Advanced Engineering Mathematics

Advanced
Engineering Mathematics

C. R. WYLIE, Jr.

Professor and Chairman, Department of Mathematics,
University of Utah

New York   Toronto   London

McGRAW-HILL BOOK COMPANY, INC.

1951

VII

ADVANCED ENGINEERING MATHEMATICS

TO MY FATHER

PREFACE

The phrase "Advanced Engineering Mathematics" admits of many interpretations. For the author it means those branches of mathematics which a student of engineering or applied science normally encounters in the first year or two following his introductory work in calculus. An almost equivalent definition would be those branches of mathematics with which the average analytical engineer must be reasonably familiar in order to carry on his own work effectively and keep abreast of current developments in his field. Specifically, the treatment in this book covers ordinary differential equations, with particular emphasis on linear equations with constant coefficients, Fourier series, operational calculus from the point of view of the Laplace transformation, separable partial differential equations and associated boundary value problems, functions of a complex variable, vector analysis, and numerical methods. In addition to these primarily mathematical topics, a chapter on electrical and mechanical vibrations has been included, not alone because of the intrinsic importance of this subject, but also because it is such a remarkable illustration of the way in which a modest amount of mathematics can unify two seemingly unrelated fields. In this presentation there has been no attempt to be rigorous for the sake of rigor itself. The author believes, however, that this book will compare favorably with others in its field in the precision of its statements and in the care with which pitfalls have been avoided or at least clearly pointed out.

In the firm conviction that a good textbook is one that can be read by a student with a minimum of assistance from his instructor and can later be used as a reference with little or no need for outside help, the author has tried to write an easy book. Clarity, no less than utility and accuracy, has been his constant goal. In an attempt to achieve this, more than the usual number of completely worked examples and carefully drawn figures have been included. In the developments there has been a conscientious attempt to make the transitions from step to step clear enough so that a student with only a good background in calculus should seldom be held up more than momentarily. To make the book reasonably self-contained, an extensive appendix has been included, covering material from the borderline between calculus, advanced calculus, and theory of equations, that might well be considered prerequisite to the rest of the book. The appendix gives a review of such topics as the elementary properties of determinants and matrices, partial differentiation, infinite series, and the expansion of functions in Taylor's series in one or more variables, hyperbolic functions, and the gamma and beta functions. Also included is a glossary of technical terms used but not defined elsewhere in the book. There are over 950 exercises of varying degrees of difficulty with which progressive mastery of the material can be measured. These range from formal problems of a purely routine nature to practical applications of considerable complexity. Hints and answers are included in many of the exercises.

There are one or two details of typography that should perhaps be noted. Throughout, words and phrases defined in the body of the text are set in boldface, and italic type has been liberally used as a sign of emphasis. To make them stand out more clearly, the worked examples are introduced by center headings and are set in type of a different size. Natural logarithms, which occur much more frequently in work of this sort, than do common logarithms, are consistently denoted by the symbol "log" without a subscript. When common logarithms are intended, the subscript 10 is always added. Instead of numbering the major divisions of the chapters consecutively throughout the book, it was decided to number them in sequence from 1 within each chapter and to use a decimal numbering system for the book as a whole. Thus Sec. 5.6 refers to the sixth section of Chapter 5, and Sec. A.4 refers to the fourth section in the appendix. A similar scheme is used in referring to the figures.

It is hardly to be expected that a book of this type should contain much, if any, original material, and the author makes only the modest claim of a minor innovation in obtaining the inverses of Laplace transforms of periodic type. The technique in question, (Sec. 6.6), for all its simplicity and usefulness, seems to have been unnoticed by previous writers on operational calculus.

In writing a textbook, even one as large as this, there is the inevitable problem of selection, and much material that one would like to present must be omitted. There is a long chapter on numerical methods, but nothing on statistics, quality control, or nomography. Bessel functions are discussed but not the Legendre polynomials. Hyperbolic functions and the gamma function have their place, but not elliptic functions. The line must be drawn somewhere, and for the student interested in topics which have not been covered, the author can only hope that study of the material which has been included will provide a sound foundation for further reading.

The indebtedness of an author to his colleagues, students, and former teachers is too great to catalogue, and to all who have given help and encouragement in the preparation of this book, I can offer here only a most inadequate acknowledgment of my appreciation. What I have tried to do in these pages, whatever its shortcomings, is the better for the friendly counsel so many have given.

C. R. WYLIE, JR.

SALT LAKE CITY, UTAH
  June, 1951

CONTENTS

CHAPTER 1

ORDINARY DIFFERENTIAL EQUATIONS OF THE FIRST ORDER

1.1 Introduction. An equation involving one or more derivatives of a function is called a **differential equation.** By a **solution** of a differential equation is meant an expression or formula for the dependent variable which does not involve any of its derivatives and which when substituted into the given equation reduces it to an identity. The study of the existence, nature, and determination of solutions of differential equations is of fundamental importance not only to the pure mathematician but also to anyone engaged in the mathematical analysis of natural phenomena.

In general, a mathematician considers it a triumph if he is able to prove that a given differential equation possesses a solution and to deduce a few of the more important properties of that solution. To a physicist or engineer, however, it is generally a great disappointment if a specific expression for the solution cannot be exhibited. The usual compromise between these two positions is some practical process by means of which the required solution can be approximated with satisfactory accuracy.

Not all differential equations are of such difficulty, however, and there are several large and very important classes of equations for which solutions can readily be found. For instance, an equation such as

$$\frac{dy}{dx} = f(x)$$

is really a differential equation, and the integral

$$y = \int f(x)dx + c$$

is a solution. More generally, the equation

$$\frac{d^n y}{dx^n} = g(x)$$

is a differential equation whose solution can be found by n successive integrations. Except in name, the process of integration is actually an example of a process for solving differential equations.

In this and the following two chapters we shall consider the differential equations which are next in difficulty after those which can be solved by

1

direct integration.   These equations form only a very small part of the class of all differential equations, and yet with a knowledge of them an engineer is equipped to handle the bulk of all applications.   To get so much for so little is indeed remarkable!

1.2 Fundamental Definitions.   If the derivatives which appear in a differential equation are total derivatives, the equation is called an **ordinary differential equation;** if partial derivatives occur, the equation is said to be a **partial differential equation.**   By the **order** of a differential equation is meant the order of the highest derivative which appears in the equation.

Example 1

The equation

$$x^2 y'' + xy' + (x^2 - n^2)y = 0$$

is an *ordinary* differential equation of the *second* order, connecting the dependent variable y with its first and second derivatives and with the independent variable x.

Example 2

The equation

$$\frac{\partial^4 u}{\partial x^4} + 2\frac{\partial^4 u}{\partial x^2\, \partial y^2} + \frac{\partial^4 u}{\partial y^4} = 0$$

is a *partial* differential equation of the *fourth* order.

At present we shall be concerned exclusively with ordinary differential equations.

An equation which is linear, that is, of the first degree, in the *dependent* variable and its derivatives is called a **linear differential equation.**   All other equations are called **nonlinear.**   In general, linear equations are much easier to solve than nonlinear ones, and most elementary applications involve equations of the linear type.

Example 3

The equation

$$y'' + 4xy' + 2y = \cos x$$

is a *linear* equation of the *second* order.   The presence of the term xy' does not alter the fact that the equation is linear because, by definition, linearity is determined solely by the way the *dependent* variable and its derivatives enter into combination among themselves.

Example 4

The equation

$$y'' + 4yy' + 2y = \cos x$$

is a *nonlinear* equation because of the occurrence of the product of y and one of its derivatives.

Example 5

The equation

$$y'' + \sin y = 0$$

is *nonlinear* because of the presence of the term $\sin y$, which is a nonlinear function of y.

As illustrated by the simple equation

$$\frac{dy}{dx} = e^{-x^2}$$

and its solution

$$y = \int e^{-x^2}\, dx + c$$

the solution of a differential equation may depend upon integrals which cannot be evaluated in terms of elementary functions. This example also illustrates the fact that a solution of a differential equation usually involves one or more arbitrary constants.

A detailed treatment of the question of how many independent arbitrary constants can appear in a solution of a differential equation is quite difficult. The usual situation is that for an equation of order n there exist solutions containing n arbitrary constants, but none containing more. However, there are equations such as

$$\left|\frac{dy}{dx}\right| + 1 = 0$$

(which has no solutions at all) and

$$\left|\frac{dy}{dx}\right| + |y| = 0$$

(which has only the single solution $y = 0$) which possess *no* solutions containing *any* arbitrary constants.

On the other hand, there are also simple differential equations which possess solutions containing more parameters than the order of the equation. For instance, it is easy to verify that

$$y = \begin{cases} c_1 x^2, & x \leqq 0 \\ c_2 x^2, & x \geqq 0 \end{cases}$$

is a solution of the first-order equation

$$x\frac{dy}{dx} = 2y$$

for *all* values of the *two* parameters c_1 and c_2. The most we can say is that in no case can the expression defining any segment of a solution of a differential equation contain more independent parameters than the order of the equation.

If a solution of a differential equation of order n contains n independent arbitrary constants, we shall call it the **general solution** of the equation. If the general solution has the property that *every* solution of the differential equation can be obtained by assigning suitable values to the constants which appear in it, we shall describe it further as the **complete solution.** Solutions which cannot be obtained from the general solution by specializing its arbitrary constants are called **singular solutions.** Singular solutions will occur rarely, if ever, in our work, and the terms **general solution** and **complete solution** can almost always be considered synonymous.

Example 6

Verify that

$$y = Ax + B(x^3 + 1)$$

is a solution of the equation

$$(2x^3 - 1)y'' - 6x^2y' + 6xy = 0$$

for all values of the constants A and B.

By differentiating y and substituting it into the differential equation as indicated and then collecting terms on A and B, we obtain at once

$$(2x^3 - 1)[6Bx] - 6x^2[A + 3Bx^2] + 6x[Ax + B(x^3 + 1)]$$
$$= (-6x^2 + 6x^2)A + (12x^4 - 6x - 18x^4 + 6x^4 + 6x)B = (0)A + (0)B = 0$$

for all values of A and B. Since the given solution contains two independent arbitrary constants, it is actually the *general* solution since the equation is of the *second* order.

Occasionally it is necessary to determine the differential equation of which a given function, involving arbitrary constants, is the general solution. This may be done by differentiating the given expression as many times as the number of constants it contains and then eliminating these constants by algebraic manipulation of the resulting equations.

Example 7

What is the differential equation having

(1) $$y = Ae^x + B \cos x$$

as its general solution?

By differentiating (1), we find

(2) $$y' = Ae^x - B \sin x$$
(3) $$y'' = Ae^x - B \cos x$$

Then, by adding and subtracting Eqs. (1) and (3), we obtain

$$A = \frac{y + y''}{2e^x}, \qquad B = \frac{y - y''}{2 \cos x}$$

Substitution of these into Eq. (2) gives

$$y' = \left(\frac{y + y''}{2e^x}\right)e^x - \left(\frac{y - y''}{2 \cos x}\right) \sin x$$

or finally

(4) $$(1 + \tan x)y'' - 2y' + (1 - \tan x)y = 0$$

Although Eq. (4) is the only differential equation having (1) for its *general* solution, it is by no means the only equation of which (1) is *a* solution. For instance, if (3) be differentiated twice more, we obtain

(5) $$y^{\text{iv}} = Ae^x + B \cos x$$

By comparing this with (1), it is evident that the given function also satisfies the very simple equation

(6) $$y^{\text{iv}} = y$$

Since Eq. (6) is of the fourth order, its general solution must contain four arbitrary constants. Hence it is clear that the given expression (1) cannot be the general solution of (6). Actually it is easy to verify that the general solution of (6) is

(7) $$y = Ae^x + B \cos x + C \sin x + De^{-x}$$

EXERCISES

Describe each of the following equations, giving its order and telling whether it is ordinary or partial, and linear or nonlinear:

1. $y'' + 3(y')^2 + 4y = 0$

2. $y' = xy$

3. $y''' + 6y'' + 4y' + y = e^x$

4. $y'' + (a + b \cos 2x)y = 0$

5. $\dfrac{\partial^2 u}{\partial x^2} + \dfrac{\partial^2 u}{\partial y^2} + \dfrac{\partial^2 u}{\partial z^2} = 0$

6. $\dfrac{d(xy')}{dx} + x^2 y = 0$

7. $\dfrac{d^2 \phi}{dt^2} + \dfrac{d\phi}{dt} + \cos \phi = 0$

8. $u \dfrac{\partial^2 u}{\partial x^2} = \dfrac{\partial^2 u}{\partial x \, \partial t}$

9. $\dfrac{\partial^2 \left(x^2 \dfrac{\partial^2 y}{\partial x^2} \right)}{\partial x^2} = \dfrac{\partial^2 y}{\partial t^2}$

10. $\dfrac{y''}{[1 + (y')^2]^{\frac{3}{2}}} = 3$

Verify that each of the following equations has the solution indicated:

11. $\dfrac{d^2 \phi}{dt^2} - 5 \dfrac{d\phi}{dt} + 4\phi = 0 \qquad \phi = ae^t + be^{4t}$

12. $\dfrac{d^3 y}{dx^3} + 4 \dfrac{dy}{dx} = 0 \qquad y = a + b \cos 2x + c \sin 2x$

13. $z' + z = x \qquad z = x - 1 + ke^{-x}$

14. $(\cos x) \dfrac{dy}{dx} + (\sin x)y = 1 \qquad y = \sin x + A \cos x$

15. $y'' + 2y' + 2y = 0 \qquad y = e^{-x}(A \cos x + B \sin x)$

16. $2xy \, dy = (y^2 - x)dx \qquad y^2 = Kx - x \log x$

17. $dy = xy^2 \, dx \qquad y = \dfrac{-2}{x^2 + c}$

18. $(xy - x^2)dy = y^2 \, dx \qquad y = Ae^{y/x}$

19. $\dfrac{d^2 z}{dx^2} = \dfrac{2z}{x^2} \qquad z = \dfrac{C}{x} + Dx^2$

20. $y'' + (y')^2 + 1 = 0 \qquad y = \log \sin (x - a) + b$

Find the differential equation of which each of the following expressions is the general solution:

21. $y = a \sin 3t + b \cos 3t$ *Ans.* $y'' + 9y = 0$
22. $y = 2c_1x + c_2x^2$ *Ans.* $x^2y'' - 2xy' + 2y = 0$
23. $y = ae^{-x} + be^{3x}$ *Ans.* $y'' - 2y' - 3y = 0$
24. $y = e^{-x} + be^{3x}$
25. $y = A + Bx + Ce^x$
26. $y = A \sin (t + B)$
27. $\theta = A \cosh 2t + B \sinh 2t$
28. $y = a \log bx$
29. Find the differential equation whose general solution defines the family of all parabolas which touch the x-axis and have their axes vertical.
         Ans. $2yy'' - (y')^2 = 0$
30. Find the differential equation whose general solution defines the family of all lines which touch the parabola $y = x^2$.

1.3 Separable First-order Equations. In many cases a first-order differential equation can be reduced by algebraic manipulations to the form

$$(1) \qquad\qquad f(x)dx + g(y)dy = 0$$

Such an equation is called **separable,** because the variables x and y have been separated from each other in such a way that x appears only in the coefficient of dx and y appears only in the coefficient of dy. An equation of this type can be solved at once by integration, giving the general solution

$$\textstyle\int f(x)dx + \int g(y)dy = C$$

where C is an arbitrary integration constant.

Other forms which should be recognized at once as being separable are

$$(2) \qquad\qquad f(x)G(y)dx + F(x)g(y)dy = 0$$

$$(3) \qquad\qquad \frac{dy}{dx} = M(x)N(y)$$

The general solution of Eq. (2) can be found by first separating variables by dividing by the product $F(x)G(y)$, giving

$$\frac{f(x)}{F(x)} dx + \frac{g(y)}{G(y)} dy = 0$$

Integration then yields the general solution

$$\int \frac{f(x)}{F(x)} dx + \int \frac{g(y)}{G(y)} dy = C$$

Similarly, the general solution of Eq. (3) can be found by first multiplying by dx and dividing by $N(y)$, giving

$$\frac{dy}{N(y)} = M(x)dx$$

Then by integration the general solution is found to be

$$\int \frac{dy}{N(y)} = \int M(x)dx + C$$

Example 1

What is the general solution of the equation

$$dx + xy\,dy + y^2\,dx = y\,dy$$

It is not immediately evident that this equation is separable. However, in any case the best first step in solving an equation of this sort is to collect terms on dx and dy. This gives

$$(1 + y^2)dx + (xy - y)dy = 0$$

or

$$(1 + y^2)dx + y(x - 1)dy = 0$$

which is of the form (2). Hence division by the product

$$(1 + y^2)(x - 1)$$

will separate the variables and reduce the equation to the standard form (1):

$$\frac{dx}{x - 1} + \frac{y\,dy}{1 + y^2} = 0$$

Integration now gives the following equation, defining the solution y as an implicit function of x:

$$\log (x - 1) + \tfrac{1}{2} \log (1 + y^2) = C$$

Although it is not necessary, this may, if desired, be written in a somewhat more convenient form by combining the logarithmic terms and proceeding as follows:

$$\log (x - 1) + \log (1 + y^2)^{\frac{1}{2}} = \log e^C$$
$$\log [(x - 1)\sqrt{1 + y^2}] = \log K$$

where K is defined to be e^C. Now if the logarithms of two numbers are equal, the numbers themselves must be equal. Hence

$$(x - 1)\sqrt{1 + y^2} = K$$

and finally

$$y^2 = \frac{K^2}{(x - 1)^2} - 1$$

Example 2

Find the solution of the differential equation

$$\frac{dy}{dx} = \frac{-2xy}{1 + y}$$

which has the property that $y = 1$ when $x = 2$.

This equation is of the form (3), and the variables may be separated by dividing by y and multiplying by $(1 + y)dx$, giving

$$\left(\frac{1 + y}{y}\right) dy = -2x\,dx \qquad \text{or} \qquad \left(\frac{1}{y} + 1\right) dy = -2x\,dx$$

Integrating this, we find the general solution

$$\log y + y = -x^2 + c$$

To determine the particular solution satisfying the requirement that $y = 1$ when $x = 2$, we substitute these values into the general solution, getting

$$\log 1 + 1 = -4 + c \qquad \text{or} \qquad c = 5$$

The required solution is therefore

$$\log y + y = 5 - x^2$$

This equation cannot be solved for y in terms of x.

It should be noted that in separating variables in the differential equation it was necessary to divide through by y; hence the possibility that $y = 0$ was implicitly ruled out. If, therefore, we had desired a particular solution with the property that $y = 0$ when $x = x_0$, such a solution, if it existed at all, could not have been found from the general formula

$$\log y + y = -x^2 + c$$

by particularizing c. Instead it would have been necessary to return to the given differential equation and search for it by some method other than the separation of variables. In this case it is obvious that the exceedingly simple function

$$y = 0$$

satisfies the differential equation identically, and thus is the appropriate special solution. Since it is not included in the general solution for any value of c, it is an example of a singular solution.

EXERCISES

Find the general solution of each of the following equations:

1. $\dfrac{dy}{dx} = -2y$ *Ans.* $y = ce^{-2x}$

2. $dx - y\,dy = x^2 y\,dy$ *Ans.* $y^2 = 2\tan^{-1} x + c$

3. $dy - dx = e^x\,dx + y^2(1 + e^x)dx$ *Ans.* $y = \tan(e^x + x + c)$

4. $e^{x+y}\,dy = x\,dx$

5. $(\cos x)(\sin y)dx - (\sin x)dy = dy$

Find the specific solution of each of the following equations which satisfies the given conditions.

6. $\dfrac{dy}{dx} = (1 - y^2)\tan x$ $x = 0,\, y = 2$ *Ans.* $y = \dfrac{3 + \cos^2 x}{3 - \cos^2 x}$

7. $2y\,dy - 2dx = 3x^2\,dx$ $x = 1,\, y = 0$ *Ans.* $y^2 = x^3 + 2x - 3$

8. $\dfrac{dx}{dy} = y^2(1 + 3x + 2x^2)$ $x = 0,\, y = 3$

9. $dx + dy = (\log x)dx$ $x = e,\, y = 0$

10. $(\cos y)(\cos x\,dx - dy) = \cos(x + y)dx$ $x = \pi,\, y = \dfrac{\pi}{2}$

1.4 Homogeneous First-order Equations. If all terms in the coefficient functions, $M(x,y)$ and $N(x,y)$, in the general first-order differential equation

$$(1) \qquad\qquad M(x,y)dx + N(x,y)dy = 0$$

are of the same degree in the variables x and y, the equation can always be reduced to one of the separable type by the substitution $y = ux$ or, equally well, by the substitution $x = vy$.

More generally, if $M(x,y)$ and $N(x,y)$ have the property that the substitution of λx for x and λy for y converts them, respectively, into the expressions

$$\lambda^n M(x,y) \qquad \text{and} \qquad \lambda^n N(x,y)$$

then Eq. (1) can always be reduced to a separable form by either of the transformations $y = ux$ or $x = vy$.

Functions with the property that the substitutions

$$x \to \lambda x \qquad \text{and} \qquad y \to \lambda y$$

merely reproduce the original forms multiplied by λ^n are called **homogeneous functions of degree** n. As a direct extension of this terminology, the differential equation (1) is called **homogeneous** when $M(x,y)$ and $N(x,y)$ are homogeneous functions *of the same degree*.

Example 1

Is the function

$$F(x,y) = x\,[\log\,\sqrt{x^2 + y^2} - \log y] + ye^{x/y}$$

homogeneous?

To decide this question, we replace x by λx and y by λy, getting

$$\begin{aligned}
F(\lambda x, \lambda y) &= \lambda x[\log\,\sqrt{\lambda^2 x^2 + \lambda^2 y^2} - \log \lambda y] + \lambda y e^{\lambda x/\lambda y} \\
&= \lambda x[(\log\,\sqrt{x^2 + y^2} + \log \lambda) - (\log y + \log \lambda)] + \lambda y e^{x/y} \\
&= \lambda\,\{x[\log\,\sqrt{x^2 + y^2} - \log y] + ye^{x/y}\} \\
&= \lambda F(x,y)
\end{aligned}$$

The given function is therefore homogeneous of degree one.

If Eq. (1), assumed now to be homogeneous, be written in the form

$$\frac{dy}{dx} = -\frac{M(x,y)}{N(x,y)}$$

it is evident that the fraction on the right is a homogeneous function of degree zero, since the same power of λ will multiply both numerator and denominator when the test substitutions $x \to \lambda x$ and $y \to \lambda y$ are made. But if

$$-\frac{M(\lambda x, \lambda y)}{N(\lambda x, \lambda y)} = -\frac{M(x,y)}{N(x,y)}$$

it follows, by assigning the value $1/x$ to the arbitrary symbol λ, that

$$-\frac{M(x,y)}{N(x,y)} = -\frac{M(\lambda x,\lambda y)}{N(\lambda x,\lambda y)} = -\frac{M(1,y/x)}{N(1,y/x)}$$

Thus an alternative standard form for a homogeneous first-order differential equation is

(2) $$\frac{dy}{dx} = R\left(\frac{y}{x}\right)$$

where $R(y/x)$ is by definition equal to

$$-\frac{M(1,y/x)}{N(1,y/x)}$$

Although in practice it is not necessary to reduce a homogeneous equation to the form (2) in order to solve it, the theory of the substitution $y = ux$ or $u = y/x$ is most easily followed when the equation is written in this form.

Now if $y = ux$, then $dy/dx = u + x(du/dx)$. Hence Eq. (2) becomes

$$u + x\frac{du}{dx} = R(u)$$

or

(3) $$x\,du = [R(u) - u]dx$$

If $R(u) \equiv u$, Eq. (2) is simply

$$\frac{dy}{dx} = \frac{y}{x}$$

and this is separable to begin with. If $R(u) \not\equiv u$, we may divide (3) by the product $x[R(u) - u]$, getting

$$\frac{du}{R(u) - u} = \frac{dx}{x}$$

The variables have now been separated, and the equation can be integrated at once. Finally, by replacing u by its value y/x, the equation defining y as a function of x is obtained.

Example 2

Find the general solution of the equation

$$(x^2 + 3y^2)dx - 2xy\,dy = 0$$

By inspection, this equation is homogeneous since all terms in the coefficient of each differential are of the second degree. Hence we set

$$y = ux \qquad \text{and} \qquad dy = u\,dx + x\,du$$

getting

$$(x^2 + 3u^2x^2)dx - 2x^2u(u\,dx + x\,du) = 0$$

or, dividing by x^2 and collecting terms,

$$(1 + u^2)dx - 2ux\,du = 0$$

Separating variables we obtain

$$\frac{dx}{x} - \frac{2u\,du}{1 + u^2} = 0$$

and then by integrating we find

$$\log x - \log(1 + u^2) = c$$

This may be written as

$$\log \frac{x}{1 + u^2} = \log e^c = \log k$$

Hence

$$\frac{x}{1 + u^2} = k$$

or

$$\frac{x}{1 + (y/x)^2} = k$$

and finally

$$x^3 = k(x^2 + y^2)$$

EXERCISES

Find the general solution of each of the following differential equations:

1. $(x - y)dx = (x + y)dy$ $\qquad\qquad\qquad$ *Ans.* $\quad x^2 - 2xy - y^2 = c$

2. $(x - y)dy = (x + y)dx$ $\qquad\quad$ *Ans.* $\quad \log k(x^2 + y^2) = 2\tan^{-1}\left(\dfrac{y}{x}\right)$

3. $(2x + y)dy = (x - 2y)dx$ $\qquad\qquad$ *Ans.* $\quad c = y^2 + 4xy - x^2$

4. $\dfrac{dy}{dx} = \tan\left(\dfrac{y}{x}\right) + \dfrac{y}{x}$ $\qquad\qquad$ **5.** $\dfrac{dy}{dx} = \left(\dfrac{y}{x}\right)^3 + 2\left(\dfrac{y}{x}\right)$

Find the specific solution of each of the following equations which satisfies the given conditions:

6. $x\,dy - y\,dx = \sqrt{x^2 + y^2}\,dx$ $\qquad x = 1, y = 0$ $\qquad$ *Ans.* $\quad y = (x^2 - 1)/2$

7. $3\dfrac{dy}{dx} = \left(\dfrac{y}{x}\right)^2 + 3\left(\dfrac{y}{x}\right) + 4$ $\qquad x = 1, y = 2$ $\quad$ *Ans.* $\quad y = 2x\tan\left(\dfrac{\pi}{4} + \log x^{\frac{2}{3}}\right)$

8. $(x^2 - y^2)dx - \dfrac{2y^3}{x}\,dy = 0$ $\qquad x = 3, y = 0$ $\quad$ *Ans.* $\quad (x^2 + y^2)\sqrt{x^2 - 2y^2} = 27$

9. $x\,dy + (x + y)dx = 0$ $\qquad x = -1, y = 1$

10. $\dfrac{dy}{dx} = \dfrac{xe^{y/x} + y}{x}$ $\qquad x = 2, y = 0$

1.5 Linear First-order Equations. By definition, the linear first-order differential equation can contain neither products nor powers involving y or y'. Hence its most general form is

$$(1) \qquad\qquad F(x)\frac{dy}{dx} + G(x)y = H(x)$$

If we divide this equation through by $F(x)$ and rename the coefficients, it appears in the more usual form

(2)
$$\frac{dy}{dx} + P(x)y = Q(x)$$

The presence of two terms on the left side of (2) involving, respectively, dy/dx and y suggests strongly that this expression is in some way related to the derivative of a product having y as one factor. If, tentatively, we consider the product zy, where z is a function yet to be determined, we have for its derivative

(3)
$$z\frac{dy}{dx} + \frac{dz}{dx}y$$

In order for this to be identical with the left side of (2), it is necessary that

$$z = 1 \quad \text{and} \quad \frac{dz}{dx} = P(x)$$

These conditions are incompatible, however, for if $z = 1$ then $dz/dx = 0$ and not $P(x)$. However, the left side of (2) need not appear in exactly its present form, for, reversing the transition from Eq. (1) to Eq. (2), we may legitimately multiply (2) by an arbitrary function of x, say $\phi(x)$, getting the equivalent equation

$$\phi(x)\frac{dy}{dx} + \phi(x)P(x)y = \phi(x)Q(x)$$

In order that the left member of this equation be the exact derivative of the product zy, as given by (3), it is necessary that

(4.1)
$$z = \phi(x)$$

(4.2)
$$\frac{dz}{dx} = \phi(x)P(x)$$

Eliminating $\phi(x)$ between these equations gives

$$\frac{dz}{dx} = zP(x) \quad \text{or} \quad \frac{dz}{z} = P(x)dx$$

from which we find by integration

$$\log z = \int P(x)dx \quad \text{or} \quad z = e^{\int P(x)dx}$$

Since, from (4.1), $z = \phi(x)$, we have thus shown that if Eq. (2) be multiplied through by the **integrating factor**

$$e^{\int P(x)dx}$$

its left member becomes the exact derivative of the product

$$yz \equiv ye^{\int P(x)dx}$$

Since the right member of (2), even after multiplication by $e^{\int P(x)dx}$, is still just a function of x alone, the equation may be solved by a single integration:

$$\left[\frac{dy}{dx} + P(x)y\right]e^{\int P(x)dx} = Q(x)e^{\int P(x)dx}$$

$$\frac{d}{dx}[ye^{\int P(x)dx}] = Q(x)e^{\int P(x)dx}$$

$$ye^{\int P(x)dx} = \int Q(x)e^{\int P(x)dx}\,dx + c$$

$$y = e^{-\int P(x)dx}\int Q(x)e^{\int P(x)dx}\,dx + ce^{-\int P(x)dx}$$

This result should *not* be remembered as a formula for the solution. Instead, an equation of this type should be solved by actually carrying out the steps just illustrated:

a. Compute the integrating factor $e^{\int P(x)dx}$.

b. Multiply the given equation by this factor.

c. Integrate both sides of the resulting equation, taking advantage of the fact that the integral of the left member is *always* just y times the integrating factor.

d. Solve the integrated equation for y.

Example 1

What is the general solution of the equation

$$\frac{dy}{dx} + (\tan x)y = \sin 2x$$

In this case $P(x) = \tan x$, and thus as an integrating factor we have

$$e^{\int P(x)dx} = e^{\int \tan x\,dx} = e^{\log \sec x} = \sec x\dagger$$

Multiplying the differential equation by this factor gives

$$(\sec x)\left[\frac{dy}{dx} + (\tan x)y\right] = (\sec x)(\sin 2x) = 2\sin x$$

Integrating this, we have

$$y \sec x = -2\cos x + c$$

or finally

$$y = -2\cos^2 x + c\cos x$$

Example 2

Find the solution of the equation

$$x^2\,dy + (2xy - x + 1)dx = 0$$

for which $y = 0$ when $x = 1$.

† Note that $e^{\log u} = u$ for any expression u.

Dividing the given equation by $x^2 \, dx$ and transposing reduces it to the form

$$(5) \qquad \frac{dy}{dx} + \frac{2y}{x} = \frac{x-1}{x^2}$$

which is a linear first-order equation.   In this case $P(x) = 2/x$, and thus the integrating factor is

$$e^{\int (2/x) \, dx} = e^{2 \log x} = e^{\log x^2} = x^2$$

Multiplying (5) by this factor gives the equation

$$x^2 \left(\frac{dy}{dx} + \frac{2y}{x} \right) = x - 1$$

Integrating this, remembering that the integral of the left member is just y times the integrating factor, we have

$$x^2 y = \frac{x^2}{2} - x + c$$

or

$$y = \frac{1}{2} - \frac{1}{x} + \frac{c}{x^2}$$

To find the specific solution which is required, we substitute the given conditions, $x = 1$, $y = 0$, into the general solution, getting

$$0 = \tfrac{1}{2} - 1 + c \qquad \text{or} \qquad c = \tfrac{1}{2}$$

The required solution is therefore

$$y = \frac{1}{2} - \frac{1}{x} + \frac{1}{2x^2}$$

EXERCISES

1. Prove that $e^{\log u} = u$.

2. Prove that no extra generality in the final answer results from using $e^{\int P(x) \, dx + c}$, instead of just $e^{\int P(x) \, dx}$, as an integrating factor of the equation

$$\frac{dy}{dx} + P(x)y = Q(x).$$

Find the general solution of each of the following equations:

3. $y' - 2y = e^{3x}$ \hfill *Ans.* $y = e^{3x} + ce^{2x}$

4. $\dfrac{dy}{dx} + \dfrac{y}{x+1} = \dfrac{1}{x^2-1}$ \hfill *Ans.* $y = \dfrac{\log (x-1) + c}{x+1}$

5. $(\sin x)dy + y(\cos x)dx = x(\sin x)dx$ \qquad **6.** $y' + 2xy = x^3$

7. $\dfrac{dy}{dx} + 3y = x$ \hfill **8.** $\dfrac{dy}{dx} - \dfrac{y}{x} = \dfrac{1}{1+x^2}$

9. $y' + \dfrac{y}{1-x} = x^2 - x$ \hfill **10.** $y'' + \dfrac{y'}{x} = x^2 + 2$

Find the specific solution of each of the following equations which satisfies the given conditions:

11. $y' = e^x + y$ $x = 0, y = 0$ *Ans.* $y = xe^x$

12. $y' = \dfrac{2x^3 + y}{x}$ $x = 2, y = 0$ *Ans.* $y = x^3 - 4x$

13. $y' + 2xy + x = e^{-x^2}$ $x = 0, y = 2$

14. $y'' + y' = e^{-2x}$ $x = 0, y = y' = 0$

15. $xy' = x \cos x - 2 \sin x - 2y$ $x = \pi, y = 1$

16. Show that the substitution $z = y^{1-n}$ will reduce the **Bernoulli equation,** $\dfrac{dy}{dx} + P(x)y = Q(x)y^n$, to a linear first-order equation in z.

Solve the following equations:

17. $\dfrac{dy}{dx} + \dfrac{y}{x} = \sqrt{y}$ *Ans.* $y = \dfrac{x^2}{9} + \dfrac{2c\sqrt{x}}{3} + \dfrac{c^2}{x}$

18. $\dfrac{dy}{dx} + \left(\dfrac{1-x}{x}\right)y = xy^2$ *Ans.* $y = \dfrac{1}{cxe^{-x} - x}$

19. $\dfrac{dy}{dx} + \dfrac{xy}{1+x^2} = (1-x^4)y^3$ 20. $(y^2 - x)dx + y\,dy = 0$

1.6 Applications of First-order Differential Equations. The mathematical formulation of physical problems involving changing quantities often leads to differential equations of the first order. The following examples will make clear how such equations arise and how they are handled.

Example 1

A tank is initially filled with 100 gal of salt solution containing 1 lb of salt per gallon. Fresh brine containing 2 lb of salt per gallon runs into the tank at the rate of 5 gal/min and the mixture, assumed to be kept uniform by stirring, runs out at the same rate. Find the amount of salt in the tank at any time, and determine how long it will take for this amount to reach 150 lb.

Let Q (lb) be the total amount of salt in solution in the tank at any time t and let dQ be the increase in this amount during the infinitesimal interval of time dt. At any time t the amount of salt per gallon of solution is therefore

$$\frac{Q}{100} \text{ (lb/gal)}$$

Now the change dQ in the total amount of salt in the tank is clearly the net gain in the interval dt due to the fresh brine running into, and mixture running out of, the tank. The rate at which salt enters the tank is

$$5 \text{ (gal/min)} \times 2 \text{ (lb/gal)} = 10 \text{ (lb/min)}$$

Hence in the interval dt the gain in salt from this source is

$$10 \text{ (lb/min)} \times dt \text{ (min)} = 10\,dt \text{ (lb)}$$

Likewise, since the concentration of salt in the mixture as it leaves the tank is the same as the concentration $Q/100$ in the tank itself, the amount of salt leaving the tank in the interval dt is

$$5 \text{ (gal/min)} \times \frac{Q}{100} \text{ (lb/gal)} \times dt \text{ (min)} = \frac{Q}{20}\,dt \text{ (lb)}$$

Therefore

(1)
$$dQ = \left(10 - \frac{Q}{20}\right) dt$$

This equation can be written in the form

(2)
$$\frac{dQ}{200 - Q} = \frac{dt}{20}$$

and handled as a separable equation, or it can be written

(3)
$$\frac{dQ}{dt} + \frac{Q}{20} = 10$$

and treated as a linear equation.

Considering it as a linear equation, we must first compute the integrating factor

$$e^{\int P \, dt} = e^{\int dt/20} = e^{t/20}$$

Multiplying Eq. (3) by this factor gives

$$e^{t/20}\left[\frac{dQ}{dt} + \frac{Q}{20}\right] = 10e^{t/20}$$

From this, by integration, we obtain

$$Qe^{t/20} = 200e^{t/20} + k$$

or

$$Q = 200 + ke^{-(t/20)}$$

Substituting the initial conditions $t = 0$, $Q = 100$, we find

$$100 = 200 + k \qquad \text{or} \qquad k = -100$$

Hence

$$Q = 200 - 100e^{-(t/20)}$$

To find how long it will be before there are 150 lb of salt in the tank, we must find t such that

$$150 = 200 - 100e^{-(t/20)}$$

or

$$e^{-(t/20)} = \tfrac{1}{2}$$

From this we have at once

$$\frac{t}{20} = \log \frac{1}{2} = -\log 2 = -.693$$

and thus

$$t = 13.9 \ (\text{min})$$

Two families of curves with the property that every member of either family cuts each member of the other family at right angles are called **orthogonal trajectories** of each other. Families of curves related in this way occur frequently in applied problems. For instance, in two-dimensional problems in the flow of heat, the curves along which the heat flow takes place and the isothermal curves, or loci of points at the same temperature, are orthogonal trajectories. Likewise in problems in the flow of electricity in thin conducting sheets, the paths along which the current flows are the orthogonal trajectories of the equipotential curves, and vice versa. The problem of finding the orthogonal trajectories of a given family of curves requires the solution of a first-order differential equation, as the following example shows.

Example 2

What are the orthogonal trajectories of the curves of the family $2x^2 + y^2 = kx$?

The fundamental idea upon which the solution of a problem such as this is based is that if two curves intersect at right angles their slopes at their common point are negative reciprocals. It is therefore necessary first to find the general expression for the slope of the curves of the given family. Now, by differentiating the given equation, we find

$$4x + 2yy' = k$$

The value of y' given by this equation is not the one we need, however, because it involves k, which varies from curve to curve. In other words it is not a general expression simultaneously valid for all curves of the family. We therefore eliminate k* between the last equation and the original equation, getting

$$2x^2 + y^2 = (4x + 2yy')x$$

or

$$y' = \frac{-2x^2 + y^2}{2xy}$$

Since the curves of the orthogonal family are by definition perpendicular to the curves of the original family at all common points, it follows that their slopes are given by the formula

$$\frac{dy}{dx} = -\frac{1}{(-2x^2 + y^2)/2xy} = \frac{2xy}{2x^2 - y^2}$$

The general solution of this homogeneous differential equation defines the required family.

To solve this equation, let $y = ux$, as usual. Then

$$u + x\frac{du}{dx} = \frac{2ux^2}{2x^2 - u^2x^2} = \frac{2u}{2 - u^2}$$

Cross multiplying and collecting terms gives

$$-u^3\,dx + x(2 - u^2)du = 0$$

Separating variables, we have

$$\frac{dx}{x} + \left(\frac{1}{u} - \frac{2}{u^3}\right) du = 0$$

* Note that this is nothing but the problem of finding the differential equation satisfied by the implicit function y defined by the given equation. Compare Example 7, Sec. 1.2.

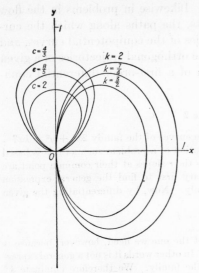

FIG. 1.1. The ellipses $2x^2 + y^2 = kx$ and their orthogonal trajectories $x^2 = -y^2 \log cy$.

and integrating,

$$\log x + \log u + \frac{1}{u^2} + \log c = 0$$

$$\log cxu = -\frac{1}{u^2}$$

$$\log \left(cx \frac{y}{x} \right) = -\frac{x^2}{y^2}$$

$$x^2 = -y^2 \log cy$$

Figure 1.1 shows several members of each family.

Example 3

A man rows with constant velocity v across a stream of width a, always heading directly for the opposite bank. If the velocity of the stream varies directly as the product of the distances from the two banks, find the equation of the path of the man. How far downstream of his starting point does he land?

Let axes be chosen as in Fig. 1.2, the origin being taken at the point from which the man starts. By hypothesis

$$v_x = \frac{dx}{dt} = \text{stream velocity} = ky(a - y)$$

$$v_y = \frac{dy}{dt} = \text{velocity with which the man rows} = v$$

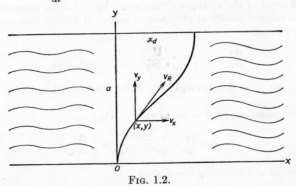

FIG. 1.2.

Hence the direction of the resultant velocity of the boat, which of course is the direction of the tangent to the path of the boat, is given by

$$\frac{dy}{dx} = \frac{v_y}{v_x} = \frac{v}{ky(a - y)}$$

This is a simple separable equation, and we can write

$$y(a - y)dy = \left(\frac{v}{k} \right) dx$$

Then integrating, we have

$$\frac{ay^2}{2} - \frac{y^3}{3} = \frac{v}{k}x + c$$

Since $y = 0$ when $x = 0$, it is evident that c must be zero. Hence the equation of the path of the boat is

$$x = \frac{k}{6v}(3ay^2 - 2y^3)$$

To find the distance downstream to the point where the man lands, we set $y = a$ and solve for x. The result is

$$x_d = \frac{ka^3}{6v}$$

Example 4

A tank having the shape of an inverted right circular cone of radius R and height h is initially filled with water. At the bottom of the tank there is a hole of radius r through which the water drains under the influence of gravity. Find the depth of the water at any time, and determine how long it will take for the tank to drain completely.

Let the origin be chosen at the vertex of the tank, and let y be the instantaneous

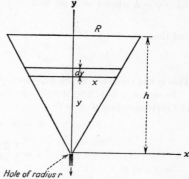

FIG. 1.3.

depth of the water. Then in the interval dt the water level will fall by the amount dy, and the resultant decrease in the volume of water will be

$$dV = (\pi x^2)dy$$

This of course must equal the volume of water which leaves the orifice during the time dt. Now from **Torricelli's law,** the velocity with which a liquid issues from an orifice is

$$v = \sqrt{2gy}$$

where g is the acceleration of gravity and y is the instantaneous height, or **head,** of the liquid above the orifice. In time dt, then, a stream of water of length $\sqrt{2gy}\,dt$ and of cross-section area πr^2 will emerge from the outlet. The volume of this amount of water is

$$dV = \pi r^2\sqrt{2gy}\,dt$$

Hence, equating the two expressions for dV, we obtain the differential equation

(4) $$\pi x^2\,dy = -\pi r^2\sqrt{2gy}\,dt$$

the minus sign indicating that as t *increases,* the depth y decreases.

Before this equation can be solved, it is necessary that x be expressed in **terms of** y. This is easily done through the use of similar right triangles, and we have

$$\frac{x}{y} = \frac{R}{h} \qquad \text{and} \qquad x^2 = \frac{R^2}{h^2}y^2$$

Therefore the differential equation (4) can be written

$$\pi \frac{R^2}{h^2} y^2 \, dy = -\pi r^2 \sqrt{2gy} \, dt$$

This is a simple separable equation which can be solved without difficulty:

$$y^{\frac{3}{2}} \, dy = -\sqrt{2g} \, \frac{r^2 h^2}{R^2} \, dt$$

$$\frac{2}{5} y^{\frac{5}{2}} = -\sqrt{2g} \, \frac{r^2 h^2}{R^2} \, t + c$$

Since $y = h$ when $t = 0$, we find

$$\tfrac{2}{5} h^{\frac{5}{2}} = c$$

and thus

$$\frac{2}{5} y^{\frac{5}{2}} = -\sqrt{2g} \, \frac{r^2 h^2}{R^2} \, t + \frac{2}{5} h^{\frac{5}{2}}$$

This is the equation which expresses the instantaneous depth y as a function of t.

To compute how long it will take the tank to empty, we must determine the value of t corresponding to $y = 0$:

$$0 = -\sqrt{2g} \, \frac{r^2 h^2}{R^2} \, t + \frac{2}{5} h^{\frac{5}{2}}$$

$$t = \frac{1}{5} \frac{R^2}{r^2} \sqrt{\frac{2h}{g}}$$

EXERCISES

1. Under certain conditions it is observed that the rate at which atmospheric pressure changes with altitude is proportional to the pressure. If the pressure is 14.7 lb/in.^{2} at sea level, and if it has fallen to one-half this value at 18,000 ft, find the formula for the pressure at any height.
2. Find the orthogonal trajectories of the curves of the family $y^2 = x - c$.
3. Find the orthogonal trajectories of the curves $y^2 - x^2 = kx$.
4. Find the orthogonal trajectories of the circles which pass through the origin and have their centers on the x-axis.
5. A body weighing w lb falls from rest under the influence of gravity. If the retarding force due to air friction is assumed to be proportional to the velocity, find the equations expressing the velocity of fall and the distance fallen, as functions of time. (Hint: Use **Newton's law**, mass $\times$ acceleration = force, to set up the differential equation.)

   Ans. $v = \dfrac{w}{k} \left(1 - e^{-(kgt/w)}\right), \qquad s = \dfrac{w}{k}\left[t - \dfrac{w}{kg}\left(1 - e^{-(kgt/w)}\right)\right]$ where k is the coefficient of air friction.
6. Verify that the answers to Exercise 5 reduce to the ideal laws

   $$v = gt \qquad \text{and} \qquad s = \tfrac{1}{2}gt^2$$

   when the coefficient of friction k approaches zero.
7. A body weighing w lb falls from rest under the influence of gravity. If the retarding force due to air friction is assumed to be proportional to the square of the velocity, find expressions for the velocity of fall and the distance fallen as functions of t. What is the equation expressing the velocity in terms of the distance fallen?

Ans. $v = v_\infty \tanh \dfrac{gt}{v_\infty},$ $s = \dfrac{v_\infty^2}{g} \log \cosh \dfrac{gt}{v_\infty},$ $v^2 = v_\infty^2[1 - e^{-(2gs/v_\infty^2)}]$ where v_∞ is the limiting velocity $\sqrt{w/k}$.

8. Verify that the answers to Exercise 7 reduce to the ideal laws

$$v = gt, \qquad s = \tfrac{1}{2}gt^2, \qquad v^2 = 2gs$$

as $k \to 0$.

9. The terminal velocity of a falling body is 192 ft/sec. Plot its distance fallen versus time for the first 20 sec of fall assuming (a) resistance proportional to the velocity and (b) resistance proportional to the square of the velocity.

10. According to **Lambert's law of absorption,** when light passes through a transparent medium the amount which is absorbed by any thin layer of the material is proportional to the amount incident on that layer and to the thickness of that layer. In his deep-sea explorations off Bermuda, Beebe observed that at a depth of 50 ft the intensity of illumination was 10 candles/ft², while at 250 ft it had fallen to 0.2 candles/ft². Find the law connecting intensity with depth in this case.

11. A rapidly rotating flywheel, after power is shut off, "coasts" to rest under the retarding influence of a friction torque which is proportional to the angular velocity ω. If the moment of inertia of the flywheel is I, and if its initial velocity is ω_0, find its instantaneous angular velocity as a function of time. How long will it take the flywheel to come to rest? (Hint: Use Newton's law in torsional form, moment of inertia $\times$ angular acceleration = torque, to set up the differential equation.)   *Ans.* The angular velocity is zero only at $t = \infty$!

12. The friction torque acting to slow down a flywheel is actually not proportional to the first power of the angular velocity ω at all speeds. As a more realistic example than Exercise 11, suppose that a flywheel of moment of inertia $I = 7.5$ lb-ft sec² coasts to rest from an initial speed of 1,000 rad/min under the influence of a retarding torque T estimated to be the following:

$$T = \begin{cases} \dfrac{\sqrt{\omega}}{10} \text{ ft-lb} & 0 < \omega < 100 \text{ rad/min} \\[2ex] \dfrac{1}{10}\left(7.5 + \dfrac{\omega^2}{40{,}000}\right) \text{ ft-lb} & 100 < \omega < 1{,}000 \text{ rad/min} \end{cases}$$

Find ω as a function of t, and determine how long it will take the flywheel to come to rest. *Ans.* The flywheel will come to rest in $1.35 + 0.42 = 1.77$ min.

13. A tank contains 1,000 gal of brine in which 500 lb of salt are dissolved. Fresh water runs into the tank at the rate of 10 gal/min and the mixture, kept uniform by stirring, runs out at the same rate. How long will it be before only 50 lb of salt are left in the tank?

14. Radium disintegrates radioactively at a rate proportional to the amount of radium instantaneously present. If one-half of any given amount of radium will disappear in 1,590 years, what fraction will disintegrate during the first century? during the tenth century?

15. When a condenser of capacity C is being charged through a resistance R by a battery supplying a voltage E, the instantaneous charge on the condenser Q satisfies the differential equation

$$R\frac{dQ}{dt} + \frac{Q}{C} = E$$

Find Q as a function of time from this equation, assuming the condenser to be initially uncharged. How long will it be before the condenser is half charged if $E = 6$ volts, $R = 100$ ohms, and $C = 1.0 \times 10^{-5}$ farad?

Ans. $Q = EC(1 - e^{-t/RC})$

16. When a switch is closed in a circuit containing a battery E, a resistance R, and an inductance L, the current i builds up at a rate given by

$$L\frac{di}{dt} + Ri = E$$

Find i as a function of time from this equation. How long will it be before the current has reached one-half its final value if $E = 6$ volts, $R = 100$ ohms, and $L = 0.1$ henry?

17. It is a fact of common experience that when a rope is wound around a rough cylinder, a small force at one end can resist a much larger force at the other. Quantitatively, it is found that throughout the portion of the rope in contact with the cylinder, the change in tension per unit length is proportional to the tension, the proportionality constant being the coefficient of friction between the rope and the cylinder divided by the radius of the cylinder. Assuming a coefficient of friction of 0.35, how many times must a rope be snubbed around a post 1 ft in diameter in order that a man holding one end can resist a force 200 times greater than he can exert? *Ans.* 2.4

18. When ethyl acetate in dilute aqueous solution is heated in the presence of a small amount of acid it decomposes according to the following equation:

$$CH_3COOC_2H_5 + H_2O \rightarrow CH_3COOH + C_2H_5OH$$
(ethyl acetate)   (water)   (acetic acid)   (ethyl alcohol)

Since this reaction takes place in dilute solution, the quantity of water which is present is so great that the loss of the small amount which combines with the ethyl acetate produces no appreciable change in the total amount. Hence of the reacting substances only the ethyl acetate suffers a measurable change in concentration. A chemical reaction of this sort in which the concentration of only one reacting substance changes is called a **first-order reaction**. It is a law of physical chemistry that the rate at which a substance is being used up, *i.e.*, transformed, in a first-order reaction is proportional to the amount of that substance instantaneously present. If the initial concentration of ethyl acetate is C_0, find the expression for its instantaneous concentration at any time t.

19. According to well-established laws of heat transfer, the amount of heat in Btu per unit time flowing through an area is proportional to the area and to the temperature gradient in degrees per unit length normal to the area, the coefficient of proportionality being known as the **thermal conductivity** of the material. On the basis of this law, how much heat will be lost per minute from 10 ft of pipe 2 in. in diameter carrying steam at 400°F if the pipe is covered with a 1-in. layer of insulating material of thermal conductivity 0.0002 Btu/(min) (°F) (in.) and if the temperature of the outer surface of the insulation is 100°F? *Ans.* 65 Btu

20. A cylindrical tank of radius r is filled with water. When the tank is rotated rapidly about its axis, centrifugal force tends to drive the water outward from the center of the tank. Under steady conditions of uniform rotation, find the equation of the curve in which the free surface of the water is intersected by a plane through the axis of the cylinder.

Ans. $y = \dfrac{\omega^2}{2g}\left(x^2 - \dfrac{r^2}{2}\right) + h$, where ω is the angular velocity of the tank and h is the initial depth of water.

21. The rate at which a solid substance dissolves varies directly as the amount of undissolved material present in the solvent and as the difference between the instantaneous concentration and the saturation concentration of the substance. If 50 lb of salt are dumped into a tank containing 200 lb of water and if the concentration at the end of 5 min is observed to be 1 part in 10, find the amount of salt in solution at any time t. The saturation concentration of salt in water is 35 parts per 100.

22. Water flows out of a vertical cylindrical tank of radius 4 ft through a hole in the bottom of radius 1 in. How long will it take the tank to empty if the water in it is initially 10 ft deep?   *Ans.*   30.4 min

23. A cylindrical tank is l ft long and has semicircular end sections of radius r ft. The tank is placed with its axis horizontal and is initially filled with water. How long will it take the tank to drain through a hole of area a sq ft at the lowest point of the tank?

$$Ans.\quad t = \frac{2}{3}\frac{l}{a}\sqrt{\frac{2}{g}}\,[(2r)^{\frac{3}{2}} - r^{\frac{3}{2}}]$$

24. A hemispherical tank of radius R is initially filled with water. How long will it take the tank to drain through a hole of radius r in the bottom of the tank?

25. Water flows into an upright circular cylinder of cross-section area A ft^2 at the rate of Q ft^3/min. At the same time the water flows out under the influence of gravity through a hole of area a ft^2 in the base of the cylinder. If the water is initially h ft deep, find the instantaneous depth as a function of t.

26. An upright cylindrical tank of radius r has a narrow crack of width w running vertically from top to bottom. If the tank is initially filled to a depth h and drains through the crack under the influence of gravity, find the instantaneous depth as a function of t. How long will it take the tank to empty? (Hint: First imagine the crack to be a series of adjacent orifices, and integrate to find the total efflux from the crack in time dt.)   *Ans.*   The tank will never empty!

27. Find the curves having the property that the length of any tangent between its point of contact and its x-intercept is equal to the abscissa of the point of contact.

28. A man rows across a river of width a, always heading directly for the point opposite his starting point. If the river flows with uniform velocity v and if the velocity with which the man can row is also v, find the equation of the path of the boat. How far downstream does the man finally land?

29. A tank and its contents weigh 100 lb. The over-all or effective heat capacity of the system is 0.5 Btu/(lb) (°F). The liquid in the tank is heated by an immersion heater which delivers 100 Btu/min. Heat is lost from the system at a rate proportional to the difference between the temperature of the system, assumed uniform throughout at any instant, and the temperature of the surrounding air, the proportionality constant being 2 Btu/(min) (°F). If the air temperature remains constant at 70° and if the initial temperature of the tank and its contents is 60°, find the temperature at any time.

30. A weight w is supported by a column having the shape of a solid of revolution. If the material of the column weighs ρ lb/ft^3, and if the radius of the upper base of the column is r_0, determine how the radius should vary in order that at all cross sections the load per unit area will be the same.   *Ans.* $r = r_0 e^{\pi \rho r_0^2 y / 2w}$

CHAPTER 2

LINEAR DIFFERENTIAL EQUATIONS WITH CONSTANT COEFFICIENTS

2.1 The General Linear Second-order Equation. The general linear differential equation of the second order can be written in the standard form

$$(1) \qquad y'' + P(x)y' + Q(x)y = R(x)$$

Clearly no loss of generality results from taking the coefficient of y'' to be 1, since this can always be accomplished by division. Because of the presence of the term $R(x)$ which is unlike the other terms in that it does not contain the dependent variable or any of its derivatives, this equation is called **nonhomogeneous.** If $R(x)$ is identically zero, we have the so-called **homogeneous*** equation

$$(2) \qquad y'' + P(x)y' + Q(x)y = 0$$

In general, neither Eq. (1) nor Eq. (2) can be solved in terms of known functions. The theory associated with such special cases as have been studied at length is, for the most part, exceedingly difficult. At this stage we shall consider in detail only the simple, though highly important, case in which $P(x)$ and $Q(x)$ are constants. However, both as an illustration of how certain properties of the solutions of a differential equation may be established even though the form of those solutions is unknown, and also because we shall need the results themselves, we shall begin by proving three fundamental theorems pertaining to the solutions of the general equations (1) and (2).

Theorem 1. If y_1 and y_2 are any solutions whatsoever of the homogeneous equation

$$(2) \qquad y'' + P(x)y' + Q(x)y = 0$$

then

$$y_3 = c_1 y_1 + c_2 y_2$$

where c_1 and c_2 are arbitrary constants, is also a solution.

---

* It is regrettable that in describing linear equations of all orders the word **homogeneous** should be used in a manner totally unlike its use in describing equations of the first order (see Sec. 1.4). The usage is universal, however, and must be accepted.

24

To prove this, it is only necessary to substitute the expression for y_3 into the given differential equation and verify that the latter is satisfied:

$$y_3'' + P(x)y_3' + Q(x)y_3$$
$$= (c_1y_1 + c_2y_2)'' + P(x)(c_1y_1 + c_2y_2)' + Q(x)(c_1y_1 + c_2y_2)$$
$$= (c_1y_1'' + c_2y_2'') + P(x)(c_1y_1' + c_2y_2') + Q(x)(c_1y_1 + c_2y_2)$$
$$= [y_1'' + P(x)y_1' + Q(x)y_1]c_1 + [y_2'' + P(x)y_2' + Q(x)y_2]c_2$$
$$= (0)c_1 + (0)c_2 = 0$$

the coefficients of c_1 and c_2 vanishing identically because, by hypothesis, y_1 and y_2 are, individually, solutions of the homogeneous equation (2).

Theorem 2.   If y_1 and y_2 are two solutions of the homogeneous equation

(2) $$y'' + P(x)y' + Q(x)y = 0$$

for which

$$W(y_1, y_2)\dagger \equiv \begin{vmatrix} y_1 & y_2 \\ y_1' & y_2' \end{vmatrix} = y_1y_2' - y_2y_1' \neq 0$$

then any solution y_3 of the homogeneous equation can be written in the form

$$y_3 = c_1y_1 + c_2y_2$$

To prove this, we shall first show that any pair of solutions of Eq. (2), say y_i and y_j, satisfy the relation

(3) $$W(y_i, y_j) = y_iy_j' - y_jy_i' = k_{ij}e^{-\int P(x)dx}$$

where k_{ij} is a suitable constant.   To establish this, we begin with the hypothesis that y_i and y_j are solutions of (2) and hence

$$y_i'' + P(x)y_i' + Q(x)y_i = 0$$
$$y_j'' + P(x)y_j' + Q(x)y_j = 0$$

If the first of these equations be multiplied by y_j and subtracted from y_i times the second, we obtain

(4) $$(y_iy_j'' - y_jy_i'') + P(x)(y_iy_j' - y_jy_i') = 0$$

Now

$$\frac{dW(y_i, y_j)}{dx} \equiv \frac{d(y_iy_j' - y_jy_i')}{dx}$$
$$= (y_iy_j'' + y_i'y_j') - (y_j'y_i' + y_jy_i'')$$
$$= (y_iy_j'' - y_jy_i'')$$

† The symbol $W(y_1, y_2)$ is customarily used to denote this combination of two functions, in honor of Hoëné Wronsky (1778–1853), Polish poet and mathematician who was one of the first to study determinants of this type.   Such determinants are usually referred to as **Wronskians.**

Hence Eq. (4) can be written

$$\frac{dW(y_i,y_j)}{dx} + P(x)W(y_i,y_j) = 0$$

This is a very simple, separable differential equation whose solution can be written down immediately

$$W(y_i,y_j) = k_{ij}e^{-\int P(x)dx}$$

where k_{ij} is an integration constant. This establishes the relation (3), which is usually known as **Abel's identity** after the Norwegian mathematical genius Niels Abel (1802–1829).

Now consider the two pairs of solutions (y_3,y_1) and (y_3,y_2), where y_3 is any solution whatsoever of the homogeneous equation (2). Applying Abel's identity (3) to each of these pairs in turn, we have

$$y_3y_1' - y_1y_3' = k_{31}e^{-\int P(x)dx}$$
$$y_3y_2' - y_2y_3' = k_{32}e^{-\int P(x)dx}$$

In general, it is possible to solve these two simultaneous equations for y_3, getting

$$y_3 = \frac{y_1k_{32}e^{-\int P(x)dx} - y_2k_{31}e^{-\int P(x)dx}}{y_1y_2' - y_2y_1'}$$

If we now apply Abel's identity to the denominator of the last expression, we obtain

$$y_3 = \frac{y_1k_{32}e^{-\int P(x)dx} - y_2k_{31}e^{-\int P(x)dx}}{k_{12}e^{-\int P(x)dx}} = \frac{k_{32}}{k_{12}}y_1 - \frac{k_{31}}{k_{12}}y_2$$

Interpreting k_{32}/k_{12} as c_1 and $-k_{31}/k_{12}$ as c_2, we have succeeded in exhibiting *any* solution, y_3, as a linear combination, $c_1y_1 + c_2y_2$, of two particular solutions, y_1 and y_2, provided only that the expression $y_1y_2' - y_2y_1'$, by which we had to divide in order to solve for y_3, does not vanish. Theorem 2 is thus established.

It is important to distinguish clearly the content of Theorems 1 and 2. The former tells us, in effect, how to obtain an infinite family of solutions of Eq. (2) whenever two solutions are known, but it does not guarantee that *all* solutions of Eq. (2) can be so obtained. Theorem 2, on the other hand, strengthens Theorem 1 by providing a condition on the particular solutions y_1 and y_2 which when it is fulfilled guarantees that the family $c_1y_1 + c_2y_2$ contains *every* solution of Eq. (2).

Theorem 3. If Y is any solution (no matter how special) of the nonhomogeneous equation

(1) $$\qquad y'' + P(x)y' + Q(x)y = R(x)$$

and if

$$c_1 y_1 + c_2 y_2$$

is the complete solution of the homogeneous equation obtained from Eq. (1) by deleting the term $R(x)$, then any solution whatsoever of Eq. (1), say $\bar{y}$, can be written

$$\bar{y} = c_1 y_1 + c_2 y_2 + Y$$

To prove this, we observe first that

$$\bar{y}'' + P(x)\bar{y}' + Q(x)\bar{y} = R(x)$$

and

$$Y'' + P(x)Y' + Q(x)Y = R(x)$$

since, by hypothesis, both $\bar{y}$ and Y are solutions of (1). If these equations be subtracted, we obtain

$$(\bar{y}'' - Y'') + P(x)(\bar{y}' - Y') + Q(x)(\bar{y} - Y) = 0$$

or

$$(\bar{y} - Y)'' + P(x)(\bar{y} - Y)' + Q(x)(\bar{y} - Y) = 0$$

Thus the quantity $(\bar{y} - Y)$ satisfies the homogeneous equation (2), and hence, whatever it may be, it must, by Theorem 2, be expressible in the form

$$(\bar{y} - Y) = c_1 y_1 + c_2 y_2$$

provided that $W(y_1, y_2) \neq 0$, that is, provided that $c_1 y_1 + c_2 y_2$ is (as we have assumed) the complete solution of (2). Hence, transposing,

$$\bar{y} = c_1 y_1 + c_2 y_2 + Y$$

and Theorem 3 is established.

The term Y, which can be *any* solution of (1), is called a **particular integral** of the nonhomogeneous equation. The expression $c_1 y_1 + c_2 y_2$, which is the complete solution of the homogeneous equation corresponding to (1), is called the **complementary function** of the nonhomogeneous equation.

The steps to be carried out in solving an equation of the form (1) can now be summarized as follows:

a. Delete the term $R(x)$ from the given equation, and then find two solutions of the remaining homogeneous equation which have a nonvanishing Wronskian. (Infinitely many such pairs exist.) Then combine these to form the complementary function, $c_1 y_1 + c_2 y_2$, of the given equation.

b. Find one particular solution, Y, of the nonhomogeneous equation itself.

c. Add the complementary function found in step *a* to the particular integral found in step *b* to obtain the general solution

$$c_1 y_1 + c_2 y_2 + Y$$

In the following paragraphs we shall examine in detail how these theoretical steps can be carried out when $P(x)$ and $Q(x)$ are constant, that is, when we have the so-called **linear differential equation with constant coefficients.**

2.2 The Homogeneous Linear Equation with Constant Coefficients. When $P(x)$ and $Q(x)$ are constant, the linear second-order differential equation may be written in the standard form

(1) $$ay'' + by' + cy = f(x)$$

A second standard form frequently encountered is based upon the so-called **operator notation.** In this, the symbol of differentiation, d/dx, is replaced by D, so that by definition

$$Dy \equiv \frac{dy}{dx}$$

As an immediate extension, the second derivative, which of course is obtained by a repetition of the process of differentiation, is written

$$D(Dy) = D^2 y$$

Similarly

$$\frac{d^3 y}{dx^3} = D(D^2 y) = D^3 y$$

$$\frac{d^4 y}{dx^4} = D(D^3 y) = D^4 y$$

. . . .

Evidently for positive integral powers of D (which are the only ones we have defined) the ordinary laws of exponents are fulfilled.

If due care is taken to see that variables are not moved across the sign of differentiation by a careless interchange of the order of factors in products, the operator D can be handled in most respects as though it were a simple algebraic quantity. For instance,

$$3D^2(x^2) - 10D(x^2) - 8(x^2) \equiv (3D^2 - 10D - 8)x^2$$
$$= (3D + 2)(D - 4)x^2 = (D - 4)(3D + 2)x^2$$

since

$$(3D^2 - 10D - 8)x^2 = 3(2) - 10(2x) - 8(x^2) = 6 - 20x - 8x^2$$
$$(3D + 2)(D - 4)x^2 = (3D + 2)(2x - 4x^2) = (6 - 24x) + (4x - 8x^2)$$
$$= 6 - 20x - 8x^2$$
$$(D - 4)(3D + 2)x^2 = (D - 4)(6x + 2x^2) = (6 + 4x) - (24x + 8x^2)$$
$$= 6 - 20x - 8x^2$$

Using the operator D, we evidently can write Eq. (1) in the alternative standard form

$$(1.1) \qquad (aD^2 + bD + c)y = f(x)$$

Many writers base the solution of Eq. (1) upon the operational properties of the symbol D. This seems both artificial and premature, and we shall postpone all operational methods until the chapter on the Laplace transformation, where operational calculus can be developed easily and efficiently in its proper setting. Until then, our use of the symbol D will be entirely a matter of notation.

Following the theory of the last section, we first attempt to find the general solution of the homogeneous equation

$$(2) \qquad ay'' + by' + cy = 0$$

or

$$(2.1) \qquad (aD^2 + bD + c)y = 0$$

obtained from (1) or (1.1) by deleting $f(x)$.

In attempting to find particular solutions of (2), it is natural to try

$$y = e^{mx}$$

where m is a constant yet to be determined, because all derivatives of this function are alike except for a numerical coefficient. Substituting into Eq. (2) and factoring e^{mx} from all terms gives

$$e^{mx}(am^2 + bm + c) = 0$$

as the condition to be satisfied in order that $y = e^{mx}$ should be a solution. Since e^{mx} can never be zero, it is thus necessary that

$$(3) \qquad am^2 + bm + c = 0$$

This purely algebraic equation is known as the **characteristic** or **auxiliary equation** of either Eq. (1) or Eq. (2). In practice it is obtained not by substituting $y = e^{mx}$ into the given differential equation and simplifying, but rather by substituting m^2 for y'', m for y', and 1 for y in the given equation, or still more simply, by equating the operational coefficient of y to zero:

$$aD^2 + bD + c = 0$$

The characteristic equation is a simple quadratic and will in general be satisfied by two values of m

$$m = \frac{-b \pm \sqrt{b^2 - 4ac}}{2a}$$

Using these two values, say m_1 and m_2, two solutions

$$y_1 = e^{m_1 x} \quad \text{and} \quad y_2 = e^{m_2 x}$$

can be constructed. From this pair, according to Theorem 1, an infinite family of solutions

(4) $$y = c_1 y_1 + c_2 y_2 \equiv c_1 e^{m_1 x} + c_2 e^{m_2 x}$$

can be formed. Moreover, by Theorem 2, if the Wronskian of these solutions is different from zero then (4) is the complete solution of Eq. (2), *i.e.*, it comprises all possible solutions of the equation. Accordingly we compute

$$W(y_1, y_2) = y_1 y_2' - y_2 y_1' = e^{m_1 x}(m_2 e^{m_2 x}) - e^{m_2 x}(m_1 e^{m_1 x})$$
$$= (m_2 - m_1)e^{(m_1 + m_2)x}$$

Since $e^{(m_1 + m_2)x}$ can never vanish, it is clear that *the general solution of Eq. (2) is always given by (4), except in the special case when $m_1 = m_2$, and the Wronskian vanishes identically.*

Example 1

What is the general solution of the differential equation

$$y'' + 7y' + 12y = 0$$

The characteristic equation in this case is

$$m^2 + 7m + 12 = 0$$

and its roots are

$$m_1 = -3, \quad m_2 = -4$$

Since these values of m are different, the complete solution is

$$y = c_1 e^{-3x} + c_2 e^{-4x}$$

Example 2

What is the general solution of the equation

$$y'' + 2y' + 5y = 0$$

The characteristic equation in this case is

$$m^2 + 2m + 5 = 0$$

and its roots are

$$m_1 = -1 + 2i, \quad m_2 = -1 - 2i$$

Since these are distinct, the general solution is

$$y = c_1 e^{(-1+2i)x} + c_2 e^{(-1-2i)x}$$

Although the last expression is undeniably the complete solution of the given equation, it is unsatisfactory for practical purposes because it involves imaginary exponentials which are awkward to handle and are not tabulated. It is therefore a matter of considerable importance to devise a more convenient form for the general solution of Eq. (2) in the case in which m_1 and m_2 are conjugate complex quantities.

To do this, let us suppose that

$$m_1 = p + iq \quad \text{and} \quad m_2 = p - iq$$

so that the general solution as first constructed is

$$y = c_1 e^{(p+iq)x} + c_2 e^{(p-iq)x}$$

By factoring out e^{px} this may be written as

$$y = e^{px}(c_1 e^{iqx} + c_2 e^{-iqx})$$

Now the expression in parentheses may be simplified by using the **Euler formulas***

$$e^{i\theta} = \cos \theta + i \sin \theta$$
$$e^{-i\theta} = \cos \theta - i \sin \theta$$

$$\cos \theta = \frac{e^{i\theta} + e^{-i\theta}}{2}$$

taking $\theta = qx$. The result of these substitutions is

$$y = e^{px}[c_1(\cos qx + i \sin qx) + c_2(\cos qx - i \sin qx)]$$
$$= e^{px}[(c_1 + c_2) \cos qx + i(c_1 - c_2) \sin qx]$$

If we now define two new constants by the equations

$$A = c_1 + c_2 \quad \text{and} \quad B = i(c_1 - c_2)$$

the general solution can finally be put in the form

$$y = e^{px}(A \cos qx + B \sin qx)$$

Example 2 (continued)

Applying this reasoning to Example 2, it is evident that $p = -1$ and $q = 2$. Hence the general solution can be written

$$y = e^{-x}(A \cos 2x + B \sin 2x)$$

Example 3

What is the general solution of the equation

$$(D^2 + 6D + 9)y = 0$$

In this case the characteristic equation

$$m^2 + 6m + 9 = 0$$

is a perfect square with roots $m_1 = -3$, $m_2 = -3$. Since these values are the same, it is impossible to build the general solution from them alone. In fact, if we write

$$y = c_1 e^{-3x} + c_2 e^{-3x}$$

*These may be recalled from the chapter on infinite series in almost any calculus text (or from the review of this material in Sec. A.4) or a more satisfactory development can be found in Sec. 9.7.

we have immediately

$$y = (c_1 + c_2)e^{-3x} = c_3 e^{-3x}$$

This cannot be the general solution of the given equation because it contains only one arbitrary constant, whereas the general solution of a second-order equation must contain two independent arbitrary constants.

To obtain the complete solution in the exceptional case, illustrated in Example 3, in which the characteristic equation has equal roots, it is necessary to have a second, independent solution. To find such a solution we may proceed as follows. Since $y = c_1 e^{m_1 x} + c_2 e^{m_2 x}$ is always a solution of the homogeneous equation (2) for all values of the constants c_1 and c_2, we may, if we choose, take

$$c_1 = -c_2 = \frac{1}{m_1 - m_2}$$

getting

$$y = \frac{e^{m_1 x} - e^{m_2 x}}{m_1 - m_2}$$

as one particular solution. In the exceptional case in which $m_2 = m_1$ this becomes an indeterminate of the form $0/0$. Evaluating it by L'Hospital's rule, i.e., differentiating numerator and denominator with respect to m_2 and then letting $m_2 = m_1$, we find in the limit

$$y = x e^{m_1 x}$$

There is thus every reason to believe that when $m_2 = m_1$ not only

$$y = e^{m_1 x} \qquad \text{but also} \qquad y = x e^{m_1 x}$$

is a solution of Eq. (2). That this is actually the case is easily verified by direct substitution, for we have

$$y = x e^{m_1 x}$$
$$y' = m_1 x e^{m_1 x} + e^{m_1 x}$$
$$y'' = m_1^2 x e^{m_1 x} + 2 m_1 e^{m_1 x}$$

Hence, substituting,

$$ay'' + by' + cy \equiv a(m_1^2 x e^{m_1 x} + 2 m_1 e^{m_1 x}) + b(m_1 x e^{m_1 x} + e^{m_1 x}) + c(x e^{m_1 x})$$
$$\text{(5)} \qquad = x e^{m_1 x}(am_1^2 + bm_1 + c) + e^{m_1 x}(2am_1 + b)$$

Now in any case, m_1 is a root of the characteristic equation and thus the entire first term in (5) vanishes identically. Moreover, when the characteristic equation has equal roots, the discriminant, $b^2 - 4ac$, must vanish. Hence in this case the general expression for the roots

$$m_1, m_2 = \frac{-b \pm \sqrt{b^2 - 4ac}}{2a}$$

reduces to

$$m_1 = m_2 = -\frac{b}{2a}$$

This value of m_1 clearly reduces the last term in (5) to zero.   This completes the proof that $y = xe^{m_1 x}$ is also a solution when $m_1 = m_2$.

It remains to verify that $y_1 = e^{m_1 x}$ and $y_2 = xe^{m_1 x}$ have a nonvanishing Wronskian:

$$
\begin{aligned}
W(y_1, y_2) &= y_1 y_2' - y_2 y_1' \\
&= e^{m_1 x}(e^{m_1 x} + xm_1 e^{m_1 x}) - xe^{m_1 x}(m_1 e^{m_1 x}) \\
&= e^{2m_1 x}
\end{aligned}
$$

Since $e^{2m_1 x}$ can never vanish, it follows that the Wronskian is always different from zero.   Thus $y_1 = e^{m_1 x}$ and $y_2 = xe^{m_1 x}$ are independent solutions, and thus the complete solution when $m_1 = m_2$ can be written

$$
y = c_1 e^{m_1 x} + c_2 xe^{m_1 x}
$$

Example 3 (continued)

Reconsidering Example 3 in the light of this analysis, we see that its general solution is

$$
y = c_1 e^{-3x} + c_2 xe^{-3x}
$$

The complete process for solving the homogeneous equation (2) in all possible cases is summarized in the accompanying table.

TABLE 2.1

Differential equation $ay'' + by' + cy = 0$ or $(aD^2 + bD + c)y = 0$
Characteristic equation $am^2 + bm + c = 0$ or $aD^2 + bD + c = 0$

Nature of the roots of the characteristic equation	Condition on the coefficients of the characteristic equation	General solution of the differential equation
Real and unequal $m_1 \neq m_2$	$b^2 - 4ac > 0$	$y = c_1 e^{m_1 x} + c_2 e^{m_2 x}$
Real and equal $m_1 = m_2$	$b^2 - 4ac = 0$	$y = c_1 e^{m_1 x} + c_2 xe^{m_1 x}$
Conjugate complex $m_1 = p + iq$ $m_2 = p - iq$	$b^2 - 4ac < 0$	$y = e^{px}(A \cos qx + B \sin qx)$

In particular applications, the two arbitrary constants in the general solution must usually be determined to fit initial conditions on y and y', or their equivalent.   The following examples will clarify the procedure.

Example 4

Find the solution of

$$
(D^2 - 4D + 4)y = 0
$$

for which $y = 1$ and $y' = -4$, when $x = 0$.

The characteristic equation of the differential equation is

$$m^2 - 4m + 4 = 0$$

Its roots are $m_1 = m_2 = 2$; hence the general solution is

$$y = c_1 e^{2x} + c_2 x e^{2x}$$

By differentiation we find

$$y' = (2c_1 + c_2)e^{2x} + 2c_2 x e^{2x}$$

Substituting the given data into the equations for y and y', respectively, we have

$$1 = c_1$$
$$-4 = 2c_1 + c_2$$

Hence

$$c_1 = 1 \qquad \text{and} \qquad c_2 = -6$$

and the required solution is

$$y = e^{2x} - 6x e^{2x}$$

Example 5

Find the solution of the equation

$$5y'' + 4y' + y = 0$$

for which $y = 0$ and $y' = 2$, when $x = 0$.

The characteristic equation here is

$$5m^2 + 4m + 1 = 0$$

and its roots are

$$m = \frac{-2 \pm i}{5}$$

Hence the general solution of the differential equation is

$$y = e^{-(2x/5)} \left(A \cos \frac{x}{5} + B \sin \frac{x}{5} \right)$$

Substituting the first of the given conditions into this expression, we find

$$A = 0$$

Differentiating the remaining portion of the general solution, we have

$$y' = B \left[-\frac{2}{5} e^{-(2x/5)} \sin \frac{x}{5} + \frac{1}{5} e^{-(2x/5)} \cos \frac{x}{5} \right]$$

Substituting the second of the initial conditions into this equation, we obtain

$$2 = \tfrac{1}{5} B \qquad \text{or} \qquad B = 10$$

The required solution is therefore

$$y = 10 e^{-(2x/5)} \sin \frac{x}{5}$$

Example 6

Find the solution of

$$3y'' + y' - 2y = 0$$

for which $y = 1$ when $x = 0$, and $y = 0$ when $x = 3$.

The characteristic equation in this case is

$$3m^2 + m - 2 = 0$$

and its roots are $m_1 = -1$ and $m_2 = \frac{2}{3}$. The general solution is therefore

$$y = c_1 e^{-x} + c_2 e^{2x/3}$$

There is no need to differentiate in this problem because neither of the given conditions involves y'. Substituting directly into the equation for y, we obtain

$$1 = c_1 + c_2$$
$$0 = c_1 e^{-3} + c_2 e^2$$

Solving these simultaneous linear equations for c_1 and c_2, we find

$$c_1 = -\frac{e^5}{1 - e^5}, \qquad c_2 = \frac{1}{1 - e^5}$$

The required solution is therefore

$$y = \frac{-e^5 e^{-x} + e^{2x/3}}{1 - e^5}$$

EXERCISES

1. Explain the difference between Dy and yD.
2. Verify that $(D + 1)(D^2 + 2)x^2 = (D^2 + 2)(D + 1)x^2$.
3. Is $(D + x)(D + 2x)e^x = (D + 2x)(D + x)e^x$? Explain.
4. What meaning, if any, can be assigned to D^{-1}? D^{-2}?

Find the general solution of each of the following equations:

5. $y'' + 3y' + 2y = 0$ *Ans.* $y = c_1 e^{-x} + c_2 e^{-2x}$
6. $4D^2 y + 4Dy + y = 0$ *Ans.* $y = c_1 e^{-(x/2)} + c_2 x e^{-(x/2)}$
7. $(D^2 - D)y = 0$ *Ans.* $y = a + be^x$
8. $10y'' + 6y' + y = 0$ ***Ans.*** $y = e^{-(3x/10)}\left(A\cos\frac{x}{10} + B\sin\frac{x}{10}\right)$
9. $9y'' + y = 0$ *Ans.* $y = A\cos\frac{x}{3} + B\sin\frac{x}{3}$
10. $y'' - 9y = 0$ *Ans.* $y = A\cosh 3x + B\sinh 3x$
11. $y'' - 8y' + 15y = 0$ 12. $y'' + y' - 2y = 0$
13. $5y'' + 6y' + y = 0$ 14. $y'' = 0$
15. $y'' + 2y' + y = 0$ 16. $y'' + 10y' + 26y = 0$
17. $2y'' + 3y' = 0$ 18. $9y'' - 12y' + 4y = 0$
19. $y'' + 20y' + 100y = 0$ 20. $2y'' - 6y' + 9y = 0$

21. Verify by direct substitution that

$$y_1 = Ae^{px}\cos qx \qquad \text{and} \qquad y_2 = Be^{px}\sin qx$$

are solutions of the equation $y'' - 2py' + (p^2 + q^2)y = 0$.

22. Show that the general solution of the equation $y'' + k^2 y = 0$ can be written in either of the forms

$$y = A\cos(kx + B) \qquad \text{or} \qquad y = C\sin(kx + D)$$

where A, B, C, D are arbitrary constants.
23. Show that the general solution of the equation $y'' - k^2 y = 0$ can be written $y = A\cosh kx + B\sinh kx$.

24. If the roots of its characteristic equation are real, show that no solution of the homogeneous differential equation can have more than one real zero.

Find the solution of each of the following equations which satisfies the given conditions.

25. $y'' + 3y' - 4y = 0$ $y = 5, y' = -5$ when $x = 0$ *Ans.* $y = 2e^{-4x} + 3e^x$
26. $y'' + 4y = 0$ $y = 0, y' = 6$ when $x = 0$ *Ans.* $y = 3 \sin 2x$
27. $25y'' + 20y' + 4y = 0$ $y = y' = 0$ when $x = 0$
28. $y'' - 5y' + 4y = 0$ $y' = 1$ when $x = 0, y' = 0$ when $x = 1$

29. $y'' - a^2y = 0$ $y = 0, y' = b$ when $x = 0$ *Ans.* $y = \dfrac{b}{a} \sinh ax$

30. $y'' - 4y = 0$ $y = 1, y' = -1$ when $x = 0$

2.3 The Nonhomogeneous Equation. Having found the complementary function for the nonhomogeneous equation

$$(1) \qquad\qquad ay'' + by' + cy = f(x)$$

by solving the related homogeneous equation, it remains to find a particular integral of (1) in order that its general solution

$$y = \text{complementary function} + \text{particular integral}$$

can be constructed. Procedures are available for finding particular integrals no matter what the form of $f(x)$ may be, and in the next section we shall examine one such method. However, in almost all cases of practical interest, $f(x)$ will be a sum of one or more terms of the following types:

> Constant
> x^n (n a positive integer)
> e^{rx}
> $\cos kx$
> $\sin kx$

or, less frequently, products of factors of these types. Particular integrals corresponding to terms of this sort can be found most easily by what is known as the method of **undetermined coefficients,** and to this we now turn our attention.

In general, this process consists in assuming a likely expression for the particular integral, Y, then substituting this "guess" into the nonhomogeneous equation, and finally determining the proper values of one or more unknown coefficients, carefully included in the tentative form, so that the trial Y will actually be a solution. In practice, it is unnecessary to start each determination with a pure guess, however, for each particular $f(x)$ requires a trial integral of a specific type, as indicated in the next table.

TABLE 2.2

Differential equation $ay'' + by' + cy = f(x)$ or $(aD^2 + bD + c)y = f(x)$

$f(x)$*	Necessary choice for the particular integral Y†
1. a (constant)	A
2. ax^n	$A_0x^n + A_1x^{n-1} + \cdots + A_{n-1}x + A_n$
3. ae^{rx}	Ae^{rx}
4. $a \cos kx$ 5. $a \sin kx$	$A \cos kx + B \sin kx$
6. $ax^ne^{rx} \cos kx$ 7. $ax^ne^{rx} \sin kx$	$(A_0x^n + \cdots + A_{n-1}x + A_n)e^{rx} \cos kx$ $\quad + (B_0x^n + \cdots + B_{n-1}x + B_n)e^{rx} \sin kx$

* When $f(x)$ consists of a sum of several terms, the appropriate particular integral is the sum of the particular integrals corresponding to these terms individually.

† Whenever a term in any of the trial integrals listed in this column is already a part of the complementary function of the given equation, it is necessary to modify the indicated choice by multiplying it by x before using it.

The following examples will clarify the application of this method.

Example 1

Find the general solution of the equation

$$(2D^2 + 3D + 1)y = 4 - e^x$$

As usual, the first step is the solution of the related homogeneous equation. In this case the characteristic equation is

$$2m^2 + 3m + 1 = 0$$

From its roots, $m_1 = -\frac{1}{2}$, $m_2 = -1$, we construct the complementary function

$$c_1e^{-\frac{1}{2}x} + c_2e^{-x}$$

Since $f(x)$ consists of the two terms 4 and $-e^x$, it is necessary either to use as a trial solution the sum of the trial integrals corresponding to each part, or else to find particular integrals for 4 and for $-e^x$ separately and add the results. Using the former method, we refer to lines 1 and 3 in Table 2.2 and assume

$$Y = A + Be^x†$$

† We must be careful not to make the mistake of taking the table too literally and writing $Y = A + Ae^x$. This amounts to the completely unwarranted assumption that the coefficient of e^x will be the same as the constant term in Y. The success of the process requires that the constants with which we begin must be arbitrary and independent, and our notation must not violate this condition.

Substituting this and its derivatives into the given equation, we find

$$2(Be^x) + 3(Be^x) + (A + Be^x) = 4 - e^x$$

or

$$6Be^x + A = 4 - e^x$$

This equation will be identically true if and only if the coefficients of like terms on both sides are the same. Hence

$$A = 4 \quad \text{and} \quad B = -\tfrac{1}{6}$$

Therefore

$$Y = 4 - \frac{e^x}{6}$$

The complete solution is thus

$$y = \text{complementary function} + Y = c_1 e^{-\frac{1}{2}x} + c_2 e^{-x} + 4 - \frac{e^x}{6}$$

Example 2

Find the general solution of the equation

$$y'' + 9y = 2x^2 + 4x + 7$$

The characteristic equation in this case is

$$m^2 + 9 = 0$$

Since its roots are $m = \pm 3i = 0 \pm 3i$, the complementary function is

$$A \cos 3x + B \sin 3x$$

According to Table 2.2, the necessary trial solutions corresponding to the respective terms in the right member of the differential equation are

$$A_0 x^2 + A_1 x + A_2, \; a_0 x + a_1, \; \text{and} \; \alpha_0$$

However, the last two are clearly contained in the first, and no extra generality is achieved by including them. Hence we assume simply

$$Y = A_0 x^2 + A_1 x + A_2$$

Substituting this into the differential equation gives

$$(2A_0) + 9(A_0 x^2 + A_1 x + A_2) = 2x^2 + 4x + 7$$

Equating coefficients of x^2, x, and the constant term x^0, we obtain the three equations

$$9A_0 = 2, \quad 9A_1 = 4, \quad 2A_0 + 9A_2 = 7$$

Hence

$$A_0 = \tfrac{2}{9}, \quad A_1 = \tfrac{4}{9}, \quad A_2 = \tfrac{59}{81}$$

and so the complete solution is

$$y = A \cos 3x + B \sin 3x + \frac{18x^2 + 36x + 59}{81}$$

Example 3

Find the general solution of the equation

$$y'' + 5y' + 6y = 3e^{-2x} + e^{3x}$$

The roots of the characteristic equation,

$$m^2 + 5m + 6 = 0$$

are $m_1 = -2$, $m_2 = -3$.   Hence the complementary function is

$$c_1 e^{-2x} + c_2 e^{-3x}$$

For the trial solution corresponding to $3e^{-2x}$ we would normally try Ae^{-2x}.   However, e^{-2x} is already a part of the complementary function, and thus, following the second footnote in Table 2.2, we must multiply this by x before including it in Y. For the term e^{3x}, the normal choice for a trial solution, namely, Be^{3x}, is satisfactory as it stands, since e^{3x} is not contained in the complementary function.   Hence we assume

$$Y = Axe^{-2x} + Be^{3x}$$

Substituting this into the differential equation, we have

$$(4Axe^{-2x} - 4Ae^{-2x} + 9Be^{3x}) + 5(-2Axe^{-2x} + Ae^{-2x} + 3Be^{3x}) + 6(Axe^{-2x} + Be^{3x})$$
$$= 3e^{-2x} + e^{3x}$$

or

$$Ae^{-2x} + 30Be^{3x} = 3e^{-2x} + e^{3x}$$

Equating coefficients of like terms, we find $A = 3$ and $B = \frac{1}{30}$.   Hence

$$Y = 3xe^{-2x} + \frac{e^{3x}}{30}$$

and the complete solution is

$$y = c_1 e^{-2x} + c_2 e^{-3x} + 3xe^{-2x} + \frac{e^{3x}}{30}$$

Example 4

What is the complete solution of the equation

$$y'' + 4y' + 5y = -2 \cos x$$

The characteristic equation is $m^2 + 4m + 5 = 0$, and its roots are $m = -2 \pm i$. Hence the complementary function is

$$e^{-2x}(A \cos x + B \sin x)$$

As particular integral we assume

$$Y = C \cos x + D \sin x$$

noting that $\cos x$ and $\sin x$ are *not* terms (but merely parts of terms) of the complementary function.   Substituting Y into the differential equation gives

$$(-C \cos x - D \sin x) + 4(-C \sin x + D \cos x) + 5(C \cos x + D \sin x) = -2 \cos x$$

or

$$(4C + 4D) \cos x + (4D - 4C) \sin x = -2 \cos x$$

Equating coefficients of the cosine and sine terms gives the simultaneous equations

$$4C + 4D = -2$$
$$-4C + 4D = 0$$

Solving these for C and D, we obtain $C = -\frac{1}{4}$, $D = -\frac{1}{4}$. Hence

$$Y = -\frac{\cos x + \sin x}{4}$$

and finally

$$y = e^{-2x}(A \cos x + B \sin x) - \frac{\cos x + \sin x}{4}$$

Example 5

What is the general solution of the equation

$$y'' - 2y' + y = xe^x - e^x$$

The characteristic equation here is $m^2 - 2m + 1 = 0$ and its roots are $m_1 = m_2 = 1$. Hence the complementary function is

$$c_1 e^x + c_2 x e^x$$

According to line 6 of Table 2.2 (with $n = r = 1$, $k = 0$) we would normally try

$$Y = (A_0 x + A_1)e^x$$

as a particular integral. (Note that the trial solution ordinarily required for $-e^x$ is automatically included in this choice.) However, these terms are already contained in the complementary function; hence following the second rule in the table, we multiply Y by x, getting as a new trial solution

$$Y = (A_0 x^2 + A_1 x)e^x$$

But this still contains a term which is a part of the complementary function, and thus we must multiply again by x before we obtain a suitable particular integral

$$Y = (A_0 x^3 + A_1 x^2)e^x$$

No term in this expression duplicates anything in the complementary function. Hence we can now proceed as usual and substitute into the differential equation, getting

$$[A_0 x^3 + (6A_0 + A_1)x^2 + (6A_0 + 4A_1)x + 2A_1]e^x$$
$$- 2[A_0 x^3 + (3A_0 + A_1)x^2 + 2A_1 x]e^x$$
$$+ (A_0 x^3 + A_1 x^2)e^x = xe^x - e^x$$

or

$$6A_0 x e^x + 2A_1 e^x = xe^x - e^x$$

This will be identically true if and only if $A_0 = \frac{1}{6}$ and $A_1 = -\frac{1}{2}$. Hence

$$Y = \left(\frac{x^3}{6} - \frac{x^2}{2}\right) e^x$$

and thus the complete solution is

$$y = c_1 e^x + c_2 x e^x - \frac{x^2 e^x}{2} + \frac{x^3 e^x}{6}$$

EXERCISES

Find the general solution of each of the following equations:

1. $y'' + 4y' + 3y = x$ *Ans.* $y = Ae^{-3x} + Be^{-x} + \dfrac{3x - 4}{9}$

2. $y'' + 3y' = 2 \sin x + \cos x$ *Ans.* $y = A + Be^{-3x} + \dfrac{\sin x - 7 \cos x}{10}$

3. $y'' + y' = 1 + 2x$ *Ans.* $y = A + Be^{-x} + x^2 - x$

4. $y'' + y = \sin x$ *Ans.* $y = A \sin x + B \cos x - \tfrac{1}{2}x \cos x$

5. $y'' - y = e^x + 2$ *Ans.* $y = Ae^x + Be^{-x} - 2 + \tfrac{1}{2}xe^x$

6. $y'' + y = \cos^2 x$ $\left(\text{Hint: } \cos^2 x = \dfrac{1 + \cos 2x}{2}\right)$

7. $y'' = \cos 3x$ **8.** $y'' - 2y' + y = 3xe^{-x}$

9. $y'' + 2y' + 10y = 3x^2$ **10.** $(D^2 + 4D + 5)y = \sin x \sin 3x$

11. $y'' + 4y' + 3y = 2e^x$ **12.** $y'' + 4y = x \sin x$

13. $y'' + y' + y = x^3 - 4$ **14.** $(D^2 + 1)y = e^x \cos x$

15. Find a particular integral of the equation

$$(D - m_1)(D - m_2)y = e^{kx}$$

Discuss the limiting case when $k \to m_1$, and explain why it is necessary to use Axe^{m_1x} as a particular integral under these conditions.   (Hint: Show that

$$\frac{e^{kx} - e^{m_1x}}{(k - m_1)(k - m_2)}$$

is a particular integral of the given equation, and consider this as $k \to m_1$.)

Find the solution of each of the following equations which satisfies the given conditions:

16. $y'' + 5y' + 4y = 20e^x$ $y = 0, y' = -2$ when $x = 0$

Ans. $y = -4e^{-x} + 2e^{-4x} + 2e^x$

17. $y'' + 9y' = 3$ $y = y' = 0$ when $x = 0$ *Ans.* $y = \dfrac{-1 + 9x + e^{-9x}}{27}$

18. $y'' + 4y' + 3y = 4e^{-x}$ $y = 0, y' = 2$ when $x = 0$

19. $y'' + 6y' + 5y = -5x + 4$ $y = 1, y' = 0,$ when $x = 0$

20. $y'' + y = \sin 2x$ $y = 1$ when $x = 0, y = 2$ when $x = \tfrac{1}{2}\pi$

2.4 Particular Integrals by the Method of Variation of Parameters.

For certain theoretical purposes, and occasionally in the applications, it is desirable to be able to find a particular integral of the equation

$$(1) \qquad\qquad ay'' + by' + cy = f(x)$$

in cases where the method of undetermined coefficients will not work, *i.e.*, when $f(x)$ is a function not covered by Table 2.2. A procedure known as **variation of parameters** will do this for all linear equations, including those with variable coefficients,

$$(2) \qquad\qquad y'' + P(x)y' + Q(x)y = R(x)$$

regardless of the form of $R(x)$, provided that the general solution of the corresponding homogeneous equation is known. It differs from the method of undetermined coefficients in that integration rather than differentiation is required, which means that the price we pay for greater generality is usually the inconvenience of integrals which cannot be evaluated in terms of familiar functions.

The fundamental idea behind the process is this. Instead of using two arbitrary *constants*, c_1 and c_2, to combine two independent solutions of the homogeneous equation

$$(3) \qquad y'' + P(x)y' + Q(x)y = 0$$

as we do in constructing the complementary function, we attempt to find two *functions of x*, say u and v, such that

$$Y = uy_1 + vy_2$$

will be a solution of the nonhomogeneous equation (2). Having two unknown functions, u and v, we require two equations for their determination. One of these will be obtained by substituting Y into the given differential equation (2); the other remains at our disposal. As the analysis proceeds it will become clear what this second condition should be.

From

$$Y = uy_1 + vy_2$$

we have, by differentiation,

$$Y' = (uy_1' + u'y_1) + (vy_2' + v'y_2)$$

Another differentiation will clearly introduce second derivatives of the unknown functions u and v, with attendant complications, unless we arrange to eliminate the first derivative terms u' and v' from Y'. This can be done if we make

$$(4) \qquad u'y_1 + v'y_2 = 0$$

which thus becomes the necessary second condition on u and v.

Proceeding now with

$$Y' = uy_1' + vy_2'$$

we find

$$Y'' = (uy_1'' + u'y_1') + (vy_2'' + v'y_2')$$

Substituting Y, Y', and Y'' into Eq. (2), we obtain

$$(uy_1'' + u'y_1' + vy_2'' + v'y_2') + P(x)(uy_1' + vy_2') + Q(x)(uy_1 + vy_2) = R(x)$$

or

$$u[y_1'' + P(x)y_1' + Q(x)y_1] + v[y_2'' + P(x)y_2' + Q(x)y_2] + u'y_1' + v'y_2' = R(x)$$

The expressions in brackets vanish because by hypothesis both y_1 and y_2 are solutions of the homogeneous equation (3). Hence we find for the other condition on u and v,

$$(5) \qquad u'y_1' + v'y_2' = R(x)$$

Solving Eqs. (4) and (5) for u' and v', we obtain

$$(6) \qquad u' = \left(-\frac{y_2}{y_1 y_2' - y_2 y_1'} \right) R(x) \qquad \text{and} \qquad v' = \left(\frac{y_1}{y_1 y_2' - y_2 y_1'} \right) R(x)$$

The functions y_1, y_2, y_1', y_2', and $R(x)$ are all known. Hence u and v can be found by a single integration. With u and v known, the particular integral

$$Y = u y_1 + v y_2$$

is completely determined.

We should notice, of course, that if $y_1 y_2' - y_2 y_1' = 0$, the solution for u' and v' cannot be carried out. However, $y_1 y_2' - y_2 y_1'$ is precisely the Wronskian of the two solutions y_1 and y_2, and if these are independent, as we suppose them to be, then their Wronskian cannot vanish.

Example 1

Find the general solution of $y'' + y = \sec x$.

By inspection we see that the complementary function in this case is

$$A \cos x + B \sin x$$

Hence, taking

$$y_1 = \cos x \qquad \text{and} \qquad y_2 = \sin x$$

we have, from Eq. (6),

$$u' = \left[-\frac{\sin x}{\cos x (\cos x) - \sin x (-\sin x)} \right] \sec x = -\tan x$$

$$v' = \left[\frac{\cos x}{\cos x (\cos x) - \sin x (-\sin x)} \right] \sec x = 1$$

Therefore

$$u = -\int \tan x \, dx = \log \cos x$$
$$v = \int dx = x$$

and thus

$$Y = u y_1 + v y_2 = (\log \cos x) \cos x + x \sin x$$

Finally

$$y = A \cos x + B \sin x + (\log \cos x) \cos x + x \sin x$$

EXERCISES

Find the general solution of each of the following equations:

1. $y'' + 4y' + 4y = \dfrac{e^{-2x}}{x^2}$ *Ans.* $y = ae^{-2x} + bxe^{-2x} - e^{-2x} \log x$

2. $y'' + 2y' + 10y = e^{-x} \sec^3 3x$

$$\text{Ans. } y = e^{-x}(A \cos 3x + B \sin 3x) + \left(\frac{-1 + 2 \sin^2 3x}{18 \cos 3x} \right) e^{-x}$$

3. $y'' + 2y' + y = e^x \log x$

4. $y'' - y = \operatorname{sech} x \tanh x$

5. $y'' + \dfrac{y}{4} = \dfrac{x^2 + 3}{\sqrt{x}}$

6. Using the method of variation of parameters, find a particular integral of the equation $y'' + \omega^2 y = \sin kx$. Discuss the limiting case when $k \to \omega$, and show that it leads to $Y = -\dfrac{x \cos \omega x}{2\omega}$.

7. Show that the general solution of the equation $y'' + k^2 y = f(x)$ can be written

$$y = A \cos kx + B \sin kx + \frac{1}{k} \int_0^x \sin k(x - s) f(s) ds$$

Derive expressions analogous to that in Exercise **7** for the general solution of each of the following equations:

8. $y'' + 2ay' + a^2 y = f(x)$
9. $y'' + 2ay' + (a^2 + b^2)y = f(x)$
10. $y'' + 2ay' + (a^2 - b^2)y = f(x)$

2.5 Equations of Higher Order. The theory of the linear equation of order higher than 2 parallels in all significant details the second-order case. For the homogeneous equation, the substitution $y = e^{mx}$ still leads to the characteristic equation, which may be obtained in a specific problem simply by replacing each derivative by the corresponding power of m. The order of this algebraic equation will be the same as the order of the differential equation itself; hence the number of roots, $m_1, m_2, m_3, \ldots$, will equal the order of the differential equation. From these roots, the solution of the differential equation can be constructed by adding together the terms that were listed in Table 2.1, Sec. 2.2, as corresponding to each of the various root types. The only extension which is necessary is required when the characteristic equation has roots of multiplicity more than 2. *If y_1 is the solution normally corresponding to a root m_1, and if this root occur k (>2) times, then not only are y_1 and xy_1 solutions (as in the second-order case), but $x^2 y_1, x^3 y_1, \ldots, x^{k-1} y_1$ are also solutions, and must be included in the complementary function.*

For the nonhomogeneous equation it is still true that the general solution is the sum of the complementary function, obtained by solving the associated homogeneous equation, and a particular integral. The particular integral can, for the important cases considered in Sec. 2.3, be found just as before by using the tentative solutions listed in Table 2.2, Sec. 2.3. Variation of parameters can be extended to those problems which the method of undetermined coefficients cannot handle. An example or two will make these ideas clear.

Example 1

Find the general solution of the equation

$$y''' + 5y'' + 9y' + 5y = 3e^{2x}$$

The characteristic equation in this case is

$$m^3 + 5m^2 + 9m + 5 = 0$$

By inspection*

$$m = -1$$

is seen to be a root.   Hence

$$c_1 e^{-x}$$

must be one term in the complementary function.   When the factor corresponding to this root is divided out of the characteristic equation, there remains the quadratic equation

$$m^2 + 4m + 5 = 0$$

Its roots are

$$m = -2 \pm i$$

and thus the complementary function must also contain

$$e^{-2x}(c_2 \cos x + c_3 \sin x)$$

The entire complementary function is therefore

$$c_1 e^{-x} + e^{-2x}(c_2 \cos x + c_3 \sin x)$$

For a particular integral, we try as usual $Y = Ae^{2x}$.   Substituting this into the differential equation gives

$$(8Ae^{2x}) + 5(4Ae^{2x}) + 9(2Ae^{2x}) + 5(Ae^{2x}) = 3e^{2x}$$

or

$$51Ae^{2x} = 3e^{2x}$$

Hence

$$A = \frac{1}{17}, \qquad Y = \frac{e^{2x}}{17}$$

and therefore

$$y = c_1 e^{-x} + e^{-2x}(c_2 \cos x + c_3 \sin x) + \frac{e^{2x}}{17}$$

Example 2

Find the general solution of the equation

$$(D^4 + 8D^2 + 16)y = -\sin x$$

The characteristic equation here is

$$m^4 + 8m^2 + 16 = 0 \qquad \text{or} \qquad (m^2 + 4)^2 = 0$$

The roots of this equation are $m = \pm 2i, \ \pm 2i$.   Hence the complementary function contains not only the terms

$$c_1 \cos 2x + c_2 \sin 2x$$

---

* In general, the most difficult feature of the solution of a linear differential equation of order higher than 2 is the determination of the roots of the characteristic equation. Of the many methods which are available for this purpose, two, Graeffe's root-squaring process and the method of interpolation, are discussed in detail in Sec. 16.1.

but also these terms multiplied by x, and is therefore

$$c_1 \cos 2x + c_2 \sin 2x + c_3 x \cos 2x + c_4 x \sin 2x$$

To find a particular integral, we try $Y = A \cos x + B \sin x$, which on substitution into the differential equation gives

$$(A \cos x + B \sin x) + 8(- A \cos x - B \sin x) + 16(A \cos x + B \sin x) = -\sin x$$

or

$$9A \cos x + 9B \sin x = -\sin x$$

This will be an identity if and only if $A = 0$ and $B = -\frac{1}{9}$. Therefore $Y = -\frac{1}{9} \sin x$, and the complete solution is

$$y = c_1 \cos 2x + c_2 \sin 2x + c_3 x \cos 2x + c_4 x \sin 2x - \frac{\sin x}{9}$$

Example 3

Find the solution of the equation

$$(D^4 + 3D^3 + 3D^2 + D)y = 2x + 8$$

for which $y = y' = y'' = y''' = 0$, when $x = 0$.

The characteristic equation in this case is

$$m^4 + 3m^3 + 3m^2 + m = 0 \qquad \text{or} \qquad m(m + 1)^3 = 0$$

Its roots are $m = 0, -1, -1, -1$, and hence the complementary function, taking due account of the triple root, is

$$a + be^{-x} + cxe^{-x} + dx^2e^{-x}$$

To find a particular integral, we would ordinarily assume

$$Y = Ax + B$$

However, one term in this expression (the constant B) duplicates a term already in the complementary function (the constant a). Hence we must multiply our original trial solution by x before using it.

Substituting the new expression

$$Y = Ax^2 + Bx$$

into the differential equation, we find

$$0 + 3(0) + 3(2A) + (2Ax + B) = 2x + 8$$

or

$$2Ax + (6A + B) = 2x + 8$$

For this to be identically true requires that $A = 1$ and $B = 2$. Hence $Y = x^2 + 2x$, and the complete solution is

$$(1) \qquad y = a + be^{-x} + cxe^{-x} + dx^2e^{-x} + x^2 + 2x$$

In order to impose the given initial conditions, it is necessary that we have expressions for y', y'', and y''' as well as for y. Hence we differentiate, getting

$$(2) \qquad y' = -be^{-x} + c(e^{-x} - xe^{-x}) + d(2xe^{-x} - x^2e^{-x}) + 2x + 2$$
$$(3) \qquad y'' = be^{-x} + c(-2e^{-x} + xe^{-x}) + d(2e^{-x} - 4xe^{-x} + x^2e^{-x}) + 2$$
$$(4) \qquad y''' = -be^{-x} + c(3e^{-x} - xe^{-x}) + d(-6e^{-x} + 6xe^{-x} - x^2e^{-x})$$

Substituting the given conditions into Eqs. (1), (2), (3), and (4), we find

$$0 = a + b$$
$$0 = -b + c +2$$
$$0 = b - 2c + 2d +2$$
$$0 = -b + 3c - 6d$$

Solving these simultaneously for a, b, c, and d gives

$$a = -12, \qquad b = 12, \qquad c = 10, \qquad d = 3$$

and finally

$$y = -12 + 12e^{-x} + 10xe^{-x} + 3x^2 e^{-x} + x^2 + 2x$$

EXERCISES

Find the general solution of each of the following equations:

1. $(D^3 + 6D^2 + 11D + 6)y = 2x$　　*Ans.*　$y = ae^{-x} + be^{-2x} + ce^{-3x} + \dfrac{6x - 11}{18}$

2. $y''' + y'' = e^x$

3. $(D^4 + 3D^3 + 3D^2 + 3D + 2)y = x^2 - x$

4. $y''' + 2y'' + 2y' = 3$

5. $y''' + 3y'' + 3y' + y = e^{-2x}$

Find the solution of each of the following equations which satisfies the given conditions:

6. $(D^4 - 16)y = 64x$　　$y = y' = y'' = y''' = 0$ when $x = 0$

　　　　　　　　　　　　　　　Ans.　$y = \sin 2x + \sinh 2x - 4x$

7. $(D^4 - 1)y = \sin 2x$　　$y = y' = 0$ when $x = 0$, $y = y' = 0$ when $x = \pi$

8. $y''' - 2y'' + 5y' = \sin x$　　$y = y' = y'' = 0$ when $x = 0$

9. $y''' + y'' + y' + y = x + 2$　　$y = 0$, $y' = \frac{3}{2}$, $y'' = 0$ when $x = 0$

10. $(D^4 + 5D^2 + 4)y = \cos 2x$　　$y = y' = y'' = 0$, $y''' = 1$ when $x = 0$

2.6 Applications. Linear differential equations with constant coefficients find their most important application in the study of electrical circuits and vibrating mechanical systems. So useful to engineers are the results of such analysis that we shall devote an entire chapter to its major features. There are of course other applications only slightly less striking, and although we cannot discuss them at length, we shall conclude this chapter with some typical examples.

Example 1

A perfectly flexible cable of length L, weighing w lb/ft, hangs over a pulley as shown in Fig. 2.1. The radius of the pulley is r, and its weight is equal to the total weight of the cable. Friction between the cable and the pulley prevents any relative slipping, although the pulley itself is free to turn without appreciable friction. At $t = 0$, the cable is released from rest in a position in which the portion hanging on one side is a ft longer than that hanging on the other. Discuss the motion of the system.

To describe the position of the system at any instant, let us take as coordinate the distance y, through which the short end of the cable has moved upward. The angle of rotation of the pulley can easily be expressed in terms of y, for as the short end of the cable is raised y ft, the point P moves a distance y to the point P'.   Hence

$$r\theta = y \quad \text{or} \quad \theta = \frac{y}{r} \quad \text{and} \quad \frac{d\theta}{dt} = \frac{1}{r}\frac{dy}{dt}$$

It will be convenient to formulate the differential equation governing this problem through the use of the so-called **energy method**.   From the fundamental law of the conservation of energy, it follows that *if no energy is lost through friction, then in a mechanical system the sum of the instantaneous kinetic and potential energies must remain*

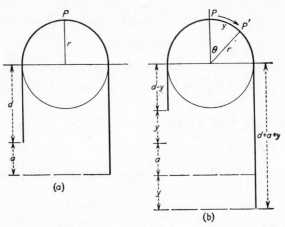

Fig. 2.1.

constant.   In the present problem we have two types of kinetic energy.   **The first is** the rotational energy of the pulley which is

$$(1) \qquad \frac{1}{2}I\left(\frac{d\theta}{dt}\right)^2 = \frac{1}{2}\left(\frac{wL}{g}\frac{r^2}{2}\right)\left(\frac{1}{r}\frac{dy}{dt}\right)^2 = \frac{1}{4}\frac{wL}{g}\left(\frac{dy}{dt}\right)^2$$

The second is the translational energy of the cable which is

$$(2) \qquad \frac{1}{2}M\left(\frac{dy}{dt}\right)^2 = \frac{1}{2}\frac{wL}{g}\left(\frac{dy}{dt}\right)^2$$

The potential energy of the system consists of the constant potential energy of the pulley and the portion of the cable in contact with it, say A, plus the varying potential energy in the hanging portions of the cable.   To compute the latter, let us take the horizontal line through the center of the pulley as the reference level.   Then if d be the initial length of the cable on the short side, the instantaneous length on this side will be $(d - y)$.   The weight of this length is $(d - y)w$, and its center of gravity is $(d - y)/2$ ft *below* the reference level.   Hence its potential energy is

$$(3) \qquad -\frac{(d - y)}{2}w(d - y) = -(d - y)^2\frac{w}{2}$$

Similarly, on the long side, the instantaneous length of the cable is $(d + a + y)$. Its weight is $(d + a + y)w$, and its center of gravity is $\dfrac{d + a + y}{2}$ ft below the reference level.   Its potential energy is therefore

$$(4) \qquad\qquad -(d + a + y)^2 \frac{w}{2}$$

Substituting from (1), (2), (3), and (4) into the relation

$$\text{K.E.} + \text{P.E.} = \text{constant}$$

we have

$$\frac{1}{4}\frac{wL}{g}\left(\frac{dy}{dt}\right)^2 + \frac{1}{2}\frac{wL}{g}\left(\frac{dy}{dt}\right)^2 + A - \frac{(d - y)^2 w}{2} - \frac{(d + a + y)^2 w}{2} = \text{constant}$$

or

$$\frac{3}{4}\frac{wL}{g}\left(\frac{dy}{dt}\right)^2 - \frac{w}{2}[(d - y)^2 + (d + a + y)^2] = C$$

Differentiating this with respect to time, we obtain

$$\frac{3}{2}\frac{wL}{g}\frac{dy}{dt}\frac{d^2y}{dt^2} - \frac{w}{2}[-2(d - y) + 2(d + a + y)]\frac{dy}{dt} = 0$$

Dividing out the factor dy/dt and collecting terms, we have the differential equation of the motion

$$\frac{3wL}{2g}\frac{d^2y}{dt^2} - 2wy = aw \qquad \text{or} \qquad \frac{d^2y}{dt^2} - \frac{4g}{3L}y = \frac{2ag}{3L}$$

The solution of this equation presents no difficulty, and we obtain at once

$$y = A_1 \cosh\left(2\sqrt{\frac{g}{3L}}\,t\right) + A_2 \sinh\left(2\sqrt{\frac{g}{3L}}\,t\right) - \frac{a}{2}$$

Since the cable starts from rest, both y and dy/dt are initially zero.   Hence

$$A_1 - \frac{a}{2} = 0 \qquad \text{and} \qquad A_2 = 0$$

and therefore

$$y = \frac{a}{2}\left[\cosh\left(2\sqrt{\frac{g}{3L}}\,t\right) - 1\right]$$

This is valid until the end of the short side of the cable is pulled up into contact with the pulley.

Example 2

A weight W_2 is suspended from a pulley of weight W_1, as shown in Fig. 2.2.   If a spring of **modulus** k, that is, a spring requiring k units of force to extend it one unit of length, is inserted in the otherwise inextensible cable which supports the pulley, find the frequency with which the system will vibrate in the vertical direction if displaced slightly from its equilibrium position.   Friction between the cable and the pulley prevents any slippage, but all other frictional effects are to be neglected.

As coordinate to describe the system we choose the vertical displacement y of the center of the pulley, the downward direction being taken as positive.   Now when the center of the pulley moves a distance y, the length of the spring must change by $2y$. Moreover, as this happens, the pulley must rotate through an angle

$$\theta = \frac{y}{R}$$

With these facts in mind we can calculate the total instantaneous energy of the system without difficulty.

The potential energy consists of two parts: (a) the potential energy of the weights W_1 and W_2 due to their position in the gravitational field and (b) the potential energy stored in the stretched spring. Taking the equilibrium position as the reference level for potential energy, we have for (a)

$$(5) \qquad\qquad -(W_1 + W_2)y$$

the minus sign indicating that a positive y corresponds to a lowering of the weight and hence a decrease in the potential energy. The potential energy stored in the

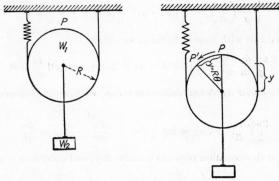

FIG. 2.2.

spring is simply the amount of work required to stretch the spring from its equilibrium elongation, say e, to its instantaneous elongation $e + 2y$. Since the force in the spring at any time is $F = $ elongation $\times$ force per unit elongation $= sk$. we have for the potential energy of type b

$$(6) \qquad W = \int F\,ds = \int_e^{e+2y} ks\,ds = k\left(\frac{s^2}{2}\right)\Big|_e^{e+2y} = 2ky^2 + 2k\,ey$$

The kinetic energy likewise consists of two parts, (a) the energy of translation of the weights W_1 and W_2, namely,

$$(7) \qquad \frac{1}{2}\left(\frac{W_1 + W_2}{g}\right)(\dot{y})^2\dagger$$

and (b) the energy of rotation of the pulley, namely,

$$\frac{1}{2}I(\dot\theta)^2 = \frac{1}{2}\left(\frac{W_1}{g}\frac{R^2}{2}\right)\left(\frac{\dot{y}}{R}\right)^2$$

$$(8) \qquad\qquad = \frac{W_1}{4g}(\dot{y})^2$$

The conservation of energy now requires that

Potential energy + kinetic energy = constant

† In problems in dynamics, first and second derivatives *with respect to time* are often indicated by placing one and two dots, respectively, over the variable in question.

or, substituting from Eqs. (5), (6), (7), and (8),

$$\frac{W_1}{4g}\,(\dot{y})^2 + \left(\frac{W_1 + W_2}{2g}\right)(\dot{y})^2 + (2ky^2 + 2k\,ey) - (W_1 + W_2)y = C$$

Differentiating this with respect to time gives us

$$\frac{W_1}{2g}\,\dot{y}\ddot{y} + \left(\frac{W_1 + W_2}{g}\right)\dot{y}\ddot{y} + 4ky\dot{y} + 2k\,e\dot{y} - (W_1 + W_2)\dot{y} = 0$$

or, dividing out $\dot{y}$ and collecting terms,

$$\left(\frac{3W_1 + 2W_2}{2g}\right)\ddot{y} + 4ky = (W_1 + W_2) - 2k\,e = 0$$

since the elongation of the spring in equilibrium e is simply

$$e = \frac{W_1 + W_2}{2k}$$

The differential equation describing the vertical movement of the system is therefore

$$\ddot{y} + \left(\frac{8kg}{3W_1 + 2W_2}\right)y = 0$$

and its general solution is

$$y = A\,\cos\left(\sqrt{\frac{8kg}{3W_1 + 2W_2}}\,t\right) + B\sin\left(\sqrt{\frac{8kg}{3W_1 + 2W_2}}\,t\right)$$

Regardless of the values of A and B, this represents vibratory motion of frequency

$$\frac{1}{2\pi}\sqrt{\frac{8kg}{3W_1 + 2W_2}} \qquad \text{cycles/unit time}$$

The bending of beams is another problem in which linear differential equations arise. To investigate this, let us imagine a beam as made up of a very large number of parallel fibers whose elastic behavior under tension or compression is described by **Hooke's law**

(9)
$$\frac{\text{Stress (lb/in.}^2)}{\text{Strain (in./in.)}} = \text{constant}$$

This proportionality constant between stress and strain is called **Young's modulus,** or the **modulus of elasticity,** and is usually denoted by the symbol E.

Now when a beam is bent, it is an observed fact that the fibers in one face of the beam are compressed while those in the opposite face are stretched. Somewhere between the upper and lower surfaces there must therefore be a transition point between the region of tension and the region of compression, where the fibers are neither stretched nor shortened. The surface separating these two regions is known as the **neutral surface** of the beam, and the curve of any particular fiber in this surface is known as the **elastic curve,** or **deflection curve,** of the beam.   The line in which the neutral surface is cut by any plane cross section of the beam is called the **neutral axis** of that section.   It is in the determination of the deflection curve that differential equations are encountered.

A second observed fact is that plane cross sections of a beam remain plane after bending if the deflection is small.   With this in mind let us consider a very short segment Δs of a bent beam, as shown in Fig. 2.3. The intersection P of the lines AB and CD is the center of curvature of the infinitesimal segment Δs, and over this small length the various fibers

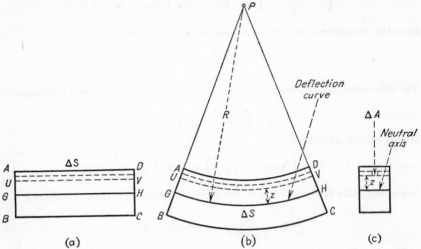

FIG. 2.3.   An infinitesimal segment of a bent beam.

such as AD, UV, GH, and BC may be regarded as arcs of circles having their centers at P.   In particular, the length $GP = HP = R$ is the radius of curvature of the deflection curve for the infinitesimal portion of the beam under consideration.

Now from plane geometry, arcs of circular sectors of the same central angle are proportional to their radii.   Hence if we let e be the amount by which a general fiber such as UV, at a distance z from the neutral surface, has changed from its original length Δs, we can write

$$\frac{\Delta s}{\Delta s - e} = \frac{R}{R - z}$$

or, simplifying,

$$\frac{z}{R} = \frac{e}{\Delta s} = \text{elongation per unit length} = \text{strain}$$

If σ be the stress, *i.e.*, the force per unit area, in the fiber UV, we then have by Hooke's law, Eq. (9),

$$\sigma = \frac{e}{\Delta s} E = \frac{zE}{R}$$

On the other hand, if the cross-section area of the fiber UV is ΔA, the actual force in the fiber is

(10) $$\Delta F = \sigma \, \Delta A = \frac{Ez \, \Delta A}{R}$$

We can now form a picture of the distribution of the forces in the individual fibers as they act perpendicular to a general cross section. The total force acting over such a cross section is then

$$F = \int_A dF = \int_A \frac{Ez}{R} \, dA \qquad \text{or finally} \qquad \frac{E}{R} \int_A z \, dA$$

since E is a constant of the material of the beam and R is a constant at any particular cross section.   If the beam bears only transverse loads, the tensile and compressive forces over any cross section must balance, leaving the net force F equal to zero, so that

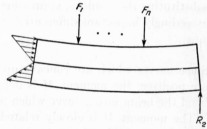

$$\frac{E}{R} \int_A z \, dA = 0$$

Since neither E nor $1/R$ can be zero, the integral must therefore vanish.

Fig. 2.4.

But if $\int_A z \, dA = 0$, the moment of the area about the axis from which z is measured is zero.   Hence, since only lines through the center of gravity have this property, it is clear that the neutral axis of any cross section (*i.e.*, the axis from which z is measured) passes through the center of gravity of that section.   If loads with a longitudinal component act on the beam, this is no longer true.

Next, for a general section we compute the total moment about the neutral axis of all the forces, ΔF, which act perpendicular to that section. From Fig. 2.3c and Eq. (10) it is clear that

$$\Delta M = z \, \Delta F = \frac{Ez^2 \, \Delta A}{R}$$

and therefore, integrating over the entire cross section,

$$M = \frac{E}{R} \int_A z^2 \, dA$$

But $\int_{A} z^2 \, dA$ is simply the moment of inertia of the cross-section area about the neutral axis.   Hence the internal moment of the fiber forces is

(11)
$$M = \frac{EI}{R}$$

This internal moment must hold in equilibrium the external moment due to the various loads acting upon the beam (Fig. 2.4).   Hence, equating EI/R to the moment of the forces which act on one side of a general cross section, we obtain an equation from which R, and eventually the deflection curve itself, can be found.

Now from calculus

$$\frac{1}{R} = \frac{y''}{[1 + (y')^2]^{\frac{3}{2}}}$$

But since we have assumed that only small deflections occur, y' is surely so small that its square can be neglected in comparison with 1.   Hence, substituting the resulting approximation for $1/R$ into (11), we obtain the exceedingly important differential equation

(12)
$$M = EIy''$$

Since curves which are concave upward have second derivatives which are positive, the moment M is defined to be positive when it tends to bend the beam into a curve which is concave upward.

The moment M is closely related to two additional quantities.   The first of these is the **shear,** V, defined to be the algebraic sum of all the

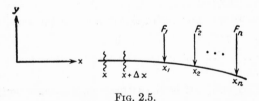

Fig. 2.5.

transverse forces which act on the beam to the right of a general cross section.   The second is the **load per unit length,** w, which acts on the beam.   We shall consider the shear positive if the net transverse force acts in the direction of the positive y-axis.   The load per unit length will be considered positive if it acts in the direction of the negative y-axis (the usual direction for loads on a beam).

Now suppose that a set of forces $F_1, F_2, \ldots, F_n$ acts on a beam as shown in Fig. 2.5.   The moment at x due to the forces is

$$M(x) = (x_1 - x)F_1 + \cdots + (x_n - x)F_n$$

and the moment at $x + \Delta x$ is

$$M(x + \Delta x) = (x_1 - \overline{x + \Delta x})F_1 + \cdots + (x_n - \overline{x + \Delta x})F_n$$

Subtracting these, we find

$$M(x + \Delta x) - M(x) = \Delta M = -\Delta x(F_1 + \cdots + F_n) = -V \Delta x$$

Hence, dividing by Δx and letting $\Delta x \to 0$, we have

(13) $\dfrac{dM}{dx} = -V$ or, using Eq. (12), $\dfrac{d(EIy'')}{dx} = -V$

Finally, in passing from x to $x + \Delta x$ along a beam which bears a distributed load w, the shear increases by the amount

$$\Delta V = w \Delta x$$

since this much force in the direction of the negative y-axis is no longer included.   Hence $dV/dx = w$ or, substituting from (13),

(14) $$\dfrac{d^2(EIy'')}{dx^2} = -w$$

Equations (12), (13), and (14) are valid whether the beam is of constant cross section or not, that is, whether I is a constant or a function of x.

Example 3

A uniform cantilever beam of length L is subjected to an oblique tensile force F at the free end.   Find the tip deflection as a function of the angle θ between the direction of the force and the initial direction of the beam.

For convenience, we take the origin at the free end of the beam, and resolve the oblique load into its longitudinal and transverse components, as shown in Fig. 2.6.

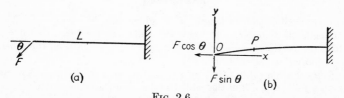

(a)   (b)

FIG. 2.6.

The moment arm of the component $F \sin \theta$, with respect to a general point of the beam P, is just x.   Hence the moment of this force is

$$-xF \sin \theta$$

the minus sign indicating that this moment tends to bend the beam so that it is convex upward.   The moment arm of the component $F \cos \theta$ is y; hence the moment itself is

$$yF \cos \theta$$

Substituting these moments into the basic equation (12), we obtain the differential equation

$$EIy'' = (F \cos \theta)y - (F \sin \theta)x$$

or

$$y'' - \left(\frac{F \cos \theta}{EI}\right) y = - \left(\frac{F \sin \theta}{EI}\right) x$$

This can be solved at once, and we find without difficulty

$$y = A \cosh \left(\sqrt{\frac{F \cos \theta}{EI}}\, x\right) + B \sinh \left(\sqrt{\frac{F \cos \theta}{EI}}\, x\right) + \left(\frac{\sin \theta}{\cos \theta}\right) x$$

Now from our choice of origin, $y = 0$ when $x = 0$. Hence $A = 0$, leaving

$$y = B \sinh \left(\sqrt{\frac{F \cos \theta}{EI}}\, x\right) + (\tan \theta)x$$

Also, when $x = L$, the slope y' is zero. Hence, differentiating and substituting,

$$0 = \sqrt{\frac{F \cos \theta}{EI}}\, B \cosh \left(\sqrt{\frac{F \cos \theta}{EI}}\, L\right) + (\tan \theta)$$

or

$$B = - \sqrt{\frac{EI}{F \cos \theta}}\, \frac{\tan \theta}{\cosh \left(\sqrt{\dfrac{F \cos \theta}{EI}}\, L\right)}$$

Therefore

$$y = \tan \theta \left[x - \sqrt{\frac{EI}{F \cos \theta}}\, \frac{\sinh \sqrt{(F \cos \theta/EI)}x}{\cosh \sqrt{(F \cos \theta/EI)}L} \right]$$

The required tip deflection is clearly equal to the value of y when $x = L$, namely,

$$\tan \theta \left[L - \sqrt{\frac{EI}{F \cos \theta}}\, \tanh \left(\sqrt{\frac{F \cos \theta}{EI}}\, L\right) \right]$$

EXERCISES

1. A perfectly flexible cable of length $2L$, weighing w lb/ft, hangs over a frictionless peg of negligible diameter. At $t = 0$, the cable is released from rest in a position in which the portion hanging on one side is a ft longer than on the other. Discuss the motion of the cable as it slips over the peg.

2. A perfectly flexible cable L ft long weighing w lb/ft lies in a straight line on a frictionless table top, a ft of the cable hanging over the edge. At $t = 0$, the cable is released and begins to slide off the edge of the table. Assuming that the height of the table is greater than L, determine the motion of the chain until it leaves the table top.

    Ans. $y = a \cosh \sqrt{(g/L)}\, t$, where y is the length of the hanging portion of the cable.

3. A weight W hangs by an inextensible cord from the circumference of a pulley of radius R and moment of inertia I. The pulley is prevented from rotating freely by a spring of strength k lb/in. attached as shown in Fig. 2.7. Considering only displacements so small that the departure of the spring from the horizontal can

be neglected, determine the natural frequency of the oscillations that occur when the system is slightly disturbed.   (Hint: Use the energy method to obtain the differential equation.)   *Ans.* $f = \dfrac{1}{2\pi} \sqrt{\dfrac{kgr^2}{Ig + WR^2}}$ cycles/unit time

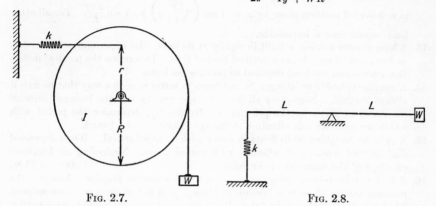

FIG. 2.7.   FIG. 2.8.

4. Under the assumption of very small motions, determine the natural frequency of the system in Fig. 2.8 if the rod is absolutely rigid and weighs W lb.

$$Ans. f = \frac{1}{2\pi} \sqrt{\frac{3kg}{4W}} \text{cycles/unit time}$$

5. A perfectly flexible chain 6 ft long, weighing 2 oz/ft, rests on the frictionless top of a table 3 ft high, 1 ft of the chain hanging over the edge.   At $t = 0$, the chain is released and begins to slide off the table.   When will it first touch the floor? How long will it be before it leaves the table completely?

6. Find the equation of the deflection curve of a uniform cantilever beam of length L bearing a uniformly distributed load of w lb/ft.

7. Show that the stress σ in a fiber at a distance z from the neutral surface of a beam can be written $\sigma = Mz/I$.

8. By first determining the work required to stretch each fiber in an infinitesimal segment of a beam Δs through the corresponding elongation e and then integrating over the entire length of the beam, show that the potential energy stored in a bent beam is

$$\frac{1}{2} E \int_0^L \frac{I\,dx}{R^2} \doteq \frac{1}{2} E \int_0^L I(y'')^2 dx$$

(Hint: First show that the work required to stretch an elastic fiber a distance x from its neutral length is equal to one-half the distance stretched times the final value of the force in the fiber.)

9. In Example 3, Sec. 2.6, evaluate the tip deflection when the force F is purely transverse, that is, when $\theta = \frac{1}{2}\pi$.

10. Extend Example 3, Sec. 2.6, by considering θ in the range from $\frac{1}{2}\pi$ to π, that is, consider F to be an oblique compressive force acting on the beam.

11. The free end of a uniform cantilever is acted upon by a tensile force whose direction coincides with that of the cantilever.   If the beam bears a uniform load of w lb/in., find the equation of the deflection curve.

12. A long slender column whose ends are constrained to remain in the same vertical line but are otherwise free (*i.e.*, are able to turn) is compressed by a load P.

Determine the possible deflection curves and the loads required to produce each one.

Ans. If $P = \left(\dfrac{n\pi}{L}\right)^2 EI$, $n = 1, 2, 3, \ldots$, the column will be in equilibrium in a deflected position given by $x = A \sin\left(\sqrt{\dfrac{P}{EI}}\, y\right) = A \sin \dfrac{n\pi y}{L}$. For all other loads equilibrium is impossible.

13. A long slender column is built in rigidly at its base. Its upper end, which is free to move out of line, bears a vertical load of P lb. Determine the possible deflection curves and the load required to produce each one.

14. A circular cylinder weighing w lb/in.^{3} floats in water in such a way that its axis is always vertical. Neglecting all forces except gravity and the buoyant force of the water as given by the principle of Archimedes, determine the period with which the cylinder will vibrate if submerged slightly and released.

15. A cylinder weighing 50 lb floats in water with its axis vertical. When depressed slightly and released, it vibrates with period 2 sec. Neglecting all frictional effects, find the diameter of the cylinder.   *Ans.* 6.73 in.

16. A hollow tube rotates about its mid-point with constant angular velocity ω, the rotation taking place in a horizontal plane. A pellet of mass m slides without friction in the interior of the tube. Find the equation of its radial motion until it emerges from the tube, assuming it starts from rest at a radial distance a from the mid-point of the tube.

CHAPTER 3

SIMULTANEOUS LINEAR DIFFERENTIAL EQUATIONS

3.1 Introduction. In many applied problems there are not one, but several dependent variables, each a function of a single independent variable, usually time. The formulation of such problems in mathematical terms frequently leads to a system of simultaneous linear differential equations, as many equations as there are dependent variables.

There are two straightforward (and closely related) methods of solving such systems. In one, the system is reduced by successive elimination of the variables until a single equation in one unknown remains. This is solved, and then working backward, the solutions for the other variables are found one by one until the problem is completed. In the other method, the ideas of complementary function and particular integral are generalized, and through their use, solutions for all the variables are constructed at the same time.

Neither method has much to recommend it over the other, and each is currently losing ground to the operational procedure we shall discuss in Chap. 6. Nonetheless we should be familiar with both, and in this chapter we shall try through examples to present each of them.

3.2 Reduction of a System to a Single Equation. Consider the following system of equations.

$$2\frac{dx}{dt} + x + 3\frac{dy}{dt} + y = e^{-t}$$

$$\frac{dx}{dt} + 5x + \frac{dy}{dt} + 7y = t$$

If we subtract twice the second equation from the first, we obtain

(1) $$-9x + \frac{dy}{dt} - 13y = e^{-t} - 2t$$

If we subtract the second equation from five times the first, we obtain

(2) $$9\frac{dx}{dt} + 14\frac{dy}{dt} - 2y = 5e^{-t} - t$$

Finally, if we differentiate Eq. (1) and add it to Eq. (2), we obtain

$$\frac{d^2y}{dt^2} + \frac{dy}{dt} - 2y = 4e^{-t} - t - 2$$

It is now a simple matter to solve this equation by the methods of Chap. 2, and we find without difficulty

(3) $$y = c_1 e^t + c_2 e^{-2t} + \tfrac{1}{2} t + \tfrac{5}{4} - 2e^{-t}$$

Various possibilities are available for finding x. By far the simplest is to use Eq. (1), which gives x directly in terms of y and its derivative. Thus

$$x = \frac{1}{9} \left[\frac{dy}{dt} - 13y + 2t - e^{-t} \right]$$

$$= \frac{1}{9} \left[\left(c_1 e^t - 2c_2 e^{-2t} + \frac{1}{2} + 2e^{-t} \right) - 13 \left(c_1 e^t + c_2 e^{-2t} + \frac{1}{2} t \right. \right.$$

$$\left. \left. + \frac{5}{4} - 2e^{-t} \right) + 2t - e^{-t} \right]$$

(4) $$= -\frac{4}{3} c_1 e^t - \frac{5}{3} c_2 e^{-2t} - \frac{7}{4} - \frac{1}{2} t + 3e^{-t}$$

Equations (3) and (4) constitute the complete solution of the original system.

In general, the steps in the reduction of a system of equations to a single equation are not as obvious as they were in the example we have just worked. For this reason it is frequently convenient to rewrite the given equations in the D notation. Then, considering the operational coefficients of the variables to be ordinary algebraic coefficients, the method of elimination will usually be apparent. To illustrate, consider the system

(5) $$(D^2 + 2D + 3)x + (3D^2 + 3D + 2)y = 0$$
$$(D^2 + D + 1)x + (2D^2 - D - 2)y = 8$$

where now the symbol D denotes d/dt and not d/dx. If the second of these equations be "multiplied" by $(D^2 + 2D + 3)$ and subtracted from $(D^2 + D + 1)$ "times" the first,* x will be eliminated and we will have

$$[(D^2 + D + 1)(3D^2 + 3D + 2) - (D^2 + 2D + 3)(2D^2 - D - 2)]y$$
$$= -(D^2 + 2D + 3)8$$

or

$$(D^4 + 3D^3 + 6D^2 + 12D + 8)y = -24$$

The roots of the characteristic equation of this equation are -1, -2, $\pm 2i$. Hence the complementary function is

$$Ae^{-t} + Be^{-2t} + C \cos 2t + D \sin 2t$$

---

* What this pseudoalgebraic procedure means, of course, is that we subtract the second derivative of the second equation plus twice the first derivative plus three times the equation itself from the sum of the first equation and its first two derivatives.

A particular integral is obviously $Y = -3$; hence the general solution is

(6) $$y = Ae^{-t} + Be^{-2t} + C \cos 2t + D \sin 2t - 3$$

To find x, we can substitute for y in either of the original differential equations and then solve the resulting equation for x. It is usually a little easier, however, to begin again with the given system and eliminate y just as we did x and then solve for x from the resulting equation. The advantage in this procedure is that the characteristic equation of the x differential equation is always the same as the one for the y equation. Moreover, we are spared the labor of finding particular integrals for all the terms arising from y and its various derivatives. Proceeding in this fashion, then, subtracting $(3D^2 + 3D + 2)$ "times" the second of Eqs. (5) from $(2D^2 - D - 2)$ "times" the first, we find

$$[(2D^2 - D - 2)(D^2 + 2D + 3) - (3D^2 + 3D + 2)(D^2 + D + 1)]x$$
$$= -(3D^2 + 3D + 2)8$$

or

$$(D^4 + 3D^3 + 6D^2 + 12D + 8)x = 16$$

The general solution of this equation can be written down at once:

(7) $$x = Ee^{-t} + Fe^{-2t} + G \cos 2t + H \sin 2t + 2$$

It is tempting now to say that (6) and (7) give the general solution of the original system. However, as a matter of principle we should substitute these expressions into at least one of the given equations and verify that they satisfy it. Choosing the second of Eqs. (5) for this purpose, we must have

$$(D^2 + D + 1)(Ee^{-t} + Fe^{-2t} + G \cos 2t + H \sin 2t + 2)$$
$$+ (2D^2 - D - 2)(Ae^{-t} + Be^{-2t} + C \cos 2t + D \sin 2t - 3) \equiv 8$$

or, performing the indicated differentiations and collecting terms,

$$(A + E)e^{-t} + (8B + 3F)e^{-2t} + (-10C - 2D - 3G + 2H) \cos 2t$$
$$+ (2C - 10D - 2G - 3H) \sin 2t + 8 \equiv 8$$

As it stands, with all eight constants perfectly arbitrary, this equation is *not* identically true.* It will be an identity if and only if

$$A + E = 0$$
$$8B + 3F = 0$$
$$-10C - 2D - 3G + 2H = 0$$
$$2C - 10D - 2G - 3H = 0$$

---

* The reason we encountered no such difficulty in the first example was that x was given explicitly in terms of y and its derivatives and was not found by solving a differential equation, and thereby introducing additional arbitrary constants.

Thus four relations must exist among the original eight arbitrary constants. Solving these equations, we find (among equivalent possibilities)

$$E = -A, \qquad F = -\tfrac{8}{3}B, \qquad G = -2(C + D), \qquad H = 2(C - D)$$

It is tedious but perfectly straightforward to verify that no new conditions on the constants are required in order for the first of Eqs. (5) to be satisfied by the solutions we have found. Therefore the correct solution of our problem is the pair of functions

$$x = -Ae^{-t} - \tfrac{8}{3}Be^{-2t} - 2(C + D) \cos 2t + 2(C - D) \sin 2t + 2$$
$$y = Ae^{-t} + Be^{-2t} + C \cos 2t + D \sin 2t - 3$$

The reduction in the number of constants from eight to four in this example illustrates the following important theorem.

Theorem 1. The number of constants in the general solution of a system of linear differential equations with constant coefficients is equal to the order of the determinant of the operational coefficients regarded as a function of D.

If the given system contains more than two differential equations, then the conditions necessary to reduce the number of constants to the figure required by Theorem 1 *cannot* be found by substituting the apparent solutions into just *one* of the original equations and equating coefficients. In fact it is necessary to substitute into *all but one* of the given equations in order to obtain enough relations between the constants.

3.3 Complementary Functions and Particular Integrals for Systems of Equations. To illustrate the extension of the ideas of characteristic equation, complementary function, and particular integral to systems of differential equations, let us consider the following set of equations.

$$(1) \quad \begin{aligned} 6 \frac{dx}{dt} + 3x - 5 \frac{dy}{dt} - y - 3 \frac{dz}{dt} &= 11 \\ \frac{dx}{dt} + \frac{dy}{dt} + y + \frac{dz}{dt} + 2z &= 0 \\ \frac{dx}{dt} + 3x + \frac{dy}{dt} - y + 2 \frac{dz}{dt} &= 0 \end{aligned}$$

As in the case of a single equation, we shall first make the system homogeneous by neglecting the terms on the right, getting

$$(2) \quad \begin{aligned} 6 \frac{dx}{dt} + 3x - 5 \frac{dy}{dt} - y - 3 \frac{dz}{dt} &= 0 \\ \frac{dx}{dt} + \frac{dy}{dt} + y + \frac{dz}{dt} + 2z &= 0 \\ \frac{dx}{dt} + 3x + \frac{dy}{dt} - y + 2 \frac{dz}{dt} &= 0 \end{aligned}$$

Now let us attempt to find solutions of this system of the form

$$x = Ae^{mt}, \qquad y = Be^{mt}, \qquad z = Ce^{mt}$$

Substituting these values into the equations in (2) and dividing out the common factor e^{mt} leads to the set of algebraic equations

(3)
$$
\begin{aligned}
(6m + 3)A - (5m + 1)B \quad\;\;\; - 3mC &= 0 \\
mA + (m + 1)B + (m + 2)C &= 0 \\
(m + 3)A + (m - 1)B + \quad\;\; 2mC &= 0
\end{aligned}
$$

To obtain solutions for x, y, and z which will not be trivial, *i.e.*, will not vanish identically, it is necessary that A, B, and C shall not all be zero. But the values $A = B = C = 0$ obviously satisfy the system (3), and in general will be the only solution of this set of equations. No other solutions are possible unless (see Theorem 12, Sec. A.1) the determinant of the coefficients in (3) is equal to zero. Thus we must have

(4)
$$
\begin{vmatrix}
(6m + 3) & -(5m + 1) & -3m \\
m & (m + 1) & (m + 2) \\
(m + 3) & (m - 1) & 2m
\end{vmatrix} = 11(m^3 - m) = 0
$$

This equation, which defines all the values of m for which nontrivial solutions can exist, is the **characteristic equation** of the system. It is, of course, nothing but the determinant of the operational coefficients of the system, equated to zero, with D replaced by m.

From the roots of this equation,

$$m_1 = 0, \qquad m_2 = 1, \qquad m_3 = -1$$

we can construct three particular solutions

$$
\begin{cases}
x_1 = A_1 e^0 = A_1 \\
y_1 = B_1 e^0 = B_1 \\
z_1 = C_1 e^0 = C_1
\end{cases}
\quad
\begin{cases}
x_2 = A_2 e^t \\
y_2 = B_2 e^t \\
z_2 = C_2 e^t
\end{cases}
\quad
\begin{cases}
x_3 = A_3 e^{-t} \\
y_3 = B_3 e^{-t} \\
z_3 = C_3 e^{-t}
\end{cases}
$$

provided that we establish the proper relations between the constants in each of the sets.

To do this, we note that the constants A_i, B_i, C_i must satisfy the equations of system 3 for the corresponding value m_i. Thus for $m_1 = 0$, we must have

$$
\begin{aligned}
3A_1 - B_1 \quad\quad\;\; &= 0 \\
B_1 + 2C_1 &= 0 \\
3A_1 - B_1 \quad\quad\;\; &= 0
\end{aligned}
$$

The third equation of this set merely duplicates the first; therefore we can neglect it and solve for B_1 and C_1 in terms of A_1 from the first pair.

Thus

$$B_1 = 3A_1 \quad \text{and} \quad C_1 = -\frac{1}{2}B_1 = -\frac{3A_1}{2}$$

and thus the first of the three particular solutions is

$$x_1 = A_1$$
$$y_1 = 3A_1$$
$$z_1 = -\frac{3A_1}{2}$$

For $m_2 = 1$, we have similarly, from Eq. (3),

$$9A_2 - 6B_2 - 3C_2 = 0$$
$$A_2 + 2B_2 + 3C_2 = 0$$
$$4A_2 \qquad\quad + 2C_2 = 0$$

If we solve for B_2 and C_2 from the last two equations, we find

$$C_2 = -2A_2 \quad \text{and} \quad B_2 = \frac{-3C_2 - A_2}{2} = \frac{5A_2}{2}$$

Substitution shows that the remaining equation (the first) is satisfied by these values, as is always the case in homogeneous systems of this kind. The particular solution corresponding to $m_2 = 1$ is therefore

$$x_2 = A_2 e^t$$
$$y_2 = \frac{5A_2 e^t}{2}$$
$$z_2 = -2A_2 e^t$$

Finally, for $m_3 = -1$, we have

$$-3A_3 + 4B_3 + 3C_3 = 0$$
$$- A_3 \qquad\quad + C_3 = 0$$
$$2A_3 - 2B_3 - 2C_3 = 0$$

If we solve the last pair for B_3 and C_3, we find

$$C_3 = A_3 \quad \text{and} \quad B_3 = A_3 - C_3 = 0$$

Substitution again confirms that the first equation is automatically satisfied by these values. The third particular solution is therefore

$$x_3 = A_3 e^{-t}$$
$$y_3 = 0$$
$$z_3 = A_3 e^{-t}$$

Since the equations of the given system (2) are all linear, sums of solutions will also be solutions.   Hence we can combine the three particular solutions into the general solution

$$x = x_1 + x_2 + x_3 = A_1 + A_2 e^t + A_3 e^{-t}$$

(5)
$$y = y_1 + y_2 + y_3 = 3A_1 + \frac{5A_2 e^t}{2}$$

$$z = z_1 + z_2 + z_3 = -\frac{3A_1}{2} - 2A_2 e^t + A_3 e^{-t}$$

This is the **complementary function** of the system.   We note that it contains three arbitrary constants as required by Theorem 1.   The relation between the constants could also have been found by substituting the original solutions into two of the three equations in (2) and equating coefficients as we did in the second example in Sec. 3.2.   When the roots of the characteristic equation are real and distinct, this is generally a less convenient way of obtaining the necessary relations, however.

To complete the problem we now need to find a particular solution or "integral" of the nonhomogeneous system (1).   To do this, we assume for x, y, and z trial solutions exactly as described in Table 3.2, Chap. 2. Thus in the present case we assume initially

$$X = a$$
$$Y = b$$
$$Z = c$$

where of course we must be careful to use different symbols for the undetermined constants in each case, since there is no reason to expect that any particular term will have the same coefficient in X, Y, and Z. However, these constant terms are like terms already present in the complementary function; hence as usual we must modify them by multiplying them by t before proceeding.   *But in the case of simultaneous equations the duplicating terms themselves must be retained together with the products of these terms and the independent variable.*   For the constant terms in the complementary function are not completely arbitrary but bear fixed ratios to each other.   Hence, unless the constant terms in X, Y, and Z are also in these same ratios (which is not to be expected), they cannot be absorbed in the complementary function.   Thus we must actually try

$$X = a_1 + a_2 t$$
$$Y = b_1 + b_2 t$$
$$Z = c_1 + c_2 t$$

Substituting these into (1), we find

$$6a_2 + 3(a_1 + a_2t) - 5b_2 - (b_1 + b_2t) - 3c_2 = 11$$
$$a_2 + b_2 + (b_1 + b_2t) + c_2 + 2(c_1 + c_2t) = 0$$
$$a_2 + 3(a_1 + a_2t) + b_2 - (b_1 + b_2t) + 2c_2 = 0$$

Collecting terms in these equations, we have

$$(6a_2 + 3a_1 - 5b_2 - b_1 - 3c_2) + (3a_2 - b_2)t = 11$$
$$(a_2 + b_2 + b_1 + c_2 + 2c_1) + (b_2 + 2c_2)t = 0$$
$$(a_2 + 3a_1 + b_2 - b_1 + 2c_2) + (3a_2 - b_2)t = 0$$

Clearly these equations will be identically true if and only if the following sets of conditions are fulfilled:

(6)
$$6a_2 + 3a_1 - 5b_2 - b_1 - 3c_2 = 11$$
$$a_2 + b_2 + b_1 + c_2 + 2c_1 = 0$$
$$a_2 + 3a_1 + b_2 - b_1 + 2c_2 = 0$$

(7)
$$3a_2 - b_2 = 0$$
$$b_2 + 2c_2 = 0$$
$$3a_2 - b_2 = 0$$

From Eqs. (7), we find

(8)
$$b_2 = 3a_2, \qquad c_2 = -\frac{3a_2}{2}$$

Substituting these values into the system (6), we obtain

(9)
$$3a_1 - b_1 \qquad = 11 + \frac{9a_2}{2}$$
$$b_1 + 2c_1 = -\frac{5a_2}{2}$$
$$3a_1 - b_1 \qquad = -a_2$$

The first and third of these equations will be incompatible unless

$$11 + \frac{9a_2}{2} = -a_2 \qquad \text{or} \qquad a_2 = -2$$

But if $a_2 = -2$, then from (8),

$$b_2 = -6 \qquad \text{and} \qquad c_2 = 3$$

Furthermore, with $a_2 = -2$, Eqs. (9) become

$$3a_1 - b_1 = 2$$
$$b_1 + 2c_1 = 5$$

and thus

$$b_1 = 3a_1 - 2, \qquad c_1 = \frac{-3a_1 + 7}{2}$$

With these values for the constants, the particular solution of the non-homogeneous system (1) becomes

$$X = a_1 - 2t$$
$$Y = 3a_1 - 2 - 6t$$
$$Z = \frac{-3a_1 + 7}{2} + 3t$$

It is interesting to note that the terms which we have not been able to evaluate completely are in precisely the ratios of the corresponding terms in the complementary function and hence can be combined with them. On the other hand we can also reason that since we are only seeking a particular solution it is legitimate now to take $a_1 = 0$, getting

$$X = -2t$$
$$Y = -2 - 6t$$
$$Z = \tfrac{7}{2} + 3t$$

These expressions constitute a **particular integral** of the original system. The complete solution can now be constructed by adding this particular integral to the complementary function:

$$x = A_1 + A_2 e^t + A_3 e^{-t} - 2t$$
$$y = 3A_1 + \tfrac{5}{2}A_2 e^t - 2 - 6t$$
$$z = -\tfrac{3}{2}A_1 - 2A_2 e^t + A_3 e^{-t} + \tfrac{7}{2} + 3t$$

EXERCISES

1. $\dfrac{dx}{dt} + 4x + 4\dfrac{dy}{dt} + 10y = 6$ *Ans.* $x = -2ae^{-t} - be^{-2t} + 9$

   $x + \dfrac{dy}{dt} + 3y = 0$ $y = ae^{-t} + be^{-2t} - 3$

2. $(D + 2)x + y = 0$ *Ans.* $x = e^{-t}[A \cos 2t + B \sin 2t] - e^t$

   $(3D + 1)x + (D + 3)y = 8e^t$ $y = e^{-t}[-(A + 2B) \cos 2t + (2A - B) \sin 2t] + 3e^t$

3. $\dfrac{dx}{dt} - 2x + 2\dfrac{dy}{dt} - 10y = 0$ 4. $\dfrac{dx}{dt} + x + 2\dfrac{dy}{dt} + y = 0$

   $2\dfrac{dx}{dt} + x + 5\dfrac{dy}{dt} - y = 0$ $\dfrac{dx}{dt} + 2\dfrac{dy}{dt} - y = 0$

5. $(D + 1)x + (4D - 2)y = t - 1$ 6. $(D + 5)x + (D + 7)y = -1$

   $(D + 2)x + (5D - 2)y = 2t - 1$ $(2D + 1)x + (3D + 1)y = 1$

7. $\dfrac{dx}{dt} + 2x + \dfrac{dy}{dt} + 11y = \sin t$

   $\dfrac{dx}{dt} + x + 5\dfrac{dy}{dt} + 6y = 0$

8. $(D^2 + 2D + 3)x + (D^2 + D + 1)y = 0$
   $(6D^2 + 28D + 60)x + (3D^2 + 4D + 20)y = 1$
9. $(D - 4)x + (D - 8)y = 0$
   $(D + 1)x + (2D + 1)y = e^{-t}$
10. $(D^2 + D + 1)x + (-4D^2 + 3D + 1)y = 0$
    $(D^2 + 2D + 3)x + (-D^2 - 4D + 15)y = e^{-t}$
11. $\dfrac{dx}{dt} - z = 0$ $Ans.$ $x = Ae^{2t} + e^{-t}[B \cos 2t + C \sin 2t]$

   $2x + \dfrac{dy}{dt} - z = 0$ $y = e^{-t}[(7B + 4C) \cos 2t + (-4B + 7C) \sin 2t]$

   $-4x + 5y + \dfrac{dz}{dt} = 0$ $z = 2Ae^{2t} + e^{-t}[(-B + 2C) \cos 2t - (2B + C) \sin 2t]$

12. $Dx - 6y + 9z = 0$ $Ans.$ $x = A + Bt + Ct^2$

   $2x + Dy - 3z = 0$ $y = \dfrac{3A + 2B + 2C}{3} + \dfrac{3B + 4C}{3} t + Ct^2$

   $x - y + Dz = 0$ $z = \dfrac{6A + 3B + 4C}{9} + \dfrac{2B + 2C}{3} t + \dfrac{2C}{3} t^2$

13. $Dx + y - 3z = e^t$ 14. $(D - 6)x - 6(D - 2)z = 0$
    $4x + Dy + 5z = 1$ $(D + 4)y - (D + 2)z = 0$
    $2x + y + Dz = 0$ $(D + 6)x + 6(D - 4)y = 0$
15. $Dx + y + z = 1 + t$
    $x + Dy + z = t$
    $x + y + Dz = 2$
16. $(D + 3)x + (D - 7)y + (D + 6)z = 0$
    $x - y + Dz = 0$
    $(D + 2)y - (2D + 3)z = 0$

Find the solution of each of the following systems which satisfies the prescribed conditions:

17. $(D - 4)x + (D - 6)y = -2$

    $x = 7, y = -4$ when $t = 0$

    $(2D + 1)x + (3D + 2)y = 0$

    $Ans.$ $x = 5e^t + 2$
             $y = -3e^t - 1$

18. $(D + 5)x + (D + 7)y = 2$

    $x = y = 0$ when $t = 0$

    $(2D + 1)x + (3D + 1)y = \sin t$

    $Ans.$ $x = \frac{4}{3}e^t - \frac{4}{3}e^{-2t} - 1 + \cos t + 2 \sin t$
             $y = -e^t + \frac{4}{5}e^{-2t} + 1 - \frac{4}{5} \cos t - \frac{7}{5} \sin t$

19. $(D^2 - D - 13)x + (D^2 + 3D + 1)y = 4$

    $x = y = 0$ when $t = 0$

    $(-D^2 - 6D + 6)x + (D^2 + 2D + 2)y = 2$

20. $\dfrac{dx}{dt} + 7y + z = 0$

    $2x + \dfrac{dy}{dt} + z = 0$ $x = y = z = 0$ when $t = 0$

    $6x - 21y + \dfrac{dz}{dt} = e^{-t}$

CHAPTER 4

MECHANICAL AND ELECTRICAL CIRCUITS

4.1 Introduction. An examination of the application of differential equations to mechanical and electrical systems is valuable for at least two reasons. In the first place, it will furnish us with useful information about the behavior of certain physical systems of great practical interest. Second, and perhaps more important, it will provide a striking example of the role which mathematics plays in unifying widely differing phenomena. For instance, we shall see that merely by renaming the variables, the analysis of the motion of a weight vibrating on a spring becomes the analysis of a simple electrical circuit. Moreover, this correspondence is not merely qualitative or descriptive. It is quantitative, in the sense that if we have given any of a wide variety of vibrating mechanical systems, an electrical circuit can be constructed whose current (or voltage, if we prefer) will give the *exact* values of the displacements of the mechanical system, when suitable scale factors are introduced. Since electrical circuits are easy to assemble, and since currents and voltages are easily measured, this affords a practical method of studying the vibration of complicated mechanical configurations, such as engine crankshafts, which are expensive to make and modify, and whose motions are difficult to record accurately. Of course mechanical models of electrical circuits can also be constructed, but there is little practical reason for so doing.

4.2 Systems with One Degree of Freedom. Systems which can be described completely by one coordinate, *i.e.*, by one physical datum such as a displacement, an angle, a current, or a voltage, are called **systems of one degree of freedom.** If a system requires more than one coordinate for its complete description, it is called a **system of several degrees of freedom.** A single differential equation suffices for the mathematical description of a system of one degree of freedom. A set of simultaneous differential equations, as many equations as there are degrees of freedom, is necessary for the analysis of systems of more than one degree of freedom. We shall begin our investigations by considering as prototypes of the general system with one degree of freedom each of the configurations shown in Fig. 4.1. In each case we assume that the elements of the system are concentrated or **lumped.** In other words, we neglect as insignificant such things as the distributed mass of the spring in Fig. 4.1*a*,

69

the distributed moment of inertia of the shaft in Fig. 4.1*b*, and the resistance of the leads in Fig. 4.1*c* and *d*.

In Fig. 4.1*a* we assume the weight to be guided, so that only vertical motion, without swinging, is possible. As indicated, the effect of friction is not neglected. Instead, we suppose that a retarding force proportional to the velocity acts at all times. Friction of this nature is known as

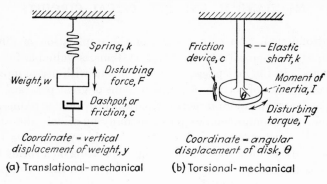

(a) Translational- mechanical   (b) Torsional- mechanical

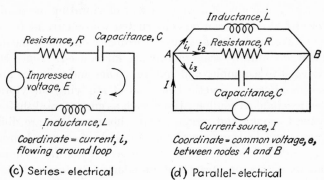

(c) Series- electrical   (d) Parallel- electrical

FIG. 4.1.   Four simple systems of one degree of freedom.

viscous friction, or **viscous damping.** Its existence is well established experimentally for moderate velocities, although for large velocities the resistance may be more nearly proportional to the square or even the cube of the velocity.

The analysis of this system is based upon Newton's law

$$\text{(1)}\qquad\qquad \text{Mass} \times \text{acceleration} = \text{force}$$

Neglecting the weight of the spring as insignificant in comparison with the main weight, we have

$$\text{(2)}\qquad\qquad \text{Vibrating mass} = \frac{w}{g}$$

Measuring the displacement y from the equilibrium position of the weight, with the positive direction upward, we have

(3)   Acceleration of the vibrating mass $= \dfrac{d^2y}{dt^2}$

The most obvious force acting on the mass is the attraction of gravity,

(4)   Gravitational force $= -w$

where the minus sign indicates that the force acts downward.   Now a weight w, when hung on a spring of modulus k, that is, a spring requiring k units of force to extend it one unit of length, will stretch the spring a distance equal to w/k in the downward, or negative, direction.   Hence when the weight moves from this equilibrium level during the course of its motion, the instantaneous elongation of the spring is

$$-\frac{w}{k} + y$$

The force which the spring exerts upon the weight at any time is therefore

Force per unit elongation $\times$ actual elongation

or

(5)   Spring force $= -k\left(-\dfrac{w}{k} + y\right) = w - ky$

the first minus sign indicating that the spring force always acts in a direction opposite to the elongation of the spring.   The velocity of the weight is $v = dy/dt$; hence, from the assumption of viscous damping,

(6)   Friction force $= -c\dfrac{dy}{dt}$

where the minus sign indicates that the resistance always acts in opposition to the velocity.   Finally, through some external agency, a disturbing force, usually periodic in nature, may act upon the system, upsetting its condition of equilibrium.   We shall consider specifically the important case in which

(7)   Disturbing force $= F_0 \cos \omega t$

Substituting from Eqs. (2), (3), (4), (5), (6), and (7) into Newton's law, Eq. (1), gives

$$\frac{w}{g}\frac{d^2y}{dt^2} = -w + (w - ky) - c\frac{dy}{dt} + F_0 \cos \omega t$$

or

$$(8) \qquad \frac{w}{g}\frac{d^2y}{dt^2} + c\frac{dy}{dt} + ky = F_0 \cos \omega t$$

We note from this equation that the gravitational force on the weight cancels identically against the portion of the elastic force due to the initial elongation of the spring.   Because of this we shall neglect gravitational forces from the outset in the analysis of problems of this sort in the future.   Equation (8) is a typical nonhomogeneous linear differential equation of the second order with constant coefficients, which, in the appropriate place, we will be able to solve without difficulty.   Before doing this, however, we shall derive the equations governing systems b, c, and d, as shown in Fig. 4.1.

The analysis of the torsional system b is based upon Newton's law in the form

(9)   Moment of inertia $\times$ angular acceleration = torque

In this case the various torques are

(10)   Elastic torque due to twisting of the shaft $= -k\theta$

$$(11) \qquad \text{Viscous damping torque} = -c\frac{d\theta}{dt}$$

(12)   Disturbing torque $= T_0 \cos \omega t$

Since the angular acceleration is $d^2\theta/dt^2$, we find on substituting into Newton's law, Eq. (9),

$$I\frac{d^2\theta}{dt^2} = -k\theta - c\frac{d\theta}{d^i} + T_0 \cos \omega t$$

or

$$(13) \qquad I\frac{d^2\theta}{dt^2} + c\frac{d\theta}{dt} + k\theta = T_0 \cos \omega t$$

This, too, is a completely familiar differential equation.

The analysis of the series or one-loop electrical circuit c is based upon **Kirchhoff's first law**: *The algebraic sum of the potential differences around any closed circuit is zero, or a voltage impressed on a closed circuit is equal to the sum of the voltage drops in the rest of the circuit.*   Using well-known electrical laws (see circuit laws in the Glossary, Sec. A.7), we have

(14)   Voltage drop across the resistance $= iR$

$$(15) \qquad \text{Voltage drop across the condenser} = \frac{1}{C}\int^t i\,dt$$

$$(16) \qquad \text{Voltage drop across the inductance} = L\frac{di}{dt}$$

Assuming the highly important case in which

(17)   Impressed voltage $= E_0 \cos \omega t$

we have, on substituting Eqs. (14), (15), (16), and (17) into Kirchhoff's law,

(18) $$L \frac{di}{dt} + iR + \frac{1}{C} \int^t i \, dt = E_0 \cos \omega t$$

Strictly speaking, this is not a differential equation but rather an **integrodifferential equation.** The operational methods which we shall develop in Chap. 6 will handle it directly; however, before we can apply the techniques we have available at this stage, we must convert it into a pure differential equation. There are two ways of doing this. The first is to regard not i but $\int^t i \, dt$ as the dependent variable of the problem. This is not merely a mathematical strategem, for the quantity

$$Q = \int^t i \, dt$$

that is, the integrated flow of current into the condenser, is precisely the electric charge or quantity of electricity instantaneously present on the condenser. In terms of Q, then, we have the equation

(19.1) $$L \frac{d^2Q}{dt^2} + R \frac{dQ}{dt} + \frac{Q}{C} = E_0 \cos \omega t$$

subject of course to the original initial conditions

$$i \Big|_{t=0} = i_0 = \frac{dQ}{dt} \Big|_{t=0}, \qquad \int^{t=0} i \, dt = Q_0$$

On the other hand, we can also convert Eq. (18) into a differential equation simply by differentiating it with respect to time, getting

(19.2) $$L \frac{d^2i}{dt^2} + R \frac{di}{dt} + \frac{i}{C} = -\omega E_0 \sin \omega t$$

The initial conditions required for an equation of this form are

$$i_0 \qquad \text{and} \qquad \frac{di}{dt} \Big|_{t=0}$$

The first of these was given for the original equation. The second can be found from the original equation, since

$$\frac{di}{dt} = \frac{1}{L} \left(E_0 \cos \omega t - iR - \frac{1}{C} \int^t i \, dt \right)$$

and the right-hand side is completely known at $t = 0$.

To establish the differential equation describing the behavior of the parallel or one node-pair electrical circuit d, we must use **Kirchhoff's second law**: *The algebraic sum of the currents flowing toward any point in an electrical circuit is zero.* Using the current laws inverse to the voltage laws we used in analyzing the series circuit c (see circuit laws in the Glossary, Sec. A.7), we have

$$(20) \qquad \text{Current through the resistance } = \frac{e}{R}$$

$$(21) \qquad \text{Current (apparently) through the condenser } = C\frac{de}{dt}$$

$$(22) \qquad \text{Current through the inductance } = \frac{1}{L}\int^{t} e\,dt$$

Assuming the important case in which the current source delivers an

$$(23) \qquad \text{Impressed current } = I_0 \cos \omega t$$

we have from Kirchhoff's second law,

$$(24) \qquad C\frac{de}{dt} + \frac{e}{R} + \frac{1}{L}\int^{t} e\,dt = I_0 \cos \omega t$$

Again, our derivation has lead to an integrodifferential equation. To convert it to a pure differential equation, we may consider $\int^{t} e\,dt = U$, say, as a new variable, getting

$$(25.1) \qquad C\frac{d^2U}{dt^2} + \frac{1}{R}\frac{dU}{dt} + \frac{U}{L} = I_0 \cos \omega t$$

Or we may simply differentiate Eq. (24) with respect to t, retaining e as independent variable, getting

$$(25.2) \qquad C\frac{d^2e}{dt^2} + \frac{1}{R}\frac{de}{dt} + \frac{e}{L} = -\omega I_0 \sin \omega t$$

In passing, we note that the quantity $U = \int^{t} e\,dt$ does not have a simple physical interpretation such as $Q = \int^{t} i\,dt$ possessed.

When we collect the differential equations which we have derived,

$$(8) \qquad \frac{w}{g}\frac{d^2y}{dt^2} + c\frac{dy}{dt} + ky = F_0 \cos \omega t \qquad \text{(translational-mechanical)}$$

$$(13) \qquad I\frac{d^2\theta}{dt^2} + c\frac{d\theta}{dt} + k\theta = T_0 \cos \omega t \qquad \text{(torsional-mechanical)}$$

$$(19.1) \qquad L\frac{d^2Q}{dt^2} + R\frac{dQ}{dt} + \frac{Q}{C} = E_0 \cos \omega t$$

$$(19.2) \qquad L\frac{d^2i}{dt^2} + R\frac{di}{dt} + \frac{i}{C} = -\omega E_0 \sin \omega t \qquad \Big\} \quad \text{(series-electrical)}$$

(25.1) $\quad C\dfrac{d^2U}{dt^2} + \dfrac{1}{R}\dfrac{dU}{dt} + \dfrac{U}{L} = I_0 \cos \omega t$

(25.2) $\quad C\dfrac{d^2e}{dt^2} + \dfrac{1}{R}\dfrac{de}{dt} + \dfrac{e}{L} = -\omega I_0 \sin \omega t$

(parallel-electrical)

their essential mathematical identity becomes apparent.   Moreover, we can see the possibility of different analogies.   For instance, if we compare the translational-mechanical and the series-electrical systems, we find that

$$\text{Mass } \frac{w}{g} \longleftrightarrow \text{inductance } L$$

$$\text{Friction } c \longleftrightarrow \text{resistance } R$$

$$\text{Spring force } k \longleftrightarrow \text{elastance } \frac{1}{C}$$

while if we compare the translational-mechanical and the parallel-electrical systems we have the less familiar correspondences

$$\text{Mass } \frac{w}{g} \longleftrightarrow \text{capacitance } C$$

$$\text{Friction } c \longleftrightarrow \text{conductance } \frac{1}{R}$$

$$\text{Spring force } k \longleftrightarrow \text{susceptance } \frac{1}{L}$$

At present we shall not pursue these analogies further.   Instead, and preparatory to this, we shall investigate one or two of the systems in detail.

4.3 The Translational-mechanical System.   The displacement y of the weight w in the translational-mechanical system has been shown to satisfy the differential equation

(1) $$\frac{w}{g}\frac{d^2y}{dt^2} + c\frac{dy}{dt} + ky = F_0 \cos \omega t$$

Following the general theory of Chap. 2, it must therefore consist of two parts.   The *complementary function,* obtained by solving Eq. (1) when the term representing the impressed force is deleted, describes the motion of the weight in the absence of any external disturbance.   This intrinsic or natural behavior of the system is called the **free motion.**   The *particular integral* describes the response of the system to a specific outside influence.   The behavior which it represents is called the **forced motion.**

The nature of the free motion of the system will depend upon the roots of the characteristic equation

$$\frac{w}{g}\,m^2 + cm + k = 0$$

namely,

$$m = -\frac{cg}{2w} \pm \frac{g}{2w}\sqrt{c^2 - \frac{4kw}{g}}$$

Since g, w, c, and k are all intrinsically positive, and since the radical $\sqrt{c^2 - (4kw/g)}$, when real, is certainly less than c, it follows that the real parts of the roots m_1 and m_2 are always negative. We must now consider three possibilities:

$$c^2 - \frac{4kw}{g} > 0$$

$$c^2 - \frac{4kw}{g} = 0$$

$$c^2 - \frac{4kw}{g} < 0$$

In the first case, $c^2 - \dfrac{4kw}{g} > 0$, there is a relatively large amount of friction, and naturally enough, the system is said to be **overdamped**. The free motion, *i.e.*, the complementary function, is now given by the expression

$$y = Ae^{m_1 t} + Be^{m_2 t}$$

where, as pointed out above, both m_1 and m_2 are negative. Thus y approaches zero as time increases indefinitely. This of course is perfectly consistent with the familiar observation that if a system upon which no external forces are acting is displaced from its equilibrium position, it will eventually return to that position as friction causes the disturbance to subside.

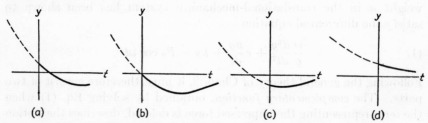

(a)   (b)   (c)   (d)

FIG. 4.2.   Displacement-time plots for free, overdamped motion.

If we set $y = 0$, we obtain the equation

$$Ae^{m_1 t} + Be^{m_2 t} = 0 \qquad \text{or} \qquad e^{(m_1 - m_2)t} = -\frac{B}{A}$$

If A and B, which will of course be determined by the initial conditions of the problem, are of opposite sign, then there is one and only one value of t which satisfies the last equation. On the other hand, since a real exponential function can never be negative, it follows that when A and B have the same sign there is no time when y is zero. A plot of the displacement y during the free motion must then have one or the other of the following general shapes (including of course the reflections of these in the t-axis). Figures 4.2a, b, and c illustrate the possibilities when A and B are of opposite sign and y can vanish once and only once. Assuming that the mass starts its motion when $t = 0$, the zero of y may, of

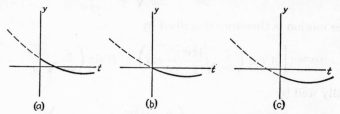

(a)   (b)   (c)

Fig. 4.3.   Displacement-time plots for free, critically damped motion.

course, occur in the physically irrelevant interval $-\infty < t < 0$. Figure 4.2d illustrates the case when A and B are of like sign and y can never vanish.

If

$$c^2 - \frac{4kw}{g} = 0$$

we have the transition case in which the roots of the characteristic equation are real and equal:

$$m_1 = m_2 = -\frac{cg}{2w}$$

This case is said to be **critically damped,** and the exact value of the damping which produces it, namely,

(2)
$$c_c = 2\sqrt{\frac{kw}{g}}$$

is known as the **critical damping.** In this case the free motion is given by

$$y = Ae^{m_1 t} + Bte^{m_1 t}$$

If we set $y = 0$, we obtain

$$Ae^{m_1 t} + Bte^{m_1 t} = 0 \qquad \text{or} \qquad t = -\frac{A}{B}$$

Thus for a critically damped system there is always one and only one value of t for which y is zero. It may however be in the physically unreal interval $-\infty < t < 0$, so that it is possible that y will never vanish in the actual motion. Figure 4.3 indicates the various possibilities. There is evidently no essential difference in the nature of the motion in the overdamped and critically damped cases.

If $c^2 - \dfrac{4kw}{g} < 0$ the motion is said to be **underdamped.** The roots of the characteristic equation in this case are the conjugate complex numbers

$$m = -\frac{cg}{2w} \pm i \frac{g}{2w} \sqrt{\frac{4kw}{g} - c^2}$$

The free motion is therefore described by

$$y = e^{-(cg/2w)t} \left[A \cos\left(\frac{g}{2w} \sqrt{\frac{4kw}{g} - c^2}\, t \right) + B \sin\left(\frac{g}{2w} \sqrt{\frac{4kw}{g} - c^2}\, t \right) \right]$$

or equally well by

$$y = G e^{-(cg/2w)t} \cos\left(\frac{g}{2w} \sqrt{\frac{4kw}{g} - c^2}\, t - H \right)$$

where A, B, G, and H are arbitrary constants. To study this motion,

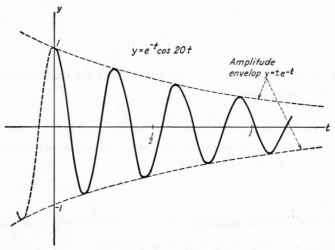

FIG. 4.4. A typical displacement-time plot for underdamped motion.

which is known as a **damped vibration,** and whose general appearance is shown in Fig. 4.4, it is convenient to introduce a simpler notation and write

$$y = G e^{-pt} \cos(qt - H)$$

where

(3) $$p = \frac{cg}{2w} \quad \text{and} \quad q = \frac{g}{2w} \sqrt{\frac{4kw}{g} - c^2}$$

This motion is not strictly periodic, because the amplitude of the cosine term is continuously decreasing. However, there are regularly spaced passages through the equilibrium position, for y vanishes whenever $\cos (qt - H) = 0$, that is, when

$$(qt - H) = \frac{\pi}{2} + n\pi \quad \text{or} \quad t = \frac{1}{q}\left(H + \frac{\pi}{2}\right) + \frac{n\pi}{q} \quad n = 0, 1, 2, \cdots$$

Hence we can speak of the "pseudo period" $2\pi/q$, and of the "pseudo frequency"

$$q = \sqrt{\omega_n^2 - p^2} = \omega_n \sqrt{1 - \gamma^2}$$

$$\frac{\omega_d}{2\pi} = \frac{q}{2\pi} = \frac{1}{2\pi}\frac{g}{2w}\sqrt{\frac{4kw}{g} - c^2} = \frac{1}{2\pi}\sqrt{\frac{kg}{w} - \frac{c^2 g^2}{4w^2}} \quad \text{cycles/unit time}$$

If $c = 0$, that is, if there is no damping in the system, the motion is strictly periodic and its frequency, which we shall call the **undamped natural frequency,** or **resonant frequency,** is

$$(4) \qquad \frac{\omega_n}{2\pi} = \frac{1}{2\pi}\frac{g}{2w}\sqrt{\frac{4kw}{g}} = \frac{1}{2\pi}\sqrt{\frac{kg}{w}} \quad \text{cycles/unit time}$$

Clearly the "frequency" when damping is present is always less than the undamped natural frequency. The ratio of these two frequencies is

$$\frac{\omega_d}{\omega_n} = \frac{\sqrt{kg/w - (c^2 g^2/4w^2)}}{\sqrt{kg/w}}$$

$$= \sqrt{1 - \frac{c^2 g}{4kw}} = \sqrt{1 - (c/c_c)^2}$$

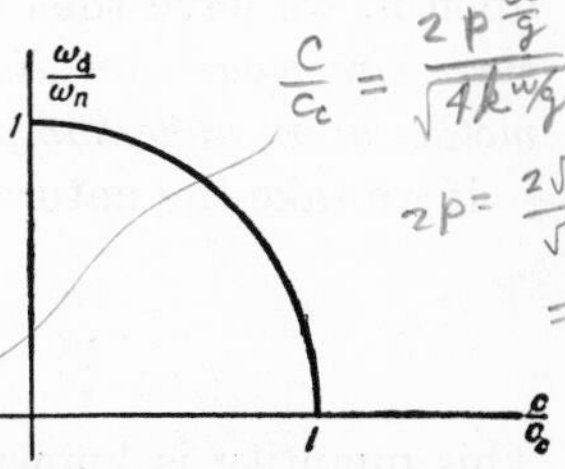

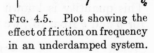

$$\frac{c}{c_c} = \frac{2p\frac{w}{g}}{\sqrt{4k\frac{w}{g}}} = \frac{c}{2\sqrt{k\frac{w}{g}}} = \gamma$$

$$2p = \frac{2\sqrt{k}}{\sqrt{w/g}}\gamma$$

$$= 2\omega_n\gamma$$

since $c_c^2 = 4kw/g$. Figure 4.5 shows a plot of ω_d/ω_n versus c/c_c. Evidently if the actual damping is only a small fraction of the critical damping, as it often is, its effect upon the frequency of the motion is insignificant. This explains why engineers usually neglect friction when they calculate the natural frequencies of systems.

FIG. 4.5. Plot showing the effect of friction on frequency in an underdamped system.

The maximum values of y occur when

$$\frac{dy}{dt} = G[-pe^{-pt}\cos (qt - H) - qe^{-pt}\sin (qt - H)] = 0$$

that is, when

$$\tan (qt - H) = -\frac{p}{q}$$

or when

$$(qt - H) = \tan^{-1}\left(-\frac{p}{q}\right) + n\pi$$

or finally when

$$t = \left(\frac{H}{q} - \frac{1}{q}\tan^{-1}\frac{p}{q}\right) + \frac{n\pi}{q} = T + \frac{n\pi}{q}$$

where T is the constant $\left(\frac{H}{q} - \frac{1}{q}\tan^{-1}\frac{p}{q}\right)$.

The ratio of successive maximum displacements is a quantity of considerable importance.   Its value is

$$\frac{y_n}{y_{n+2}} = \frac{y[T + (n\pi/q)]}{y[T + (n+2)\pi/q]} = \frac{Ge^{-p[T+(n\pi/q)]}\cos\left[q\left(T + \frac{n\pi}{q}\right) - H\right]}{Ge^{-p[T+(n+2)\pi/q]}\cos\left[q\left(T + \frac{n+2}{q}\pi\right) - H\right]}$$

$$= e^{2\pi p/q}\frac{\cos(qT + n\pi - H)}{\cos(qT + n\pi - H + 2\pi)}$$

$$= e^{2\pi p/q}$$

Since this result depends only on the parameters of the system and not upon n, we have thus established the remarkable result that *the ratio of successive maximum displacements remains constant throughout the entire motion of an underdamped system.*

If we take the natural logarithm of the last expression, we have

$$\log\left(\frac{y_n}{y_{n+2}}\right) = \frac{2\pi p}{q}$$

This quantity is known as the **logarithmic decrement** δ.   Substituting for p and q from (3), we find

$$\delta = \frac{2\pi p}{q} = 2\pi\frac{cg/2w}{(g/2w)\sqrt{(4kw/g) - c^2}}$$

$$= 2\pi\frac{c}{\sqrt{c_c^2 - c^2}}$$

$$= 2\pi\frac{(c/c_c)}{\sqrt{1 - (c/c_c)^2}}$$

Solved for c/c_c, this becomes

(5) $$\frac{c}{c_c} = \frac{\delta}{\sqrt{\delta^2 + 4\pi^2}}$$

Since y_n and y_{n+2} are quantities which are relatively easy to measure,

δ can easily be computed. Then from the last expression the fraction of critical damping which is present in a given system can be found at once.

To find a particular integral of the differential equation

(6)
$$\frac{w}{g} \frac{d^2y}{dt^2} + c \frac{dy}{dt} + ky = F_0 \cos \omega t$$

we assume as usual

$$Y = A \cos \omega t + B \sin \omega t$$

Substituting this into (6) gives

$$\frac{w}{g} (-\omega^2 A \cos \omega t - \omega^2 B \sin \omega t) + c(-\omega A \sin \omega t + \omega B \cos \omega t)$$
$$+ k(A \cos \omega t + B \sin \omega t) = F_0 \cos \omega t$$

Equating coefficients of the sine and cosine terms gives the two conditions

$$\left(k - \omega^2 \frac{w}{g}\right) A + \omega c B = F_0$$

$$-\omega c A + \left(k - \omega^2 \frac{w}{g}\right) B = 0$$

Solving these simultaneously, we find

$$A = \frac{\left(k - \omega^2 \dfrac{w}{g}\right)}{\left(k - \omega^2 \dfrac{w}{g}\right)^2 + (\omega c)^2} F_0$$

$$B = \frac{\omega c}{\left(k - \omega^2 \dfrac{w}{g}\right)^2 + (\omega c)^2} F_0$$

Hence

$$Y = F_0 \frac{\left(k - \omega^2 \dfrac{w}{g}\right) \cos \omega t + (\omega c) \sin \omega t}{\left(k - \omega^2 \dfrac{w}{g}\right)^2 + (\omega c)^2}$$

$$= \frac{F_0}{\sqrt{\left(k - \omega^2 \dfrac{w}{g}\right)^2 + (\omega c)^2}} \left[\frac{\left(k - \omega^2 \dfrac{w}{g}\right)}{\sqrt{\left(k - \omega^2 \dfrac{w}{g}\right)^2 + (\omega c)^2}} \cos \omega t \right.$$
$$\left. + \frac{\omega c}{\sqrt{\left(k - \omega^2 \dfrac{w}{g}\right)^2 + (\omega c)^2}} \sin \omega t \right]$$

Now by referring to the triangle shown in Fig. 4.6 it is evident that Y can be written in either of the equivalent forms

$$Y = \frac{F_0}{\sqrt{\left(k - \omega^2 \dfrac{w}{g}\right)^2 + (\omega c)^2}} (\cos \omega t \cos \alpha + \sin \omega t \sin \alpha)$$

(7.1)
$$= \frac{F_0 \cos (\omega t - \alpha)}{\sqrt{\left(k - \omega^2 \dfrac{w}{g}\right)^2 + (\omega c)^2}}$$

$$Y = \frac{F_0}{\sqrt{\left(k - \omega^2 \dfrac{w}{g}\right)^2 + (\omega c)^2}} (\cos \omega t \sin \beta + \sin \omega t \cos \beta)$$

(7.2)
$$= \frac{F_0 \sin (\omega t + \beta)}{\sqrt{\left(k - \omega^2 \dfrac{w}{g}\right)^2 + (\omega c)^2}}$$

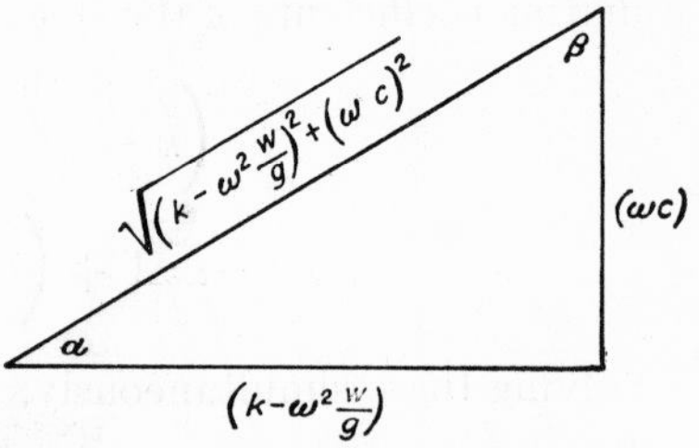

The first of these is the more convenient because it involves the same function (the cosine) as the excitation term in the differential equation. Hence the lag or lead of the response with

$$\left(k - \omega^2 \frac{W}{g}\right)$$

Fig. 4.6.

respect to the disturbing force can easily be inferred. Accordingly, we continue with the first expression for Y.

If we divide the numerator and denominator by k, we obtain

$$Y = \frac{F_0/k}{\sqrt{[1 - (\omega^2 w/kg)]^2 + (\omega c/k)^2}} \cos (\omega t - \alpha)$$

$$= \frac{F_0/k}{\sqrt{\left(1 - \dfrac{\omega^2}{kg/w}\right)^2 + \left[\left(\dfrac{\omega}{\sqrt{kg/w}}\right)\left(\dfrac{2c}{\sqrt{4kw/g}}\right)\right]^2}} \cos (\omega t - \alpha)$$

$$= \frac{\delta_{st}}{\sqrt{\left(1 - \dfrac{\omega^2}{\omega_n^2}\right)^2 + \left(2 \dfrac{\omega}{\omega_n} \dfrac{c}{c_c}\right)^2}} \cos (\omega t - \alpha)$$

where $\delta_{st} \equiv F_0/k$ is the **static deflection** which a *constant* force of magnitude F_0 would produce in a spring of modulus k.

The quantity

(8)
$$M = \frac{1}{\sqrt{\left(1 - \dfrac{\omega^2}{\omega_n^2}\right)^2 + \left(2 \dfrac{\omega}{\omega_n} \dfrac{c}{c_c}\right)^2}}$$

is called the **magnification ratio.**   It is the factor by which the static deflection produced in a spring of modulus k by a constant force F_0 must be multiplied in order to give the amplitude of the vibrations which result when the same force acts dynamically with frequency ω.   Curves of the magnification ratio plotted against the **frequency ratio** ω/ω_n for various values of the **damping ratio** c/c_c are shown in Fig. 4.7.

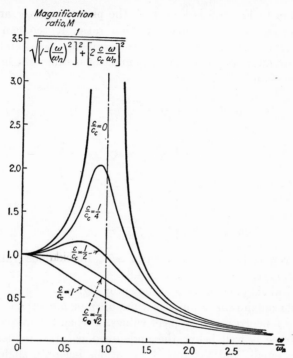

FIG. 4.7.   Curves of the magnification ratio as a function of the impressed frequency ratio, for various amounts of damping.

An inspection of Fig. 4.7 reveals the following interesting facts:

a. M is 1, regardless of the amount of friction, if $\omega/\omega_n = 0$.

b. If $0 < c/c_c < 1/\sqrt{2}$, M rises to a maximum as ω/ω_n increases from 0, the peak value occurring in all cases *before* the impressed frequency ω reaches the undamped natural frequency, or resonant frequency of the system, ω_n.

c. The smaller the amount of friction, the larger the maximum of M, until for the condition of undamped resonance, namely, $c/c_c = 0$ and $\omega = \omega_n$, infinite magnification, *i.e.*, a response of infinite amplitude, occurs.

d. If $c/c_c \geqq 1/\sqrt{2}$, the magnification ratio decreases steadily as ω/ω_n increases from zero.

e. For all values of c/c_c, M approaches zero as the impressed frequency is raised indefinitely above the undamped natural frequency of the system. The angle

$$\alpha = \tan^{-1} \frac{\omega c}{k - \omega^2 \dfrac{w}{g}}$$

which appears in Fig. 4.6 is known as the **phase angle** or **angle of lag** of the response. Like the magnification ratio, it too can easily be expressed in terms of the dimensionless parameters ω/ω_n and c/c_c. To do this, we divide numerator and denominator in the right-hand side of the last expression by k, getting

$$\alpha = \tan^{-1} \left[\frac{\omega c/k}{1 - (\omega^2 w/kg)} \right]$$

$$= \tan^{-1} \left(\frac{\dfrac{\omega}{\sqrt{kg/w}} \dfrac{2c}{\sqrt{4kw/g}}}{1 - \dfrac{\omega^2}{kg/w}} \right)$$

$$= \tan^{-1} \frac{2 \dfrac{\omega}{\omega_n} \dfrac{c}{c_c}}{1 - (\omega/\omega_n)^2}$$

Plots of α versus the frequency ratio ω/ω_n for various values of the damping ratio c/c_c are shown in Fig. 4.8.

The physical significance of α is shown in Fig. 4.9. The displacement Y reaches its maxima α/ω units of time *after* or *later* than the driving force reaches its corresponding peak values. When the frequency of the disturbing force is well below the undamped natural frequency of the system, α is small, and the forced vibrations lag only slightly behind the driving force. When the impressed frequency is equal to the natural frequency, the response of the system lags the excitation by one-quarter of a cycle. As ω increases indefinitely, the lag of the response approaches half a cycle, or in other words the response becomes 180° out of phase with respect to the driving force.

The results of our detailed study of the vibrating weight can now be summarized. The complete motion of the system consists of two parts. The first is given by the complementary function of the underlying differential equation, and may be either oscillatory or nonoscillatory according as the amount of friction which is present is less than or more than the critical damping figure for the system. In any case, however, this part of the solution contains factors which decay exponentially and thus becomes vanishingly small in a very short time. For this reason it is

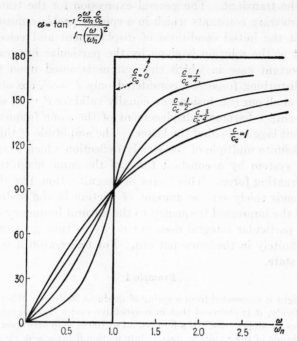

$$\alpha = \tan^{-1} \frac{2\frac{\omega}{\omega_n}\frac{c}{c_c}}{1 - \left(\frac{\omega}{\omega_n}\right)^2}$$

FIG. 4.8.   Curves of the phase angle as a function of the impressed frequency ratio, for various amounts of damping.

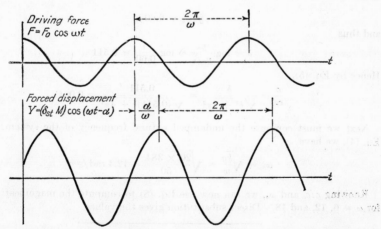

FIG. 4.9.   Plot showing the significance of the phase angle as a measure of the time by which the response lags the excitation.

known as the **transient.** The general expression for the transient contains two arbitrary constants which in a specific problem must be determined to fit the initial conditions of displacement and velocity. The second part of the solution is given by the particular integral. In the highly important case in which the system is acted upon by a pure harmonic disturbing force (we considered only $F = F_0 \cos \omega t$ but without exception all our conclusions are equally valid for $F = F_0 \sin \omega t$), this term represents a harmonic displacement of the same frequency as the excitation but lagging behind the latter. The amplitude of this displacement is a definite multiple of the steady deflection which would be produced in a system by a constant force of the same magnitude as the actual, alternating force. This factor of magnification, like the amount of lag, depends solely on the amount of friction in the system and on the ratio of the impressed frequency to the natural frequency of the system. The particular integral does not decay as time goes on but continues indefinitely in the same pattern. For this reason it is known as the **steady state.**

Example 1

A 50-lb weight is suspended from a spring of modulus 20 lb/in. When the system is vibrating freely, it is observed that in consecutive cycles the maximum displacement decreases by 40 per cent. If a force equal to 10 cos ωt lb acts upon the system, find the amplitude of the resultant steady-state motion if (a) $\omega = 6$, (b) $\omega = 12$, and (c) $\omega = 18$, rad/sec.

The first step here must be to determine the amount of damping which is present in the system. From the given data it is clear that

$$y_{n+2} = 0.60 y_n$$

and thus

$$\delta = \log \frac{y_n}{y_{n+2}} = \log \frac{1}{0.60} = 0.511$$

Hence by Eq. (5),

$$\frac{c}{c_c} = \frac{\delta}{\sqrt{\delta^2 + 4\pi^2}} = \frac{0.511}{\sqrt{(0.511)^2 + 4\pi^2}} = 0.081$$

Next we must compute the undamped natural frequency of the system. Using Eq. (4), we have

$$\omega_n = \sqrt{\frac{kg}{w}} = \sqrt{\frac{20 \times 384}{50}} = 12.4 \text{ rad/sec}$$

Knowing c/c_c and ω_n, we can now use Eq. (8) to compute the magnification ratio for $\omega = 6$, 12, and 18. Direct substitution gives the values

ω	6	12	18
M	1.30	5.94	0.88

Finally, it is clear that a 10-lb force, acting statically, will stretch a spring of modulus 20 lb/in. a distance

$$\delta_{st} = \tfrac{10}{20} = 0.5 \text{ in.}$$

Hence, multiplying this static deflection by the appropriate values of the magnification ratio, we find for the amplitude of the steady-state motion the values

ω	6	12	18
Amplitude	0.65	2.97	0.44

The amplitude corresponding to the impressed frequency $\omega = 12$ is much larger than either of the others because this frequency very nearly coincides with the natural frequency of the system, $\omega_n = 12.4$.

Example 2

A system containing a negligible amount of damping is disturbed from its equilibrium position by the sudden application at $t = 0$ of a force equal to $F_0 \sin \omega t$. Discuss the subsequent motion of the system if ω is close to the natural frequency ω_n.

The differential equation to be solved here is

$$\frac{w}{g}\frac{d^2y}{dt^2} + ky = F_0 \sin \omega t$$

The complementary function is clearly

$$A \cos \sqrt{\frac{kg}{w}}\, t + B \sin \sqrt{\frac{kg}{w}}\, t$$

and it is easy to verify that a particular integral is

$$Y = \frac{F_0}{k - \omega^2 \dfrac{w}{g}} \sin \omega t$$

Hence, using Eq. (4), the general solution can be written

$$y = A \cos \omega_n t + B \sin \omega_n t + \frac{F_0 g}{w} \frac{\sin \omega t}{\omega_n^2 - \omega^2}$$

Since $y = 0$ when $t = 0$, we must have $A = 0$, leaving

$$y = B \sin \omega_n t + \frac{F_0 g}{w} \frac{\sin \omega t}{\omega_n^2 - \omega^2}$$

and

$$v = \frac{dy}{dt} = B\omega_n \cos \omega_n t + \frac{F_0 g}{w} \frac{\omega \cos \omega t}{\omega_n^2 - \omega^2}$$

Substituting $v = 0$ and $t = 0$ in the last equation, we obtain

$$0 = B\omega_n + \frac{F_0 g \omega}{w(\omega_n^2 - \omega^2)} \qquad \text{or} \qquad B = -\frac{F_0 g}{w} \frac{\omega}{\omega_n(\omega_n^2 - \omega^2)}$$

Hence

$$y = \frac{F_0 g}{w(\omega_n^2 - \omega^2)} \left(-\frac{\omega}{\omega_n} \sin \omega_n t + \sin \omega t \right)$$

Now we are supposing that the impressed frequency ω is very close to the natural frequency ω_n. Hence for descriptive purposes we may legitimately set $\omega/\omega_n = 1$, obtaining

$$y \doteq \frac{F_0 g}{w} \frac{\sin \omega t - \sin \omega_n t}{\omega_n^2 - \omega^2}$$

If we convert the difference of the sine terms into a product, we get

$$y = -\frac{F_0 g}{w} \frac{2 \cos \left(\dfrac{\omega + \omega_n}{2} t \right) \sin \left(\dfrac{\omega - \omega_n}{2} t \right)}{(\omega + \omega_n)(\omega - \omega_n)}$$

If we now let ϵ denote the small quantity $(\omega - \omega_n)/2$ and note that $(\omega + \omega_n)/2$ is approximately equal to ω, we can write

$$y \doteq -\frac{F_0 g}{w} \frac{\sin \epsilon t}{2\epsilon \omega} \cos \omega t$$

Since ϵ is a small quantity, the period, $2\pi/\epsilon$, of the term $\sin \epsilon t$ is large. Hence the form of the last expression shows that y can be regarded as essentially a periodic

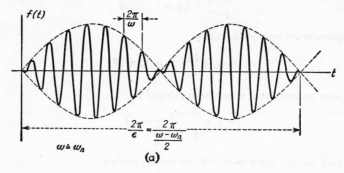

(a)

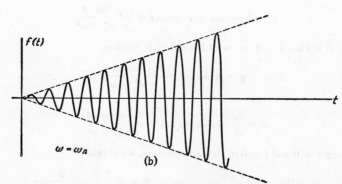

(b)

FIG. 4.10. Plot showing the phenomenon of beats.

function, $\cos \omega t$, of frequency ω, with the slowly varying amplitude

$$-\frac{F_0 g}{w} \frac{\sin \epsilon t}{2\epsilon\omega}$$

Figure 4.10 shows the general nature of this behavior when ω is nearly but not quite equal to ω_n, and in the limiting case when $\omega = \omega_n$ and conditions of **pure resonance** exist.

This is one of the simplest illustrations of the phenomenon of **beats**, which occurs whenever an impressed frequency is close to a natural frequency of a system, or whenever two slightly different frequencies are impressed upon a system regardless of what its natural frequencies may be. A wave form, such as that shown in Fig. 4.10a, whose amplitude is periodically varying is said to be **amplitude modulated**, and the dotted curves to which the actual wave periodically rises and falls are called its **envelope**.

EXERCISES

1. If friction is neglected, show that the natural frequency of a system consisting of a mass on an elastic suspension is approximately

$$\frac{3.13}{\sqrt{\delta_{st}}} \qquad \text{cycles/sec}$$

where δ_{st} is the deflection, in inches, produced in the suspension when the mass hangs in static equilibrium.

2. A heavy motor of unknown weight is set upon a felt mounting pad of unknown spring constant. What is the natural frequency of the system if the motor is observed to compress the pad $\frac{1}{16}$ in.?

3. If the roots of the characteristic equation in the overdamped case are $m = -r \pm s$, show that the complementary function can be written as

$$y = Ae^{-rt} \cosh (st + B)$$

or as

$$y = Ce^{-rt} \sinh (st + D)$$

according as it has no real zero or one real zero (see Fig. 4.2).

4. If y_0 and v_0 are, respectively, the initial displacement and initial velocity with which an overdamped system starts its motion, show that

$$\frac{w}{g} \left(\frac{v_0}{y_0}\right)^2 + c \left(\frac{v_0}{y_0}\right) + k > 0$$

is the condition that the complementary function have a real zero.

5. In addition to the condition of Exercise 4, what further requirement is necessary to ensure that the zero of the complementary function will be positive, *i.e.*, will occur during the actual motion?

6. An overdamped system begins to move from its equilibrium position with velocity v_0. Show that the maximum displacement occurs when

$$t = \frac{1}{\omega_n \sqrt{(c/c_c)^2 - 1}} \tanh^{-1} \sqrt{1 - \left(\frac{c_c}{c}\right)^2}$$

(Hint: Use the results of Exercise 3.)

7. In Exercise 6 show that the maximum displacement is

$$y_{max} = \frac{v_0}{\omega_n}\left(\tan\frac{\alpha}{2}\right)^{\sec\alpha}$$

where $\alpha = \sin^{-1}(c_c/c)$.

8. Investigate the answers to Exercises 6 and 7 in the limit when c/c_c approaches 1. Check your results by working directly with the equation of the transient for the critically damped case.

9. Show that the maximum displacements during the free motion of an underdamped system do not occur midway between the zeros of the complementary function but precede the mid-points by the constant amount

$$\frac{1}{\omega_n}\frac{\sin^{-1}(c/c_c)}{\sqrt{1-(c/c_c)^2}}$$

10. Investigate the motion of a weight hanging on a spring when the disturbing force is equal to $F_0 \sin \omega t$ instead of $F_0 \cos \omega t$. In particular show that Eqs. (8) and (9) for the magnification ratio and angle of lag, respectively, are still the same.

11. Investigate the motion of a weight hanging from a spring if a constant force F_0 is suddenly applied to the weight. Are the concepts of magnification ratio and angle of lag relevant in this case?

12. Show that the maxima of the curves of the magnification ratio versus frequency ratio occur when

$$\frac{\omega}{\omega_n} = \sqrt{1-2\left(\frac{c}{c_c}\right)^2}$$

13. A weight of 64 lb hangs from a spring of modulus 36 lb/in. During the free motion of the system it is observed that the maximum displacement of the weight decreases to one-tenth of its value in 5 cycles of the motion. Find the amplitude of the steady-state motion produced by a force equal to 6 sin 15t lb. By what time interval does this steady-state motion lag the driving force in this case?

14. A weight of 128 lb hangs from a spring of modulus 75 lb/in. The damping in the system is 28 per cent of critical. Determine the motion of the weight if it is pulled downward 2 in. from its equilibrium position and suddenly released.

15. A motor weighing 640 lb and designed to be run at 1,760 rpm has become unbalanced, the unbalanced force being estimated to be 150 lb at the normal operating speed. The elastic mounting on which the motor rests has a modulus of 30 tons/in. Neglecting damping, what will be the amplitude of the forced vibrations? If damping equal to $\frac{1}{8}c_c$ be provided, what will be the amplitude of the forced vibrations?

16. A weight of 96 lb hangs on a spring of modulus 25 lb/in. A force equal to 19.5 cos 4t lb acts on the weight. If the actual damping is 60 per cent of critical and if the weight begins to move from rest from an initial displacement of 0.7 in. find the equation of its subsequent motion.

17. Solve Exercise 16 if instead of the force 19.5 cos 4t, a constant force of 50 lb is suddenly applied to the system when it is in its equilibrium position.

18. A uniform bar of length l and weight w rests on two horizontal rollers which rotate inward in opposition to each other with constant angular velocity. The coefficient of friction (assumed to be "dry" or Coulomb friction) between the bar and the rollers is μ. When the bar is displaced slightly from a symmetrical position, it executes small horizontal oscillations in a direction perpendicular to the axes of the cylinders.   Determine the period of this motion, and show how the value of μ may thus be found experimentally.

19. In many applications involving forces arising from rotating parts which have become unbalanced, the amplitude of the sinusoidal disturbing force acting on a system is not constant but varies directly as the square of the frequency.   If a weight suspended from a spring is acted upon by a force of this character, determine the steady-state motion.   In particular, determine the form of the magnification ratio and the angle of lag.

20. Show that the maximum points on the plots of the magnification ratio versus the frequency ratio under the conditions of Exercise 19 always occur at values of the impressed frequency, ω, which are greater than the natural frequency of the system ω_n.

4.4 The Series Electrical Circuit.   All the results which we derived in the last section may, after a suitable change in terminology, be applied to any of the other systems which we have considered.   However, the concepts which are central in one field are not always of equal importance in related fields, and it seems desirable to illustrate the minor differences in the application of our general theory to various classes of systems by considering one of the electrical circuits in some detail.

For the simple series circuit with an alternating impressed voltage, we derived (among several equivalent forms) the equation

(1) $$L \frac{d^2Q}{dt^2} + R \frac{dQ}{dt} + \frac{1}{C} Q = E_0 \cos \omega t$$

and on comparing this with the differential equation of the vibrating weight

$$\frac{w}{g} \frac{d^2y}{dt^2} + c \frac{dy}{dt} + ky = F_0 \cos \omega t$$

we noted the correspondence

$$\text{Charge } Q \longleftrightarrow \text{displacement } y$$
$$\text{Inductance } L \longleftrightarrow \text{mass } \frac{w}{g}$$
$$\text{Resistance } R \longleftrightarrow \text{friction } c$$
$$\text{Elastance } \frac{1}{C} \longleftrightarrow \text{spring modulus } k$$
$$\text{Voltage } E \longleftrightarrow \text{force } F$$

and implicitly,

$$\text{Current } i \equiv \frac{dQ}{dt} \longleftrightarrow \text{velocity } v \equiv \frac{dy}{dt}$$

Extending this correspondence to the derived results, we can infer from the undamped natural frequency of the mechanical system

$$\omega_n = \sqrt{\frac{kg}{w}}$$

that the electrical circuit has a natural frequency

$$\Omega_n = \sqrt{\frac{1}{LC}}$$

when no resistance is present. Furthermore, the concept of critical damping

$$c_c = \sqrt{\frac{4kw}{g}}$$

leads to the concept of critical resistance

$$R_c = \sqrt{\frac{4L}{C}}$$

which determines whether the free behavior of the electrical system will be oscillatory or nonoscillatory.

The notion of magnification ratio can also be extended to the electrical case, but it is not customary to do so because the extension would relate to Q (the analogue of the displacement y), whereas in most electrical problems it is not Q but i which is the variable of interest. To see how a related concept arises in the electrical case, let us convert the particular integral Y, given by Eq. (7.2) of the last section, into its electrical equivalent. The result is found by direct substitution to be

$$Q = \frac{E_0 \sin (\omega t + \beta)}{\sqrt{\left(\dfrac{1}{C} - \omega^2 L\right)^2 + (\omega R)^2}}, \qquad \beta = \tan^{-1}\left(\frac{\dfrac{1}{C} - \omega^2 L}{\omega R}\right)$$

To obtain the current i, we differentiate this, getting

$$\frac{dQ}{dt} = i = \frac{E_0 \omega \cos (\omega t + \beta)}{\sqrt{\left(\dfrac{1}{C} - \omega^2 L\right)^2 + (\omega R)^2}}$$

or, dividing numerator and denominator by ω,

(2) $$i = \frac{E_0 \cos (\omega t - \delta)}{\sqrt{R^2 + [\omega L - (1/\omega C)]^2}}$$

where

(3) $$\delta = -\beta = \tan^{-1}\left[\frac{\omega L - (1/\omega C)}{R}\right]$$

This shows that the steady-state current produced by an alternating voltage is of the same frequency as the voltage but lags the voltage by

δ/ω units of time, or

$$\frac{\delta/\omega}{2\pi/\omega} = \frac{\delta}{2\pi} \qquad \text{cycles}$$

The amplitude of the steady-state current is obtained by dividing the voltage amplitude E_0 by the expression

(4) $$\sqrt{R^2 + [\omega L - (1/\omega C)]^2}$$

By analogy with Ohm's law, $I = E/R$, the quantity (4) appears as a generalized resistance, or **impedance** as it is usually called. The impedance while not the analogue of the magnification ratio is clearly a similar concept. Since impedance is defined as

$$\frac{\text{Voltage}}{\text{Current}}$$

the mechanical quantity corresponding to this is the ratio

$$\frac{\text{Force}}{\text{Velocity}}$$

This is called the **mechanical impedance** by some writers, and in certain mechanical problems has proved a useful notion.

A somewhat different approach to the determination of the particular integral, or steady-state current, is sometimes taken by electrical engineers. Given either a cosine *or* a sine voltage, they write the basic differential equation (1) in the form

(5) $$L \frac{d^2Q}{dt^2} + R \frac{dQ}{dt} + \frac{Q}{C} = E_0 e^{j\omega t} = E_0(\cos \omega t + j \sin \omega t)\dagger$$

trusting that real and imaginary terms will somehow retain their identity throughout the process. If this be the case, then the real part of the particular integral corresponding to $E_0 e^{j\omega t}$ will be the particular integral for $E_0 \cos \omega t$, and the imaginary part will be the particular integral for $E_0 \sin \omega t$.

To see that this is actually so, we must first find a particular integral of (5). We do this as usual by assuming

$$Q = A e^{j\omega t}$$

and substituting into the differential equation. This gives

$$L(-\omega^2 A e^{j\omega t}) + R(j\omega A e^{j\omega t}) + \frac{1}{C} A e^{j\omega t} = E_0 e^{j\omega t}$$

$\dagger$ To avoid confusing $i = \sqrt{-1}$ with i = current, we shall throughout the rest of this chapter follow the standard practice of writing $\sqrt{-1} = j$.

which will be an identity if and only if

$$A = \frac{E_0}{-\omega^2 L + j\omega R + \dfrac{1}{C}}$$

Hence

$$Q = \frac{E_0 e^{j\omega t}}{j\omega R - \omega^2 L + (1/C)}$$

From this we find, by differentiation,

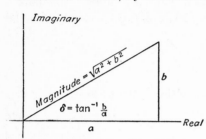

FIG. 4.11. Plot showing the relation between the magnitude, angle, and components of a general complex number.

$$\frac{dQ}{dt} = i = \frac{E_0 j\omega e^{j\omega t}}{j\omega R - \omega^2 L + (1/C)}$$
$$= \frac{E_0 e^{j\omega t}}{R + j[\omega L - (1/\omega C)]}$$

To find the real and imaginary parts of this expression, it is convenient to recall that any complex number, $a + jb$, can be written

$$a + jb = (\text{magnitude}) \; e^{j(\text{angle})}$$

where the magnitude and the angle are related to the components a and b, as shown in Fig. 4.11.

Applied to the denominator of i, this gives

$$R + j\left(\omega L - \frac{1}{\omega C}\right) = \sqrt{R^2 + \left(\omega L - \frac{1}{\omega C}\right)^2} \; e^{j\delta}$$

where

$$\delta = \tan^{-1}\left[\frac{\omega L - (1/\omega C)}{R}\right]$$

Hence we can rewrite i in the form

$$i = \frac{E_0 e^{j\omega t}}{\sqrt{R^2 + [\omega L - (1/\omega C)]^2} \; e^{j\delta}}$$
$$= \frac{E_0 e^{j(\omega t - \delta)}}{\sqrt{R^2 + [\omega L - (1/\omega C)]^2}}$$
$$= E_0 \frac{\cos(\omega t - \delta) + j\sin(\omega t - \delta)}{\sqrt{R^2 + [\omega L - (1/\omega C)]^2}}$$

Comparing this with Eqs. (2) and (3), it is clear that the real part here is exactly the particular integral corresponding to $E_0 \cos \omega t$, as we derived it directly. Similarly, had we taken the trouble to work it out explicitly, we would have found for the particular integral corresponding to $E_0 \sin \omega t$

precisely the imaginary part of the last expression. Since it is much easier to find the particular integral corresponding to an exponential term than it is to find the particular integral for a cosine or sine term, the advantage of using $E_0 e^{j\omega t}$ in place of $E_0 \cos \omega t$ or $E_0 \sin \omega t$ is obvious.

The expression

$$R + j\left(\omega L - \frac{1}{\omega C}\right) \qquad \text{or} \qquad j\omega L + R + \frac{1}{j\omega C}$$

is called the **complex impedance** Z. Its magnitude, which we defined earlier [Eq. (4)] simply as the impedance, might also be called the **attenuation,** since the larger its value, the smaller or more *attenuated* is the resultant current. The angle δ of the complex impedance is the **phase shift.** The real part of Z is clearly a resistance. The imaginary part of Z is called the **reactance.** The reciprocal of Z is called the **admittance.** The real part of the admittance is called the **conductance,** and the imaginary part is called the **susceptance.**

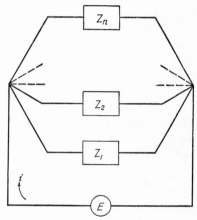

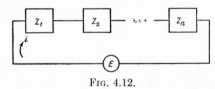

FIG. 4.12.   FIG. 4.13.

The most striking property of the complex impedance, as every electrical engineer knows, is that when any electrical elements are connected in series or in parallel, the corresponding impedances combine just as simple resistances do. Thus the current through a series of Z's can be found simply by dividing the impressed voltage by the single impedance

$$Z = Z_1 + Z_2 + \cdots + Z_n$$

Similarly, the current through a set of elements connected in parallel can be found by dividing the impressed voltage by the single impedance Z defined by the relation

$$\frac{1}{Z} = \frac{1}{Z_1} + \frac{1}{Z_2} + \cdots + \frac{1}{Z_n}$$

This makes it actually unnecessary to use differential equations in determining the *steady-state behavior* of an electrical system (or of a mechanical system, if the concept of mechanical impedance be used). *For the transient behavior this is not true, however.*

Example 1

A series circuit in which both the charge and the current are initially zero contains the elements $L = 1$, $R = 1,000$, $C = 6.25 \times 10^{-6}$. If a constant emf of 24 volts is suddenly switched into the circuit, find the peak value of the resultant current.

The differential equation which we must solve is

$$\frac{d^2Q}{dt^2} + 1,000\frac{dQ}{dt} + \frac{Q}{6.25 \times 10^{-6}} = 24$$

subject to the conditions that $Q = i = 0$, when $t = 0$. The characteristic equation in this case is

$$m^2 + 1,000m + \frac{10^6}{6.25} = 0$$

and its roots are $m_1 = -200$, $m_2 = -800$. Hence the complementary function is

$$c_1 e^{-200t} + c_2 e^{-800t}$$

To find a particular integral, we assume $Q = A$, and substitute into the differential equation, getting without difficulty

$$A = 150 \times 10^{-6}$$

The complete solution is therefore

$$Q = c_1 e^{-200t} + c_2 e^{-800t} + 150 \times 10^{-6}$$

and, differentiating,

$$\frac{dQ}{dt} = i = -200 c_1 e^{-200t} - 800 c_2 e^{-800t}$$

Substituting the initial conditions for Q and i gives the pair of equations

$$c_1 + c_2 + 150 \times 10^{-6} = 0$$
$$c_1 + 4c_2 = 0$$

from which we find at once

$$c_1 = -200 \times 10^{-6}, \qquad c_2 = 50 \times 10^{-6}$$

Hence

$$i = 0.04(e^{-200t} - e^{-800t})$$

To find the time when i is a maximum, we must equate to zero the time derivative of i:

$$0.04(-200 e^{-200t} + 800 e^{-800t}) = 0$$

Dividing out $(0.04)800 e^{-200t}$ and transposing, we have

$$e^{-600t} = \tfrac{1}{4}$$

from which, using logarithms,

$$t = 0.0023 \text{ sec}$$

The maximum value of i can now be found by substituting this value of t into the general expression for i. The result is

$$i_{max} = 0.019 \text{ amp}$$

EXERCISES

1. In Example 1 plot the potential difference across each element as a function of time for $0 < t < 0.01$

2. In Example 1 suppose that 10 msec after the voltage is impressed on the circuit it is suddenly removed. Find the voltage across the condenser as a function of time, and plot it for $0 < t < 0.02$.

3. A series circuit contains the elements $L = 1$, $R = 600$, $C = 4 \times 10^{-6}$. Initially there is neither charge nor current in the circuit. If a constant voltage of 28 is suddenly switched into the circuit at $t = 0$, find the resultant current as a function of time.

4. A 1-μf condenser with an initial charge $Q_0 = 10^{-5}$ coulomb is discharged through a resistance of 120 ohms and an inductance of 0.01 henry connected in series with it. Find the resultant current as a function of time.

5. A voltage $E = 120 \cos 120\pi t$ is suddenly switched into a series circuit containing the elements $L = 1$, $R = 800$, $C = 4 \times 10^{-6}$. What is the resultant steady-state current?

6. A series circuit in which $Q_0 = i_0 = 0$ contains the elements $L = 1$, $R = 1,000$, $C = 4 \times 10^{-6}$. A voltage $E = 110 \sin 50\pi t$ is suddenly switched into the circuit. Find the resultant current as a function of time.

7. A condenser $C = 5 \times 10^{-6}$, a resistance $R = 20$, and an inductance $L = 0.1$ are connected in parallel. A current source delivering a constant current of 0.01 is suddenly connected across the common terminals of the elements. Find the resultant voltage as a function of time.

8. A series circuit in which $Q_0 = i_0 = 0$ contains the elements $L = 0.02$, $R = 250$, and $C = 2 \times 10^{-6}$. A constant voltage of 28 is suddenly switched into the circuit. Find the time it takes for the potential difference across the condenser to reach one-half of its terminal value.

9. A constant voltage is suddenly switched into a nonoscillatory RLC circuit in which $Q_0 = i_0 = 0$. Show that the voltage across the condenser can never overshoot its terminal value.

10. For what values of ω is the impedance $Z = \sqrt{R^2 + \left(\omega L - \frac{1}{\omega C}\right)^2}$ a minimum?

    Compare this with the corresponding property of the magnification ratio. Explain.

4.5 Systems with Several Degrees of Freedom.

The laws of Newton and Kirchhoff, together with the mathematical theory of simultaneous linear differential equations which we developed in Chap. 3, form the basis of the analysis of large classes of systems with more than one degree of freedom. The details of such applications can best be made clear through examples.

Example 1

A uniform bar 4 ft long and weighing 16 lb/ft is supported as shown in Fig. 4.14a, on springs of moduli 24 and 15 lb/in., respectively. If the springs are guided so that only vertical displacement of the center of the bar is possible, find the undamped natural frequencies of the system.

This is a system with two degrees of freedom, because to specify it completely two coordinates are required, for instance, the vertical displacement of the center of gravity of the bar y and the angle of rotation of the bar about its center of gravity θ. As shown in Fig. 4.14b, the instantaneous deflections of the springs are

$$y + 24 \sin \theta \qquad \text{and} \qquad y - 24 \sin \theta$$

or, if we make the usual assumption that the angular deflection is small, approximately

$$y + 24\theta \qquad \text{and} \qquad y - 24\theta$$

Hence the forces which the springs apply to the ends of the bar are

$$15(y + 24\theta) \qquad \text{and} \qquad 24(y - 24\theta)$$

Newton's law applied to the translation of the center of gravity of the bar therefore gives*

$$\frac{64}{384} \frac{d^2y}{dt^2} = -15(y + 24\theta) - 24(y - 24\theta)$$

or

(1) $$\frac{d^2y}{dt^2} + 234y - 1{,}296\theta = 0$$

Similarly, computing the torques applied to the ends of the bar by the spring forces and then applying Newton's law in torsional form to the rotation of the bar about its

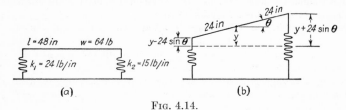

$$\text{F}_{\text{IG}}.\ 4.14.$$

center of gravity, we have (recalling that the moment of inertia of a uniform bar about its mid-point is $ml^2/12$)

$$\frac{64}{384} \frac{(48)^2}{12} \frac{d^2\theta}{dt^2} = -24[15(y + 24\theta)] + 24[24(y - 24\theta)]$$

or

(2) $$8\frac{d^2\theta}{dt^2} - 54y + 5{,}616\theta = 0$$

To find the solutions of the simultaneous differential equations (1) and (2), we can set up the characteristic equation and proceed as we did in Chap. 3, or we may take advantage of the fact that because friction was neglected neither of these equations contains any first derivative terms. To capitalize on this, as vibration engineers

* As pointed out in the derivation of Eq. (8), Sec. 4.2, we can neglect the gravitational force on the bar and the portion of the elastic forces due to the compression of the springs in their equilibrium position. An equivalent point of view is to imagine that the motion takes place not in a vertical plane but on a frictionless horizontal plane, so that gravitational effects are irrelevant.

usually do, we assume solutions of the special form*

$$y = A \cos \omega t \qquad \text{and} \qquad \theta = B \cos \omega t$$

and substitute them into the differential equations, dividing out the common factor $\cos \omega t$, as we do. The result is the pair of algebraic equations

$$-\omega^2 A + 234A - 1,296B = 0$$
$$-8\omega^2 B - 54A + 5,616B = 0$$

or

$$(-\omega^2 + 234)A - 1,296B = 0$$
$$-54A + (-8\omega^2 + 5,616)B = 0$$

In order that there should be nontrivial values of A and B satisfying these equations, it is necessary that the determinant of the coefficients should vanish. This gives the equation

$$\begin{vmatrix} (-\omega^2 + 234) & -1,296 \\ -54 & (-8\omega^2 + 5,616) \end{vmatrix} = 8\omega^4 - 7,488\omega^2 + 1,244,160 = 0$$

Solving this we find

$$\omega_1^2 = 216, \qquad \omega_2^2 = 720$$

or

$$\omega_1 = 6\sqrt{6}, \qquad \omega_2 = 12\sqrt{5} \qquad \text{rad/sec}$$

For these frequencies and for these only, there are nontrivial solutions of the two simultaneous differential equations. These, then, are the natural frequencies of the system. Converted from radians per second to cycles per second, they are

$$f_1 = \frac{6\sqrt{6}}{2\pi} = 2.34 \qquad \text{and} \qquad f_2 = \frac{12\sqrt{5}}{2\pi} = 4.27$$

This problem is typical of many in the field of mechanical vibrations, in that only the natural frequencies were required. Accordingly there was no need to construct the general solution or to determine the arbitrary constants to fit prescribed conditions.

Example 2

In the circuit shown in Fig. 4.15 find the current in each loop as a function of time if all charges and currents are zero when the switch is closed at $t = 0$.

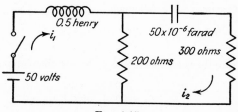

0.5 henry
i_1
50 volts
50×10^{-6} farad
200 ohms
300 ohms
i_2

FIG. 4.15.

We take as variables the currents i_1 and i_2 flowing in the respective loops, noting that the current in the common branch is therefore $i_1 - i_2$. Applying Kirchhoff's

* The assumptions $y = C \sin \omega t$ and $\theta = D \sin \omega t$ would have worked just as well.

first law to each loop, we obtain the equations

$$0.5 \frac{di_1}{dt} + 200(i_1 - i_2) = 50$$

$$200(i_2 - i_1) + 300i_2 + \frac{1}{50 \times 10^{-6}} \int i_2 \, dt = 0$$

or, letting $Q_2 = \int i_2 \, dt$,

$$\frac{di_1}{dt} + 400i_1 - 400 \frac{dQ_2}{dt} = 100$$

$$-2i_1 + 5 \frac{dQ_2}{dt} + 200Q_2 = 0$$

The characteristic equation of this system is

$$\begin{vmatrix} (m + 400) & -400m \\ -2 & (5m + 200) \end{vmatrix} = 5(m^2 + 280m + 16,000) = 0$$

From its roots, $m_1 = -80$ and $m_2 = -200$, we can construct the expressions

$$i_1 = a_1 e^{-80t} + b_1 e^{-200t}$$
$$Q_2 = a_2 e^{-80t} + b_2 e^{-200t}$$

which, after the constants are properly related, will constitute the complementary function of the system.

Substituting these expressions into the second of the two differential equations, we obtain

$$-2(a_1 e^{-80t} + b_1 e^{-200t}) + 5(-80a_2 e^{-80t} - 200b_2 e^{-200t}) + 200(a_2 e^{-80t} + b_2 e^{-200t}) = 0$$

or

$$(-2a_1 - 200a_2)e^{-80t} + (-2b_1 - 800b_2)e^{-200t} = 0$$

This will be identically true if and only if

$$a_1 = -100a_2 \qquad \text{and} \qquad b_1 = -400b_2$$

Therefore the complementary function is

$$i_1 = -100a_2 e^{-80t} - 400b_2 e^{-200t}$$
$$Q_2 = a_2 e^{-80t} + b_2 e^{-200t}$$

To find a particular integral, we assume

$$i_1 = A_1$$
$$Q_2 = A_2$$

Substituting these into the nonhomogeneous system of differential equations gives

$$400A_1 = 100$$
$$-2A_1 + 200A_2 = 0$$

Hence

$$A_1 = \tfrac{1}{4} \qquad \text{and} \qquad A_2 = \tfrac{1}{400}$$

and therefore the general solution of the system is

$$i_1 = -100a_2 e^{-80t} - 400b_2 e^{-200t} + \tfrac{1}{4}$$
$$Q_2 = a_2 e^{-80t} + b_2 e^{-200t} + \tfrac{1}{400}$$

Since $i_1 = 0$ and $Q_2 = 0$ when $t = 0$, we must have

$$0 = -100a_2 - 400b_2 + \tfrac{1}{4}$$
$$0 = a_2 + b_2 + \tfrac{1}{400}$$

From these we find without difficulty that

$$a_2 = -\tfrac{1}{240} \quad \text{and} \quad b_2 = \tfrac{1}{600}$$

The required currents are therefore

$$i_1 = \tfrac{5}{12}e^{-80t} - \tfrac{2}{3}e^{-200t} + \tfrac{1}{4}$$
$$i_2 = \frac{dQ_2}{dt} = \frac{1}{3}\,e^{-80t} - \frac{1}{3}\,e^{-200t}$$

Evidently $i_2 = 0$ when $t = 0$, as required.

EXERCISES

Find the natural frequencies of the following systems:

1.

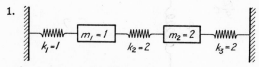

FIG. 4.16.

Ans. $\omega_1 = 1$, $\omega_2 = 2$

2.

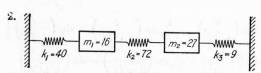

FIG. 4.17.

3.

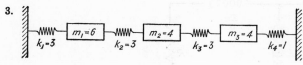

FIG. 4.18.

4.

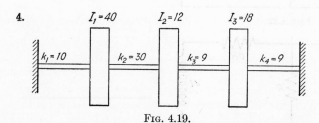

FIG. 4.19.

Ans. $\omega_1 = \tfrac{1}{2}$, $\omega_2 = 1$, $\omega_3 = 2$

Find the currents in the following circuits as functions of time if in each case the key is closed at an instant when all charges and currents are zero.

5.

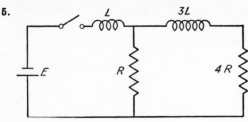

FIG. 4.20.

Ans. $i_1 = \dfrac{E}{R}\left(-\dfrac{1}{8}e^{-\frac{2R}{L}t} - \dfrac{9}{8}e^{-\frac{2R}{3L}t} + \dfrac{5}{4}\right)$; $i_2 = \dfrac{E}{R}\left(\dfrac{1}{8}e^{-\frac{2R}{L}t} - \dfrac{3}{8}e^{-\frac{2R}{3L}t} + \dfrac{1}{4}\right)$

6.

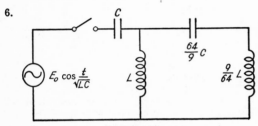

FIG. 4.21.

Ans. $i_1 = E_0\sqrt{\dfrac{C}{L}}\left[\dfrac{243}{80}\sin\left(\dfrac{3t}{\sqrt{LC}}\right) - \dfrac{1}{240}\sin\left(\dfrac{t}{3\sqrt{LC}}\right) - \sin\left(\dfrac{t}{\sqrt{LC}}\right)\right]$

$i_2 = E_0\sqrt{\dfrac{C}{L}}\left[\dfrac{27}{10}\sin\left(\dfrac{3t}{\sqrt{LC}}\right) + \dfrac{1}{30}\sin\left(\dfrac{t}{3\sqrt{LC}}\right) - \sin\left(\dfrac{t}{\sqrt{LC}}\right)\right]$

7.

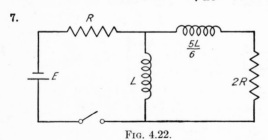

FIG. 4.22.

8.

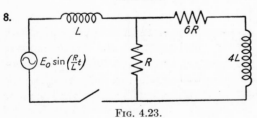

FIG. 4.23.

In the following circuits the currents are initially zero, the charge on the condenser in the closed loop is (necessarily) zero, but the condenser in the open loop bears a charge Q_0.   Find each current as a function of time after the closing of the switch.

9.

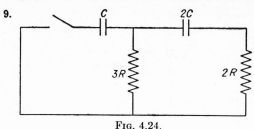

Fig. 4.24.

10.

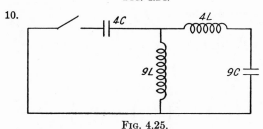

Fig. 4.25.

4.6 Electromechanical Analogies. Although we have pointed out repeatedly the mathematical similarity between certain simple mechanical and electrical systems, we have not as yet shown how to make the correspondence exact, so that numerical results for one system can be obtained experimentally from another.   To see how this can be done let us consider, as an illustration, the torsional-mechanical and parallel-electrical circuits that we discussed in Sec. 4.2.   There we derived the equation

$$(1) \qquad I\frac{d^2\theta}{dt^2} + c\frac{d\theta}{dt} + k\theta = T_0\cos\omega_1 t$$

for the torsional system, and either of the equations

$$(2.1) \qquad C\frac{d^2u}{dt^2} + \frac{1}{R}\frac{du}{dt} + \frac{1}{L}u = I_0\cos\omega_2 t \qquad u = \int^t e\,dt$$

$$(2.2) \qquad C\frac{d^2e}{dt^2} + \frac{1}{R}\frac{de}{dt} + \frac{1}{L}e = -I_0\,\omega_2\sin\omega_2 t$$

for the electrical circuit.   If we base the analysis of the electrical system on Eq. (2.1), the *voltage* $e = du/dt$ corresponds to the *angular velocity* $d\theta/dt$ in the torsional case.   If we use Eq. (2.2), the *voltage* e corresponds to the *angular displacement* θ.   From either point of view we make the analogy exact by reducing the differential equations to a dimensionless form.

To do this for Eq. (1), let ν_1 be an arbitrary frequency, let α be an arbitrary angle, and let X and τ be dimensionless variables defined by

$$X = \frac{\theta}{\alpha}, \qquad \tau = \nu_1 t$$

Then

$$\frac{d\theta}{dt} = \frac{d(\alpha X)}{dt} = \alpha \frac{dX}{dt} = \alpha \frac{dX}{d\tau}\frac{d\tau}{dt} = \alpha \nu_1 \frac{dX}{d\tau}$$

and similarly

$$\frac{d^2\theta}{dt^2} = \alpha \nu_1^2 \frac{d^2X}{d\tau^2}$$

Under these substitutions Eq. (1) becomes

$$I\alpha\nu_1^2 \frac{d^2X}{d\tau^2} + c\alpha\nu_1 \frac{dX}{d\tau} + k\alpha X = T_0 \cos\left(\frac{\omega_1}{\nu_1}\tau\right)$$

or, dividing by $I\alpha\nu_1^2$,

$$(3) \qquad \frac{d^2X}{d\tau^2} + \left(\frac{c}{I\nu_1}\right)\frac{dX}{d\tau} + \left(\frac{k}{I\nu_1^2}\right)X = \left(\frac{T_0}{I\alpha\nu_1^2}\right)\cos\left(\frac{\omega_1}{\nu_1}\tau\right)$$

In this form the equation is entirely dimensionless, for not only are the variables X and τ dimensionless, but so too are the coefficients. In fact

$T_0 = $ torque $ = $ force $\times$ distance has dimensions $\dfrac{ML}{T^2}L = \dfrac{ML^2}{T^2}$

$I = $ moment of inertia has dimensions ML^2

$\alpha = $ angle is dimensionless

$\omega_1,\ \nu_1 = $ frequencies are of dimension $\dfrac{1}{T}$

$c = $ torque per unit angular velocity has dimensions $\dfrac{ML^2/T^2}{1/T} = \dfrac{ML^2}{T}$

$k = $ torque per unit angle has dimensions $\dfrac{ML^2}{T^2}$

and thus

$$\left[\frac{c}{I\nu_1}\right] = \frac{ML^2/T}{ML^2\,(1/T)} = [0]$$

$$\left[\frac{k}{I\nu_1^2}\right] = \frac{ML^2/T^2}{ML^2\,(1/T^2)} = [0]$$

$$\left[\frac{T_0}{I\alpha\nu_1^2}\right] = \frac{ML^2/T^2}{ML^2\,(1/T^2)} = [0]$$

$$\left[\frac{\omega_1}{\nu_1}\right] = \frac{1/T}{1/T} = [0]$$

To reduce Eq. (2.1) to a dimensionless form, let v be an arbitrary value of $u = \int^t e\,dt$, and let ν_2 be an arbitrary frequency. Then in terms of the dimensionless variables

$$X = \frac{u}{v} \quad \text{and} \quad \tau = \nu_2 t$$

we have

$$\frac{du}{dt} = v\nu_2 \frac{dX}{d\tau} \quad \text{and} \quad \frac{d^2u}{dt^2} = v\nu_2^2 \frac{d^2X}{d\tau^2}$$

These substitutions reduce Eq. (2.1) to the form

$$C v\nu_2^2 \frac{d^2X}{d\tau^2} + \frac{1}{R} v\nu_2 \frac{dX}{d\tau} + \frac{1}{L} vX = I_0 \cos\frac{\omega_2}{\nu_2}\tau$$

or, dividing by $C v\nu_2^2$,

$$(4.1) \qquad \frac{d^2X}{d\tau^2} + \left(\frac{1}{CR\nu_2}\right)\frac{dX}{d\tau} + \left(\frac{1}{CL\nu_2^2}\right)X = \left(\frac{I_0}{C v\nu_2^2}\right)\cos\left(\frac{\omega_2}{\nu_2}\tau\right)$$

Again we have achieved a completely dimensionless form, for

$[R]$ = volts per ampere
$[C]$ = charge per volt = (amperes $\times$ T) per volt
$[L]$ = volts per unit rate of change of current = (volts $\times$ T) per ampere
$[v] = \int^t e\,dt$ = volts $\times$ T

and so

$$\left[\frac{1}{CR\nu_2}\right] = \frac{1}{\dfrac{\text{ampere} \times T}{\text{volts}} \dfrac{\text{volts}}{\text{ampere}} \dfrac{1}{T}} = [0]$$

$$\left[\frac{1}{CL\nu_2^2}\right] = \frac{1}{\dfrac{\text{ampere} \times T}{\text{volts}} \dfrac{\text{volts} \times T}{\text{ampere}} \dfrac{1}{T^2}} = [0]$$

$$\left[\frac{I_0}{C v\nu_2^2}\right] = \frac{\text{ampere}}{(\text{volts} \times T) \dfrac{\text{ampere} \times T}{\text{volts}} \dfrac{1}{T^2}} = [0]$$

$$\left[\frac{\omega_2}{\nu_2}\right] = \frac{1/T}{1/T} = [0]$$

In a precisely similar way, by letting ϵ be an arbitrary voltage, ν_3 be an arbitrary frequency, and then expressing Eq. (2.2) in terms of the dimensionless variables

$$X = \frac{e}{\epsilon} \quad \text{and} \quad \tau = \nu_3 t$$

we obtain the dimensionless equation

$$(4.2) \qquad \frac{d^2X}{d\tau^2} + \left(\frac{1}{CR\nu_3}\right)\frac{dX}{d\tau} + \left(\frac{1}{CL\nu_3^2}\right)X = \left(-\frac{I_0\,\omega_2}{C\epsilon\nu_3^2}\right)\sin\left(\frac{\omega_2}{\nu_3}\tau\right)$$

Suppose now that we have a torsional system for which we desire to make an exact electrical model with voltage corresponding to angular velocity. This means that we have given the mechanical parameters

$$I, c, k, T_0, \text{ and } \omega_1$$

and can choose as convenient, or necessary, the electrical parameters

$$C, R, L, I_0, \text{ and } \omega_2$$

and the arbitrary scale factors

$$\alpha, \nu_1 \text{ and } v, \nu_2$$

Comparing Eqs. (3) and (4.1) it is clear that they will be *identical*, provided only that the corresponding dimensionless groups are numerically equal:

$$\frac{c}{I\nu_1} = \frac{1}{CR\nu_2}$$

$$\frac{k}{I\nu_1^2} = \frac{1}{CL\nu_2^2}$$

$$\frac{T_0}{I\alpha\nu_1^2} = \frac{I_0}{Cv\nu_2^2}$$

$$\frac{\omega_1}{\nu_1} = \frac{\omega_2}{\nu_2}$$

Of the nine quantities apparently at our disposal, namely,

$$C, R, L, I_0, \omega_2, \alpha, \nu_1, v, \text{ and } \nu_2$$

only seven are essentially arbitrary, because only the ratios

$$\frac{\alpha}{v} \qquad \text{and} \qquad \frac{\nu_1}{\nu_2}$$

are significant. However, since these quantities need satisfy only the four relations noted above, it is clear that we have ample opportunity for suiting our convenience (*e.g.*, availability of electrical elements in the laboratory) in constructing our model.

Now suppose that the electrical counterpart of the given torsional system has been built and that the appropriate initial conditions have been determined from the relations

$$\frac{\theta}{\alpha} \leftarrow X \rightarrow \frac{u}{v}$$

$$\frac{1}{\alpha\nu_1}\frac{d\theta}{dt} \leftarrow \frac{dX}{d\tau} \rightarrow \frac{1}{v\nu_2}\frac{du}{dt} = \frac{e}{v\nu_2}$$

If the voltage in the electrical circuit under these conditions be measured and plotted dimensionlessly as

$$\frac{dX}{d\tau} \equiv \frac{e}{\nu\nu_2} \qquad \text{versus} \qquad \tau = \nu_2 t$$

the resulting graph will be identical with the dimensionless plot of

$$\frac{dX}{d\tau} \equiv \frac{1}{\alpha\nu_1}\frac{d\theta}{dt} \qquad \text{versus} \qquad \tau = \nu_1 t$$

But from the dual interpretations

$$\frac{1}{\alpha\nu_1}\frac{d\theta}{dt} \leftarrow \frac{dX}{d\tau} \rightarrow \frac{e}{\nu\nu_2}$$

$$\nu_1 t \leftarrow \tau \rightarrow \nu_2 t$$

it is clear that

$$\frac{d\theta}{dt} = \left(\frac{\alpha\nu_1}{\nu\nu_2}\right) e$$

and

$$t\bigg|_{\text{torsional system}} = \left(\frac{\nu_2}{\nu_1}\right) t\bigg|_{\text{electrical system}}$$

Hence, having plotted e versus t for the electrical circuit, it is only necessary to regraduate the axes so that

$$\text{One unit on } e\text{-scale} = \frac{\alpha\nu_1}{\nu\nu_2} \text{ units on } \frac{d\theta}{dt}\text{-scale}$$

and

$$\text{One unit on electrical } t\text{-scale} = \frac{\nu_2}{\nu_1} \text{ units on mechanical } t\text{-scale}$$

in order to obtain an exact plot of the angular velocity $d\theta/dt$. The angular displacement can of course be found as the area under the $(d\theta/dt,t)$ curve.

A system with a single degree of freedom is so simple to analyze mathematically that there is no practical reason for constructing a model of it. This is not the case, however, when there are several degrees of freedom, especially if the behavior of a system for a number of values of its parameters is to be determined. In such cases the ease with which electrical components can be connected and disconnected, and the ease with which currents and voltages can be measured, often makes it convenient to study a complicated mechanical system by making experimental measurements on an electrical analogue.

The theory of this procedure is a direct extension of that which we have just developed. However, in constructing equivalent circuits a certain amount of ingenuity is required, which only practice can supply.

Lacking the time for this, we shall conclude our discussion with a few general observations and an example or two.

When we first consider making an electrical model of a mechanical system, we have always two distinct possibilities. The model may be either a series circuit or a parallel circuit. If we choose the series analogy, we have as corresponding elements

$$\text{Mass } M \text{ or moment of inertia } I \longleftrightarrow \text{inductance } L$$
$$\text{Friction } c \longleftrightarrow \text{resistance } R$$
$$\text{Springs } k \longleftrightarrow \text{elastance } \frac{1}{C}$$
$$\text{Force } F \text{ or torque } T \longleftrightarrow \text{voltage } E$$

and depending upon the point of view we take toward the electrical circuit

$$\left.\begin{array}{r}\text{Displacement}\\ \text{Velocity}\end{array}\right\} \longleftrightarrow \text{current}$$

From the last set of corresponding elements it is clear that components of a mechanical system between whose ends there is the same displace-

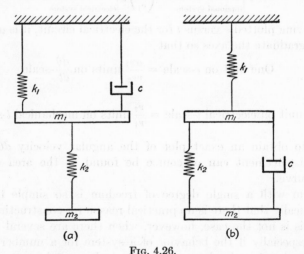

(a)   (b)

FIG. 4.26.

ment or velocity difference correspond to electrical elements through which the same current flows. Now elements in apparent **mechanical parallel,** such as the spring and dashpot, k_1 and c in Fig. 4.26a, or k_2 and c in Fig. 4.26b, have the same displacement and velocity differences across their terminals. Hence they correspond to electrical elements with the same current through them, *i.e.*, to electrical elements in *series* Moreover, elements in apparent **mechanical series** experience displacements and velocities totaling the displacement or velocity across the entire combination. Therefore the current through their analogues, as a whole, is the sum of the currents through the individual analogues. Such elements must then be in electrical *parallel*.

To construct the series circuit equivalent to the configuration shown in Fig. 4.26a we note that m_1, c, and k_1 all experience the same displacement. Hence their images are elements in series. Also the displacement of m_2 is the sum of the displacement of m_1 and the displacement across k_2. Hence the analogues of m_2, k_2, and the combination (m_1, c, k_1) must be in parallel. Figure 4.27a shows the circuit meeting these require-

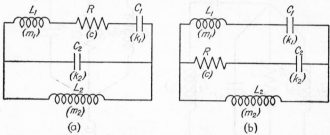

FIG. 4.27.   The series-circuit analogues of the mechanical systems shown in Fig. 4.26.

ments. The elements in parentheses indicate the original mechanical components. In the circuit shown in Fig. 4.27b, the dashpot c experiences the displacement of k_2 rather than the displacement of k_1 and m_1. Hence its image must be in series with the image of k_2, as shown in Fig. 4.27b.

If we choose the parallel-circuit analogy, we have the correspondences

$$\text{Mass } M \text{ or moment of inertia } I \longleftrightarrow \text{capacitance } C$$

$$\text{Friction } c \longleftrightarrow \text{conductance } \frac{1}{R}$$

$$\text{Springs } k \longleftrightarrow \text{susceptance } \frac{1}{L}$$

$$\text{Force } F \text{ or torque } T \longleftrightarrow \text{current } I$$

and, as we choose,

$$\left.\begin{array}{c}\text{Displacement}\\\text{Velocity}\end{array}\right\} \longleftrightarrow \text{voltage}$$

From the last set of corresponding elements we see that components in *mechanical parallel*, *i.e.*, elements whose terminals experience the same displacement or velocity difference, correspond to elements across which there is the same voltage difference, in other words to elements in *electrical parallel*. Moreover, elements which are in *mechanical series*, and hence experience displacement or velocity differences totaling the difference across the combination as a whole, correspond to elements whose voltage differences add to the total voltage difference across the entire combination, *i.e.*, to elements in *electrical series*.

To construct the parallel circuit analogous to Fig. 4.26a, we observe that m_1, c, and k_1 have images which must be in parallel, while the images of m_2 and k_2 must be in series with this combination. Figure 4.28a shows one arrangement of a circuit meeting these requirements. If the common

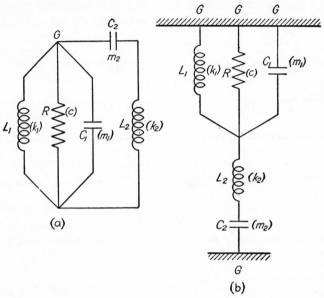

Fig. 4.28.　The parallel-circuit analogue of the mechanical system shown in Fig. 4.26a.

terminal G in Fig. 4.28a be taken as the ground, the circuit may be redrawn as shown in Fig. 4.28b. The geometric resemblance of this to the original mechanical configuration is remarkable, and illustrates one reason for the recent increase in the popularity of the parallel analogy.*

In Fig. 4.26b we note that the dashpot is in parallel with the spring k_2 rather than with m_1 and k_1. Hence the equivalent circuit is as shown in Fig. 4.29.

To make exact the correspondence between the mechanical systems shown in Fig. 4.26 and their electrical analogues we must, as in the case of systems with a single degree of freedom, reduce the underlying dif-

---

* The parallel-circuit analogy is the basis of the so-called **mobility method** of solving vibration problems. See, for example, F. A. Firestone, "The Mobility Method of Computing the Vibration of Linear Mechanical and Acoustical Systems, Mechanical-electrical Analogies," *J. Applied Phys.*, 1938, pp. 373–387.

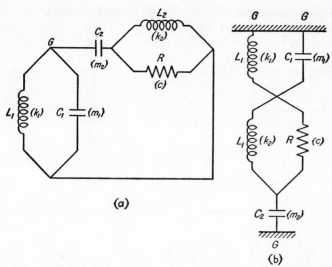

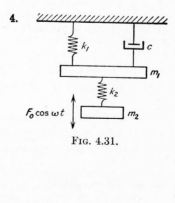

FIG. 4.29.   The parallel-circuit analogue of the mechanical system shown in Fig. 4.26b.

ferential equations to dimensionless form, and determine the physical components of the image so that corresponding dimensionless groups of parameters will be numerically equal.

EXERCISES

1. Reduce the differential equation of the translational system with one degree of freedom to a dimensionless form.
2. Reduce the differential equation of the series circuit with one degree of freedom to a dimensionless form.

Draw the series and parallel networks which are analogous to the following mechanical systems:

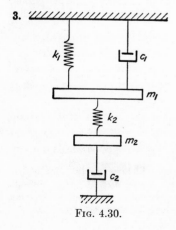

3.

FIG. 4.30.

4.

$F_0 \cos \omega t$

FIG. 4.31.

5.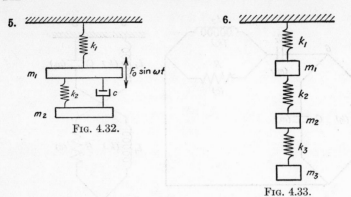

FIG. 4.32.

6.

FIG. 4.33.

7.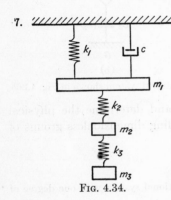

FIG. 4.34.

8.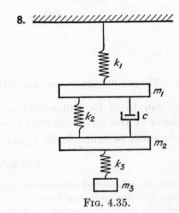

FIG. 4.35.

9. Set up the differential equations for the system of Exercise 5 and its series analogue, reduce them to dimensionless form, and determine the corresponding dimensionless groups of parameters.

10. Set up the differential equations for the system of Exercise 5 and its parallel analogue, reduce them to dimensionless form, and determine the corresponding dimensionless groups of parameters.

CHAPTER 5

FOURIER SERIES AND INTEGRALS

5.1 Introduction. In Chap. 2 we learned that nonhomogeneous differential equations containing terms of the form

$$A \cos \omega t \qquad \text{and} \qquad B \sin \omega t$$

could easily be solved for all values of ω. Then in Chap. 4 we discovered that such differential equations were fundamental in the study of physical systems subjected to simple periodic disturbances. In many cases, however, the forces, torques, or voltages which act on a system, although periodic, are by no means as simple as pure sine and cosine waves. For instance, the voltage impressed on an electric circuit might consist of the series of pulses shown in Fig. 5.1, or the disturbing influence acting on a

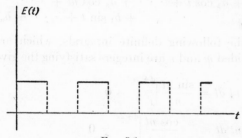

Fig. 5.1.

mechanical system might be a force of constant magnitude whose direction is periodically and instantaneously reversed, as in Fig. 5.2.

If general periodic functions of this sort could be expressed in the form of a series

$$f(t) = \tfrac{1}{2}a_0\dagger + a_1 \cos t + a_2 \cos 2t + \cdots + a_n \cos nt + \cdots$$
$$+ b_1 \sin t + b_2 \sin 2t + \cdots + b_n \sin nt + \cdots$$

it is clear that our power to solve physical problems would be greatly increased, since the terms of such a series could, individually, be handled without difficulty. The possibility of such expansions, and their deter-

† The introduction of the factor $\tfrac{1}{2}$ is a conventional device to render more symmetric the final formulas for the coefficients.

113

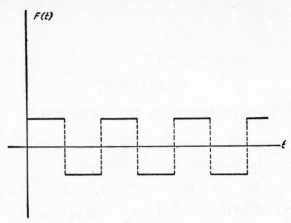

FIG. 5.2.

mination when they exist, are the subject matter of Fourier* analysis, to which we shall devote this chapter.

5.2 The Euler Coefficients. To obtain expressions for the coefficients a_n and b_n in the expansion

(1) $\quad f(t) = \tfrac{1}{2}a_0 + a_1 \cos t + \cdots + a_n \cos nt + \cdots$
$$+ b_1 \sin t + \cdots + b_n \sin nt + \cdots$$

we shall need the following definite integrals, which are valid for all values of d, provided m and n are integers satisfying the given restrictions.

(2) $\quad \displaystyle\int_d^{d+2\pi} \cos nt \, dt = \frac{\sin nt}{n}\bigg|_d^{d+2\pi} = 0 \qquad\qquad n \neq 0$

(3) $\quad \displaystyle\int_d^{d+2\pi} \sin nt \, dt = -\frac{\cos nt}{n}\bigg|_d^{d+2\pi} = 0 \qquad\qquad n \neq 0$

(4) $\quad \displaystyle\int_d^{d+2\pi} \cos mt \cos nt \, dt = \frac{1}{2}\left[\frac{\sin (m-n)t}{m-n} + \frac{\sin (m+n)t}{m+n}\right]_d^{d+2\pi} = 0$
$$m \neq n$$

(5) $\quad \displaystyle\int_d^{d+2\pi} \cos^2 nt \, dt = \left[\frac{t}{2} + \frac{\sin 2nt}{4n}\right]_d^{d+2\pi} = \pi \qquad\qquad n \neq 0$

(6) $\quad \displaystyle\int_d^{d+2\pi} \sin mt \cos nt \, dt = -\frac{1}{2}\left[\frac{\cos (m-n)t}{m-n} + \frac{\cos (m+n)t}{m+n}\right]_d^{d+2\pi} = 0$
$$m \neq n$$

---

* Named for Jacques Fourier (1768–1830), French mathematician and confidant of Napoleon, who first undertook the systematic study of such expansions in a memorable monograph, "Théorie analytique de la chaleur," published in 1822. The use of Fourier series in special problems dates from the time of Daniel Bernoulli (1700–1782) who used them to solve certain problems connected with vibrating strings.

$$(7) \quad \int_d^{d+2\pi} \sin nt \cos nt \, dt = \left. \frac{\sin^2 nt}{2n} \right|_d^{d+2\pi} = 0 \qquad\qquad n \neq 0$$

$$(8) \quad \int_d^{d+2\pi} \sin mt \sin nt \, dt = \frac{1}{2}\left[\frac{\sin (m-n)t}{m-n} - \frac{\sin (m+n)t}{m+n} \right]_d^{d+2\pi} = 0$$
$$m \neq n$$

$$(9) \quad \int_d^{d+2\pi} \sin^2 nt \, dt = \left[\frac{t}{2} - \frac{\sin 2nt}{4n} \right]_d^{d+2\pi} = \pi \qquad\qquad n \neq 0 \quad \Leftarrow$$

With these integrals available, the determination of a_n and b_n proceeds as follows.

To find a_0, assume that the series (1) can legitimately be integrated term by term from $t = d$ to $t = d + 2\pi$.   Then

$$\int_d^{d+2\pi} f(t)dt = \tfrac{1}{2}a_0 \int_d^{d+2\pi} dt + a_1 \int_d^{d+2\pi} \cos t \, dt + \cdots$$
$$+ a_n \int_d^{d+2\pi} \cos nt \, dt + \cdots + b_1 \int_d^{d+2\pi} \sin t \, dt + \cdots$$
$$+ b_n \int_d^{d+2\pi} \sin nt \, dt + \cdots$$

The integral on the left can always be evaluated, since $f(t)$ is a given function.   At worst some method of approximate integration such as the trapezoidal rule will be required.   The first term on the right is simply

$$\tfrac{1}{2}a_0 t \Big|_d^{d+2\pi} = \pi a_0$$

By Eq. (2) all integrals with a cosine in the integrand vanish, and by Eq. (3) all integrals containing a sine vanish.   Hence the integrated result reduces to

$$\int_d^{d+2\pi} f(t)dt = \pi a_0$$

or

$$(10) \qquad\qquad a_0 = \frac{1}{\pi} \int_d^{d+2\pi} f(t)dt$$

To find a_n ($n = 1,2,3 \ldots$), multiply each side of (1) by $\cos nt$ and then integrate from d to $d + 2\pi$, assuming again that termwise integration is justified.   This gives

$$\int_d^{d+2\pi} f(t) \cos nt \, dt = \frac{1}{2} a_0 \int_d^{d+2\pi} \cos nt \, dt + a_1 \int_d^{d+2\pi} \cos nt \cos t \, dt$$
$$+ \cdots + a_n \int_d^{d+2\pi} \cos^2 nt \, dt + \cdots + b_1 \int_d^{d+2\pi} \cos nt \sin t \, dt$$
$$+ \cdots + b_n \int_d^{d+2\pi} \cos nt \sin nt \, dt + \cdots$$

The integral on the left is completely determinate. By Eqs. (2) and (4) all integrals on the right containing only cosine terms vanish except the one involving $\cos^2 nt$, which, by Eq. (5), is equal to π. Finally, by Eqs. (6) and (7), every integral which contains a sine is zero. Hence

$$\int_d^{d+2\pi} f(t) \cos nt \, dt = a_n \pi$$

or

$$(11) \qquad a_n = \frac{1}{\pi} \int_d^{d+2\pi} f(t) \cos nt \, dt$$

To determine b_n, we continue essentially the same procedure. We multiply (1) by $\sin nt$ and then integrate from d to $d + 2\pi$, getting

$$\int_d^{d+2\pi} f(t) \sin nt \, dt = \tfrac{1}{2}a_0 \int_d^{d+2\pi} \sin nt \, dt + a_1 \int_d^{d+2\pi} \sin nt \cos t \, dt$$

$$+ \cdots + a_n \int_d^{d+2\pi} \sin nt \cos nt \, dt + \cdots + b_1 \int_d^{d+2\pi} \sin nt \sin t \, dt$$

$$+ \cdots + b_n \int_d^{d+2\pi} \sin^2 nt \, dt + \cdots$$

As before, every integral on the right vanishes but one, leaving

$$\int_d^{d+2\pi} f(t) \sin nt \, dt = b_n \int_d^{d+2\pi} \sin^2 nt \, dt = \pi b_n$$

and so

$$(12) \qquad b_n = \frac{1}{\pi} \int_d^{d+2\pi} f(t) \sin nt \, dt$$

Formulas (10), (11), and (12) are known as the **Euler formulas,** and the series (1), when its coefficients have these values, is known as the **Fourier series** of $f(t)$. In most applications, the interval over which $f(t)$ is to be expanded is either $(-\pi, +\pi)$ or $(0, 2\pi)$, so that d in the Euler formulas is usually either $-\pi$ or 0. Actually, the formula for a_0 need not be listed, for it can be obtained from the general expression for a_n by putting $n = 0$. It was to achieve this that we wrote the constant term as $\tfrac{1}{2}a_0$ in the original expansion.

We must be careful at this stage not to delude ourselves with the belief that we have proved that a function, $f(t)$, has a Fourier expansion which is a valid representation of it. What our analysis has shown is merely that *if* $f(t)$ has an expansion of the form (1), *then* the coefficients in that series must be given by the Euler formulas. Questions concerning the convergence of Fourier series and, if they converge, the conditions under which they will represent the function which generated them, are many and difficult, and are by no means completely answered yet.

These problems can safely be left to the curiosity of mathematicians, however, for almost any conceivable engineering application is covered by the famous theorem of Dirichlet.*

If $f(t)$ is a bounded function of period 2π, and if in any one period it has at most a finite number of maxima and minima and a finite number of discontinuities,† then the Fourier series of $f(t)$ converges to $f(t)$ at all points where $f(t)$ is continuous, and converges to the average of the right- and left-hand limits of $f(t)$ at each point where $f(t)$ is discontinuous.

The **Dirichlet conditions,** so-called, make it clear that a function need not be continuous in order to possess a valid Fourier expansion. This means that a function may consist of a number of disjointed pieces of different curves, each given by a different equation, and still be repre-

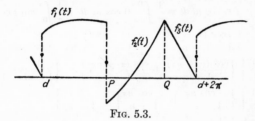

FIG. 5.3.

sentable by a Fourier series. In using the Euler formulas to find the coefficients in the expansion of such a function, it will therefore be necessary to break up the range of integration $(d, d + 2\pi)$ to correspond to the various segments of the function. Thus in Fig. 5.3 the function $f(t)$ is defined by three different expressions $f_1(t)$, $f_2(t)$, $f_3(t)$ on successive portions of the period interval $d < t < d + 2\pi$. Hence it is necessary to write the Euler formulas as

$$a_n = \frac{1}{\pi} \int_d^{d+2\pi} f(t) \cos nt \, dt = \frac{1}{\pi} \int_d^P f_1(t) \cos nt \, dt + \frac{1}{\pi} \int_P^Q f_2(t) \cos nt \, dt$$
$$+ \frac{1}{\pi} \int_Q^{d+2\pi} f_3(t) \cos nt \, dt$$

$$b_n = \frac{1}{\pi} \int_d^{d+2\pi} f(t) \sin nt \, dt = \frac{1}{\pi} \int_d^P f_1(t) \sin nt \, dt + \frac{1}{\pi} \int_P^Q f_2(t) \sin nt \, dt$$
$$+ \frac{1}{\pi} \int_Q^{d+2\pi} f_3(t) \sin nt \, dt$$

Incidentally, according to the theorem of Dirichlet, the Fourier series of the function shown in Fig. 5.3 will converge to the average values, indicated by dots, at the discontinuities at d, P, and $d + 2\pi$.

* Peter Gustave Lejeune Dirichlet (1805–1859) was a great German mathematician.
† Since $f(t)$ is assumed to be bounded, these discontinuities can only be finite jumps.

Example 1

What is the Fourier expansion of the periodic function whose definition in one period is

$$f(t) = 0 \qquad -\pi < t < 0$$
$$f(t) = \sin t \qquad 0 < t < \pi$$

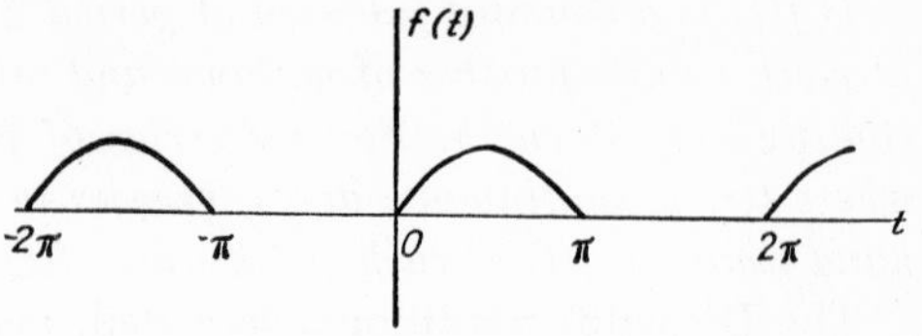

Fig. 5.4.

In this case, taking $d = -\pi$ in the Euler formulas, we have

[margin handwritten: $a_0 = \frac{1}{\pi} \int_{-\pi}^{\pi} f(t)\,dt$
$= \frac{-\cos t}{\pi} \Big|_{0}^{\pi}$ $\frac{2\pi}{\pi}$ *?*
$= \frac{2}{\pi}$ ✓ *]*

$$a_n = \frac{1}{\pi} \int_{-\pi}^{\pi} f(t) \cos nt\, dt = \frac{1}{\pi} \int_{-\pi}^{0} 0 \cos nt\, dt + \frac{1}{\pi} \int_{0}^{\pi} \sin t \cos nt\, dt$$

$$= \frac{1}{\pi}\left[-\frac{1}{2}\left\{ \frac{\cos(1-n)t}{1-n} + \frac{\cos(1+n)t}{1+n} \right\} \right]_{0}^{\pi}$$ *[margin: ← eq.121 Eshbach P.1-136]*

$$= -\frac{1}{2\pi}\left[\left\{ \frac{\cos(\pi - n\pi)}{1-n} + \frac{\cos(\pi + n\pi)}{1+n} \right\} - \left\{ \frac{1}{1-n} + \frac{1}{1+n} \right\} \right]$$

$$= -\frac{1}{2\pi}\left[\left\{ \frac{-\cos n\pi}{1-n} + \frac{-\cos n\pi}{1+n} \right\} - \frac{2}{1-n^2} \right]$$

$$= \frac{\cos n\pi + 1}{\pi(1 - n^2)} \qquad n \neq 1$$

$$a_1 = \frac{1}{\pi}\int_{0}^{\pi} \sin t \cos t\, dt = \frac{1}{\pi}\frac{\sin^2 t}{2}\Big|_{0}^{\pi} = 0$$

$$b_n = \frac{1}{\pi}\int_{-\pi}^{\pi} f(t) \sin nt\, dt = \frac{1}{\pi}\int_{-\pi}^{0} 0 \sin nt\, dt + \frac{1}{\pi}\int_{0}^{\pi} \sin t \sin nt\, dt$$

$$= \frac{1}{\pi}\left[\frac{1}{2}\left\{ \frac{\sin(1-n)t}{1-n} - \frac{\sin(1+n)t}{1+n} \right\} \right]_{0}^{\pi}$$

$$= 0 \qquad n \neq 1$$

$$b_1 = \frac{1}{\pi}\int_{0}^{\pi} \sin^2 t\, dt = \frac{1}{\pi}\left[\frac{t}{2} - \frac{\sin 2t}{4} \right]_{0}^{\pi} = \frac{1}{2}$$

Hence

$$f(t) = \frac{1}{\pi} + \frac{\sin t}{2} - \frac{2}{\pi}\left[\frac{\cos 2t}{3} + \frac{\cos 4t}{15} + \frac{\cos 6t}{35} + \frac{\cos 8t}{63} + \cdots \right]$$

Plots showing the accuracy with which the first n terms of this series represent the given function are shown in Fig. 5.5 for $n = 1, 2, 3$. For $n = 4, 5, \ldots$, the partial sums are almost indistinguishable from $f(t)$.

Interesting numerical series can frequently be obtained from Fourier series by evaluating them at specific points. For instance, if we set $t = \frac{1}{2}\pi$ in the above expansion, we find

$$1 = \frac{1}{\pi} + \frac{1}{2} - \frac{2}{\pi}\left[-\frac{1}{3} + \frac{1}{15} - \frac{1}{35} + \frac{1}{63} - \cdots \right]$$

or

$$\frac{1}{1\cdot 3} - \frac{1}{3\cdot 5} + \frac{1}{5\cdot 7} - \frac{1}{7\cdot 9} + \cdots = \frac{\pi - 2}{4}$$

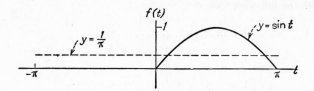

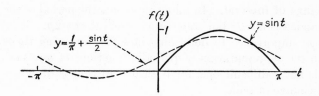

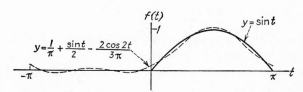

FIG. 5.5. The approximation of a function by the first few terms of its Fourier expansion.

EXERCISES

Determine the Fourier expansions of the following functions:

1. $f(t) = t$ $\qquad -\pi < t < \pi$ $\qquad$ *Ans.* $a_n \equiv 0$, $b_n = (-1)^{n+1}\dfrac{2}{n}$

2. $f(t) = -t$ $\qquad -\pi < t < 0$ $\qquad$ *Ans.* $a_0 = \pi$, $a_n = \dfrac{2(\cos n\pi - 1)}{\pi n^2}$, $b_n \equiv 0$

$\quad\;\; f(t) = t$ $\qquad\;\; 0 < t < \pi$

3. $f(t) = \pi^2 - t^2$ $\qquad -\pi < t < \pi$ $\qquad$ *Ans.* $a_0 = \dfrac{4\pi^2}{3}$, $a_n = \dfrac{-4\cos n\pi}{n^2}$, $b_n \equiv 0$

4. $f(t) = 1$ $\qquad -\pi < t < 0$ $\qquad$ *Ans.* $a_0 = \dfrac{3}{2}$, $a_n = \dfrac{1 - \cos n\pi}{\pi^2 n^2}$, $b_n = \dfrac{\cos n\pi}{n\pi}$

$\quad\;\; f(t) = 1 - \dfrac{t}{\pi}$ $\qquad 0 < t < \pi$ $\qquad$ **8.** $f(t) = 2$ $\qquad 0 < t < \dfrac{2\pi}{3}$

5. $f(t) = \sin \tfrac{1}{2}t$ $\qquad -\pi < t < \pi$ $\qquad\quad\;\; f(t) = 1$ $\qquad \dfrac{2\pi}{3} < t < \dfrac{4\pi}{3}$

6. $f(t) = 0$ $\qquad -\pi < t < 0$

$\quad\;\; f(t) = t^2$ $\qquad\;\; 0 < t < \pi$ $\qquad\quad\;\; f(t) = 0$ $\qquad \dfrac{4\pi}{3} < t < 2\pi$

7. $f(t) = 1$ $\qquad 0 < t < \tfrac{1}{2}\pi$ $\qquad$ **9.** $f(t) = \cos t$ $\qquad -\pi < t < 0$

$\quad\;\; f(t) = 0$ $\qquad \tfrac{1}{2}\pi < t < 2\pi$ $\qquad\quad\;\; f(t) = \sin t$ $\qquad 0 < t < \pi$

10. Establish the following numerical results:

$$1 + \frac{1}{2^2} + \frac{1}{3^2} + \frac{1}{4^2} + \frac{1}{5^2} + \cdots = \frac{\pi^2}{6}$$

$$1 - \frac{1}{2^2} + \frac{1}{3^2} - \frac{1}{4^2} + \frac{1}{5^2} - \cdots = \frac{\pi^2}{12}$$

$$1 + \frac{1}{3^2} + \frac{1}{5^2} + \frac{1}{7^2} + \frac{1}{9^2} + \cdots = \frac{\pi^2}{8}$$

(Hint: Use the results of Exercise 6.)

5.3 Change of Interval. In many problems the period of the function to be expanded is not 2π but some other interval, say $2p$. It is therefore a matter of importance to determine how the foregoing theory can be applied to the representation of periodic functions of any period. The problem is not a difficult one, for basically all that is involved is a proportional change of scale.

Analytically, such a change of scale is represented by the substitution

$$x = \frac{\pi t}{p} \qquad \text{or} \qquad t = \frac{px}{\pi}$$

for when $t = d$, then $x = \pi d/p = D$, say, and when $t = d + 2p$, then $x = \pi(d + 2p)/p = \pi d/p + 2\pi = D + 2\pi$. Thus, when the substitution $t = px/\pi$ is made in the equation, $y = f(t)$, of a function of period $2p$, we obtain the function

$$y = f\left(\frac{px}{\pi}\right)$$

and this, *as a function of* x, say $F(x)$, is of period 2π.

As a function of x of period 2π, $f(px/\pi) \equiv F(x)$ can, of course be expanded into a Fourier series by the preceding theory, giving

(1) $F(x) = \frac{1}{2}a_0 + a_1 \cos x + a_2 \cos 2x + \cdots + a_n \cos nx + \cdots$
$$+ b_1 \sin x + b_2 \sin 2x + \cdots + b_n \sin nx + \cdots$$

where as usual

(2) $a_n = \frac{1}{\pi} \int_D^{D+2\pi} F(x) \cos nx \, dx, \qquad b_n = \frac{1}{\pi} \int_D^{D+2\pi} F(x) \sin nx \, dx$

If in these expressions we now make the inverse substitutions

$$x = \frac{\pi t}{p}, \qquad dx = \frac{\pi}{p} \, dt, \qquad x = D \sim t = d, \qquad x = D + 2\pi \sim t = d + 2p$$

the expansion (1) becomes

(3) $F\left(\frac{\pi t}{p}\right) \equiv f(t) = \frac{1}{2} a_0 + a_1 \cos \frac{\pi t}{p} + a_2 \cos \frac{2\pi t}{p} + \cdots + a_n \cos \frac{n\pi t}{p}$
$$+ \cdots + b_1 \sin \frac{\pi t}{p} + b_2 \sin \frac{2\pi t}{p} + \cdots + b_n \sin \frac{n\pi t}{p} + \cdots$$

was $p = \pi$

and the coefficient formulas (2) become

$$(4.1) \qquad a_n = \frac{1}{p} \int_d^{d+2p} f(t) \cos \frac{n\pi t}{p} \, dt$$

$$(4.2) \qquad b_n = \frac{1}{p} \int_d^{d+2p} f(t) \sin \frac{n\pi t}{p} \, dt$$

Using Eqs. (4.1) and (4.2), the series (3) can be constructed in any particular problem without the necessity of introducing the auxiliary variable x. In most applications d will either be $-p$ or 0.

Example 1

What is the Fourier expansion of the function whose definition in a single period is

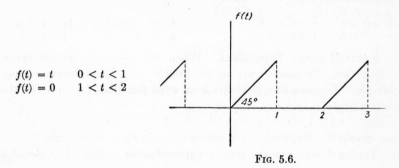

$$f(t) = t \qquad 0 < t < 1$$
$$f(t) = 0 \qquad 1 < t < 2$$

FIG. 5.6.

In this case the length of the period of the function is 2. Hence $p = 1$, and from (4.1) and (4.2) (taking $d = 0$), we have

$$a_n = \frac{1}{1} \int_0^2 f(t) \cos \frac{n\pi t}{1} \, dt = \int_0^1 t \cos n\pi t \, dt + \int_1^2 0 \cos n\pi t \, dt$$

$$= \left[\frac{1}{n^2\pi^2} \cos n\pi t + \frac{t}{n\pi} \sin n\pi t \right]_0^1$$

$$= \frac{\cos n\pi - 1}{n^2\pi^2}$$

$$= -\frac{2}{n^2\pi^2} \qquad n \text{ odd}$$

$$= 0 \qquad n \text{ even} \qquad\qquad\qquad n \neq 0$$

$$a_0 = \frac{1}{1} \int_0^2 f(t)\,dt = \int_0^1 t \, dt + \int_1^2 0 \, dt = \frac{t^2}{2} \Big|_0^1 = \frac{1}{2}$$

$$b_n = \frac{1}{1} \int_0^2 f(t) \sin \frac{n\pi t}{1} \, dt = \int_0^1 t \sin n\pi t \, dt + \int_1^2 0 \sin n\pi t \, dt$$

$$= \left[\frac{1}{n^2\pi^2} \sin n\pi t - \frac{t}{n\pi} \cos n\pi t \right]_0^1$$

$$= -\frac{\cos n\pi}{n\pi}$$

Substituting these values into the series (3), we obtain

$$f(t) = \frac{1}{4} - \frac{2}{\pi^2}\left[\cos \pi t + \frac{\cos 3\pi t}{9} + \frac{\cos 5\pi t}{25} + \cdots\right]$$
$$+ \frac{1}{\pi}\left[\sin \pi t - \frac{\sin 2\pi t}{2} + \frac{\sin 3\pi t}{3} - \cdots\right]$$

$$\frac{\pi}{p} = \frac{\pi}{1}$$

EXERCISES

Determine the Fourier expansions of the following functions:

1. $f(t) = 0$ $-2 < t < -1$ $Ans.$ $a_0 = \frac{1}{2},\, a_n = \frac{4}{n^2\pi^2}\left(1 - \cos \frac{n\pi}{2}\right) b_n \equiv 0$
   $f(t) = 1 + t$ $-1 < t < 0$
   $f(t) = 1 - t$ $0 < t < 1$
   $f(t) = 0$ $1 < t < 2$
2. $f(t) = 0$ $-3 < t < -1$
   $f(t) = 1 + \cos \pi t$ $-1 < t < 1$
   $f(t) = 0$ $1 < t < 3$
3. $f(t) = t$ $0 < t < 1$ 4. $f(t) = \cos t$ $-\frac{1}{2}\pi < t < \frac{1}{2}\pi$
   $f(t) = 0$ $1 < t < 3$ 5. $f(t) = t - t^3$ $-1 < t < 1$

5.4 Half-range Expansions. When $f(t)$ possesses certain symmetry properties, the coefficients in its Fourier expansion become especially simple. Suppose first that $f(t)$ is an **even function,** *i.e.*, suppose that

$$f(-t) = f(t)$$

or, geometrically, that $f(t)$ is symmetrical in the vertical axis.

Taking $d = -p$ in the general expression for a_n [Eq. (4.1), Sec. 5.3], we can write

$$a_n = \frac{1}{p} \int_{-p}^{p} f(t) \cos \frac{n\pi t}{p}\, dt = \frac{1}{p} \int_{-p}^{0} f(t) \cos \frac{n\pi t}{p}\, dt + \frac{1}{p} \int_{0}^{p} f(t) \cos \frac{n\pi t}{p}\, dt$$

Now in the integral from $-p$ to 0, make the substitution

$$t = -s, \qquad dt = -ds$$

This integral then becomes

(1) $$\frac{1}{p} \int_{p}^{0} f(-s) \cos \left(\frac{-n\pi s}{p}\right) (-ds)$$

But $f(-s) = f(s)$, from the hypothesis that $f(t)$ is an even function. Moreover, the cosine is also an even function, and thus

$$\cos \left(\frac{-n\pi s}{p}\right) = \cos \frac{n\pi s}{p}$$

Finally, the negative sign associated with ds in (1) may be eliminated by changing the limits back to the normal order, 0 to p. The integral (1) then becomes

$$\frac{1}{p} \int_0^p f(s) \cos \frac{n\pi s}{p} ds$$

and thus a_n can be written

$$a_n = \frac{1}{p} \int_0^p f(s) \cos \frac{n\pi s}{p} ds + \frac{1}{p} \int_0^p f(t) \cos \frac{n\pi t}{p} dt$$

$$= \frac{2}{p} \int_0^p f(t) \cos \frac{n\pi t}{p} dt$$

since the two integrals are identical, except for the dummy variable of integration, which is immaterial.

Similarly, we can write

$$b_n = \frac{1}{p} \int_{-p}^0 f(t) \sin \frac{n\pi t}{p} dt + \frac{1}{p} \int_0^p f(t) \sin \frac{n\pi t}{p} dt$$

Again, putting

$$t = -s, \qquad dt = -ds$$

in the first integral, we have

$$b_n = \frac{1}{p} \int_p^0 f(-s) \sin \left(\frac{-n\pi s}{p} \right) (-ds) + \frac{1}{p} \int_0^p f(t) \sin \frac{n\pi t}{p} dt$$

But

$$f(-s) = f(s) \qquad \text{by hypothesis}$$

and

$$\sin \left(\frac{-n\pi s}{p} \right) = - \sin \frac{n\pi s}{p}$$

Hence, reversing the limits on the first integral, as before, we find

$$b_n = - \frac{1}{p} \int_0^p f(s) \sin \frac{n\pi s}{p} ds + \frac{1}{p} \int_0^p f(t) \sin \frac{n\pi t}{p} dt = 0$$

since, except for the irrelevant variable of integration, the two integrals are identical in all but sign.

Thus we have shown that *if a periodic function f(t) is even, its Fourier expansion contains no sine terms, that is, $b_n = 0$ for all values of n. In this case the coefficients of the cosine terms are given by the simpler formula*

(2)
$$a_n = \frac{2}{p} \int_0^p f(t) \cos \frac{n\pi t}{p} dt$$

Now suppose that $f(t)$ is an **odd function**, *i.e.*, suppose that

$$f(-t) = -f(t)$$

or, geometrically, that $f(t)$ is symmetric in the origin. Then proceeding just as before, we can write

$$a_n = \frac{1}{p} \int_{-p}^{0} f(t) \cos \frac{n\pi t}{p} \, dt + \frac{1}{p} \int_{0}^{p} f(t) \cos \frac{n\pi t}{p} \, dt$$

$$= \frac{1}{p} \int_{p}^{0} f(-s) \cos \left(\frac{-n\pi s}{p} \right) (-ds) + \frac{1}{p} \int_{0}^{p} f(t) \cos \frac{n\pi t}{p} \, dt$$

$$= -\frac{1}{p} \int_{0}^{p} f(s) \cos \frac{n\pi s}{p} \, ds + \frac{1}{p} \int_{0}^{p} f(t) \cos \frac{n\pi t}{p} \, dt$$

$$= 0$$

$$b_n = \frac{1}{p} \int_{-p}^{0} f(t) \sin \frac{n\pi t}{p} \, dt + \frac{1}{p} \int_{0}^{p} f(t) \sin \frac{n\pi t}{p} \, dt$$

$$= \frac{1}{p} \int_{p}^{0} f(-s) \sin \left(\frac{-n\pi s}{p} \right) (-ds) + \frac{1}{p} \int_{0}^{p} f(t) \sin \frac{n\pi t}{p} \, dt$$

$$= \frac{1}{p} \int_{0}^{p} f(s) \sin \frac{n\pi s}{p} \, ds + \frac{1}{p} \int_{0}^{p} f(t) \sin \frac{n\pi t}{p} \, dt$$

$$= \frac{2}{p} \int_{0}^{p} f(t) \sin \frac{n\pi t}{p} \, dt$$

Thus *if a periodic function, $f(t)$, is odd, its Fourier expansion contains no*

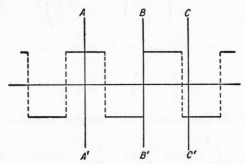

Fig. 5.7. Plot showing how oddness and evenness depend on the choice of axes.

cosine terms, that is, $a_n = 0$ for all values of n. In this case the coefficients of the sine terms are given by the simpler formula

$$(3) \qquad\qquad b_n = \frac{2}{p} \int_{0}^{p} f(t) \sin \frac{n\pi t}{p} \, dt$$

It should be emphasized here that oddness and evenness are not intrinsic properties of a graph, but depend upon its relation to the vertical axis of the coordinate system. Thus in Fig. 5.7 if the line AA' be chosen as the vertical axis, the function becomes even and its Fourier expansion will contain nothing but cosine terms. On the other hand, if BB' be chosen as the vertical axis, the function becomes odd, and only sine terms appear in its expansion. If, finally, a general line, such as CC' be taken as axis, the function is neither odd nor even and both sines and cosines will appear in its Fourier series.

The observations we have just made about the Fourier coefficients of odd and even functions serve to reduce by half the labor of expanding such functions. However, their principal value is that under certain conditions they make it possible to expand a function in terms of cosines only or in terms of sines only, whichever we choose.

Let us suppose that the conditions of a problem require us to consider the values of a function *only* in the interval from 0 to p. In other words, conditions of periodicity are irrelevant to the problem, and what the function may be *outside* the range 0 to p is completely immaterial. This being the case, we can invent any extension we please to define the function from $-p$ to 0 before we use the Euler formulas to find the Fourier coefficients. Between $-p$ and 0 the series constructed from these coefficients will, of course, represent whatever extension we created over this interval, but *irrespective of this extension* the series will converge to the given function between 0 and p, as required.

In particular, if we extend the function by reflecting it in the vertical axis, so that $f(-t) = f(t)$, the original function plus its extension is even, and hence its Fourier expansion will contain only cosine terms, whose coefficients, as we showed above, will be given by

$$a_n = \frac{2}{p} \int_0^p f(t) \cos \frac{n\pi t}{p}\, dt$$

On the other hand, if we extend the function by reflecting it in the origin, so that $f(-t) = -f(t)$, the extended function is odd, and its Fourier expansion will have coefficients

$$a_n = 0, \qquad b_n = \frac{2}{p} \int_0^p f(t) \sin \frac{n\pi t}{p}\, dt$$

Thus, simply by imagining the appropriate extension of a function originally defined only for $0 < t < p$, we can obtain expansions representing the function on this interval and containing only cosine terms or only sine terms, as we please. Such series are known as **half-range expansions.**

Example 1

Find the half-range expansions of the function

$$f(t) = t - t^2 \qquad 0 < t < 1$$

The half-range cosine expansion is based on imagining an even extension of $(t - t^2)$

over the interval $(-1,0)$. However, once we understand the reasoning underlying the procedure we need give no thought to the extension, but can write directly

$$b_n = 0$$

and then from (2),

$$
\begin{aligned}
a_n &= \frac{2}{1} \int_0^1 (t - t^2) \cos \frac{n\pi t}{1} \, dt \\
&= 2 \left[\left(\frac{\cos n\pi t}{n^2\pi^2} + \frac{t}{n\pi} \sin n\pi t \right) - \left(\frac{2t}{n^2\pi^2} \cos n\pi t - \frac{2}{n^3\pi^3} \sin n\pi t + \frac{t^2}{n\pi} \sin n\pi t \right) \right]_0^1 \\
&= 2 \left[\left(\frac{\cos n\pi - 1}{n^2\pi^2} \right) - \left(\frac{2 \cos n\pi}{n^2\pi^2} \right) \right] \\
&= -\frac{2(1 + \cos n\pi)}{n^2\pi^2} \qquad\qquad\qquad\qquad n \neq 0
\end{aligned}
$$

$$
a_0 = \frac{2}{1} \int_0^1 (t - t^2) \, dt = 2 \left[\frac{t^2}{2} - \frac{t^3}{3} \right]_0^1 = \frac{1}{3}
$$

Hence it is possible to represent $f(t) = t - t^2$ for $0 < t < 1$ by the series

$$
(4) \qquad f(t) = \frac{1}{6} - \frac{4}{\pi^2} \left[\frac{\cos 2\pi t}{4} + \frac{\cos 4\pi t}{16} + \frac{\cos 6\pi t}{36} + \frac{\cos 8\pi t}{64} + \cdots \right]
$$

The half-range sine expansion is based upon extending $(t - t^2)$ over the interval $(-1,0)$ by reflection in the origin. However, all we need do to obtain the expansion is to note that

$$a_n = 0$$

and then use (3) to compute b_n:

$$
\begin{aligned}
b_n &= \frac{2}{1} \int_0^1 (t - t^2) \sin \frac{n\pi t}{1} \, dt \\
&= 2 \left[\left(\frac{1}{n^2\pi^2} \sin n\pi t - \frac{t}{n\pi} \cos n\pi t \right) - \left(\frac{2t}{n^2\pi^2} \sin n\pi t + \frac{2}{n^3\pi^3} \cos n\pi t - \frac{t^2}{n\pi} \cos n\pi t \right) \right]_0^1 \\
&= 2 \left[\left(-\frac{\cos n\pi}{n\pi} \right) - \left(\frac{2(\cos n\pi - 1)}{n^3\pi^3} - \frac{\cos n\pi}{n\pi} \right) \right] \\
&= \frac{4(1 - \cos n\pi)}{n^3\pi^3}
\end{aligned}
$$

Hence it is also possible to represent $f(t)$ for $0 < t < 1$ in the form

$$
(5) \qquad f(t) = \frac{8}{\pi^3} \left[\frac{\sin \pi t}{1} + \frac{\sin 3\pi t}{27} + \frac{\sin 5\pi t}{125} + \frac{\sin 7\pi t}{343} + \cdots \right]
$$

Series (4) and (5) are by no means the only Fourier series which will represent $(t - t^2)$ on the interval $(0,1)$. They are merely the most convenient or most useful ones. In fact, with every possible extension of $(t - t^2)$ from 0 to -1 there is associated a series yielding $(t - t^2)$ for $0 < t < 1$. For instance, a third such series might be obtained by letting the extension be simply the function defined by $(t - t^2)$ itself for $-1 < t < 0$. In that case

$$
\begin{aligned}
a_n &= \frac{1}{1} \int_{-1}^1 (t - t^2) \cos \frac{n\pi t}{1} \, dt \\
&= \left[\left(\frac{\cos n\pi t}{n^2\pi^2} + \frac{t}{n\pi} \sin n\pi t \right) - \left(\frac{2t}{n^2\pi^2} \cos n\pi t - \frac{2}{n^3\pi^3} \sin n\pi t + \frac{t^2}{n\pi} \sin n\pi t \right) \right]_{-1}^1 \\
&= -\frac{4 \cos n\pi}{n^2\pi^2} \qquad\qquad\qquad\qquad n \neq 0
\end{aligned}
$$

$$a_0 = \frac{1}{1} \int_{-1}^{1} (t - t^2) dt = \left[\frac{t^2}{2} - \frac{t^3}{3} \right]_{-1}^{1} = -\frac{2}{3}$$

$$b_n = \frac{1}{1} \int_{-1}^{1} (t - t^2) \sin \frac{n\pi t}{1} \, dt$$

$$= \left[\left(\frac{1}{n^2\pi^2} \sin n\pi t - \frac{t}{n\pi} \cos n\pi t \right) - \left(\frac{2t}{n^2\pi^2} \sin n\pi t + \frac{2}{n^3\pi^3} \cos n\pi t - \frac{t^2}{n\pi} \cos n\pi t \right) \right]_{-1}^{1}$$

$$= -\frac{2 \cos n\pi}{n\pi}$$

Hence it is also possible to write

$$(6) \quad f(t) = -\frac{1}{3} + \frac{4}{\pi^2} \left[\frac{\cos \pi t}{1} - \frac{\cos 2\pi t}{4} + \frac{\cos 3\pi t}{9} - \frac{\cos 4\pi t}{16} + \cdots \right]$$

$$+ \frac{2}{\pi} \left[\frac{\sin \pi t}{1} - \frac{\sin 2\pi t}{2} + \frac{\sin 3\pi t}{3} - \frac{\sin 4\pi t}{4} + \cdots \right]$$

Figures 5.8a, b, and c show the entire periodic functions which are represented, respectively, by the series (4), (5), and (6).

Figure 5.8 and the associated expansions illustrate another interesting and important fact. In Fig. 5.8c the graph as a whole is not continuous but has jumps at $t = \pm 1, \pm 3, \pm 5$, ... In the corresponding series (6), the coefficients (of the sine terms) diminish only as fast as $1/n$ decreases. On the other hand, the graph in Fig. 5.8a is everywhere continuous but has corners, or points, where the tangent changes direction suddenly, at $t = 0, \pm 1, \pm 2, \ldots$ In the corresponding series (4), the coefficients all become small much more rapidly than in (6); as fast as $1/n^2$, in fact. Finally in Fig. 5.8b the graph is not only continuous but the derivative is also continuous, *i.e.*, there are no points where the tangent changes direction abruptly. This smoother behavior is reflected in the coefficients in the corresponding series (5), which in this case approach zero as $1/n^3$ does.

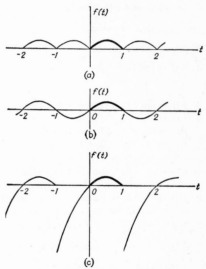

FIG. 5.8.   Plot showing different periodic functions coinciding over the interval (0,1).

These observations may be summed up and generalized in the following statement: *The Fourier coefficients of a function satisfying the Dirichlet conditions always decrease in magnitude at least as fast as $1/n$, for sufficiently large n. If the function has one or more discontinuities, the coefficients can decrease no faster than this. If the function is everywhere continuous but* *has one or more points where its derivative is discontinuous, its coefficients decrease as $1/n^2$. In general, if a function and its various derivatives all satisfy the Dirichlet conditions, and if the kth derivative is the first which is not everywhere continuous, then the Fourier coefficients of the function approach zero as $1/n^{k+1}$, for sufficiently large n.* More concisely though less accurately, we can say that the smoother the function, the faster its Fourier expansion converges.

Closely associated with the last result are the following observations which we state here without proof. *The integral of any periodic function $f(t)$ which satisfies the Dirichlet conditions can be found by termwise integration of the Fourier series of the function. If, in addition, the function is everywhere continuous and possesses a derivative $f'(t)$ which satisfies the Dirichlet conditions, then, wherever it exists, $f'(t)$ can be found by termwise differentiation of the Fourier series of $f(t)$.*

EXERCISES

1. In the exercises at the end of the last two sections tell which of the functions are even and which are odd.

Expand the following:

2. $f(t) = e^t$ in a cosine series for $0 < t < 1$ Ans. $a_n = \dfrac{2[(-1)^n e - 1]}{1 + n^2\pi^2}$, $(b_n = 0)$

3. $f(t) = \cos t$ in a sine series for $0 < t < 2\pi$

$$Ans. \quad (a_n = 0), \ b_n = \frac{2n(1 - \cos n\pi)}{\pi(n^2 - 4)} \qquad n \neq 2, \ b_2 = 0$$

4. $f(t) = \sin t$ in a cosine series for $0 < t < 2\pi$

5. $f(t) = 1 \quad 0 < t < 1$
   $f(t) = 0 \quad 1 < t < k$, in a cosine series

6. $f(t) = t^2 \quad\quad 0 < t < 1$
   $f(t) = 2 - t \quad 1 < t < 2$, in a sine series

7. Obtain a series, different from the half-range sine expansion, which will represent $(t - t^2)$ for $0 < t < 1$ and whose coefficients will decrease as $1/n^3$.

8. Is it possible to obtain a series representing $(t - t^2)$ for $0 < t < 1$ whose coefficients will decrease as $1/n^4$?

9. If $f(t) = 1 \quad\quad\quad 0 < t < a$

   $f(t) = \dfrac{t - 1}{a - 1} \quad a < t < 1$

   $f(t) = 0 \quad\quad 1 < t < 2$

   and if a is only slightly less than 1, discuss the behavior of the coefficients in the half-range cosine expansion of $f(t)$ for small and medium values of n as well as for $n \to \infty$.

10. Find a function whose half-range cosine series will have coefficients decreasing as $1/n^4$. Determine the expansion.

11. If $f(t)$, originally defined only for $0 < t < p$, is extended from p to $2p$ by reflection in the line $t = p$, show that the half-range sine expansion of the extended function contains no terms of the form

$$\sin \frac{n\pi t}{2p}, \qquad n \text{ even}$$

and determine the coefficients of the terms

$$\sin \frac{n\pi t}{2p}, \qquad n \text{ odd}$$

$$\textit{Ans.} \quad b_n = \frac{2}{p} \int_0^p f(t) \sin \frac{n\pi t}{2p}\, dt, \qquad n \text{ odd}$$

12. Determine how $f(t)$ must be extended from p to $2p$ so that the half-range cosine expansion of the extended function will contain no terms of the form

$$\cos \frac{n\pi t}{2p}, \qquad n \text{ even}$$

Derive a formula for the nonzero coefficients.

5.5 Alternative Forms of Fourier Series. The original form of the Fourier series of a function, as derived in Secs. 5.2 and 5.3, can be converted into several other trigonometric forms and into one in which imaginary exponentials appear instead of real trigonometric functions. For instance, in the series

$$f(t) = \frac{1}{2} a_0 + a_1 \cos \frac{\pi t}{p} + a_2 \cos \frac{2\pi t}{p} + \cdots + a_n \cos \frac{n\pi t}{p} + \cdots$$
$$+ b_1 \sin \frac{\pi t}{p} + b_2 \sin \frac{2\pi t}{p} + \cdots + b_n \sin \frac{n\pi t}{p} + \cdots$$

we can group together the terms of the same frequency and apply to each pair the usual procedure for reducing the sum of a sine and cosine of the same angle to a single term:

$$f(t) = \frac{1}{2} a_0 + \sqrt{a_1^2 + b_1^2} \left[\frac{a_1}{\sqrt{a_1^2 + b_1^2}} \cos \frac{\pi t}{p} + \frac{b_1}{\sqrt{a_1^2 + b_1^2}} \sin \frac{\pi t}{p} \right]$$
$$+ \cdots \cdots \cdots \cdots \cdots \cdots \cdots \cdots \cdots \cdots$$
$$+ \sqrt{a_n^2 + b_n^2} \left[\frac{a_n}{\sqrt{a_n^2 + b_n^2}} \cos \frac{n\pi t}{p} + \frac{b_n}{\sqrt{a_n^2 + b_n^2}} \sin \frac{n\pi t}{p} \right]$$
$$+ \cdots \cdots \cdots \cdots \cdots \cdots \cdots \cdots \cdots \cdots$$

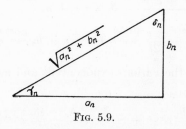

FIG. 5.9.

If we now define the angles γ_n and δ_n from the triangle shown in **Fig. 5.9**, and set $A_0 = \frac{1}{2} a_0$ and $A_n = \sqrt{a_n^2 + b_n^2}$, the last series can be written

$$f(t) = A_0 + A_1 \left(\cos \frac{\pi t}{p} \cos \gamma_1 + \sin \frac{\pi t}{p} \sin \gamma_1 \right)$$
$$+ \cdot \cdot \cdot \cdot \cdot \cdot \cdot \cdot \cdot \cdot \cdot \cdot \cdot \cdot$$
$$+ A_n \left(\cos \frac{n\pi t}{p} \cos \gamma_n + \sin \frac{n\pi t}{p} \sin \gamma_n \right)$$
$$+ \cdot \cdot \cdot \cdot \cdot \cdot \cdot \cdot \cdot \cdot \cdot \cdot \cdot \cdot$$

$$(1) \quad = A_0 + A_1 \cos \left(\frac{\pi t}{p} - \gamma_1 \right) + \cdot \cdot \cdot + A_n \cos \left(\frac{n\pi t}{p} - \gamma_n \right) + \cdot \cdot \cdot$$

or equally well

$$f(t) = A_0 + A_1 \left(\cos \frac{\pi t}{p} \sin \delta_1 + \sin \frac{\pi t}{p} \cos \delta_1 \right)$$
$$+ \cdot \cdot \cdot \cdot \cdot \cdot \cdot \cdot \cdot \cdot \cdot \cdot \cdot \cdot$$
$$+ A_n \left(\cos \frac{n\pi t}{p} \sin \delta_n + \sin \frac{n\pi t}{p} \cos \delta_n \right)$$
$$+ \cdot \cdot \cdot \cdot \cdot \cdot \cdot \cdot \cdot \cdot \cdot \cdot \cdot$$

$$(2) \quad = A_0 + A_1 \sin \left(\frac{\pi t}{p} + \delta_1 \right) + \cdot \cdot \cdot + A_n \sin \left(\frac{n\pi t}{p} + \delta_n \right) + \cdot \cdot \cdot$$

In either of these forms, the quantity $A_n = \sqrt{a_n^2 + b_n^2}$ is the resultant amplitude of the components of frequency $n\pi/p$, that is, the **amplitude of the nth harmonic** in the expansion. The phase angles

$$\gamma_n = \tan^{-1} \left(\frac{b_n}{a_n} \right) \qquad \text{and} \qquad \delta_n = \tan^{-1} \left(\frac{a_n}{b_n} \right)$$

measure the lag or lead of the nth harmonic with reference to a pure cosine or a pure sine wave of the same frequency.

The complex exponential form of a Fourier series is obtained by substituting the exponential equivalents of the sine and cosine terms into the original form of the series:

$$f(t) = \frac{1}{2} a_0 + a_1 \frac{e^{i\pi t/p} + e^{-(i\pi t/p)}}{2} + \cdot \cdot \cdot + a_n \frac{e^{ni\pi t/p} + e^{-(ni\pi t/p)}}{2} + \cdot \cdot \cdot$$
$$+ b_1 \frac{e^{i\pi t/p} - e^{-(i\pi t/p)}}{2i} + \cdot \cdot \cdot + b_n \frac{e^{ni\pi t/p} - e^{-(ni\pi t/p)}}{2i} + \cdot \cdot \cdot$$

Collecting terms on the various exponentials and noting that $1/i = -i$ gives

$$f(t) = \frac{1}{2} a_0 + \frac{a_1 - ib_1}{2} e^{i\pi t/p} + \cdot \cdot \cdot + \frac{a_n - ib_n}{2} e^{ni\pi t/p} + \cdot \cdot \cdot$$
$$+ \frac{a_1 + ib_1}{2} e^{-(i\pi t/p)} + \cdot \cdot \cdot + \frac{a_n + ib_n}{2} e^{-(ni\pi t/p)} + \cdot \cdot \cdot$$

If we now define

$$c_0 = \frac{1}{2}\, a_0, \qquad c_n = \frac{a_n - ib_n}{2}, \qquad c_{-n} = \frac{a_n + ib_n}{2}$$

the last series can be written more symmetrically in the form

$$f(t) = \cdots + c_{-n}e^{-(ni\pi t/p)} + \cdots + c_{-1}e^{-(i\pi t/p)} + c_0 \\ + c_1 e^{i\pi t/p} + \cdots + c_n e^{ni\pi t/p} + \cdots$$

or simply

$$(3) \qquad\qquad f(t) = \sum_{n=-\infty}^{\infty} c_n e^{ni\pi t/p}$$

Now when it is used at all, this exponential form is used as a basic form in its own right; *i.e.*, it is not obtained by transformation from the trigonometric form but is constructed directly from the given function. To do this requires that expressions be available for the direct evaluation of the coefficients c_n. These may be found easily from the definitions of c_0, c_n, and c_{-n}. For

$$c_n = \frac{a_n - ib_n}{2} = \frac{1}{2}\left[\frac{1}{p}\int_d^{d+2p} f(t)\cos\frac{n\pi t}{p}\, dt - i\frac{1}{p}\int_d^{d+2p} f(t)\sin\frac{n\pi t}{p}\, dt\right]$$

$$= \frac{1}{2p}\int_d^{d+2p} f(t)\left(\cos\frac{n\pi t}{p} - i\sin\frac{n\pi t}{p}\right)dt$$

$$= \frac{1}{2p}\int_d^{d+2p} f(t)e^{-(ni\pi t/p)}\, dt$$

$$c_{-n} = \frac{a_n + ib_n}{2} = \frac{1}{2}\left[\frac{1}{p}\int_d^{d+2p} f(t)\cos\frac{n\pi t}{p}\, dt + i\frac{1}{p}\int_d^{d+2p} f(t)\sin\frac{n\pi t}{p}\, dt\right]$$

$$= \frac{1}{2p}\int_d^{d+2p} f(t)\left(\cos\frac{n\pi t}{p} + i\sin\frac{n\pi t}{p}\right)dt$$

$$= \frac{1}{2p}\int_d^{d+2p} f(t)e^{ni\pi t/p}\, dt$$

$$c_0 = \frac{1}{2}\, a_0 = \frac{1}{2p}\int_d^{d+2p} f(t)dt$$

Clearly, whether the index n is positive, negative, or zero, c_n is given by the one formula

$$(4) \qquad\qquad c_n = \frac{1}{2p}\int_d^{d+2p} f(t)e^{-(ni\pi t/p)}\, dt$$

As usual, d will almost always be either $-p$ or 0.

In the complex representation defined by (3) and (4), a certain symmetry between the expressions for a function and for its Fourier coefficients is evident.   In fact, the expressions

$$f(t) = \sum_{n=-\infty}^{\infty} c_n e^{ni\pi t/p}$$

$$c_n = \frac{1}{2p} \int_{-p}^{p} f(t) e^{-(ni\pi t/p)} \, dt$$

are of essentially the same structure, as the following correlation reveals

$$t \longleftrightarrow n$$
$$f(t) \longleftrightarrow c_n \equiv c(n)$$
$$e^{ni\pi t/p} \longleftrightarrow e^{-(ni\pi t/p)}$$

$$\sum_{n=-\infty}^{\infty} \Big(\qquad \Big) \longleftrightarrow \frac{1}{2p} \int_{-p}^{p} \Big(\qquad \Big) \, dt$$

This duality is worthy of note, and as our development proceeds to the Fourier integral and the Laplace transform, it will become still more striking and fundamental.

Example 1

Find the complex form of the Fourier series of the function whose definition in one period is

$$f(t) = e^{-t} \qquad -1 < t < 1$$

Since $p = 1$, we have from (4) taking $d = -1$,

$$
\begin{aligned}
c_n &= \frac{1}{2} \int_{-1}^{1} e^{-t} e^{-ni\pi t} \, dt \\
&= \frac{1}{2} \int_{-1}^{1} e^{-(1+ni\pi)t} \, dt \\
&= \frac{1}{2} \left[\frac{e^{-(1+ni\pi)t}}{-(1+ni\pi)} \right]_{-1}^{1} \\
&= \frac{e^{-(1+ni\pi)} - e^{(1+ni\pi)}}{-2(1+ni\pi)} \\
&= \frac{ee^{ni\pi} - e^{-1}e^{-ni\pi}}{2(1+ni\pi)}
\end{aligned}
$$

Now $e^{i\pi} = \cos \pi + i \sin \pi = -1$ and thus $e^{ni\pi} = e^{-ni\pi} = (-1)^n$.   Therefore

$$
\begin{aligned}
c_n &= \frac{(-1)^n}{(1+ni\pi)} \left(\frac{e - e^{-1}}{2} \right) \\
&= \frac{(-1)^n \sinh 1}{(1+ni\pi)} \frac{(1-ni\pi)}{(1-ni\pi)} \\
&= \frac{(-1)^n (1-ni\pi) \sinh 1}{(1 + n^2\pi^2)}
\end{aligned}
$$

The expansion of $f(t)$ is therefore

$$f(t) = \sum_{n=-\infty}^{\infty} (-1)^n \frac{(1 - ni\pi)\sinh 1}{(1 + n^2\pi^2)} e^{ni\pi t}$$

This can be converted into the real trigonometric form without difficulty, for we have by definition

$$c_n = \frac{a_n - ib_n}{2}$$

$$c_{-n} = \frac{a_n + ib_n}{2}$$

and thus, by adding and subtracting,

$$a_n = c_n + c_{-n}, \qquad b_n = i(c_n - c_{-n})$$

Therefore in this problem

$$a_n = \frac{(-1)^n(1 - ni\pi)\sinh 1}{(1 + n^2\pi^2)} + \frac{(-1)^n(1 + ni\pi)\sinh 1}{(1 + n^2\pi^2)}$$

$$= \frac{(-1)^n \, 2\sinh 1}{(1 + n^2\pi^2)}$$

$$b_n = i\left[\frac{(-1)^n(1 - ni\pi)\sinh 1}{(1 + n^2\pi^2)} - \frac{(-1)^n(1 + ni\pi)\sinh 1}{(1 + n^2\pi^2)}\right]$$

$$= \frac{(-1)^n 2n\pi \sinh 1}{(1 + n^2\pi^2)}$$

$$\tfrac{1}{2}a_0 = c_0 = \sinh 1$$

Hence we can also write

$$f(t) = \sinh 1 - 2\sinh 1\left[\frac{\cos \pi t}{1 + \pi^2} - \frac{\cos 2\pi t}{1 + 4\pi^2} + \frac{\cos 3\pi t}{1 + 9\pi^2} - \cdots\right]$$
$$- 2\pi \sinh 1\left[\frac{\sin \pi t}{1 + \pi^2} - \frac{2\sin 2\pi t}{1 + 4\pi^2} + \frac{3\sin 3\pi t}{1 + 9\pi^2} - \cdots\right]$$

5.6 Applications. Although we shall see other uses of Fourier series in later chapters, their most important application at the present stage is the representation of periodic disturbances acting on physical systems.

Example 1

Determine the forced vibrations of the system shown in Fig. 5.10a if the disturbing force is as shown in Fig. 5.10b.

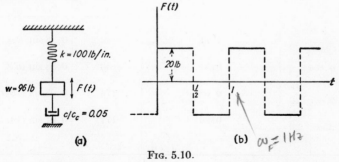

FIG. 5.10.

Our first step must be to obtain the Fourier expansion of the driving force. Since this is clearly an odd function of t, no cosine terms can be present, and thus we need only compute

$$b_n = \frac{2}{\frac{1}{2}} \int_0^{\frac{1}{2}} 20 \sin \left(\frac{n\pi t}{\frac{1}{2}} \right) dt$$

$$= 80 \left[-\frac{\cos 2n\pi t}{2n\pi} \right]_0^{\frac{1}{2}}$$

$$= 40 \frac{1 - \cos n\pi}{n\pi}$$

$$= 0 \qquad n \text{ even}$$

$$= \frac{80}{n\pi} \qquad n \text{ odd}$$

Hence

$$F(t) = \frac{80}{\pi} \left[\sin 2\pi t + \frac{\sin 6\pi t}{3} + \frac{\sin 10\pi t}{5} + \frac{\sin 14\pi t}{7} + \cdots \right]$$

Since we are concerned only with the forced or steady-state motion of the system, we need determine only the particular integral corresponding to $F(t)$. This can be done very simply using the ideas of Sec. 4.3, for it is only necessary to apply the proper magnification ratio and phase shift to each component of the driving force. Preparatory to doing this we must determine the static deflections that would be produced in the system by steady forces having the magnitudes of the various components of $F(t)$. These are given by

$$(\delta_{st})_n = \frac{(80/n\pi) \text{ lb}}{100 \text{ lb/in.}} = \frac{4}{5n\pi} \text{ in.} \qquad n \text{ odd}$$

Then we must calculate the undamped natural frequency of the system, which is

$$\omega_n = \sqrt{\frac{kg}{w}} = \sqrt{\frac{100 \times 384}{96}} = 20 \text{ rad/sec}$$

The rest of the work can best be presented in tabular form

Term	δ_{st}	$\dfrac{\omega}{\omega_n}$	$M = \dfrac{1}{\sqrt{\left(1 - \dfrac{\omega^2}{\omega_n^2}\right)^2 + \left(2 \dfrac{c}{c_c} \dfrac{\omega}{\omega_n}\right)^2}}$	$\alpha = \tan^{-1} \dfrac{2 \dfrac{c}{c_c} \dfrac{\omega}{\omega_n}}{1 - \dfrac{\omega^2}{\omega_n^2}}$	Steady-state term $= \delta_{st} M \sin (\omega t - \alpha)$
1	$\dfrac{4}{5\pi}$	$\dfrac{2\pi}{20}$	1.11	2°	$0.28 \sin (2\pi t - 2°)$
2	$\dfrac{4}{15\pi}$	$\dfrac{6\pi}{20}$	6.83	40°	$0.58 \sin (6\pi t - 40°)$
3	$\dfrac{4}{25\pi}$	$\dfrac{10\pi}{20}$	0.68	174°	$0.03 \sin (10\pi t - 174°)$
4	$\dfrac{4}{35\pi}$	$\dfrac{14\pi}{20}$	0.26	177°	$0.01 \sin (14\pi t - 177°)$
$\cdots$	$\cdots$	$\cdots$	$\cdots$	$\cdots$	$\cdots$

Figure 5.11 shows the forced vibrations plotted as a function of time.

This problem illustrates an exceedingly important but sometimes misunderstood characteristic of forced vibrations. If the driving force is not a pure sine or cosine wave, its Fourier expansion will contain terms with frequencies above the fundamental or apparent frequency of the excitation. If the frequency of one of these terms happens to be close to the resonant or natural frequency of the system, the large value of the corresponding magnification ratio may offset many times the smaller amplitude of the harmonic and make the resultant term the dominant part of the entire response. If and when this happens, the response will appear (mysteriously, to an observer ignorant of the underlying analysis) to be of a higher frequency than the force that produces it. Figure 5.11 shows this clearly, for although the force alternates only once per second, the weight is seen to move up and down three times per second.

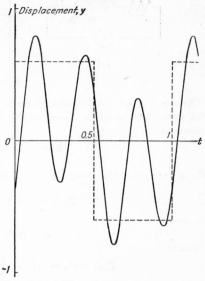

FIG. 5.11. Plot showing a response of apparent frequency greater than the excitation producing it.

Example 2

Find the steady-state current produced in the circuit shown in Fig. 5.12a by the voltage shown in Fig. 5.12b.

The first step is to find the Fourier expansion of the voltage. Since we plan to use the concept of the complex impedance, it will be convenient to use the complex exponential form of the Fourier series. Hence we compute

$$c_n = \frac{1}{0.01} \int_0^{0.005} E_0 e^{-(ni\pi t/0.005)} \, dt \quad \text{(interval from 0.005 to 0.01 = 0}$$
$$\text{as } f(t) = 0)$$

$$= 100E_0 \frac{e^{-(ni\pi t/0.005)}}{-\dfrac{ni\pi}{0.005}} \Bigg]_0^{0.005}$$

$$= E_0 \frac{(1 - e^{-ni\pi})}{2ni\pi}$$

$$= 0, \qquad n \text{ even, } n \neq 0$$

$$= \frac{E_0}{ni\pi} = -\frac{iE_0}{n\pi} \qquad n \text{ odd}$$

$$c_0 = \frac{1}{0.01} \int_0^{0.005} E_0 \, dt = 100E_0 t \Big]_0^{0.005} = \frac{E_0}{2}$$

Therefore

$$E = E_0 \left[\cdots + \frac{ie^{-600i\pi t}}{3\pi} + \frac{ie^{-200i\pi t}}{\pi} + \frac{1}{2} - \frac{ie^{200i\pi t}}{\pi} - \frac{ie^{600i\pi t}}{3\pi} - \cdots \right]$$

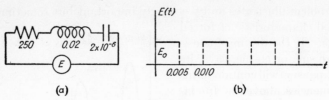

FIG. 5.12.

Now in Sec. 4.4, we showed that the steady-state current produced by a voltage of the form $Ae^{i\omega t}$ could be found simply by dividing the voltage by the complex impedance

$$Z(\omega) = R + i\left(\omega L - \frac{1}{\omega C}\right)$$

Using the data of the present problem, we have

$$Z(\omega) = 250 + i\left(0.02\omega - \frac{10^6}{2\omega}\right)$$

or, since

$$\omega = 200n\pi \qquad n \text{ odd}$$

we have

$$Z(\omega) = Z_n = 250 + i\left(4n\pi - \frac{2,500}{n\pi}\right) \qquad n \text{ odd}$$

Hence, dividing each term in the expansion of the voltage by the value of Z for the corresponding frequency, we find

$$I(t) = \sum_{n=-\infty}^{\infty} D_n e^{200ni\pi t}† \qquad n \text{ odd}$$

where

$$D_n = \frac{c_n}{Z_n} = -\frac{E_0 i}{n\pi} \frac{1}{250 + i\left(4n\pi - \dfrac{2,500}{n\pi}\right)} = \frac{-iE_0}{250n\pi + i(4\pi^2 n^2 - 2,500)} \qquad n \text{ odd}$$

If we desire the real trigonometric form of this expansion,
$I(t) = \frac{1}{2}a_0 + a_1 \cos 200\pi t + a_2 \cos 600\pi t + \cdots + b_1 \sin 200\pi t + b_2 \sin 600\pi t + \cdots$
we have at once

$$a_n = D_n + D_{-n}$$
$$= -E_0 i\left[\frac{1}{250n\pi + i(4\pi^2 n^2 - 2,500)} + \frac{1}{-250n\pi + i(4\pi^2 n^2 - 2,500)}\right]$$
$$= -\frac{2E_0(4\pi^2 n^2 - 2,500)}{(250n\pi)^2 + (4n^2\pi^2 - 2,500)^2} \qquad n \text{ odd}$$
$$b_n = i(D_n - D_{-n})$$
$$= E_0\left[\frac{1}{250n\pi + i(4\pi^2 n^2 - 2,500)} - \frac{1}{-250n\pi + i(4n^2\pi^2 - 2,500)}\right]$$
$$= \frac{500n\pi E_0}{(250n\pi)^2 + (4n^2\pi^2 - 2,500)^2} \qquad n \text{ odd}$$

† Because of the presence of the condenser, the impedance for the component of zero frequency is infinite. Hence the term $\frac{1}{2}E_0$ makes no contribution to the steady-state current.

EXERCISES

1. In Example 1 discuss the effect of (a) doubling the amount of friction and (b) changing the spring to one of modulus 120 lb/in.

2. Discuss the steady-state motion of the following system.

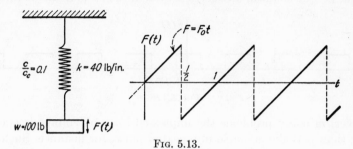

Fig. 5.13.

3. Discuss the steady-state motion of the following system.

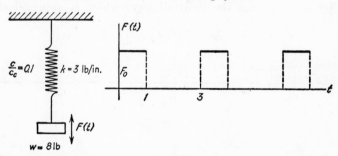

Fig. 5.14.

4. What is the steady-state current in the following circuit?

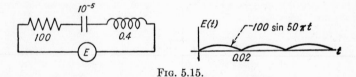

Fig. 5.15.

5. What is the steady-state current in the following circuit?

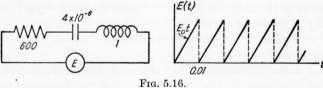

Fig. 5.16.

5.7 The Fourier Integral as the Limit of a Fourier Series. The properties of Fourier series so far developed are adequate to accomplish the expansion of any periodic function satisfying the Dirichlet conditions, and, in connection with the theory of Chap. 4, enable us to find the response of a mechanical or electrical system to any periodic disturbance.

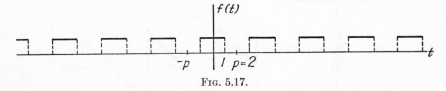

FIG. 5.17.

However, in many problems the impressed force or voltage is aperiodic rather than periodic, a single unrepeated pulse, for instance. Such functions evidently cannot be handled directly through the use of Fourier series, for such series necessarily define only periodic functions. Nonetheless, by investigating the limit (if any) which is approached by a

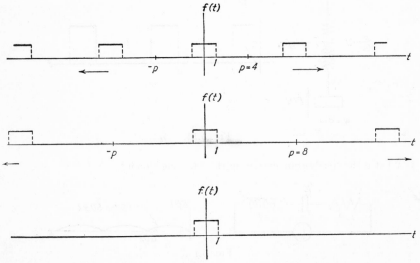

FIG. 5.18. Plot showing a periodic function becoming nonperiodic as its period increases indefinitely.

Fourier series as the period of the given function is made longer and longer and finally allowed to become infinite, a suitable representation can perhaps be obtained. An example is probably the best way to introduce the theory of this process.

Consider, then, the function $f(t)$ shown in Fig. 5.17, in the limit as $p \to \infty$, as suggested by Fig. 5.18. This function is clearly even, and thus its Fourier expansion contains only cosine terms, whose coefficients are given by

$$a_n = \frac{2}{p} \int_0^1 1 \cos \frac{n\pi t}{p}\, dt$$

$$= \frac{2}{p} \frac{\sin (n\pi t/p)}{n\pi/p} \bigg|_0^1$$

$$= \frac{2}{p} \left(\frac{p}{n\pi}\right) \sin \frac{n\pi}{p}$$

$$a_0 = \frac{2}{p} \int_0^1 1\, dt = \frac{2}{p}$$

$f(t) = 1$ (unity height)

It will now help us to visualize what happens as $p \to \infty$ if we plot the amplitude a_n as a function of n, or better still as a function of the frequency, $n\pi/p$, for different values of p.   Figure 5.19 shows such plots

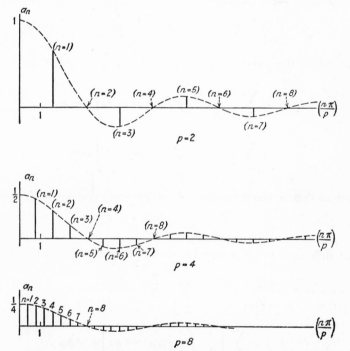

FIG. 5.19.   Plot showing the behavior of the Fourier coefficients of a function as the period of the function becomes infinite.

for $p = 2, 4$, and 8.   The plots are all very much alike.   In fact, they differ in only two respects: (a) in the vertical scale, which is inversely proportional to the length of the period, and (b) in the crowding together of the ordinates, caused by the reduction of the frequency interval $\Delta\omega$

between successive harmonics, which also varies inversely with the period:

$$\Delta\omega = \frac{(n+1)\pi}{p} - \frac{n\pi}{p} = \frac{\pi}{p}$$

The characteristic crowding together of the amplitudes, and the accompanying decrease of their magnitudes, suggest that in the limit when $p \rightarrow \infty$ and the given function becomes aperiodic, the Fourier representation, now a sum of continuously distributed infinitesimal terms, becomes an integral. This is actually the case, as the following outline of steps reveals.

If we begin with the complex exponential form of a Fourier series, P./32

$$f(t) = \sum_{-\infty}^{\infty} c_n e^{in\pi t/p}$$

$$c_n = \frac{1}{2p} \int_{-p}^{p} f(t) e^{-(in\pi t/p)} \, dt \equiv \frac{1}{2p} \int_{-p}^{p} f(s) e^{-(in\pi s/p)} \, ds$$

and substitute the second expression for c_n into $f(t)$, we obtain

$$f(t) = \sum_{-\infty}^{\infty} \left[\frac{1}{2p} \int_{-p}^{p} f(s) e^{-(in\pi s/p)} \, ds \right] e^{in\pi t/p}$$

$$= \sum_{-\infty}^{\infty} \left[\frac{1}{2\pi} \int_{-p}^{p} f(s) e^{-(in\pi s/p)} \, ds \right] e^{in\pi t/p} \frac{\pi}{p}$$

Now let us denote the frequency of the general component by

$$\omega_n \equiv \frac{n\pi}{p}$$

and the difference in frequency between consecutive harmonics by

$$\Delta\omega \equiv \frac{\pi}{p}$$

Then $f(t)$ can be written

$$f(t) = \sum_{-\infty}^{\infty} \left[\frac{1}{2\pi} \int_{-p}^{p} f(s) e^{-i\omega_n s} \, ds \right] e^{i\omega_n t} \, \Delta\omega$$

In this form, $f(t)$ appears as the sum of products of the infinitesimal $\Delta\omega$ times the value of the function of ω,

$$\left[\frac{1}{2\pi} \int_{-p}^{p} f(s) e^{-i\omega s} \, ds \right] e^{i\omega t}$$

at a point ω_n in each interval $\Delta\omega$. The limit of such a sum is a definite integral,* and thus, as $p \to \infty$ and $f(t)$ becomes aperiodic, we can write

$$(1) \qquad f(t) = \int_{-\infty}^{\infty} \left[\frac{1}{2\pi} \int_{-\infty}^{\infty} f(s)e^{-i\omega s}\, ds \right] e^{i\omega t}\, d\omega$$

This is one form of what is called a **Fourier integral.** It is a valid representation of $f(t)$, provided that in every finite interval $f(t)$ satisfies the Dirichlet conditions and that the integral

$$\int_{-\infty}^{\infty} |f(t)|\, dt$$

exists. Under these conditions the Fourier integral gives the value of $f(t)$ at all points where $f(t)$ is continuous, and it gives the average of the right- and left-hand limits at all points where $f(t)$ is discontinuous.

The Fourier integral can be written in various forms. For instance, we can write†

$$f(t) = \int_{-\infty}^{\infty} g(\omega)e^{i\omega t}\, d\omega$$

where

$$(2) \qquad g(\omega) = \frac{1}{2\pi} \int_{-\infty}^{\infty} f(s)e^{-i\omega s}\, ds$$

These two expressions, in which the symmetry between $f(t)$ and its **coefficient function** $g(\omega)$ is unmistakable, constitute what is known as a **Fourier transform pair.** Elaborate tables of such pairs have been prepared for engineering use.‡

---

* The situation is not quite as simple as we have made it seem, for the structure of the function

$$\left[\frac{1}{2\pi} \int_{-p}^{p} f(s)e^{-i\omega s}\, ds \right] e^{i\omega t}$$

depends on p as well as upon ω. Hence as p increases, the function we are evaluating changes, and the elementary theory of the definite integral is not strictly applicable. Moreover, the fact that the summation extends over an infinite range makes additional investigation of the limiting process necessary. The modifications necessary to make our conclusions rigorous can be found in more advanced treatments such as "Fourier Series and Boundary Value Problems" by R. V. Churchill, McGraw-Hill Book Company, Inc., pp. 88–90, New York, 1941.

† Some authors associate the factor $1/2\pi$ with the integral for $f(t)$ instead of with the integral for $g(\omega)$, as we have done.

‡ G. A. Campbell and R. M. Foster, "Fourier Integrals for Practical Applications," D. Van Nostrand Company, Inc., New York, 1948.

On the other hand, we can legitimately move the factor $e^{i\omega t}$ into the inner integral in (1) since it does not involve the variable s of that integration. This gives

(3) $$f(t) = \frac{1}{2\pi} \int_{-\infty}^{\infty} \int_{-\infty}^{\infty} f(s)e^{-i\omega(s-t)} \, ds \, d\omega$$

In this we can replace the exponential by its trigonometric equivalent, getting

$$f(t) = \frac{1}{2\pi} \int_{-\infty}^{\infty} \int_{-\infty}^{\infty} f(s)[\cos \omega(s - t) - i \sin \omega(s - t)] ds \, d\omega$$

If we break this up into two integrals, we get

$$f(t) = \frac{1}{2\pi} \int_{-\infty}^{\infty} \int_{-\infty}^{\infty} f(s) \cos \omega(s - t) ds \, d\omega$$
$$- \frac{i}{2\pi} \int_{-\infty}^{\infty} \int_{-\infty}^{\infty} f(s) \sin \omega(s - t) ds \, d\omega$$

Now $\sin \omega(s - t)$ is an odd function of ω. Hence the second integral vanishes because of the ω integration from $-\infty$ to ∞. This could have been foreseen, since $f(t)$ is entirely real. Thus we obtain the real trigonometric representation

(4) $$f(t) = \frac{1}{2\pi} \int_{-\infty}^{\infty} \int_{-\infty}^{\infty} f(s) \cos \omega(s - t) ds \, d\omega$$

Since the integrand is now an even function of ω, we need perform the ω integration only between 0 and ∞, provided we multiply the result by 2. This gives us the modified form,

(4.1) $$f(t) = \frac{1}{\pi} \int_{0}^{\infty} \int_{-\infty}^{\infty} f(s) \cos \omega(s - t) ds \, d\omega$$

If $f(t)$ is itself either an odd or an even function, further simplifications are possible. To see this, expand the term $\cos \omega(s - t)$ in the integrand of (4), getting

$$f(t) = \frac{1}{2\pi} \int_{-\infty}^{\infty} \int_{-\infty}^{\infty} f(s) \cos \omega s \cos \omega t \, ds \, d\omega$$
$$+ \frac{1}{2\pi} \int_{-\infty}^{\infty} \int_{-\infty}^{\infty} f(s) \sin \omega s \sin \omega t \, ds \, d\omega$$

and then write the inner integrals as the sums of integrals over $(-\infty, 0)$ and $(0, \infty)$. Then

$$f(t) = \frac{1}{2\pi} \int_{-\infty}^{\infty} \int_{-\infty}^{0} f(s) \cos \omega s \cos \omega t \, ds \, d\omega$$

$$+ \frac{1}{2\pi} \int_{-\infty}^{\infty} \int_{0}^{\infty} f(s) \cos \omega s \cos \omega t \, ds \, d\omega$$

$$+ \frac{1}{2\pi} \int_{-\infty}^{\infty} \int_{-\infty}^{0} f(s) \sin \omega s \sin \omega t \, ds \, d\omega$$

$$+ \frac{1}{2\pi} \int_{-\infty}^{\infty} \int_{0}^{\infty} f(s) \sin \omega s \sin \omega t \, ds \, d\omega$$

Next make the substitution

$$s = -z, \qquad ds = -dz$$

in the integrals from $-\infty$ to 0:

$$(5) \quad f(t) = \frac{1}{2\pi} \int_{-\infty}^{\infty} \int_{\infty}^{0} f(-z) \cos (-\omega z) \cos \omega t (-dz) d\omega$$

$$+ \frac{1}{2\pi} \int_{-\infty}^{\infty} \int_{0}^{\infty} f(s) \cos \omega s \cos \omega t \, ds \, d\omega$$

$$+ \frac{1}{2\pi} \int_{-\infty}^{\infty} \int_{\infty}^{0} f(-z) \sin (-\omega z) \sin \omega t (-dz) d\omega$$

$$+ \frac{1}{2\pi} \int_{-\infty}^{\infty} \int_{0}^{\infty} f(s) \sin \omega s \sin \omega t \, ds \, d\omega$$

Now if $f(t)$ is an even function, so that $f(-z) = f(z)$, the first integral in (5) becomes identical with the second, when the minus sign attached to dz is used to reverse the order of the limits on the inner integral. Similarly the third and fourth integrals turn out to be equal but of opposite sign. Hence we have simply

$$(6) \qquad f(t) = \frac{1}{\pi} \int_{-\infty}^{\infty} \int_{0}^{\infty} f(s) \cos \omega s \cos \omega t \, ds \, d\omega \qquad f(t) \text{ even}$$

This is called the **Fourier cosine integral,** and is analogous to the half-range cosine expansion of a periodic function which is even.

If $f(t)$ is an odd function, so that $f(-z) = -f(z)$, then the first and second integrals in (5) cancel each other and the third and fourth combine, giving

$$(7) \qquad f(t) = \frac{1}{\pi} \int_{-\infty}^{\infty} \int_{0}^{\infty} f(s) \sin \omega s \sin \omega t \, ds \, d\omega \qquad f(t) \text{ odd}$$

This is the **Fourier sine integral,** and is the analogue of the half-range sine expansion of an odd periodic function.

For some purposes it is convenient to have the Fourier sine and cosine integral representations displayed as transform pairs. Thus we can write

(6.1)
$$f(t) = \int_{-\infty}^{\infty} g(\omega) \cos \omega t \, d\omega$$
$$g(\omega) = \frac{1}{\pi} \int_{0}^{\infty} f(s) \cos \omega s \, ds \qquad f(t) \text{ even}$$

and

(7.1)
$$f(t) = \int_{-\infty}^{\infty} g(\omega) \sin \omega t \, d\omega$$
$$g(\omega) = \frac{1}{\pi} \int_{0}^{\infty} f(s) \sin \omega s \, ds \qquad f(t) \text{ odd}$$

Equations (6), (6.1), (7), and (7.1) can of course all be modified by performing the ω integrations only from 0 to ∞ and multiplying the results by 2.

To illustrate the Fourier integral representation of an aperiodic function, let us return to the isolated pulse which we considered briefly at the beginning of this section (Fig. 5.18). Since this function is clearly even, we can use (6), getting

$$\begin{aligned} f(t) &= \frac{1}{\pi} \int_{-\infty}^{\infty} \int_{0}^{1} \cos \omega s \cos \omega t \, ds \, d\omega \\ &= \frac{1}{\pi} \int_{-\infty}^{\infty} \cos \omega t \left[\frac{\sin \omega s}{\omega} \right]_{0}^{1} d\omega \\ &= \frac{1}{\pi} \int_{-\infty}^{\infty} \frac{\cos \omega t \sin \omega}{\omega} d\omega \\ &= \frac{2}{\pi} \int_{0}^{\infty} \frac{\cos \omega t \sin \omega}{\omega} d\omega \end{aligned}$$

the last step following, since the integrand is an even function of ω. Thus, although it is impossible to find an elementary antiderivative for the last integral, we know that as a definite integral it must equal 1 if t is between -1 and $+1$, must equal $\frac{1}{2}$ if $t = \pm 1$, and must vanish if t is numerically greater than 1.

In the case of Fourier series representation of a periodic function it was a matter of some interest to determine how well the first few terms of the expansion represented the function. The corresponding problem in the aperiodic case is to investigate how well the Fourier integral represents a function when only the components in the lower part of the frequency range are taken into account. Suppose, therefore, that we consider only the frequencies below ω_0. In this case we have as an approximation to $f(t)$ the finite integral

$$\frac{2}{\pi} \int_0^{\omega_0} \frac{\cos \omega t \sin \omega}{\omega} \, d\omega$$

Now

$$\cos a \sin b = \frac{\sin (a + b) - \sin (a - b)}{2}$$

and thus we can write the last integral as

$$\frac{1}{\pi} \int_0^{\omega_0} \frac{\sin \omega(t + 1)}{\omega} \, d\omega - \frac{1}{\pi} \int_0^{\omega_0} \frac{\sin \omega(t - 1)}{\omega} \, d\omega$$

In the first of these let $\omega(t + 1) = u$, and in the second let $\omega(t - 1) = u$
Then we have for the approximation of $f(t)$

$$\frac{1}{\pi} \int_0^{\omega_0(t+1)} \frac{\sin u}{u} \, du - \frac{1}{\pi} \int_0^{\omega_0(t-1)} \frac{\sin u}{u} \, du$$

Although these integrals possess no antiderivatives which can be expressed in terms of elementary functions, they occur often enough in applied mathematics to be named and tabulated. Specifically

$$\int_0^x \frac{\sin u}{u} \, du$$

is known as the **sine integral** function of x, and is written si (x). It is tabulated, among other places, in Jahnke-Emde, "Tables of Functions." Using this notation, the approximation to $f(t)$ may be written

$$\frac{1}{\pi} \text{si } \omega_0(t + 1) - \frac{1}{\pi} \text{si } \omega_0(t - 1)$$

Figure 5.20 shows this approximation for $\omega_0 = 8$, 16, and 32 rad/sec.

5.8 From the Fourier Integral to the Laplace Transform. In many applications of the Fourier integral

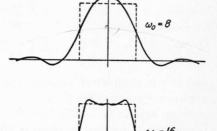
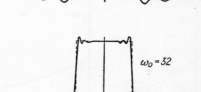

Fig. 5.20. Plot showing the approximation of a function by its Fourier integral taken only over frequencies less than ω_0.

the function to be represented is identically zero before some instant, usually $t = 0$. When this is the case, the general Fourier transform pair, given by Eqs. (2), Sec. 5.7, becomes the **unilateral Fourier transform.***

---

* Note that for later convenience we have here chosen to incorporate the factor $1/2\pi$ in the integral for $f(t)$ rather than in the integral for $g(\omega)$, as we did earlier.

$$f(t) = \frac{1}{2\pi} \int_{-\infty}^{\infty} g(\omega)e^{i\omega t}\, d\omega$$

(1)

$$g(\omega) = \int_{0}^{\infty} f(s)e^{-i\omega s}\, ds$$

Useful as this is in many applications, it is still inadequate to represent such a simple function as the so-called **unit step function,** $u(t)$:

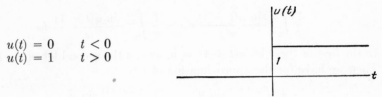

$$u(t) = 0 \qquad t < 0$$
$$u(t) = 1 \qquad t > 0$$

Fig. 5.21.   The unit step function, $u(t)$.

In fact, for this function,

$$g(\omega) = \int_{0}^{\infty} 1 \cdot e^{-i\omega s}\, ds$$

$$= \left. \frac{e^{-i\omega s}}{-i\omega} \right|_{0}^{\infty}$$

$$= \left. \frac{\cos \omega s - i \sin \omega s}{-i\omega} \right|_{0}^{\infty}$$

and this is completely meaningless, since the cosine and sine of infinite arguments are undefined.

As an artifice to handle this case (and others like it) the function e^{-at} is sometimes inserted in place of the unit step function.   Since e^{-at} has a unilateral Fourier transform, as we shall soon see, and since when a

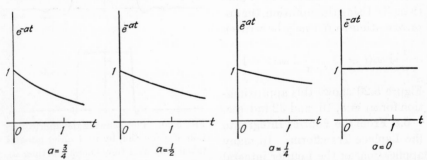

Fig. 5.22.   Plot showing how $e^{-at}(t > 0)$ approaches the unit step function when a approaches zero.

approaches zero, e^{-at}, considered for $t > 0$, approaches the unit step function, it is natural to hope that the order of the operations of letting $a \to 0$ and taking the Fourier transform can be interchanged.   If this is possible, then we can postpone letting $a \to 0$ until *after* the transform has been safely taken, and all will be well.

In the present problem the development proceeds as follows. Instead of transforming $u(t)$ we transform e^{-at}, getting

$$g(\omega) = \int_0^\infty e^{-as} e^{-i\omega s}\, ds$$

$$= \int_0^\infty e^{-(a+i\omega)s}\, ds$$

$$= \left. \frac{e^{-(a+i\omega)s}}{-(a+i\omega)} \right|_0^\infty$$

$$= \frac{1}{a+i\omega}$$

since the factor e^{-as} now ensures that the antiderivative vanishes at the upper limit. Thus

$$f(t) = \frac{1}{2\pi} \int_{-\infty}^\infty g(\omega) e^{i\omega t}\, d\omega$$

$$= \frac{1}{2\pi} \int_{-\infty}^\infty \frac{e^{i\omega t}}{a+i\omega}\, d\omega$$

$$= \frac{1}{2\pi} \int_{-\infty}^\infty \frac{\cos \omega t + i \sin \omega t}{a+i\omega}\, \frac{a-i\omega}{a-i\omega}\, d\omega$$

$$= \frac{1}{2\pi} \int_{-\infty}^\infty \frac{(a \cos \omega t + \omega \sin \omega t) + i(a \sin \omega t - \omega \cos \omega t)}{a^2 + \omega^2}\, d\omega$$

[handwritten margin notes:]
odd
$f(-\omega) = -f(\omega)$
✓ $-\omega \times \cos(-\omega t) = -(\omega \cos \omega t)$
✓ $\sin(-\omega t) = -(\sin \omega t)$

Now the imaginary part of the integrand, namely,

$$\frac{a \sin \omega t - \omega \cos \omega t}{a^2 + \omega^2}$$

[handwritten margin notes:]
even
$f(-\omega) = f(\omega)$
$-\omega \cos(-\omega t) = \omega \cos \omega t$ ✗
$-\omega \sin(-\omega t) = \omega \sin \omega t$ ✓
$-\omega(-\sin \omega t) = \omega \sin \omega t$ ✓

is an odd function of ω, and hence will vanish when integrated between the limits $-\infty$ and ∞. On the other hand, the real part of the integrand is an even function of ω, and thus we can write

$$f(t) = \frac{1}{\pi} \int_0^\infty \frac{a \cos \omega t + \omega \sin \omega t}{a^2 + \omega^2}\, d\omega = \frac{1}{\pi} \int_0^\infty \frac{a \cos \omega t}{a^2 + \omega^2}\, d\omega + \frac{1}{\pi} \int_0^\infty \frac{\omega \sin \omega t}{a^2 + \omega^2}\, d\omega$$

In the first integral in the right member let $\omega = az$. Then

$$f(t) = \frac{1}{\pi} \int_0^\infty \frac{\cos atz}{1 + z^2}\, dz + \frac{1}{\pi} \int_0^\infty \frac{\omega \sin \omega t}{a^2 + \omega^2}\, d\omega$$

We are now in a position to let a approach zero. As this happens,

$$f(t) \equiv e^{-at} \to u(t)$$

and thus we obtain

$$u(t) = \frac{1}{\pi} \int_0^\infty \frac{dz}{1 + z^2} + \frac{1}{\pi} \int_0^\infty \frac{\sin \omega t}{\omega}\, d\omega = \frac{1}{2} + \frac{1}{\pi} \int_0^\infty \frac{\sin \omega t}{\omega}\, d\omega$$

[handwritten note:] $= \pi/2$

This establishes the value of another definite integral, without benefit of an antiderivative.

The use which we have just made of the so-called **convergence factor** e^{-at} is both artificial and clumsy, and it would be desirable to make this procedure more systematic. To do this let us define

$$F(t) = 0 \qquad\qquad t < 0$$
$$F(t) = e^{-at}f(t) \qquad t > 0$$

where $f(t)$ is the function of actual interest. Then applying the unilateral Fourier transform to $F(t)$, we have

$$F(t) = e^{-at}f(t) = \frac{1}{2\pi} \int_{-\infty}^{\infty} g(\omega)e^{i\omega t}d\omega$$

where

$$g(\omega) = \int_{0}^{\infty} F(s)e^{-i\omega s}\,ds$$
$$= \int_{0}^{\infty} [e^{-as}f(s)]e^{-i\omega s}\,ds$$
$$= \int_{0}^{\infty} f(s)e^{-(a+i\omega)s}\,ds$$

We can now multiply both sides of the expression for $F(t)$ by e^{at} getting

$$f(t) = \frac{e^{at}}{2\pi} \int_{-\infty}^{\infty} g(\omega)e^{i\omega t}\,d\omega$$
$$= \frac{1}{2\pi} \int_{-\infty}^{\infty} g(\omega)e^{(a+i\omega)t}\,d\omega$$

Moreover, from the last form of the expression for $g(\omega)$, it is clear that ω enters only through the binomial $(a + i\omega)$. To emphasize this fact, we shall write $g(a + i\omega)$ in place of $g(\omega)$. Then the equations of the transform pair become

$$f(t) = \frac{1}{2\pi} \int_{-\infty}^{\infty} g(a + i\omega)e^{(a+i\omega)t}\,d\omega$$
$$g(a + i\omega) = \int_{0}^{\infty} f(s)e^{-(a+i\omega)s}\,ds$$

Finally, let us put $a + i\omega = \sigma$, and note that

$$d\omega = \frac{d(a + i\omega)}{i} = \frac{d\sigma}{i}$$

and that when $\omega = -\infty$, $\sigma = a - i\infty$ and when $\omega = \infty$, $\sigma = a + i\infty$. Then we have the pair of equations

$$f(t) = \frac{1}{2\pi i} \int_{a-i\infty}^{a+i\infty} g(\sigma) e^{\sigma t}\, d\sigma$$

$$g(\sigma) = \int_0^\infty f(s) e^{-\sigma s}\, ds$$

These constitute a **Laplace transform pair.** * The function $g(\sigma)$ is known as the **Laplace transform** of $f(t)$. The integral for $f(t)$ is known as the **complex inversion integral.**

We have thus naturally and inevitably encountered the Laplace transformation through our attempt to supply the unilateral Fourier transformation with a "built-in" convergence factor. This transformation is the foundation of the modern form of the **operational calculus,** which was originated in quite another form by the English electrical engineer Oliver Heaviside around 1890. In the next chapter we shall develop an extensive list of formulas for the use of the Laplace transform itself, although the meaning and use of the inversion integral we must leave to the chapters on complex variable theory.

* Named after Pierre Simon de Laplace (1749–1827), one of the greatest mathematicians of all time, who used such transforms in his researches in the theory of probability.

CHAPTER 6

THE LAPLACE TRANSFORMATION

6.1 Introduction. In the last chapter we traced the evolution of the Laplace transformation from the unilateral Fourier integral. Our development there made it clear that for the Laplace transform of $f(t)$ to exist, and for $f(t)$ to be recoverable from its transform, it is sufficient (a) that in every finite interval $f(t)$ should satisfy the Dirichlet conditions and (b) that there should exist a value a such that the integral from 0 to ∞ of the product

$$|e^{-at}f(t)| = e^{-at}|f(t)|$$

should exist. Essentially equivalent to these requirements are the more usual conditions (a) that $f(t)$ should be at least piecewise continuous (see the Glossary, Sec. A.7) over every finite interval $0 \leqq t_1 \leqq t \leqq t_2$ and (b) that $f(t)$ should be of **exponential order,** *i.e.,* that there should exist a constant a such that the product

$$e^{-at}|f(t)|$$

is bounded for all values of t greater than some finite number T.

With a function $f(t)$ satisfying either of these sets of conditions, the Laplace transformation associates a function of s which we shall denote by $\mathcal{L}[f(t)]$ or, where no confusion can result, simply by $\mathcal{L}(f)$ and which is given by the formula

$$(1) \qquad \mathcal{L}(f) = \int_0^\infty f(t)e^{-st}\,dt$$

The function $f(t)$ whose transform is a given function of s, say $\phi(s)$, we shall call the **inverse** of $\phi(s)$, and shall denote by $\mathcal{L}^{-1}(\phi)$. From the concluding discussion of the last chapter we know that the function having $\phi(s)$ for its transform is given by the complex inversion integral

$$(2) \qquad f(t) = \frac{1}{2\pi i}\int_{a-i\infty}^{a+i\infty} \phi(s)e^{st}\,ds$$

However, we shall make no use of this fact in the present chapter.

In succeeding paragraphs we shall find that many relatively complicated operations upon $f(t)$, such as differentiation and integration for

150

instance, can be replaced by simple algebraic operations, such as multiplication or division by s, upon the transform $\mathcal{L}(f)$. This is analogous to the way in which such operations as multiplication and division of numbers are replaced by the simpler processes of addition and subtraction when we work not with the numbers themselves but with their logarithms. Our primary task in this chapter is to develop tables of transforms which can be used, like tables of logarithms, for facilitating the manipulation of functions, and by means of which we can recover the proper function of t from its Laplace transform at the end of a problem.

6.2 The General Method. The utility of the Laplace transformation is based primarily upon the following four theorems.

Theorem 1. The Laplace transform of a sum is the sum of the transforms of the individual terms.

Proof. By definition

$$\mathcal{L}(f + g) = \int_0^\infty (f + g)e^{-st}\, dt$$
$$= \int_0^\infty fe^{-st}\, dt + \int_0^\infty ge^{-st}\, dt$$
$$= \mathcal{L}(f) + \mathcal{L}(g)$$

Q.E.D.

Theorem 2. The Laplace transform of a constant times a function is the constant times the transform of the function.

Proof. By definition

$$\mathcal{L}(cf) = \int_0^\infty (cf)e^{-st}\, dt$$
$$= c \int_0^\infty fe^{-st}\, dt$$
$$= c\mathcal{L}(f)$$

The properties guaranteed by Theorems 1 and 2 are the definitive properties of a **linear operator.**

Theorem 3. If $f(t)$ is a function of exponential order which is continuous and whose derivative is at least piecewise continuous over every finite interval $0 \le t_1 \le t \le t_2$, and if $f(t)$ approaches the value $f(0^+)$* as t approaches zero from the right, then the Laplace transform of the derivative of $f(t)$ is given by the formula

$$\mathcal{L}(f') = s\mathcal{L}(f) - f(0^+)$$

Proof. By definition

$$\mathcal{L}(f') = \int_0^\infty f'e^{-st}\, dt$$

---

* If $f(t)$ is continuous at the origin, $f(0^+)$ is just the (unique) value of the function at that point, $f(0)$.

If we use integration by parts on this integral, choosing

$$u = e^{-st}, \qquad\qquad dv = f' \, dt$$
$$du = -se^{-st} \, dt, \qquad v = f$$

we have

$$\mathcal{L}(f') = \left[e^{-st} f \right]_0^\infty + s \int_0^\infty f e^{-st} \, dt$$

From the hypothesis that $f(t)$ is of exponential order, it is clear that the integrated portion of the last expression vanishes at the upper limit, leaving

$$\mathcal{L}(f') = -f(0^+) + s \int_0^\infty f e^{-st} \, dt$$
$$= s\mathcal{L}(f) - f(0^+)$$

If $f'(t)$ is not everywhere continuous, the range of integration $(0, \infty)$ in the original integral must be broken up to correspond to the discontinuities of $f'(t)$. Since $f(t)$ is assumed to be everywhere continuous, the final result is exactly the same, however.

Q.E.D.

Corollary. If both $f(t)$ and $f'(t)$ are of exponential order and continuous for $0 \leq t$, and if $f''(t)$ is at least piecewise continuous over every finite interval $0 \leq t_1 \leq t \leq t_2$, then

$$\mathcal{L}(f'') = s^2 \mathcal{L}(f) - sf(0^+) - f'(0^+)$$

where $f(0^+)$ and $f'(0^+)$ are the values which $f(t)$ and $f'(t)$ approach, respectively, as t approaches 0 from the right.

Proof. By Theorem 3 we can write

$$\mathcal{L}(f'') = \mathcal{L}[(f')'] = s\mathcal{L}(f') - f'(0^+)$$
$$= s[s\mathcal{L}(f) - f(0^+)] - f'(0^+)$$
$$= s^2\mathcal{L}(f) - sf(0^+) - f'(0^+)$$

Q.E.D.

If the transform of a function contains the factor s, it is frequently useful to employ Theorem 3 in reverse in finding the function itself. Thus if

$$\mathcal{L}(F) = s\phi(s)$$

and if $f(t)$ is a function such that

$$\mathcal{L}(f) = \phi(s) \qquad \text{and} \qquad f(0^+) = 0$$

then, by Theorem 3,

$$\mathcal{L}(f') = s\mathcal{L}(f) - f(0^+) = s\mathcal{L}(f) = s\phi(s) = \mathcal{L}(F)$$

Hence*

$$F(t) = f'(t)$$

Realizing this, we can, if it appears convenient, suppress the factor s, determine the inverse of $\phi(s)$, namely, $f(t)$, and then differentiate $f(t)$ to find the required function $F(t)$. Likewise if a transform contains the factor s^k we may find its inverse by suppressing s^k, determining the inverse of what remains, and then differentiating this function k times with respect to t.

Theorem 4. If $f(t)$ is of exponential order and at least piecewise continuous, then the Laplace transform of $\int_a^t f(t)dt$ is given by the formula

$$\mathcal{L}\left[\int_a^t f(t)dt\right] = \frac{1}{s}\mathcal{L}(f) + \frac{1}{s}\int_a^0 f(t)dt$$

Proof. By definition

$$\mathcal{L}\left[\int_a^t f(t)dt\right] = \int_0^\infty \left[\int_a^t f(t)dt\right]e^{-st}\,dt$$

If we integrate this by parts, letting

$$u = \int_a^t f(t)dt, \qquad dv = e^{-st}\,dt$$

$$du = f(t)dt, \qquad v = \frac{e^{-st}}{-s}$$

we have

$$\mathcal{L}\left[\int_a^t f(t)dt\right] = \left[\frac{e^{-st}}{-s}\int_a^t f(t)dt\right]_0^\infty + \frac{1}{s}\int_0^\infty f(t)e^{-st}\,dt$$

As an immediate consequence of the fact that $f(t)$ is of exponential order it is clear that the integrated portion of the last expression vanishes at the upper limit. Hence we have simply

$$\mathcal{L}\left[\int_a^t f(t)dt\right] = \frac{1}{s}\int_a^0 f(t)dt + \frac{1}{s}\int_0^\infty f(t)e^{-st}\,dt$$

$$= \frac{1}{s}\mathcal{L}(f) + \frac{1}{s}\int_a^0 f(t)dt$$

Q.E.D.

* This of course assumes the "obvious" theorem that if two functions have the same transform they are identical. This is strictly true if the functions are continuous. If discontinuities are permitted, the most we can say is that two functions with the same transform cannot differ over any interval of positive length, although they may differ at various isolated points. A detailed discussion of this result (Lerch's theorem) would take us too far afield.

Theorem 4, like Theorem 3, is also useful in finding the inverses of transforms.   Thus if

$$\mathcal{L}(F) = \frac{1}{s}\,\phi(s)$$

and if $f(t)$ is a function such that

$$\mathcal{L}(f) = \phi(s)$$

then by Theorem 4

$$\mathcal{L}\left[\int_0^t f(t)dt\right] = \frac{1}{s}\,\mathcal{L}(f) = \frac{1}{s}\,\phi(s) = \mathcal{L}(F)$$

Therefore

$$F(t) = \int_0^t f(t)dt$$

In other words we may, if we choose, neglect the factor $1/s$ in a transform, determine the inverse $f(t)$ of what remains, and then integrate $f(t)$ from 0 to t to find the required function $F(t)$.   In the same way, the factor $1/s^k$ can be neglected in a transform, provided that the inverse of the remaining portion be integrated k times from 0 to t.

Although we need many more formulas before the Laplace transformation can be applied effectively to specific problems, Theorems 1 to 4 allow us to outline all the essential steps in the usual application of this method to the solution of differential equations.   Suppose that we have given the equation

$$ay'' + by' + cy = f(t)$$

If we take the Laplace transform of both sides, we have

$$\mathcal{L}(ay'' + by' + cy) = \mathcal{L}(f)$$

By Theorem 1 this can be written

$$\mathcal{L}(ay'') + \mathcal{L}(by') + \mathcal{L}(cy) = \mathcal{L}(f)$$

Then, by Theorem 2, we have

$$a\mathcal{L}(y'') + b\mathcal{L}(y') + c\mathcal{L}(y) = \mathcal{L}(f)$$

Now applying Theorem 3 and its corollary to the first two terms on the left, we have

$$a[s^2\mathcal{L}(y) - sy_0 - y_0'] + b[s\mathcal{L}(y) - y_0] + c\mathcal{L}(y) = \mathcal{L}(f)$$

where y_0 and y_0' are the given initial values of y and y'.   Collecting terms on $\mathcal{L}(y)$ and transposing all other terms to the right member of the equation, we find that

$$(as^2 + bs + c)\mathcal{L}(y) = \mathcal{L}(f) + (as + b)y_0 + ay_0'$$

and finally

$$\mathcal{L}(y) = \frac{\mathcal{L}(f) + (as + b)y_0 + ay_0'}{as^2 + bs + c}$$

Now $f(t)$ is a given function of t; hence its Laplace transform is a perfectly definite function of s (although we have as yet no formulas for finding it). Moreover, y_0 and y_0' are definite numbers, known from the data of the problem, and thus the transform of y is a completely known function of s. If, then, we had available a table of transforms, we could find in it the function y having the right-hand side of the last equation for its transform, *and this function would be the solution to our problem, initial conditions and all.*

This brief discussion illustrates the two great advantages of the Laplace transformation in solving differential equations: first, the way in which it reduces the problem to one in algebra; second, the automatic way in which it takes care of initial conditions without the necessity of constructing a general solution and then specializing the arbitrary constants which it contains. Clearly, our immediate task is to implement this process by establishing an adequate table of transforms.

EXERCISES

1. Which of the following functions are of exponential order?

    (a) t^n (b) e^{3t}

    (c) $\cosh^2 t$ (d) $\dfrac{1}{t}$

                (e) e^{t^2}

2. If a function is of exponential order and is piecewise continuous for $0 \leqq t$, show that its integral from 0 to t is also of exponential order. Explain how this result was used implicitly in the proof of Theorem 4.

3. Show that the derivative of a function of exponential order is not necessarily of exponential order. (Hint: Construct a counterexample.)

4. What is the Laplace transform of $\dfrac{d^3y}{dt^3}$? of $\dfrac{d^ny}{dt^n}$?

5. What is the Laplace transform of $\displaystyle\int_0^t \int_0^t f(t)dt\, dt$?

6. Show that $\mathcal{L}[f(at)]$ is equal to $\dfrac{1}{a} \mathcal{L}[f(t)]\Big|_{s \to \frac{s}{a}}$

6.3 The Transforms of Special Functions. Among all the functions whose transforms we might now think of tabulating, the most important are the simple ones

$$e^{-at},\ \cos bt,\ \sin bt,\ t^n,\ \text{and}\ u(t) \equiv \begin{cases} 0, & t < 0 \\ 1, & t > 0 \end{cases}$$

Once we know the transforms of these functions, nearly all the formulas we shall need can be obtained through the use of a few additional general theorems. The specific results are the following.

Formula 1. $\mathcal{L}(e^{-at}) = \dfrac{1}{s + a}$

Formula 2. $\mathcal{L}(\cos bt) = \dfrac{s}{s^2 + b^2}$

Formula 3. $\mathcal{L}(\sin bt) = \dfrac{b}{s^2 + b^2}$

Formula 4. $\mathcal{L}(t^n) = \begin{cases} \dfrac{\Gamma(n + 1)}{s^{(n+1)}}, & n \text{ a general positive number} \\[2ex] \dfrac{n!}{s^{(n+1)}}, & n \text{ a positive integer} \end{cases}$

Formula 5. $\mathcal{L}[u(t)] = \dfrac{1}{s}$

To prove Formula 1, we have simply

$$\begin{aligned} \mathcal{L}(e^{-at}) &= \int_0^\infty e^{-at}e^{-st}\,dt = \int_0^\infty e^{-(s+a)t}\,dt \\ &= \frac{e^{-(s+a)t}}{-(s + a)}\bigg|_0^\infty \\ &= \frac{1}{s + a} \end{aligned}$$

To prove Formula 2, we have

$$\begin{aligned} \mathcal{L}(\cos bt) &= \int_0^\infty (\cos bt)e^{-st}\,dt \\ &= \frac{e^{-st}}{s^2 + b^2}(-s\cos bt + b\sin bt)\bigg|_0^\infty \\ &= \frac{s}{s^2 + b^2} \end{aligned}$$

To prove Formula 3, we have

$$\begin{aligned} \mathcal{L}(\sin bt) &= \int_0^\infty (\sin bt)e^{-st}\,dt \\ &= \frac{e^{-st}}{s^2 + b^2}(-s\sin bt - b\cos bt)\bigg|_0^\infty \\ &= \frac{b}{s^2 + b^2} \end{aligned}$$

To prove Formula 4, we have

$$\mathcal{L}(t^n) = \int_0^\infty t^n e^{-st}\,dt$$

If n is a small positive integer, it is entirely practical to integrate this by parts. However, for all other cases it is either necessary, or at least convenient, to reduce the integral to the standard integral for the gamma function (Sec. A.6) by the substitution

$$st = z, \qquad dt = \frac{dz}{s}$$

Then

$$
\begin{aligned}
\mathcal{L}(t^n) &= \int_0^\infty \left(\frac{z}{s}\right)^n e^{-z} \frac{dz}{s} \\
&= \frac{1}{s^{(n+1)}} \int_0^\infty z^{(n+1)-1} e^{-z}\, dz \\
&= \frac{1}{s^{(n+1)}} \Gamma(n+1)
\end{aligned}
$$

Since $\Gamma(n+1) = n!$ when n is a positive integer, this establishes the second part of the formula also.

Formula 5 can be obtained immediately by taking $n = 0$ in Formula 4, or we can write

$$\mathcal{L}[u(t)] = \int_0^\infty 1 \cdot e^{-st}\, dt = \frac{e^{-st}}{-s}\Big|_0^\infty = \frac{1}{s}$$

Example 1

What is the Laplace transform of cosh bt?

Since $\cosh bt = \dfrac{e^{bt} + e^{-bt}}{2}$, we have

$$
\begin{aligned}
\mathcal{L}(\cosh bt) &= \mathcal{L}\left(\frac{e^{bt} + e^{-bt}}{2}\right) = \frac{1}{2}\mathcal{L}(e^{bt}) + \frac{1}{2}\mathcal{L}(e^{-bt}) \\
&= \frac{1}{2}\left(\frac{1}{s-b} + \frac{1}{s+b}\right) \\
&= \frac{s}{s^2 - b^2}
\end{aligned}
$$

The analogy with Formula 2, for the transform of cos bt, is apparent.

Example 2

If $\mathcal{L}(y) = \dfrac{1}{s(s+1)(s+2)}$, what is y?

None of our formulas yields a transform resembling this one. However, using the method of partial fractions, we can write

$$\frac{1}{s(s+1)(s+2)} = \frac{A}{s} + \frac{B}{s+1} + \frac{C}{s+2} = \frac{A(s+1)(s+2) + Bs(s+2) + Cs(s+1)}{s(s+1)(s+2)}$$

For this to be an identity we must have

$$1 = A(s+1)(s+2) + Bs(s+2) + Cs(s+1)$$

Setting $s = 0$, $s = -1$, and $s = -2$ in turn, we find from this that

$$A = \tfrac{1}{2}, \qquad B = -1, \qquad C = \tfrac{1}{2}$$

Hence

$$\mathcal{L}(y) = \frac{1}{2}\left(\frac{1}{s} - \frac{2}{s+1} + \frac{1}{s+2}\right)$$

Now Formulas 1 and 5 are applicable to the individual terms, giving

$$y = \tfrac{1}{2}u(t) - e^{-t} + \tfrac{1}{2}e^{-2t} = \tfrac{1}{2} - e^{-t} + \tfrac{1}{2}e^{-2t} \qquad t > 0$$

On the other hand, we could have suppressed the factor $1/s$ in $\mathcal{L}(y)$, leaving

$$\frac{1}{(s+1)(s+2)} \equiv \frac{1}{s+1} - \frac{1}{s+2}$$

By Formula 1 the inverse of this is

$$e^{-t} - e^{-2t}$$

Finally, having suppressed $1/s$, we must, as we pointed out in connection with Theorem 4, integrate from 0 to t to obtain y:

$$y = \int_0^t (e^{-t} - e^{-2t})dt = \left[-e^{-t} - \frac{e^{-2t}}{-2}\right]_0^t = \frac{1}{2} - e^{-t} + \frac{1}{2}e^{-2t}$$

as before.

Example 3

Solve for y from the simultaneous equations

$$y' + y + 3\int_0^t z\,dt = \cos t + 3\sin t$$
$$2y' + 3z' + 6z = 0$$

if $y_0 = -3$ and $z_0 = 2$.

We begin by taking the Laplace transform of each equation:

$$\mathcal{L}(y') + \mathcal{L}(y) + 3\mathcal{L}\left(\int_0^t z\,dt\right) = \mathcal{L}(\cos t) + 3\mathcal{L}(\sin t)$$
$$2\mathcal{L}(y') + 3\mathcal{L}(z') + 6\mathcal{L}(z) = 0$$

Using Theorems 3 and 4, and Formulas 2 and 3, this becomes

$$[s\mathcal{L}(y) + 3] + \mathcal{L}(y) + \frac{3}{s}\mathcal{L}(z) = \frac{s}{s^2+1} + \frac{3}{s^2+1}$$
$$2[s\mathcal{L}(y) + 3] + 3[s\mathcal{L}(z) - 2] + 6\mathcal{L}(z) = 0$$

Collecting terms and transposing, we obtain

$$(s+1)\mathcal{L}(y) + \frac{3}{s}\mathcal{L}(z) = \frac{s+3}{s^2+1} - 3$$
$$2s\mathcal{L}(y) + 3(s+2)\mathcal{L}(z) = 0$$

Since it is y which we want, we first solve these (algebraic) equations for $\mathcal{L}(y)$, getting

$$\mathcal{L}(y) = \frac{\begin{vmatrix} \left(\dfrac{s+3}{s^2+1} - 3\right) & \dfrac{3}{s} \\[2mm] 0 & 3(s+2) \end{vmatrix}}{\begin{vmatrix} s+1 & \dfrac{3}{s} \\[2mm] 2s & 3(s+2) \end{vmatrix}} = \frac{\left(\dfrac{s+3}{s^2+1} - 3\right) 3(s+2)}{3s(s+3)}$$

$$= \frac{s+2}{s(s^2+1)} - 3\left[\frac{s+2}{s(s+3)}\right]$$

Applying the method of partial fractions to this expression, we have

$$\mathcal{L}(y) = \left(\frac{2}{s} + \frac{-2s+1}{s^2+1}\right) - \left(\frac{1}{s+3} + \frac{2}{s}\right)$$

$$= -2\left(\frac{s}{s^2+1}\right) + \frac{1}{s^2+1} - \frac{1}{s+3}$$

Finally, writing the inverse of each of these terms, we have

$$y = -2\cos t + \sin t - e^{-3t} \qquad t > 0$$

6.4 Further General Theorems. One of the most useful properties of the Laplace transformation is embodied in the following theorem.

Theorem 1. $\mathcal{L}[e^{-at}f(t)] = \mathcal{L}[f(t)]\Big|_{s \to s+a}$

Proof. By definition

$$\mathcal{L}[e^{-at}f(t)] = \int_0^\infty [e^{-at}f(t)]e^{-st}\,dt$$

$$= \int_0^\infty f(t)e^{-(s+a)t}\,dt$$

and this is in structure exactly the Laplace transform of $f(t)$ itself except that $(s + a)$ takes the place of s.

Q.E.D.

In words, this theorem says that the transform of e^{-at} times a function of t is equal to the transform of the function, with s replaced by $(s + a)$. In the reverse sense, this theorem tells us that if we replace $(s + a)$ by s, that is, if we replace s by $(s - a)$, then the inverse of this modified function must be multiplied by e^{-at} in order to obtain the inverse of the original transform. By means of this theorem we can easily establish the following important formulas.

Formula 1. $\mathcal{L}(e^{-at}\cos bt) = \dfrac{s+a}{(s+a)^2 + b^2}$

Formula 2. $\mathcal{L}(e^{-at}\sin bt) = \dfrac{b}{(s+a)^2 + b^2}$

Formula 3. $\mathcal{L}(e^{-at}t^n) = \dfrac{\Gamma(n+1)}{(s+a)^{(n+1)}}$ n a general positive number

$\qquad\qquad\qquad\quad = \dfrac{n!}{(s+a)^{(n+1)}}$ n a positive integer

Example 1

If $\mathcal{L}(y) = \dfrac{s}{(s-3)^5}$, what is y?

In this case let us first suppress the factor s, leaving $\dfrac{1}{(s-3)^5}$. By Formula 3 the inverse of this is

$$\frac{t^4 e^{3t}}{4!}$$

Since we neglected the factor s, we must differentiate this function in order to obtain the proper expression for y. Hence

$$y = \frac{d}{dt}\left(\frac{t^4 e^{3t}}{4!}\right) = \frac{4t^3 e^{3t} + 3t^4 e^{3t}}{24}$$

Example 2

What is the solution of the equation $y'' + 2y' + y = e^{-t}$, for which $y(0) = 0$ and $y'(0) = 1$?

Transforming both sides of the given equation, we have

$$[s^2\mathcal{L}(y) - 1] + 2[s\mathcal{L}(y)] + \mathcal{L}(y) = \frac{1}{s+1}$$

$$(s^2 + 2s + 1)\mathcal{L}(y) = \frac{1}{s+1} + 1$$

$$\mathcal{L}(y) = \frac{1}{(s+1)^3} + \frac{1}{(s+1)^2}$$

Applying Formula 3 to each of these terms, we have at once

$$y = \frac{t^2 e^{-t} + 2t e^{-t}}{2}$$

In this example the characteristic equation of the differential equation has repeated roots, and moreover the term on the right-hand side is a part of the complementary function; yet neither of these features requires any special treatment in the operational solution of the problem. This is another of the many advantages of the Laplace transform method of solving differential equations.

In some problems a system is acted upon by a disturbance which begins not at $t = 0$ but at some later time, say $t = a$. The analytical representation of such functions and the nature of their Laplace transforms is therefore a matter of some importance. To illustrate, suppose that we wish an expression describing the function shown in Fig. 6.1a, the curve being congruent to the right half of the parabola $y = t^2$, shown

in Fig. 6.1b. It is not enough to recall from analytic geometry the
formula for the translation of axes and write

$$f(t) = (t - a)^2$$

because this equation (even with the usual reservation that $t > 0$)
defines the curve shown in Fig. 6.1c and not the required graph. However, if we take the unit step function and translate it a units to the right

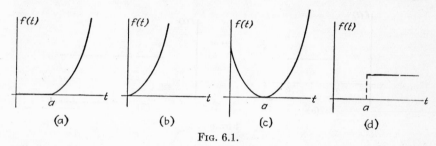

FIG. 6.1.

by writing $u(t - a)$, we obtain the function shown in Fig. 6.1d. Since
this vanishes for $t < a$ and is equal to 1 for $t > a$, the product

$$(t - a)^2 u(t - a)$$

will define precisely the arc we want. More generally, the expression

$$f(t - a)u(t - a)$$

represents the function obtained by translating $f(t)$ a units to the right
and "cutting it off," i.e., making it vanish identically, to the left of a.
The transforms of such functions are given by the following theorem.

Theorem 2. $\mathcal{L}[f(t - a)u(t - a)] = e^{-as}\mathcal{L}[f(t)]$ $a \geq 0$

Proof.   By definition

$$\mathcal{L}[f(t - a)u(t - a)] = \int_0^\infty [f(t - a)u(t - a)]e^{-st}\,dt$$

$$= \int_a^\infty f(t - a)e^{-st}\,dt$$

since the integration effectively commences not at $t = 0$ but at $t = a$,
because $f(t - a)u(t - a)$ vanishes identically to the left of this point.
Now let

$$t - a = \tau, \qquad dt = d\tau$$

Then the last integral becomes

$$\int_0^\infty f(\tau)e^{-s(\tau+a)}\,d\tau = e^{-as}\int_0^\infty f(\tau)e^{-s\tau}\,d\tau$$

$$= e^{-as}\mathcal{L}(f)$$

Q.E.D.

As a result to be used in finding inverses, this theorem asserts that suppressing the factor e^{-as} in a transform requires that the inverse of what remains be translated a units to the right and cut off to the left of the point $t = a$.

Example 3

What is the equation of the function shown in Fig. 6.2a?

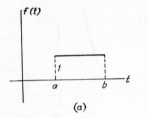
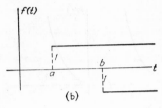

FIG. 6.2.

Clearly, we can regard this function as the sum of the two functions shown in Fig. 6.2b, that is, as

$$u(t - a) - u(t - b)$$

Example 4

What is the equation of the function shown in Fig. 6.3?

To obtain the segment of this function between 1 and 2, we must multiply the expression $(t - 1)$ by a factor which will equal zero to the left of 1, unity between 1 and 2, and zero to the right of 2.   By Example 3 such a function is

$$u(t - 1) - u(t - 2)$$

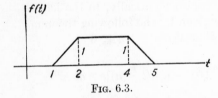

FIG. 6.3.

Hence

$$(t - 1)[u(t - 1) - u(t - 2)]$$

defines the given function between 1 and 2 and vanishes elsewhere.   Similarly

$$u(t - 2) - u(t - 4)$$

defines the given function between 2 and 4 and vanishes elsewhere, and

$$(5 - t)[u(t - 4) - u(t - 5)]$$

defines the given function between 4 and 5 and vanishes elsewhere.   The complete representation of the function is therefore the sum of the last three expressions

$$(t - 1)[u(t - 1) - u(t - 2)] + [u(t - 2) - u(t - 4)] + (5 - t)[u(t - 4) - u(t - 5)]$$
$$= (t - 1)u(t - 1) - (t - 2)u(t - 2) - (t - 4)u(t - 4) + (t - 5)u(t - 5)$$

Example 5

What is the transform of the function shown in **Fig. 6.4?**
The equation of the function is obviously

$$f(t) = -(t - 1)(t - 2)[u(t - 1) - u(t - 2)]$$

However, we cannot apply Theorem 2 until the individual terms in $f(t)$ appear as functions of a single binomial argument $(t - a)$.   Hence we write

$$f(t) = -(t - 1)(\overline{t - 1} - 1)u(t - 1) + (\overline{t - 2} + 1)(t - 2)u(t - 2)$$
$$= -[(t - 1)^2 - (t - 1)]u(t - 1) + [(t - 2)^2 + (t - 2)]u(t - 2)$$

Now Theorem 2 can be applied, and we find

$$\mathcal{L}(f) = -\left(\frac{2}{s^3} - \frac{1}{s^2}\right)e^{-s} + \left(\frac{2}{s^3} + \frac{1}{s^2}\right)e^{-2s}$$

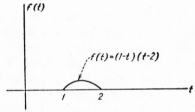

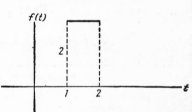

FIG. 6.4.   FIG. 6.5.

Example 6

Find the solution of the equation $y' + 3y + 2 \int_0^t y\, dt = f(t)$ for which $y(0) = 1$, if $f(t)$ is the function shown in Fig. 6.5.

In this case, $f(t) = 2u(t - 1) - 2u(t - 2)$, and thus the differential equation can be written

$$y' + 3y + 2 \int_0^t y\, dt = 2u(t - 1) - 2u(t - 2)$$

Taking transforms, we have

$$[s\mathcal{L}(y) - 1] + 3\mathcal{L}(y) + \frac{2}{s}\mathcal{L}(y) = \frac{2e^{-s}}{s} - \frac{2e^{-2s}}{s}$$

or

$$(s^2 + 3s + 2)\mathcal{L}(y) = 2e^{-s} - 2e^{-2s} + s$$

and

$$\mathcal{L}(y) = \frac{s}{(s + 1)(s + 2)} + \frac{2e^{-s}}{(s + 1)(s + 2)} - \frac{2e^{-2s}}{(s + 1)(s + 2)}$$

The first term can be written

$$\frac{2}{s + 2} - \frac{1}{s + 1}$$

Hence its inverse is

$$2e^{-2t} - e^{-t}$$

If the exponential factors are suppressed in the second and third terms of $\mathcal{L}(y)$, the algebraic portion which remains can be written

$$2\left(\frac{1}{s+1} - \frac{1}{s+2}\right)$$

The inverse of this is

$$2e^{-t} - 2e^{-2t}$$

However, because the factors e^{-s} and e^{-2s} were neglected, it is necessary to take the last expression, translate it one unit to the right and cut it off to the left of $t = 1$, and also translate it two units to the right and cut it off to the left of $t = 2$, in order to obtain the inverses of the original terms. This gives for y

$$y = [2e^{-2t} - e^{-t}] + 2[e^{-(t-1)} - e^{-2(t-1)}]$$
$$\cdot u(t - 1) - 2[e^{-(t-2)} - e^{-2(t-2)}]u(t - 2)$$

Plots of these three terms, as well as of their sum, that is, y itself, are shown in Fig. 6.6.

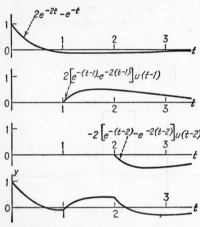

We have already made repeated use of Theorems 3 and 4 of Sec. 6.2 on the transforms of derivatives and integrals. On the other hand, it is sometimes convenient or necessary to consider the derivatives and integrals of transforms. The basis for this is contained in the next two theorems.

FIG. 6.6. Plot showing the solution of Example 6.

Theorem 3. If $\mathcal{L}[f(t)] = \phi(s)$, then $\mathcal{L}[tf(t)] = -\phi'(s)$ or equally well, if $\mathcal{L}^{-1}[\phi(s)] = f(t)$, then $\mathcal{L}^{-1}[\phi'(s)] = -tf(t)$.

Proof. By hypothesis

$$\phi(s) = \mathcal{L}(f) = \int_0^\infty f(t)e^{-st}\,dt$$

Differentiating this with respect to s,* we obtain

$$\phi'(s) = \int_0^\infty f(t)[-te^{-st}]\,dt$$
$$= \int_0^\infty [-tf(t)]e^{-st}\,dt$$
$$= \mathcal{L}[-tf(t)]$$

which is just another way of writing either

$$\mathcal{L}[tf(t)] = -\phi'(s) \equiv -\frac{d\mathcal{L}(f)}{ds}$$

* See Sec. A.2 for Leibnitz' rule for differentiating a definite integral with respect to a parameter.

or
$$\mathcal{L}^{-1}[\phi'(s)] = -tf(t)$$

Q.E.D.

The extension to repeated differentiation of the transform is obvious.

Theorem 4.   If $\mathcal{L}[f(t)] = \phi(s)$ and if $f(t)/t$ has a limit as $t \to 0^+$, then

$$\mathcal{L}\left[\frac{f(t)}{t}\right] = \int_s^\infty \phi(s)ds$$

or equally well, if

$$\mathcal{L}^{-1}[\phi(s)] = f(t) \qquad \text{then} \qquad \mathcal{L}^{-1}\left[\int_s^\infty \phi(s)ds\right] = \frac{f(t)}{t}$$

Proof.   By hypothesis

$$\phi(s) = \mathcal{L}(f) = \int_0^\infty f(t)e^{-st}\,dt$$

If we integrate both sides of this equation from s to ∞, we obtain

$$\int_s^\infty \phi(s)ds = \int_s^\infty \left[\int_0^\infty f(t)e^{-st}\,dt\right]ds$$

But under the assumptions we have made about $f(t)$, the order of integration in the repeated integral can legitimately be reversed, giving

$$\int_s^\infty \phi(s)ds = \int_0^\infty \left[\int_s^\infty f(t)e^{-st}\,ds\right]dt$$

or, since t is independent of s,

$$\begin{aligned}
\int_s^\infty \phi(s)ds &= \int_0^\infty f(t)\left[\int_s^\infty e^{-st}\,ds\right]dt \\
&= \int_0^\infty f(t)\left[\frac{e^{-st}}{-t}\right]_s^\infty dt \\
&= \int_0^\infty \frac{f(t)}{t}\,e^{-st}\,dt \\
&= \mathcal{L}\left[\frac{f(t)}{t}\right]
\end{aligned}$$

Q.E.D.

The extension to repeated integration of the transform is obvious.

Example 7

What is $\mathcal{L}(t^2 \sin 2t)$?

By a repeated application of Theorem 3, we have

$$\mathcal{L}(t^2 \sin 2t) = (-1)^2 \frac{d^2 \mathcal{L}(\sin 2t)}{ds^2}$$

$$= \frac{d^2}{ds^2} \left(\frac{2}{s^2 + 4} \right)$$

$$= \frac{12s^2 - 16}{(s^2 + 4)^3} \quad \checkmark$$

Example 8

What is y if $\mathcal{L}(y) = \log \frac{s+1}{s-1}$?

By hypothesis

$$y = \mathcal{L}^{-1} \left(\log \frac{s+1}{s-1} \right)$$

Hence, using the second form of Theorem 3, we can write

$$-ty = \mathcal{L}^{-1} \left[\frac{d}{ds} \left(\log \frac{s+1}{s-1} \right) \right]$$

$$= \mathcal{L}^{-1} \left(\frac{1}{s+1} - \frac{1}{s-1} \right)$$

$$= e^{-t} - e^t$$

Therefore

$$y = \frac{e^t - e^{-t}}{t} = \frac{2 \sinh t}{t}$$

Example 9

What is $\mathcal{L} \left(\frac{\sin kt}{t} \right)$?

By Theorem 4, we have

$$\mathcal{L} \left(\frac{\sin kt}{t} \right) = \int_s^\infty \mathcal{L}(\sin kt) ds$$

$$= \int_s^\infty \frac{k}{s^2 + k^2} ds$$

$$= \tan^{-1} \frac{s}{k} \Big|_s^\infty$$

$$= \frac{\pi}{2} - \tan^{-1} \frac{s}{k}$$

$$= \cot^{-1} \frac{s}{k}$$

Example 10

If $\mathcal{L}(y) = \frac{s}{(s^2 - 1)^2}$, what is y?

By hypothesis

$$y = \mathcal{L}^{-1} \left[\frac{s}{(s^2 - 1)^2} \right]$$

Hence from the second form of Theorem 4 we have

$$\frac{y}{t} = \mathcal{L}^{-1}\left[\int_s^\infty \frac{s}{(s^2-1)^2}\,ds\right]$$

$$= \mathcal{L}^{-1}\left[\frac{-1}{2(s^2-1)}\Big|_s^\infty\right]$$

$$= \mathcal{L}^{-1}\left[\frac{1}{4}\left(\frac{1}{s-1}-\frac{1}{s+1}\right)\right]$$

$$= \frac{e^t - e^{-t}}{4}$$

Therefore

$$y = t\left(\frac{e^t - e^{-t}}{4}\right) = \frac{t \sinh t}{2}$$

EXERCISES

Find the Laplace transform of each of the following functions:

1. $\sinh 2t$

2. $\cos(at + b)$

3. $t^2 + 2t + 3$

4. te^{-5t}

5. $t \cos 2t$

6. $t^2 e^{-3t}$

7. $(t-1)^2 u(t-1)$

8. $\sin(t-2)$

9. $tu(t-1)$

10. $\sin(t-2)u(t-2)$

11. $(\cos t)(\cos 2t)$ (Hint: Convert the given product to a sum.)

12. $\sin^3 2t$ *Ans.* $\dfrac{3}{2}\left(\dfrac{1}{s^2+4} - \dfrac{1}{s^2+36}\right)$

13. $te^{-t}\sin t$ *Ans.* $\dfrac{2(s+1)}{(s^2+2s+2)^2}$

14. $\displaystyle\int_0^t \frac{\sin t}{t}\,dt$ *Ans.* $\dfrac{\cot^{-1}s}{s}$

15. $\dfrac{1 - e^t}{t}$ *Ans.* $\log\left(\dfrac{s-1}{s}\right)$

16. $(t^2-1)u(t-1)$ *Ans.* $\left(\dfrac{2}{s^3} + \dfrac{2}{s^2}\right)e^{-s}$

17. $t^2 u(t-3)$

18. $u(t-1)u(t-2)$

19. $t \cos^2 t$

20. $\dfrac{1 - \cos t}{t^2}$

21. $f(t) = \begin{cases} \sin t, & 0 < t < \pi \\ 0, & \pi < t < \infty \end{cases}$

22. $f(t) = \begin{cases} t, & 0 < t < 2 \\ 2, & 2 < t < \infty \end{cases}$

23.

24.

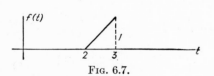

FIG. 6.7.

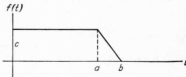

FIG. 6.8.

Find $f(t)$ if

25. $\mathcal{L}(f) = \dfrac{s}{(s+2)^2}$

26. $\mathcal{L}(f) = \dfrac{1}{(s+a)^5}$

27. $\mathcal{L}(f) = \dfrac{1}{s^2(s+1)}$

28. $\mathcal{L}(f) = \dfrac{cs+d}{(s+a)^2+b^2}$

29. $\mathcal{L}(f) = \dfrac{cs+d}{(s+a)^2-b^2}$

30. $\mathcal{L}(f) = \dfrac{1}{s}\tan^{-1}s$

Ans. $\left(\dfrac{t^2+4t+2}{2}\right)e^t$

31. $\mathcal{L}(f) = \dfrac{s^2}{(s-1)^3}$

Ans. $(1-\cos t)e^{-t}$

32. $\mathcal{L}(f) = \dfrac{1}{(s+1)(s^2+2s+2)}$

33. $\mathcal{L}(f) = \dfrac{e^{-2s}}{(s^2-4)}$

Ans. $\dfrac{e^{2(t-2)}-e^{-2(t-2)}}{4}u(t-2)$

34. $\mathcal{L}(f) = \log\dfrac{1-s^2}{s^2}$

Ans. $\dfrac{2-e^t-e^{-t}}{t}$

35. $\mathcal{L}(f) = s\log\dfrac{s-1}{s+1}+2$

Ans. $\dfrac{2(\sinh t - t\cosh t)}{t^2}$

36. $\mathcal{L}(f) = \dfrac{1+2s}{(s+2)^2(s-1)^2}$

Ans. $\dfrac{t(e^t-e^{-2t})}{3}$

37. $\mathcal{L}(f) = \dfrac{e^{-s}+2e^{-2s}}{(s+2)}$

38. $\mathcal{L}(f) = \log\dfrac{1+s}{s}$

39. $\mathcal{L}(f) = \log\dfrac{s+a}{s+b}$

40. $\mathcal{L}(f) = \log\dfrac{s^2+1}{s(s+1)}$

41. $\mathcal{L}(f) = \dfrac{e^{-2s}}{(s^2+9)}$

42. $\mathcal{L}(f) = \dfrac{s+2}{(s^2+4s+5)^2}$

Solve the following differential equations:

43. $\dfrac{d^2x}{dt^2}+4\dfrac{dx}{dt}+13x=2e^{-t} \qquad x_0=0,\,x_0'=-1$

Ans. $x = \dfrac{-e^{-2t}(\cos 3t + 2\sin 3t)+e^{-t}}{5}$

44. $\dfrac{dy}{dt}+2y+2\displaystyle\int_0^t y\,dt = u(t-a) \qquad y_0=-2$

Ans. $y = -2e^{-t}(\cos t - \sin t)+e^{-(t-a)}\sin(t-a)u(t-a)$

45. $\dfrac{d^2y}{dt^2}+2\dfrac{dy}{dt}+5y=u(t) \qquad y_0=-1,\,y_0'=0$

46. $\dfrac{dy}{dt}+4y+5\displaystyle\int_0^t y\,dt = e^{-t} \qquad y_0=0$

47. $\dfrac{dy}{dt}+2y+\displaystyle\int_0^t y\,dt = \cos t \qquad y_0=1$

48. $\dfrac{d^2y}{dt^2}+4\dfrac{dy}{dt}+3y=f(t) \qquad$ where $f(t)=\begin{cases}1, & 0<t<2 \\ 0, & 2<t<\infty\end{cases}$ and $y_0=y_0'=0$

49. $\dfrac{dx}{dt}-4x+3\displaystyle\int_0^t = f(t) \qquad$ where $f(t)=\begin{cases}0, & 0<t<2 \\ t-2, & 2<t<4 \\ 2, & 4<t<\infty\end{cases}$ and $x_0=1$

50. $\dfrac{dx}{dt}-4x-\dfrac{dy}{dt}+2y=0$

$$x_0=0,\,y_0=1$$

$2\dfrac{dx}{dt}+12x-8y = u(t-3)$

Ans. $y = \cos 2t + 3\sin 2t + \dfrac{1}{2}\left[-1+\cos 2(t-3)+\dfrac{\sin 2(t-3)}{2}\right]u(t-3)$

6.5 The Heaviside Expansion Theorems. The frequent use we have had to make of partial fractions indicates clearly the importance of this technique in operational calculus. It is therefore highly desirable to have the procedure systematized as much as possible. The following theorems, usually associated with the name of Heaviside, are of great utility in this connection.

Theorem 1. If $y = \mathcal{L}^{-1}\left[\dfrac{p(s)}{q(s)}\right]$, where $p(s)$ and $q(s)$ are polynomials, and the order of $q(s)$ is greater than the order of $p(s)$, then the term in y corresponding to an unrepeated linear factor $(s - a)$ of $q(s)$ is

$$\frac{p(a)}{q'(a)} e^{at} \qquad \text{or} \qquad \frac{p(a)}{Q(a)} e^{at}$$

where $Q(s)$ is the product of all the factors of $q(s)$ except $(s - a)$.

Proof. In the usual partial fraction breakdown of $p(s)/q(s)$, an unrepeated linear factor $(s - a)$ of $q(s)$ will have corresponding to it a fraction of the form

$$\frac{A}{s - a}$$

If we denote the sum of the fractions corresponding to all the other factors of $q(s)$ by $h(s)$, we can therefore write

$$\frac{p(s)}{q(s)} = \frac{A}{s - a} + h(s)$$

Multiplying this identity by $(s - a)$ gives

$$\frac{(s - a)p(s)}{q(s)} \equiv \frac{p(s)}{q(s)/(s - a)} = A + (s - a)h(s)$$

If we now let s approach a, the second term in the right member vanishes, and we have

$$A = \lim_{s \to a}\left[\frac{p(s)}{q(s)/(s - a)}\right]$$

The limit of the numerator here is evidently $p(a)$. The denominator appears as an indeterminate of the form $0/0$. However, if we evaluate it as usual by differentiating numerator and denominator and then letting s approach a, we obtain just $q'(a)$. Hence

$$A = \frac{p(a)}{q'(a)}$$

On the other hand, we could have eliminated the indeterminacy before passing to the limit simply by canceling $(s - a)$ into $q(s)$, which by hypothesis contains this factor. Doing this, we obtain the equivalent form of A

$$A = \frac{p(a)}{Q(a)}$$

Finally, taking inverses, it is clear that the term

$$\frac{A}{s-a}$$

gives rise to the term

$$Ae^{at} = \frac{p(a)}{q'(a)} e^{at} = \frac{p(a)}{Q(a)} e^{at}$$

in the inverse y.

Q.E.D.

If $q(s)$ contains only unrepeated linear factors, then by applying Theorem 1 to each factor we obtain the following important result.

Corollary. If $y = \mathcal{L}^{-1}\left[\dfrac{p(s)}{q(s)}\right]$ and if $q(s)$ is completely factorable into the unrepeated linear factors

$$(s - a_1), \qquad (s - a_2), \ldots, \qquad (s - a_n)$$

then

$$y = \sum_{i=1}^{n} \frac{p(a_i)}{q'(a_i)} e^{a_i t} = \sum_{i=1}^{n} \frac{p(a_i)}{Q(a_i)} e^{a_i t}$$

Theorem 2. If $y = \mathcal{L}^{-1}\left[\dfrac{p(s)}{q(s)}\right]$, where $p(s)$ and $q(s)$ are polynomials and the order of $q(s)$ is greater than the order of $p(s)$, then the terms in y corresponding to a repeated linear factor $(s - a)^r$ of $q(s)$ are

$$e^{at}\left[\frac{\phi^{(r-1)}(a)}{(r-1)!} + \frac{\phi^{(r-2)}(a)}{(r-2)!}\frac{t}{1!} + \cdots + \frac{\phi'(a)}{1!}\frac{t^{r-2}}{(r-2)!} + \phi(a)\frac{t^{r-1}}{(r-1)!}\right]$$

where $\phi(s)$ is the quotient of $p(s)$ and all the factors of $q(s)$ except $(s - a)^r$.

Proof. From the elementary theory of partial fractions, a repeated linear factor $(s - a)^r$ in $q(s)$ gives rise to the component fractions

$$\frac{A_1}{(s-a)} + \frac{A_2}{(s-a)^2} + \cdots + \frac{A_{r-1}}{(s-a)^{r-1}} + \frac{A_r}{(s-a)^r}$$

If we let $h(s)$ denote, as before, the sum of the fractions corresponding to all the other factors of $q(s)$, we have

$$\frac{p(s)}{q(s)} \equiv \frac{\phi(s)}{(s-a)^r} = \frac{A_1}{(s-a)} + \frac{A_2}{(s-a)^2}$$

$$+ \cdots + \frac{A_{r-1}}{(s-a)^{r-1}} + \frac{A_r}{(s-a)^r} + h(s)$$

Multiplying this identity by $(s - a)^r$ gives

$$\phi(s) = A_1(s - a)^{r-1} + A_2(s - a)^{r-2} + \cdots + A_{r-1}(s - a) + A_r$$
$$+ [(s - a)^r h(s)]$$

If we put $s = a$ in this expression, we obtain

$$A_r = \phi(a)$$

If we now differentiate $\phi(s)$, we have

$$\phi'(s) = A_1(r - 1)(s - a)^{r-2} + A_2(r - 2)(s - a)^{r-3} + \cdots + A_{r-1}$$
$$+ [r(s - a)^{r-1} h(s) + (s - a)^r h'(s)]$$

Again setting $s = a$, we find this time

$$A_{r-1} = \phi'(a)$$

Continuing in this fashion, and noting that the first $(r - 1)$ derivatives of the product $(s - a)^r h(s)$ will all vanish when $s = a$, we obtain successively

$$\phi''(a) = 2!A_{r-2}$$
$$\phi'''(a) = 3!A_{r-3}$$
$$\cdots \cdots \cdots \cdots$$
$$\phi^{(r-1)}(a) = (r - 1)!A_1$$

or

$$A_{r-k} = \frac{\phi^{(k)}(a)}{k!} \qquad k = 0, 1, \ldots (r - 1)$$

The terms in the expansion of $p(s)/q(s)$ which correspond to the factor $(s - a)^r$ are therefore

$$\frac{\phi^{(r-1)}(a)}{(r - 1)!} \frac{1}{(s - a)} + \frac{\phi^{(r-2)}(a)}{(r - 2)!} \frac{1}{(s - a)^2} + \cdots$$
$$+ \frac{\phi'(a)}{1!} \frac{1}{(s - a)^{r-1}} + \phi(a)\frac{1}{(s - a)^r}$$

Recalling that

$$\mathcal{L}^{-1}\left[\frac{1}{(s - a)^n}\right] = \frac{t^{n-1}e^{at}}{(n - 1)!}$$

it is evident that the terms in y which arise from these fractions are

$$\frac{\phi^{(r-1)}(a)}{(r - 1)!} e^{at} + \frac{\phi^{(r-2)}(a)}{(r - 2)!} \frac{te^{at}}{1!} + \cdots + \frac{\phi'(a)}{1!} \frac{t^{r-2}e^{at}}{(r - 2)!} + \phi(a) \frac{t^{r-1}e^{at}}{(r - 1)!}$$

If we factor out e^{at} we have precisely the assertion of the theorem.

Q.E.D.

Theorem 3. If $y = \mathcal{L}^{-1}\left[\dfrac{p(s)}{q(s)}\right]$, where $p(s)$ and $q(s)$ are polynomials and the order of $q(s)$ is greater than the order of $p(s)$, then the terms in y

corresponding to an unrepeated quadratic factor $[(s + a)^2 + b^2]$ of $q(s)$ are

$$\frac{e^{-at}}{b} (\phi_i \cos bt + \phi_r \sin bt)$$

where ϕ_r and ϕ_i are, respectively, the real and imaginary parts of

$$\phi(-a + ib)$$

and $\phi(s)$, as before, is the quotient of $p(s)$ and all the factors of $q(s)$ except $[(s + a)^2 + b^2]$.

Proof. An unrepeated quadratic factor $[(s + a)^2 + b^2]$ of $q(s)$ gives rise to a component fraction of the form

$$\frac{As + B}{(s + a)^2 + b^2}$$

in the partial fraction expansion of $p(s)/q(s)$. If we let $h(s)$ denote the fractions corresponding to all the other factors of $q(s)$, we can write

$$\frac{p(s)}{q(s)} \equiv \frac{\phi(s)}{(s + a)^2 + b^2} = \frac{As + B}{(s + a)^2 + b^2} + h(s)$$

Multiplying this identity by $(s + a)^2 + b^2$, we obtain

$$\phi(s) = As + B + [(s + a)^2 + b^2]h(s)$$

Now let $\underline{s = -a + ib}$. This value of course makes $[(s + a)^2 + b^2]$ vanish; hence the last product drops out, leaving

$$\phi(-a + ib) = (-a + ib)A + B$$

or, writing $\phi(-a + ib) = \phi_r + i\phi_i$,

$$\phi_r + i\phi_i = -aA + B + ibA$$

Equating real and imaginary terms in the last identity, we find

$$\phi_r = -aA + B, \qquad \phi_i = bA$$

or, solving for A and B,

$$A = \frac{\phi_i}{b}, \qquad B = \phi_r + \frac{a}{b}\phi_i = \frac{b\phi_r + a\phi_i}{b}$$

Thus the partial fraction which corresponds to the quadratic factor $[(s + a)^2 + b^2]$ is

$$\frac{As + B}{(s + a)^2 + b^2} = \frac{1}{b}\left[\frac{\phi_i s + (b\phi_r + a\phi_i)}{(s + a)^2 + b^2}\right]$$

$$= \frac{1}{b}\left[\frac{(s + a)\phi_i}{(s + a)^2 + b^2} + \frac{b\phi_r}{(s + a)^2 + b^2}\right]$$

The inverse of this expression is evidently

$$\frac{1}{b} \left[\phi_i e^{-at} \cos bt + \phi_r e^{-at} \sin bt \right]$$

Factoring out e^{-at} gives the assertion of the theorem.

Q.E.D.

There is a fourth theorem dealing with repeated quadratic factors but because of its complexity and limited usefulness we shall not develop it here.

Example 1

If $\mathcal{L}(f) = \dfrac{s^2 + 2}{s(s+1)(s+2)}$, what is $f(t)$?

The roots of the denominator are $s = 0$, $s = -1$, $s = -2$. Hence we must compute the values of

$$p(s) = s^2 + 2$$

and

$$q'(s) = 3s^2 + 6s + 2$$

for these values of s. These are

$$p(0) = 2, \qquad p(-1) = 3, \qquad p(-2) = 6$$
$$q'(0) = 2, \qquad q'(-1) = -1, \qquad q'(-2) = 2$$

From the corollary of Theorem 1 we now have at once

$$f(t) = \frac{2}{2} e^{0t} + \frac{3}{-1} e^{-t} + \frac{6}{2} e^{-2t} = 1 - 3e^{-t} + 3e^{-2t}$$

Example 2

If $\mathcal{L}(y) = \dfrac{s}{(s+2)^2(s^2 + 2s + 2)}$, what is y?

Considering first the repeated linear factor, we identify

$$\phi(s) = \frac{s}{(s^2 + 2s + 2)} \qquad \text{and} \qquad \phi'(s) = \frac{-s^2 + 2}{(s^2 + 2s + 2)^2}$$

Evaluating these for the root $s = -2$, we obtain

$$\phi(-2) = -1 \qquad \text{and} \qquad \phi'(-2) = -\tfrac{1}{2}$$

Hence, by Theorem 2, the terms in y corresponding to $(s+2)^2$ are

$$e^{-2t} \left(-\frac{1}{2} - t \right) = -\frac{(1 + 2t)e^{-2t}}{2}$$

For the quadratic factor

$$s^2 + 2s + 2 \equiv (s+1)^2 + 1^2$$

we have

$$\phi(s) = \frac{s}{(s+2)^2}$$

Hence

$$\phi(-a + ib) = \phi(-1 + i) = \frac{-1 + i}{[(-1 + i) + 2]^2}$$
$$= \frac{-1 + i}{(1 + i)^2}$$
$$= \frac{-1 + i}{2i}$$
$$= \frac{1}{2} + \frac{i}{2}$$

and thus

$$\phi_r = \phi_i = \frac{1}{2}$$

The term in y corresponding to the factor $(s^2 + 2s + 2)$ is therefore

$$\frac{e^{-t}(\cos t + \sin t)}{2}$$

Adding the two partial inverses, we have finally

$$y = -\frac{(1 + 2t)e^{-2t}}{2} + \frac{e^{-t}(\cos t + \sin t)}{2}$$

EXERCISES

Find the functions which have the following transforms:

1. $\dfrac{s + 1}{(s + 2)(s^2 + 4)}$ *Ans.* $f(t) = \dfrac{\cos 2t + 3 \sin 2t - e^{-2t}}{8}$

2. $\dfrac{s}{(s + 1)^2(s^2 + 1)}$ *Ans.* $f(t) = \dfrac{-te^{-t} + \sin t}{2}$

3. $\dfrac{s + 2}{(s^2 + 1)(s^2 + 4)}$ *Ans.* $f(t) = \dfrac{2 \cos t + 4 \sin t - 2 \cos 2t - 2 \sin 2t}{6}$

4. $\dfrac{s^2 + s + 1}{s^3 + 6s^2 + 11s + 6}$ 5. $\dfrac{s^3 - 1}{s^4 + 8s^3 + 19s^2 + 12s}$

Solve the following differential equations:

6. $y''' - 2y'' - y' + 2y = u(t - 2)$ $y_0 = y_0' = 0,\ y_0'' = 1$

    Ans. $y = \dfrac{e^{-t} - 3e^t + 2e^{2t}}{6} + \dfrac{u(t - 2)}{2} - \left[\dfrac{e^{-(t-2)} + 3e^{(t-2)} - e^{2(t-2)}}{6}\right] u(t - 2)$

7. $y^{iv} + 2y''' + 2y'' + 2y' + y = e^t$ $y_0 = y_0' = y_0'' = y_0''' = 0$

8. $x'' + 2x + \displaystyle\int_0^t y\, dt = t$

$$x_0 = 1,\ x_0' = -1$$

$x'' + 2x' + y = \sin 2t$

       Ans. $x = -\dfrac{7e^t}{5} + \dfrac{5 + t - t^2}{2} - \dfrac{2 \cos 2t + \sin 2t}{20}$

9. $(D^2 + D + 1)x + (D - 1)y = u(t)$

$$x_0 = x_0' = y_0 = 0,\ y_0' = 2$$

$(D^2 + 2D + 3)x + (3D^2 + 4D - 3)y = u(t - 1)$

10. $y' - 3z = 5$

   $y - z' - w = 3 - 2t$ $y_0 = 1, z_0 = 0, w_0 = -1$

   $z + w' = -1$

6.6 Transforms of Periodic Functions. The application of the Laplace transformation to the important case of general periodic functions is based upon the following theorem.

Theorem 1. If $f(t)$ is of period a, then $\mathcal{L}(f) = \dfrac{\displaystyle\int_0^a f(t)e^{-st}\,dt}{1 - e^{-as}}.$

Proof. By definition

$$\mathcal{L}(f) = \int_0^\infty f(t)e^{-st}\,dt$$

$$= \int_0^a f(t)e^{-st}\,dt + \int_a^{2a} f(t)e^{-st}\,dt + \int_{2a}^{3a} f(t)e^{-st}\,dt + \cdots$$

Now in the second integral let $t = \tau + a$, in the third integral let

$$t = \tau + 2a$$

and in general let $t = \tau + na$ in the $(n + 1)$st integral. In each case $dt = d\tau$, and the new limits become 0 and a, respectively. Then

$$\mathcal{L}(f) = \int_0^a f(\tau)e^{-s\tau}\,d\tau + \int_0^a f(\tau + a)e^{-s(\tau+a)}\,d\tau + \int_0^a f(\tau + 2a)e^{-s(\tau+2a)}\,d\tau$$

$$+ \cdots$$

$$= \int_0^a f(\tau)e^{-s\tau}\,d\tau + e^{-as}\int_0^a f(\tau + a)e^{-s\tau}\,d\tau + e^{-2as}\int_0^a f(\tau + 2a)e^{-s\tau}\,d\tau$$

$$+ \cdots$$

But $f(\tau) = f(\tau + a) = f(\tau + 2a) = \cdots = f(\tau + na) = \cdots$ for all τ, since, by hypothesis, $f(t)$ is of period a. Thus we have

$$\mathcal{L}(f) = \int_0^a f(\tau)e^{-s\tau}\,d\tau + e^{-as}\int_0^a f(\tau)e^{-s\tau}\,d\tau + e^{-2as}\int_0^a f(\tau)e^{-s\tau}\,d\tau + \cdots$$

$$= (1 + e^{-as} + e^{-2as} + \cdots)\int_0^a f(\tau)e^{-s\tau}\,d\tau$$

If the infinite geometric progression be explicitly summed, we obtain the result of the theorem

$$\mathcal{L}(f) = \frac{\displaystyle\int_0^a f(t)e^{-st}\,dt}{1 - e^{-as}}$$

Q.E.D.

$$\sum_{n=0}^{\infty} \varepsilon^{-n\tau s} = 1 + \varepsilon^{-\tau s} + \varepsilon^{-2\tau s} + \cdots = \frac{1}{1 - \varepsilon^{-\tau s}}$$

Example 1

Find the transform of the rectangular wave shown in Fig. 6.9.

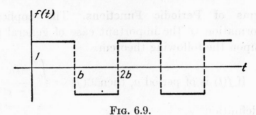

FIG. 6.9.

The period here is $2b$.   Hence, by Theorem 1,

$$
\begin{aligned}
\mathcal{L}(f) &= \frac{1}{1 - e^{-2bs}} \int_0^{2b} f(t) e^{-st} \, dt \\
&= \frac{1}{1 - e^{-2bs}} \left(\int_0^b 1 \cdot e^{-st} \, dt + \int_b^{2b} -1 \cdot e^{-st} \, dt \right) \\
&= \frac{1}{1 - e^{-2bs}} \left(\frac{e^{-st}}{-s} \Big|_0^b - \frac{e^{-st}}{-s} \Big|_b^{2b} \right) \\
&= \frac{1}{1 - e^{-2bs}} \left(\frac{1 - 2e^{-bs} + e^{-2bs}}{s} \right) \\
&= \frac{(1 - e^{-bs})^2}{s(1 - e^{-bs})(1 + e^{-bs})} \\
&= \frac{1 - e^{-bs}}{s(1 + e^{-bs})} \\
&= \frac{e^{\frac{1}{2}bs} - e^{-\frac{1}{2}bs}}{s(e^{\frac{1}{2}bs} + e^{-\frac{1}{2}bs})} \\
&= \frac{1}{s} \tanh \frac{1}{2} bs
\end{aligned}
$$

Example 2

What is the transform of the function shown in Fig. 6.10?

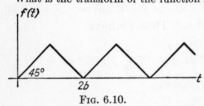

FIG. 6.10.

This problem is a reminder that an attractive new technique is not always simpler than familiar procedures. The function shown in Fig. 6.10 is nothing but the integral of the function transformed in Example 1. Hence by Theorem 4, Sec. 6.2, on the transforms of integrals of functions, the answer here is just $1/s$ times the answer to Example 1, that is,

$$
\frac{1 - e^{-bs}}{s^2(1 + e^{-bs})} \qquad \text{or} \qquad \frac{1}{s^2} \tanh \frac{1}{2} bs
$$

Example 3

Find the transform of the saw-tooth wave shown in Fig. 6.11. Here the period is a, and thus

$$\mathcal{L}(f) = \frac{1}{1 - e^{-as}} \int_0^a te^{-st}\, dt$$

$$= \frac{1}{1 - e^{-as}} \left[\frac{e^{-st}}{s^2}(-st - 1) \right]_0^a$$

$$= \frac{1 - (1 + as)e^{-as}}{s^2(1 - e^{-as})}$$

$$= \frac{(1 + as) - (1 + as)e^{-as} - as}{s^2(1 - e^{-as})}$$

$$= \frac{1 + as}{s^2} - \frac{a}{s(1 - e^{-as})}$$

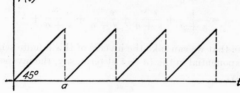

FIG. 6.11.

Example 4

What is the Laplace transform of the **staircase function**

$$f(t) = n + 1, \qquad nk < t < (n + 1)k \qquad n = 0, 1, 2, \ldots$$

Tne required transform can easily be found by direct calculation. However, it is even simpler to obtain it by considering $f(t)$ to be the difference of the two functions

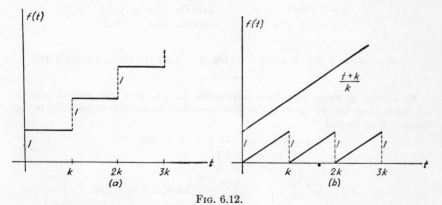

FIG. 6.12.

shown in Fig. 6.12b. The transform of the linear function $(t + k)/k$ can be found at once by Formula 4, Sec. 6.3. The transform of the saw-tooth function was obtained in the last example. Hence

$$\mathcal{L}(f) = \frac{1}{k}\left[\frac{1}{s^2} + \frac{k}{s} \right] - \frac{1}{k}\left[\frac{1 + ks}{s^2} - \frac{k}{s(1 - e^{-ks})} \right]$$

$$= \frac{1}{s(1 - e^{-ks})}$$

Example 5

If the Laplace transform of $f(t)$ is $\dfrac{1}{(s+a)(1-e^{-ks})}$ what is $f(t)$?

Since we have not yet encountered a periodic function having the given function of s for its transform, we must make a direct attack upon the problem. To do this, let us reverse the derivation of Theorem 1 and replace $1/(1-e^{-ks})$ by the geometric series of which it is the sum, getting

$$\mathcal{L}(f) = \frac{1}{s+a}(1 + e^{-ks} + e^{-2ks} + e^{-3ks} + \cdots)$$

$$= \frac{1}{s+a} + \frac{e^{-ks}}{s+a} + \frac{e^{-2ks}}{s+a} + \frac{e^{-3ks}}{s+a} + \cdots$$

Now let us assume that we can take the inverse of this infinite series term by term. If we neglect the exponential in the $(n+1)$st term, say, the inverse of what remains is immediate, namely,

$$e^{-at}$$

But having neglected the exponential e^{-nks}, we must translate the function e^{-at} to the right a distance of nk and then cut it off to the left of $t = nk$. When this is done for each term, we have

$$f(t) = e^{-at} + e^{-a(t-k)}u(t-k) + e^{-a(t-2k)}u(t-2k) + e^{-a(t-3k)}u(t-3k) + \cdots$$

The function $f(t)$ is thus equal to

e^{-at}	over the interval $(0,k)$
$e^{-at} + e^{ak}e^{-at}$	over the interval $(k,2k)$
$e^{-at} + e^{ak}e^{-at} + e^{2ak}e^{-at}$	over the interval $(2k,3k)$

. . . .

$$e^{-at} + e^{ak}e^{-at} + e^{2ak}e^{-at} + \cdots + e^{nak}e^{-at} \qquad \text{over the interval } (nk, \overline{n+1}k)$$

. . . .

To obtain a more convenient expression for $f(t)$ over the general interval $nk < t < (n+1)k$, we can sum the finite geometric progression defining $f(t)$ in this range. Thus we find

$$f(t) = e^{-at}(1 + e^{ak} + e^{2ak} + \cdots + e^{nak})$$

$$= e^{-at}\left[\frac{(e^{ak})^{n+1} - 1}{e^{ak} - 1}\right]$$

$$= \frac{e^{-a(t-\overline{n+1}k)}}{e^{ak} - 1} - \frac{e^{-at}}{e^{ak} - 1} \qquad nk < t < (n+1)k$$

Now let us define $\tau = t - \overline{n+1}k$, so that τ ranges from $-k$ to 0 as t ranges from nk to $(n+1)k$. If we make this substitution in the first fraction only, $f(t)$ assumes the symmetric form

$$f(t) = \frac{e^{-a\tau}}{e^{ak} - 1} - \frac{e^{-at}}{e^{ak} - 1}$$

The second term is a continuous function, dying away rapidly as t increases. The first term is completely independent of n, that is, gives the same set of values over each interval, since no matter what n may be, τ always ranges from $-k$ to 0.   Moreover, the first term is discontinuous, since at the left end of any interval its value is

$$\frac{e^{-a(-k)}}{e^{ak} - 1}$$

while at the right end its value is

$$\frac{1}{e^{ak} - 1}$$

Therefore the periodic function which it represents has a jump of

$$\frac{e^{ak}}{e^{ak} - 1} - \frac{1}{e^{ak} - 1} \equiv 1$$

at each of the points $t = k$, $2k$, $3k$, ...

In Fig. 6.13 the discontinuous periodic function represented by the first term in

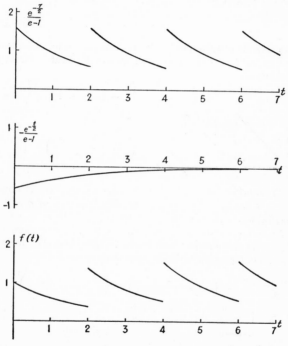

FIG. 6.13.   Plot showing the inverse of $\phi(s) = \dfrac{1}{(s + \frac{1}{2})(1 - e^{-2s})}$.

$f(t)$, the continuous transient term represented by the second fraction, and $f(t)$ itself are shown for $a = \frac{1}{2}$ and $k = 2$.

Example 6

What is the solution of the equation $y' + 3y + 2 \int_0^t y \, dt = f(t)$ if $y(0) = 1$ and if $f(t)$ is the function shown in Fig. 6.14?

Taking the transform of each side of the given equation, using the result of Example 3 to transform $f(t)$, we have

$$[s\mathcal{L}(y) - 1] + 3\mathcal{L}(y) + \frac{2}{s}\mathcal{L}(y) = \frac{1+s}{s^2} - \frac{1}{s(1 - e^{-s})}$$

or

$$\mathcal{L}(y) = \frac{s^2 + s + 1}{s(s + 1)(s + 2)} - \frac{1}{(s + 1)(s + 2)(1 - e^{-s})}$$

The inverse of the first fraction can be found immediately by the corollary of the first Heaviside theorem:

$$\tfrac{1}{2} - e^{-t} + \tfrac{3}{2}e^{-2t}$$

To find the inverse of the second fraction, we must write

$$\frac{1}{(s + 1)(s + 2)(1 - e^{-s})} = \left(\frac{1}{s + 1} - \frac{1}{s + 2}\right)\frac{1}{1 - e^{-s}}$$

$$= \frac{1}{(s + 1)(1 - e^{-s})} - \frac{1}{(s + 2)(1 - e^{-s})}$$

and then use the results of Example 5. In this case $k = 1$, and thus the inverse over a general interval $n < t < n + 1$ is

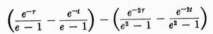

$$\left(\frac{e^{-\tau}}{e - 1} - \frac{e^{-t}}{e - 1}\right) - \left(\frac{e^{-2\tau}}{e^2 - 1} - \frac{e^{-2t}}{e^2 - 1}\right)$$

or

$$\left(\frac{e^{-\tau}}{e - 1} - \frac{e^{-2\tau}}{e^2 - 1}\right) - \left(\frac{e^{-t}}{e - 1} - \frac{e^{-2t}}{e^2 - 1}\right)$$

$$-1 < \tau < 0$$

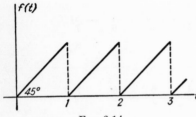

FIG. 6.14.

The second term is obviously a continuous function of t, and is simply an additional contribution to the transient of the system. The periodic function defined by the first bracketed expression is also continuous in this case, because the unit jumps which each of its terms exhibits at $t = 1, 2, 3, \ldots$, just cancel each other.

The entire solution for y is therefore

$$y = \frac{1 - 2e^{-t} + 3e^{-2t}}{2} + \left(\frac{e^{-t}}{e - 1} - \frac{e^{-2t}}{e^2 - 1}\right) - \left(\frac{e^{-\tau}}{e - 1} - \frac{e^{-2\tau}}{e^2 - 1}\right)$$

$$= \underbrace{\left(-\frac{e - 2}{e - 1}e^{-t} + \frac{3e^2 - 5}{2(e^2 - 1)}e^{-2t}\right)}_{\text{(transient)}} + \underbrace{\left(\frac{1}{2} - \frac{e^{-\tau}}{e - 1} + \frac{e^{-2\tau}}{e^2 - 1}\right)}_{\text{(steady state)}} \quad -1 < \tau < 0$$

Fig. 6.15 shows a plot of the component terms, and of y itself.

The analysis of equations like the one considered in Example 6 is so important that a table of additional results similar to the one obtained in Example 5 would be highly desirable. Using for the most part only the procedure illustrated in Example 5, such a table can easily be developed (Table 6.2, page 183), as we shall now show.

To avoid unnecessary writing, let us first define the following functions over the general interval $nk < x < (n+1)k$, where k is an arbitrary positive number and n is a non-negative integer (Table 6.1, page 182).

The functions $\phi_1(x,k)$ and $\phi_2(x,k)$ are, respectively, the staircase function and the Morse dot function. The functions $\phi_3(x,k)$ and $\phi_4(x,k)$ are the integrals of $\phi_1(x,k)$ and $\phi_2(x,k)$, respectively. The function $\phi_5(x,a,k)$ is precisely the one we encountered in the solution of Example 5. The others, while somewhat more complicated, arise in the same way and may be plotted just as easily when the parameters a, b, and k are known.

In Table 6.2 are listed the inverses of all the elementary periodic-type transforms which are likely to be encountered. Of course, as Example 6 illustrated, it is usually necessary to employ the method of partial fractions before the results in Table 6.2 can be applied.

Formulas 1 to 4 in Table 6.2 are obvious applications of Theorem 1 and of Theorem 4, Sec. 6.2. Formula 5 was derived in detail in Example 5, and the derivations of Formulas 6 to 10 follow almost exactly the same pattern. All that is necessary is to express as complex exponentials the sines and cosines which appear in the inverses of the

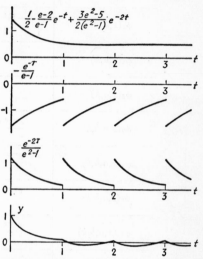

FIG. 6.15.   Plot showing the solution of Example 6.

individual terms. The expression for $f(t)$ over any interval is then, as in Example 5, just a finite geometric progression which can be summed and then converted to a purely real form without difficulty.

The derivations of Formulas 11 and 12 are somewhat different because of the repeated factor in the denominator of the transforms. To illustrate the necessary modifications in these and similar cases, we shall derive Formula 12 in detail.

In the transform

$$\frac{1}{(s+a)^2(1+e^{-ks})}$$

let

$$\frac{1}{1+e^{-ks}}$$

TABLE 6.1

Definition of functional symbol	Definition of function over general interval $nk < x < (n+1)k$
$\phi_1(x,k)$	$n + 1$
$\phi_2(x,k)$	$\dfrac{(-1)^n + 1}{2}$
$\phi_3(x,k)$	$(n+1)x - \dfrac{n(n+1)k}{2}$
$\phi_4(x,k)$	$\left[\dfrac{(-1)^n + 1}{2}\right]x + \dfrac{k}{4}[1 - (-1)^n(2n+1)]$
$\phi_5(x,a,k)$	$\dfrac{e^{-ax}}{e^{ak} - 1}$
$\phi_6(x,a,k)$	$\dfrac{e^{-ax}}{e^{ak} + 1}$
$\phi_7(x,a,b,k)$	$\dfrac{e^{-ax}\cos b(x+k) - e^{-a(x+k)}\cos bx}{2(\cosh ak - \cos bk)}$
$\phi_8(x,a,b,k)$	$\dfrac{e^{-ax}\cos b(x+k) + e^{-a(x+k)}\cos bx}{2(\cosh ak + \cos bk)}$
$\phi_9(x,a,b,k)$	$\dfrac{e^{-ax}\sin b(x+k) - e^{-a(x+k)}\sin bx}{2(\cosh ak - \cos bk)}$
$\phi_{10}(x,a,b,k)$	$\dfrac{e^{-ax}\sin b(x+k) + e^{-a(x+k)}\sin bx}{2(\cosh ak + \cos bk)}$
$\phi_{11}(x,a,k)$	$\dfrac{(x+k)e^{-ax} - xe^{-a(x+k)}}{2(\cosh ak - 1)}$
$\phi_{12}(x,a,k)$	$\dfrac{(x+k)e^{-ax} + xe^{-a(x+k)}}{2(\cosh ak + 1)}$

be expanded into an infinite series. Then we have for the transform

$$\frac{1}{(s+a)^2}[1 - e^{-ks} + e^{-2ks} - e^{-3ks} + e^{-4ks} - \cdots + (-1)^n e^{-nks} + \cdots]$$

If the exponential e^{-nks} in the $(n+1)$st term be neglected, the inverse of what remains is just te^{-at}. But having neglected the factor e^{-nks}, we must translate the function te^{-at} nk units to the right and cut it off to the left of $t = nk$ before we obtain the proper inverse. When this is done for each term, we have

$$f(t) = te^{-at} - (t-k)e^{-a(t-k)}u(t-k) + \cdots$$
$$+ (-1)^n(t-nk)e^{-a(t-nk)}u(t-nk) \cdots$$

TABLE 6.2

Laplace transform	Inverse over general interval $nk < t < (n + 1)k$ $-k < \tau < 0$
1. $\dfrac{1}{s(1 - e^{-ks})}$	$\phi_1(t,k)$
2. $\dfrac{1}{s(1 + e^{-ks})}$	$\phi_2(t,k)$
3. $\dfrac{1}{s^2(1 - e^{-ks})}$	$\phi_3(t,k)$
4. $\dfrac{1}{s^2(1 + e^{-ks})}$	$\phi_4(t,k)$
5. $\dfrac{1}{(s + a)(1 - e^{-ks})}$	$\phi_5(\tau,a,k) - \phi_5(t,a,k)$
6. $\dfrac{1}{(s + a)(1 + e^{-ks})}$	$(-1)^n\phi_6(\tau,a,k) + \phi_6(t,a,k)$
7. $\dfrac{s + a}{[(s + a)^2 + b^2][1 - e^{-ks}]}$	$\phi_7(\tau,a,b,k) - \phi_7(t,a,b,k)$
8. $\dfrac{s + a}{[(s + a)^2 + b^2][1 + e^{-ks}]}$	$(-1)^n\phi_8(\tau,a,b,k) + \phi_8(t,a,b,k)$
9. $\dfrac{b}{[(s + a)^2 + b^2][1 - e^{-ks}]}$	$\phi_9(\tau,a,b,k) - \phi_9(t,a,b,k)$
10. $\dfrac{b}{[(s + a)^2 + b^2][1 + e^{-ks}]}$	$(-1)^n\phi_{10}(\tau,a,b,k) + \phi_{10}(t,a,b,k)$
11. $\dfrac{1}{(s + a)^2(1 - e^{-ks})}$	$\phi_{11}(\tau,a,k) - \phi_{11}(t,a,k)$
12. $\dfrac{1}{(s + a)^2(1 + e^{-ks})}$	$(-1)^n\phi_{12}(\tau,a,k) + \phi_{12}(t,a,k)$

For $f(t)$ over the interval $nk < t < (n + 1)k$, we therefore have the finite sum

$$\sum_{j=0}^{n} (-1)^j(t - jk)e^{-a(t-jk)}$$

or, factoring out e^{-at} and incorporating $(-1)^j$ in the remaining exponential

(1) $$f(t) = e^{-at} \sum_{j=0}^{n} (t - jk)(-e^{ak})^j \qquad nk < t < (n + 1)k$$

Because of the factor $(t - jk)$ (which entered because $s + a$ was a repeated factor of the denominator of the transform) this expression for $f(t)$ is *not* a geometric progression. It may still be summed, however, by using the following important theorem from the calculus of finite differences.*

Theorem 2. If α ($\neq 1$) is a constant, real or complex, $\phi(j)$ a polynomial of order m, and if $\beta = \alpha/(\alpha - 1)$, then the sum

$$\sum_{j=0}^{n} \alpha^j \phi(j) \equiv \phi(0) + \alpha\phi(1) + \alpha^2\phi(2) + \cdots + \alpha^n\phi(n)$$

is equal to

$$\alpha^j V(j) \Big]_{j=0}^{j=n+1} \equiv \alpha^{n+1} V(n+1) - V(0)$$

where

$$V(j) = \frac{1}{\alpha - 1}[1 - \beta\Delta + \beta^2\Delta^2 - \cdots + (-1)^m\beta^m\Delta^m]\phi(j)$$

and Δ is the ordinary difference operator (Sec. 16.2) defined by the properties

$$\Delta F(j) = F(j+1) - F(j)$$
$$\Delta^2 F(j) = \Delta F(j+1) - \Delta F(j)$$
$$\cdot \quad \cdot \quad \cdot \quad \cdot \quad \cdot \quad \cdot \quad \cdot \quad \cdot \quad \cdot \quad \cdot \quad \cdot \quad \cdot$$

To apply the summation method of this theorem to our problem, we make the following identifications

$$\alpha = (-e^{ak}), \qquad \beta = \frac{e^{ak}}{e^{ak}+1}, \qquad \phi(j) = t - jk, \qquad m = 1$$

Then

$$V(j) = \frac{1}{-e^{ak}-1}\left[1 - \frac{e^{ak}}{e^{ak}+1}\Delta\right](t - jk)$$

$$= \frac{1}{-e^{ak}-1}\left[(t - jk) - \frac{e^{ak}}{e^{ak}+1}\{(t - \overline{j+1}\,k) - (t - jk)\}\right]$$

$$= \frac{1}{-e^{ak}-1}\left[(t - jk) + \frac{ke^{ak}}{e^{ak}+1}\right]$$

$$= -\frac{(t - jk)(e^{ak}+1) + ke^{ak}}{(e^{ak}+1)^2}$$

$$= -\frac{(t - \overline{j-1}\,k)e^{ak} + (t - jk)}{e^{2ak} + 2e^{ak} + 1}$$

$$= -\frac{(t - \overline{j-1}\,k) + (t - jk)e^{-ak}}{e^{ak} + 2 + e^{-ak}}$$

$$= -\frac{(t - \overline{j-1}\,k) + (t - jk)e^{-ak}}{2(\cosh ak + 1)}$$

* L. M. Milne-Thompson, "The Calculus of Finite Differences," Macmillan & Co., Ltd., London, p. 46, 1933.

The required sum is therefore

$$\alpha^j V(j)\Big]_{j=0}^{j=n+1} = \left[-(-e^{ak})^j \frac{(t - \overline{j - 1}\, k) + (t - jk)e^{-ak}}{2(\cosh ak + 1)} \right]_{j=0}^{j=n+1}$$

$$= -(-e^{ak})^{n+1} \left[\frac{(t - nk) + (t - \overline{n+1}\, k)e^{-ak}}{2(\cosh ak + 1)} \right]$$

$$+ \left[\frac{(t + k) + te^{-ak}}{2(\cosh ak + 1)} \right]$$

$$= (-1)^n \frac{(t - nk)e^{a(n+1)k} + (t - \overline{n+1}\, k)e^{ank}}{2(\cosh ak + 1)}$$

$$+ \frac{(t + k) + te^{-ak}}{2(\cosh ak + 1)}$$

From (1), the required inverse is e^{-at} times this sum, or

$$(-1)^n \frac{(t - nk)e^{-a(t - \overline{n+1}\, k)} + (t - \overline{n+1}\, k)e^{-a(t-nk)}}{2(\cosh ak + 1)}$$

$$+ \frac{(t + k)e^{-at} + te^{-a(t+k)}}{2(\cosh ak + 1)}$$

To achieve the more symmetric form given in Table 6.2, let

$$t - \overline{n+1}\, k = \tau$$

in the first fraction.   Then we have for the inverse

$$(-1)^n \frac{(\tau + k)e^{-a\tau} + \tau e^{-a(\tau+k)}}{2(\cosh ak + 1)} + \frac{(t + k)e^{-at} + te^{-a(t+k)}}{2(\cosh ak + 1)}$$

$$= (-1)^n \phi_{12}(\tau,a,k) + \phi_{12}(t,a,k)$$

as asserted.

The second term in this expression is obviously a continuous function of t which decays rapidly as t increases (assuming that a is positive). That the first, or periodic, term is also continuous can be seen by evaluating it at the right end ($\tau = 0$) of a general interval and at the left end ($\tau = -k$) of the next interval and verifying that these are the same:

Right end value ($\tau = 0$) in $(n + 1)$st interval $= \dfrac{(-1)^n k}{2(\cosh ak + 1)}$

Left end value ($\tau = -k$) in $(n + 2)$nd interval $= \dfrac{(-1)^{n+1}(-k)}{2(\cosh ak + 1)}$

The transient or t-evaluated components of all inverses in Table 6.2 are continuous for all $t > 0$.   This is true of the periodic or τ-evaluated components if and only if the order of the polynomial part of the denominator of the transform exceeds the order of the numerator by more than 1. If this is not the case, there is a jump of $+1$ at each of the points

$$t = k, 2k, 3k, \ldots$$

if the transform contains $(1 - e^{-ks})$, and a jump of $(-1)^n$ if the transform contains $(1 + e^{-ks})$.

Example 7

A simple series circuit contains the elements $R = 400$, $L = 0.2$, $C = 10^{-6}$. At $t = 0$, while the circuit is completely passive, an exponential "saw-tooth" voltage wave, equal to $E_0 e^{-5,000t}$ throughout one period and repeating itself every 0.002 sec, is switched into the circuit. Find the total response of the circuit and also the steady-state current.

The differential equation to be solved is

$$0.2 \frac{di}{dt} + 400i + 10^6 \int_0^t i \, dt = E(t)$$

Taking the Laplace transform of both sides, we obtain

$$\mathcal{L}(i) \left(0.2s + 400 + \frac{10^6}{s} \right) = E_0 \frac{\int_0^{0.002} e^{-5,000t} e^{-st} \, dt}{1 - e^{-0.002s}} = E_0 \frac{\int_0^{0.002} e^{-(s+5,000)t} \, dt}{1 - e^{-0.002s}}$$

or

$$\mathcal{L}(i) \frac{s^2 + 2,000s + 5 \times 10^6}{5s} = E_0 \frac{1 - e^{-(0.002s+10)}}{(s + 5,000)(1 - e^{-0.002s})}$$
$$= E_0 \frac{1 - e^{-10} + e^{-10}(1 - e^{-0.002s})}{(s + 5,000)(1 - e^{-0.002s})}$$
$$= E_0 \frac{e^{-10}}{s + 5,000} + E_0 \frac{1 - e^{-10}}{(s + 5,000)(1 - e^{-0.002s})}$$

Hence

$$\mathcal{L}(i) = \frac{5E_0 e^{-10} s}{(s + 5,000)(s + 1,000^2 + 2,000^2)}$$
$$+ \frac{5E_0(1 - e^{-10})s}{(s + 5,000)(s + 1,000^2 + 2,000^2)(1 - e^{-0.002s})}$$

By simple partial fraction manipulations we find

$$\frac{s}{(s + 5,000)(s + 1,000^2 + 2,000^2)} = \frac{1}{4,000} \left[-\frac{1}{s + 5,000} + \frac{s + 1,000}{(s + 1,000^2 + 2,000^2)} \right]$$

From this point the entire solution can be written down at once:

$$i = \frac{5E_0 e^{-10}}{4,000} [-e^{-5,000t} + e^{-1,000t} \cos 2,000t]$$
$$- \frac{5E_0(1 - e^{-10})}{4,000} [\phi_5(\tau, 5,000, 0.002) - \phi_5(t, 5,000, 0.002)]$$
$$+ \frac{5E_0(1 - e^{-10})}{4,000} [\phi_7(\tau, 1,000, 2,000, 0.002) - \phi_7(t, 1,000, 2,000, 0.002)]$$

The steady-state current is described by the terms in τ:

$$i_{ss} = -\frac{5E_0(1 - e^{-10})}{4,000} [\phi_5(\tau, 5,000, 0.002) - \phi_7(\tau, 1,000, 2,000, 0.002)]$$

or written out at length

$$i_{ss} = -\frac{E_0(1 - e^{-10})}{800} \left[\frac{e^{-5,000\tau}}{e^{10} - 1} \right.$$
$$\left. - \frac{e^{-1,000\tau} \cos 2,000(\tau + 0.002) - e^{-1,000(\tau+0.002)} \cos 2,000\tau}{2(\cosh 2 - \cos 4)} \right]$$

This function, plotted for $-0.002 < \tau < 0$, defines one complete cycle of the steady-state current. Of course the unit jumps in ϕ_5 and $-\phi_7$ at the ends of each period just cancel, leaving the steady-state current continuous, as of course it must be.

The operational solution of a problem like this, leading as it does to a relatively simple, finite expression for the response, is in general to be preferred to the use of Fourier series, which leaves the answer in the form of an infinite series.

EXERCISES

Find the transforms of the following periodic functions:

1.

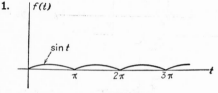

Fig. 6.16.

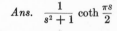

$Ans. \quad \dfrac{1}{s^2 + 1} \coth \dfrac{\pi s}{2}$

2.

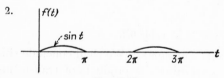

Fig. 6.17.

3.

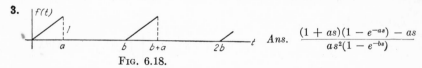

Fig. 6.18.

$Ans. \quad \dfrac{(1 + as)(1 - e^{-as}) - as}{as^2(1 - e^{-bs})}$

4.

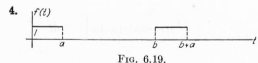

Fig. 6.19.

5.

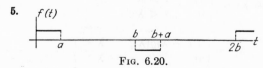

Fig. 6.20.

6. What is $\mathcal{L}^{-1}\left[\dfrac{s}{(s+1)(s^2+1)(1-e^{-2s})}\right]$?

7. What is $\mathcal{L}^{-1}\left[\dfrac{e^{-s}}{s(s+1)(1+e^{-2s})}\right]$?

Solve each of the following differential equations, and plot one cycle of the steady-state solution:

8. $\dfrac{dy}{dt} + 4y + 3\displaystyle\int_0^t y\,dt = f(t) \equiv$

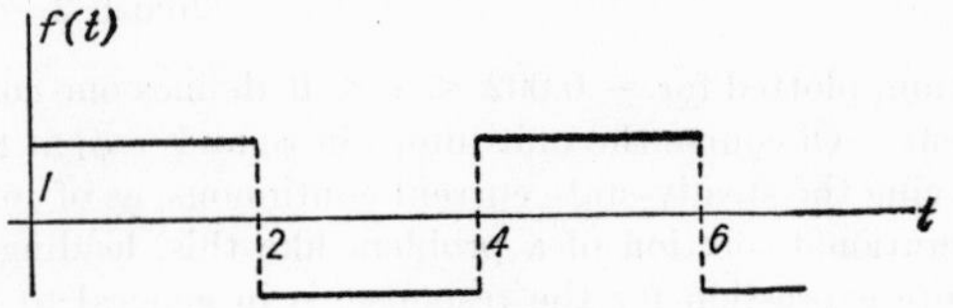

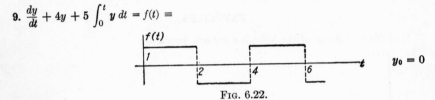

FIG. 6.21.

$y_0 = 0$

9. $\dfrac{dy}{dt} + 4y + 5\displaystyle\int_0^t y\,dt = f(t) \equiv$

FIG. 6.22.

$y_0 = 0$

10. $\dfrac{d^2y}{dt^2} + y = f(t) \equiv$

FIG. 6.23.

$y_0 = y_0' = 0$

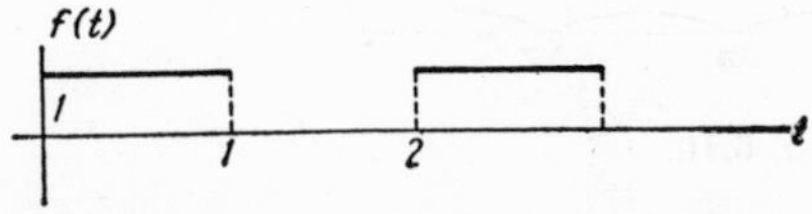

11. to 15. Derive Formulas 7, 8, 9, 10, and 11 in Table 6.2.

6.7 Convolution and the Duhamel Formulas. We shall conclude this chapter by establishing a result concerning the products of transforms which is of considerable theoretical as well as practical importance.

Theorem 1.

$$\mathcal{L}[f(t)]\mathcal{L}[g(t)] = \mathcal{L}\left[\int_0^t f(t-\lambda)g(\lambda)d\lambda\right] = \mathcal{L}\left[\int_0^t f(\lambda)g(t-\lambda)d\lambda\right]$$

Proof. By definition

(1) $\qquad \mathcal{L}\left[\displaystyle\int_0^t f(t-\lambda)g(\lambda)d\lambda\right] = \int_0^\infty\left[\int_0^t f(t-\lambda)g(\lambda)d\lambda\right]e^{-st}\,dt$

Now

$$u(t-\lambda) = \begin{cases} 1, & t > \lambda \\ 0, & t < \lambda \end{cases}$$

and thus

$$f(t-\lambda)g(\lambda)u(t-\lambda) = \begin{cases} f(t-\lambda)g(\lambda), & \lambda < t \\ 0, & \lambda > t \end{cases}$$

Since this product vanishes for all values of λ greater than t, the inner integration in (1) can be extended to ∞ if the factor $u(t - \lambda)$ be inserted in the integrand.   Hence

$$(2) \quad \mathcal{L}\left[\int_0^t f(t - \lambda)g(\lambda)d\lambda \right] = \int_0^\infty \left[\int_0^\infty f(t - \lambda)g(\lambda)u(t - \lambda)d\lambda \right] e^{-st}\, dt$$

Now our usual implicit assumptions about the functions we transform are sufficient to permit the order of integration in (2) to be interchanged:

$$(3) \quad \mathcal{L}\left[\int_0^t f(t - \lambda)g(\lambda)d\lambda \right] = \int_0^\infty \left[\int_0^\infty f(t - \lambda)g(\lambda)u(t - \lambda)e^{-st}\, dt \right] d\lambda$$
$$= \int_0^\infty g(\lambda) \left[\int_0^\infty f(t - \lambda)u(t - \lambda)e^{-st}\, dt \right] d\lambda$$

Because of the presence of $u(t - \lambda)$, the inner integrand is identically zero for all $t < \lambda$.   Hence the inner integration effectively starts not at $t = 0$ but at $t = \lambda$.   Therefore

$$(4) \quad \mathcal{L}\left[\int_0^t f(t - \lambda)g(\lambda)d\lambda \right] = \int_0^\infty g(\lambda) \left[\int_\lambda^\infty f(t - \lambda)e^{-st}\, dt \right] d\lambda$$

Now in the integral on the right in (4) let

$$t - \lambda = \tau, \qquad dt = d\tau$$

Then

$$\mathcal{L}\left[\int_0^t f(t - \lambda)g(\lambda)d\lambda \right] = \int_0^\infty g(\lambda) \left[\int_0^\infty f(\tau)e^{-s(\tau + \lambda)}\, d\tau \right] d\lambda$$
$$= \int_0^\infty g(\lambda)e^{-s\lambda} \left[\int_0^\infty f(\tau)e^{-s\tau}\, d\tau \right] d\lambda$$
$$= \left[\int_0^\infty f(\tau)e^{-s\tau}\, d\tau \right] \left[\int_0^\infty g(\lambda)e^{-s\lambda}\, d\lambda \right]$$
$$= \mathcal{L}[f(t)]\mathcal{L}[g(t)]$$

From symmetry, the second form of the theorem can be obtained by interchanging $f(t)$ and $g(t)$.

Q.E.D.

The **convolution** or **Faltung integral**

$$\int_0^t f(t - \lambda)g(\lambda)d\lambda$$

is frequently denoted simply by

$$f(t) * g(t)$$

In this symbolism Theorem 1 becomes

$$\mathcal{L}(f)\mathcal{L}(g) = \mathcal{L}(f * g) = \mathcal{L}(g * f)$$

Example 1

If $\mathcal{L}(f) = \dfrac{2}{(s+1)(s^2+4)}$, what is $f(t)$?

Since

$$\mathcal{L}(e^{-t}) = \frac{1}{s+1} \qquad \text{and} \qquad \mathcal{L}(\sin 2t) = \frac{2}{s^2+4}$$

it is obvious that

$$\mathcal{L}(f) = \mathcal{L}(e^{-t})\mathcal{L}(\sin 2t)$$

Hence, by the convolution theorem,

$$
\begin{aligned}
f(t) &= \int_0^t e^{-(t-\lambda)} \sin 2\lambda \, d\lambda \\
&= e^{-t} \int_0^t e^\lambda \sin 2\lambda \, d\lambda \\
&= e^{-t} \left[\frac{e^\lambda}{1+2^2} (\sin 2\lambda - 2 \cos 2\lambda) \right]_0^t \\
&= \frac{e^{-t}}{5} \left[e^t (\sin 2t - 2 \cos 2t) - (-2) \right] \\
&= \frac{\sin 2t - 2 \cos 2t}{5} + \frac{2e^{-t}}{5}
\end{aligned}
$$

This can readily be checked by using the Heaviside expansion theorems.

Example 2

Find a particular integral of the differential equation

$$y'' + 2ay' + (a^2 + b^2)y = f(t)$$

where $f(t)$ is any function possessing a Laplace transform.

Taking the Laplace transform of the given equation, and assuming that

$$y(0) = y'(0) = 0,$$

which is legitimate since only a particular solution is desired, we find

$$\mathcal{L}(y) = \frac{1}{(s+a)^2 + b^2} \mathcal{L}(f)$$

Now

$$\frac{1}{(s+a)^2 + b^2} = \mathcal{L}\left(\frac{e^{-at} \sin bt}{b} \right)$$

Hence

$$\mathcal{L}(y) = \mathcal{L}(f)\mathcal{L}\left(\frac{e^{-at} \sin bt}{b} \right)$$

and thus, by the convolution theorem,

$$y = \frac{1}{b} \int_0^t f(t - \lambda)e^{-a\lambda} \sin b\lambda \, d\lambda$$

or equally well

$$y = \frac{1}{b} \int_0^t f(\lambda) e^{-a(t-\lambda)} \sin b(t - \lambda) d\lambda$$

$$= \frac{e^{-at}}{b} \int_0^t f(\lambda) e^{a\lambda} \sin b(t - \lambda) d\lambda$$

It is interesting to compare this procedure with the method of variation of parameters, as developed in Sec. 2.4, for the determination of particular integrals of linear differential equations. The two give identical results.

An especially important application of the convolution theorem makes it possible to determine the response of a system to a general excitation if its response to a unit step function is known. To develop this idea, we shall need the concept of indicial admittance, which we shall present here in relation to electric circuits, where it first arose.

Suppose that we have an electrical network consisting of a number of loops, one and only one of which, say the jth, contains a voltage source $E(t)$. Suppose further that there is no initial storage of energy in the system, *i.e.*, suppose that at $t = 0$ all charges and currents are zero. If we set up the differential equations of such a system and take the Laplace transform of each, we will obtain a set of algebraic equations of the form

$$\left(a_{11}s + b_{11} + \frac{c_{11}}{s}\right) \mathcal{L}(i_1) + \cdots + \left(a_{1k}s + b_{1k} + \frac{c_{1k}}{s}\right) \mathcal{L}(i_k) + \cdots$$

$$+ \left(a_{1n}s + b_{1n} + \frac{c_{1n}}{s}\right) \mathcal{L}(i_n) = 0$$

$$\cdots \cdots \cdots \cdots \cdots \cdots \cdots \cdots \cdots \cdots \cdots \cdots \cdots$$

$$\left(a_{j1}s + b_{j1} + \frac{c_{j1}}{s}\right) \mathcal{L}(i_1) + \cdots + \left(a_{jk}s + b_{jk} + \frac{c_{jk}}{s}\right) \mathcal{L}(i_k) + \cdots$$

$$+ \left(a_{jn}s + b_{jn} + \frac{c_{jn}}{s}\right) \mathcal{L}(i_n) = \mathcal{L}(E)$$

$$\cdots \cdots \cdots \cdots \cdots \cdots \cdots \cdots \cdots \cdots \cdots \cdots \cdots$$

$$\left(a_{n1}s + b_{n1} + \frac{c_{n1}}{s}\right) \mathcal{L}(i_1) + \cdots + \left(a_{nk}s + b_{nk} + \frac{c_{nk}}{s}\right) \mathcal{L}(i_k) + \cdots$$

$$+ \left(a_{nn}s + b_{nn} + \frac{c_{nn}}{s}\right) \mathcal{L}(i_n) = 0$$

where the a's, b's, and c's are constants depending on the components of the system. On the right-hand side only the jth equation will contain a term different from zero because, first, only the jth loop contains a voltage source, and second, all initial currents and charges are zero, so that there are no initial values to be transposed to the right members of any of the equations. If we now put

$$z_{jk} = a_{jk}\, s + b_{jk} + \frac{c_{jk}}{s}$$

and solve for the transform of one of the currents, say the kth, we obtain

$$\mathcal{L}(i_k) = \frac{\begin{vmatrix} z_{11} & \cdots & 0 & \cdots & z_{1n} \\ \cdots & \cdots & \cdots & \cdots & \cdots \\ z_{j1} & \cdots & \mathcal{L}(E) & \cdots & z_{jn} \\ \cdots & \cdots & \cdots & \cdots & \cdots \\ z_{n1} & \cdots & 0 & \cdots & z_{nn} \end{vmatrix}}{\begin{vmatrix} z_{11} & \cdots & z_{1k} & \cdots & z_{1n} \\ \cdots & \cdots & \cdots & \cdots & \cdots \\ z_{j1} & \cdots & z_{jk} & \cdots & z_{jn} \\ \cdots & \cdots & \cdots & \cdots & \cdots \\ z_{n1} & \cdots & z_{nk} & \cdots & z_{nn} \end{vmatrix}}$$

or simply

$$\mathcal{L}(i_k) = \frac{\mathcal{L}(E)}{Z(s)}$$

where $Z(s)$ is the quotient of the determinant of the coefficients of the system and the cofactor of the element in the jth row and kth column of this determinant.

If $E(t)$ is the unit step function, then

$$\mathcal{L}(E) = \frac{1}{s}$$

and we have

$$\mathcal{L}(i_k) = \frac{1}{sZ(s)}$$

The current defined by this transform is called the **indicial admittance**, $A(t)$. In other words

$$\mathcal{L}(A) = \frac{1}{sZ(s)}$$

$A(t)$ of course depends upon the point where the voltage source is inserted in the circuit and upon the branch in which the resultant current is considered. Thus there is actually a function $A(t)$ for every pair of input and output points, and it would be more accurate to write $A_{jk}(t)$ than just $A(t)$, as we have done.

Now return to the transform of i_k in the general case,

$$\mathcal{L}(i_k) = \frac{\mathcal{L}(E)}{Z(s)}$$

and divide both sides by s, getting

$$\frac{1}{s}\mathcal{L}(i_k) = \frac{\mathcal{L}(E)}{sZ(s)} = \mathcal{L}(A)\mathcal{L}(E)$$

Hence, by the convolution theorem,

$$\frac{1}{s}\mathcal{L}(i_k) = \mathcal{L}\left[\int_0^t A(t-\lambda)E(\lambda)d\lambda\right] = \mathcal{L}\left[\int_0^t A(\lambda)E(t-\lambda)d\lambda\right]$$

or

$$\mathcal{L}(i_k) = s\mathcal{L}\left[\int_0^t A(t-\lambda)E(\lambda)d\lambda\right] = s\mathcal{L}\left[\int_0^t A(\lambda)E(t-\lambda)d\lambda\right]$$

But from Theorem 3, Sec. 6.2, that is, $\mathcal{L}(f') = s\mathcal{L}(f)$ if $f(0) = 0$, it follows that

$$i_k = \frac{d}{dt}\left[\int_0^t A(t-\lambda)E(\lambda)d\lambda\right] = \frac{d}{dt}\left[\int_0^t A(\lambda)E(t-\lambda)d\lambda\right]$$

Performing the indicated differentiations (see Theorem 2, Sec. A.2), we have either

(5)
$$i_k = \int_0^t A'(t-\lambda)E(\lambda)d\lambda + A(0)E(t)$$

or

(6)
$$i_k = \int_0^t A(\lambda)E'(t-\lambda)d\lambda + A(t)E(0)$$

Since $A(t)$ is by definition the response to a unit voltage of a system in which there are no initial currents, it follows that $A(0) = 0$. Hence Eq. (5) becomes simply

(7)
$$i_k = \int_0^t A'(t-\lambda)E(\lambda)d\lambda$$

By making the simple change of variable $\tau = t - \lambda$ in the integrals in Eqs. (6) and (7), we obtain the related expressions

(8)
$$i_k = A(t)E(0) + \int_0^t A(t-\tau)E'(\tau)d\tau$$

(9)
$$i_k = \int_0^t A'(\tau)E(t-\tau)d\tau$$

We have thus established the following four formulas giving the current produced by a general voltage in terms of the (experimentally accessible) current $A(t)$ produced by a unit step voltage, E, A, and i, referring, of course, to a definite pair of input and output points.

(6)
$$i = A(t)E(0) + \int_0^t A(\lambda)E'(t-\lambda)d\lambda$$

(7)
$$i = \int_0^t A'(t-\lambda)E(\lambda)d\lambda$$

(8) $$i = A(t)E(0) + \int_0^t A(t - \lambda)E'(\lambda)d\lambda$$

(9) $$i = \int_0^t A'(\lambda)E(t - \lambda)d\lambda$$

Equations (8) and (9) could also have been obtained from Eqs. (7) and (6), respectively, by integrating the latter by parts.

Some writers refer to all these formulas as **Duhamel's formulas,** although others insist the attribution is unwarranted. Formula 8, which is the one most frequently encountered, is usually referred to as **Duhamel's integral,** or the **Boltzman-Hopkinson principle of superposition.**

It is possible to obtain these integrals by physical reasoning as follows. Let the impressed voltage $E(t)$ be given, and imagine it approximated by a series of step functions, as shown in Fig. 6.24. The first step function is of noninfinitesimal magnitude $E(0)$. All later step functions in the approximation are of infinitesimal magnitude, and their contributions in the limit will have to be taken into account by integration. Specifically, since

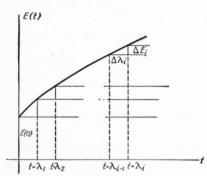

$$\frac{\Delta E}{\Delta \lambda} \doteq \frac{dE}{dt}\bigg|_{t=\lambda} = E'(\lambda)$$

we have for the height ΔE_i of the general infinitesimal step function, the approximate expression

$$\Delta E_i \doteq E'(\lambda_i)\Delta \lambda_i$$

FIG. 6.24. Plot showing the synthesis of a general voltage by means of step functions.

Now if $A(t)$ is the indicial admittance of the system (for the proper pair of input and output points, of course), the first step voltage produces a current equal to

$$E(0)A(t)$$

from the very definition of the indicial admittance. For the second step voltage there is a lag of $t = \lambda_1$ units of time before it begins to act. Hence the (infinitesimal) current which it produces is

$$\Delta E_1 A(t - \lambda_1)$$

or

$$E'(\lambda_1)\Delta\lambda_1 A(t - \lambda_1)$$

Similarly the third step voltage produces the current

$$E'(\lambda_2)\Delta\lambda_2 A(t - \lambda_2)$$

and in general the $(i + 1)$st step voltage produces the current

$$E'(\lambda_i)\Delta\lambda_i A(t - \lambda_i)$$

If these contributions to the total current are added, we obtain for the current flowing at a general time t,

$$
\begin{aligned}
i &= E(0)A(t) + E'(\lambda_1)\Delta\lambda_1 A(t - \lambda_1) + E'(\lambda_2)\Delta\lambda_2 A(t - \lambda_2) + \cdots \\
&\qquad\qquad\qquad\qquad\qquad + E'(\lambda_i)\Delta\lambda_i A(t - \lambda_i) + \cdots \\
&= E(0)A(t) + \Sigma E'(\lambda_i)A(t - \lambda_i)\Delta\lambda_i
\end{aligned}
$$

the summation extending over all the step voltages which have begun to act up to the instant t.   In the limit when $\Delta\lambda_i \to 0$ and the height of each step voltage [after the first, $E(0)$] approaches zero, the sum in the last expression becomes an integral, and we have (8).

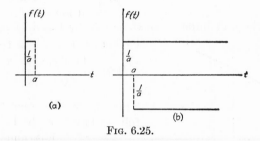

FIG. 6.25.

To obtain a physical derivation, or interpretation, of Formula 7 we must first determine the physical meaning of the derivative, $A'(t)$, of the indicial admittance.   To do this, we shall need the concept of a unit impulse.

Suppose that we have the function shown in Fig. 6.25a.   This consists of a suddenly applied force of constant magnitude acting for a definite interval and then suddenly ceasing, the product of duration and magnitude being unity.   If a is very small, the period of application is small but the magnitude of the force is very great.   It is sometimes advantageous to pursue this idea to the limit, and imagine a force of arbitrarily large magnitude acting for an infinitesimal time.   This is what is meant by an **impulse**, or a **unit impulse** if the product of the duration and magnitude remains 1 as we pass to the limit.   To determine the transform of a unit impulse, consider Fig. 6.25b, which shows how the pulse in Fig. 6.25a can be represented as the difference of two step functions,

$$\frac{u(t) - u(t - a)}{a}$$

Transforming this we have

$$\frac{1}{a}\left(\frac{1}{s} - \frac{e^{-as}}{s}\right) = \frac{1 - e^{-as}}{as}$$

As $a \to 0$, this transform becomes an indeterminate of the form $0/0$. Evaluating it as usual, we obtain

$$\frac{s}{s} = 1$$

for the limit.   Just as we gave a name, $A(t)$, to the response of a system to a unit step voltage, so we define $h(t)$ to be the response of a system to a unit impulse.

Now we have seen that in general

$$\mathcal{L}(i) = \frac{\mathcal{L}(E)}{Z(s)}$$

Hence if E is the unit impulse, so that $\mathcal{L}(E) = 1$ and i becomes $h(t)$, we have

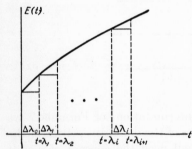

$$\mathcal{L}[h(t)] = \frac{1}{Z(s)} = s\,\frac{1}{sZ(s)} = s\mathcal{L}[A(t)]$$

Thus, from Theorem 3, Sec. 6.2, it follows that

$$h(t) = \frac{dA(t)}{dt} = A'(t)$$

Fig. 6.26.   Plot showing the synthesis of a general voltage by means of impulses.

In words, *the response of a system to a unit impulse is the derivative of the response of the system to a unit step function.*

Now let $E(t)$, in the general case, be approximated by a series of infinitesimal impulses, as shown in Fig. 6.26.   For the first impulse, whose magnitude* is $E(\lambda_0)\Delta\lambda_0$, the (infinitesimal) resultant current is the product of the magnitude of the impulse and the current response to a unit impulse, namely, $h(t) \equiv A'(t)$:

$$E(\lambda_0)\Delta\lambda_0 A'(t)$$

The second impulse does not occur until $t = \lambda_1$; hence the current which it produces is

$$E(\lambda_1)\Delta\lambda_1 A'(t - \lambda_1)$$

* The magnitude of an impulse is measured by the area of its representative figure *i.e.*, by voltage $\times$ duration.

and in general, the current produced by the $(i + 1)$st impulse is

$$E(\lambda_i)\Delta\lambda_i A'(t - \lambda_i)$$

If these contributions to the total current are added, we obtain for the current flowing at a general time t,

$$i = E(\lambda_0)\Delta\lambda_0 A'(t) + E(\lambda_1)\Delta\lambda_1 A'(t - \lambda_1) + \cdots$$
$$+ E(\lambda_i)\Delta\lambda_i A'(t - \lambda_i) + \cdots$$
$$= \Sigma E(\lambda_i)A'(t - \lambda_i)\Delta\lambda_i$$

the summation extending over all impulses which have acted on the system up to the time t. In the limit when each $\Delta\lambda \to 0$, the last sum becomes an integral, and we have Formula 7.

Example 3

If $y_0 = y_0' = 0$, find the solution of the differential equation $y'' + 5y' + 4y = f(t)$, when $f(t)$ is (a) the unit step function and (b) the unit impulse. Use these results in (8) and (7), respectively, to find the solution of the given equation when $f(t) = e^{-2t}$, and check this solution by solving directly when $f(t) = e^{-2t}$.

If $f(t) = u(t)$, then, taking the Laplace transform of the given equation, we have

$$\mathcal{L}(y) = \frac{1}{s(s + 1)(s + 4)}$$

and by an immediate application of the first Heaviside expansion theorem we find

$$y(t) \equiv A(t) = \frac{1}{4} - \frac{e^{-t}}{3} + \frac{e^{-4t}}{12}$$

If $f(t)$ is the unit impulse, then we have similarly

$$\mathcal{L}(y) = \frac{1}{(s + 1)(s + 4)}$$

and

$$y(t) \equiv h(t) = \frac{e^{-t}}{3} - \frac{e^{-4t}}{3}$$

We note in passing that $h(t)$ is the derivative of $A(t)$.

Now according to Eq. (8), the solution of the given differential equation when $f(t) = e^{-2t}$ is

$$y = A(t)f(0) + \int_0^t A(t - \lambda)f'(\lambda)d\lambda$$
$$= \left(\frac{1}{4} - \frac{e^{-t}}{3} + \frac{e^{-4t}}{12}\right)(1) + \int_0^t \left(\frac{1}{4} - \frac{e^{-(t-\lambda)}}{3} + \frac{e^{-4(t-\lambda)}}{12}\right)(-2e^{-2\lambda})d\lambda$$
$$= \frac{1}{4} - \frac{e^{-t}}{3} + \frac{e^{-4t}}{12} - \frac{1}{2}\int_0^t e^{-2\lambda}d\lambda + \frac{2e^{-t}}{3}\int_0^t e^{-\lambda}d\lambda - \frac{e^{-4t}}{6}\int_0^t e^{2\lambda}\,d\lambda$$
$$= \frac{1}{4} - \frac{e^{-t}}{3} + \frac{e^{-4t}}{12} - \frac{1}{2}\left(\frac{1 - e^{-2t}}{2}\right) + \frac{2e^{-t}}{3}(1 - e^{-t}) - \frac{e^{-4t}}{6}\left(\frac{e^{2t} - 1}{2}\right)$$
$$= \frac{e^{-t}}{3} + \frac{e^{-4t}}{6} - \frac{e^{-2t}}{2}$$

Likewise, according to Eq. (7), the solution when $f(t) = e^{-2t}$ can be written

$$
\begin{aligned}
y &= \int_0^t A'(t - \lambda) f(\lambda) d\lambda = \int_0^t h(t - \lambda) f(\lambda) d\lambda \\
&= \int_0^t \left(\frac{e^{-(t-\lambda)}}{3} - \frac{e^{-4(t-\lambda)}}{3} \right) e^{-2\lambda} d\lambda \\
&= \frac{e^{-t}}{3} + \frac{e^{-4t}}{6} - \frac{e^{-2t}}{2}
\end{aligned}
$$

as before.

In this simple illustration it is of course even easier to find the solution of

$$ y'' + 5y' + 4y = e^{-2t} $$

by direct attack. For we have immediately

$$ \mathcal{L}(y) = \frac{1}{(s + 1)(s + 4)(s + 2)} $$

and, by the first Heaviside expansion theorem,

$$ y = \frac{e^{-t}}{3} + \frac{e^{-4t}}{6} - \frac{e^{-2t}}{2} $$

as before.

EXERCISES

Using the convolution theorem, find y if

1. $\mathcal{L}(y) = \dfrac{1}{(s^2 + 1)^2}$

2. $\mathcal{L}(y) = \dfrac{s^2 + s}{(s^2 + 1)(s^2 + 2s + 2)}$

3. $\mathcal{L}(y) = \dfrac{1}{(s^2 + 2)^2 - 4s^2}$

4. Find the solution of $y' + 3y + 2 \displaystyle\int_0^t y \, dt = f(t)$ for which $y_0 = 0$, when $f(t) = u(t)$ and when $f(t) = t$, and verify that these solutions satisfy (8).

5. Find the solution of $y'' + 3y' + 2y = f(t)$ for which $y_0 = y_0' = 0$ when $f(t)$ is the unit impulse and when $f(t) = t$, and verify that these solutions satisfy (7).

CHAPTER 7

PARTIAL DIFFERENTIAL EQUATIONS

7.1 Introduction. In our previous work we have seen how the analysis of mechanical and electrical systems containing lumped parameters leads frequently to total differential equations. However, assumptions to the effect that all masses exist as mass points, that all springs are weightless, or that the elements of an electrical circuit are concentrated in ideal resistances, inductances, and condensers rather than continuously distributed are often not sufficiently accurate. In such

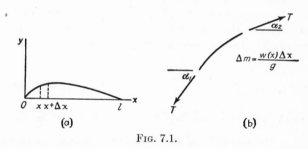

Fig. 7.1.

cases a more realistic analysis usually leads to one or more partial differential equations which must be solved to obtain a description of the behavior of the system. In this chapter we shall discuss such equations as they commonly arise in engineering and in physics. We shall begin our study by examining in detail the derivation from physical principles of certain typical partial differential equations. Then, knowing the forms of most frequent occurrence, we shall investigate methods of solution and their application to specific problems.

7.2 The Derivation of Equations. One of the first problems to be attacked through the use of partial differential equations was that of the vibration of a stretched, flexible string. Today, after nearly 250 years, it is still an excellent initial example.

Suppose, then, that we have an elastic string, stretched under a tension T between two points a distance l apart. The weight of the string per unit length after it is stretched we suppose to be a known function $w(x)$ of the distance x from one end of the string. In formulating the problem we assume that

199

a. The motion takes place entirely in one plane, and in this plane each particle moves at right angles to the equilibrium position of the string.

b. The deflections of the string during the motion are so small that the resulting change in length of the string has no effect upon the tension T.

c. The string is perfectly flexible, *i.e.*, can transmit force only in the direction of its length.

d. The force of gravity is negligible in comparison with the tension T.

e. The effect of friction can be neglected.

f. The slope of the deflection curve is at all points and at all times so small that sin α can be replaced by tan α, where α is the inclination angle of the tangent to the deflection curve.

With these assumptions in mind, let us consider a general infinitesimal segment of the string as a free body (Fig. 7.1*b*). By assumption *a*, the mass of such an element is $\Delta m = w(x)\Delta x/g$. By assumption *b*, the forces which act at the ends of the element are the same, namely, T. By assumption *c*, these forces are directed along the respective tangents to the deflection curve. By assumptions *d* and *e*, there are no other forces acting on the element. Hence the transverse motion of Δm is produced solely by the components of these forces which are normal to the length of the string:

$$T \sin \alpha_2 = T \sin \alpha \Big|_{x+\Delta x} \qquad \text{and} \qquad T \sin \alpha_1 = T \sin \alpha \Big|_x$$

The acceleration produced in Δm by these forces is approximately $\dfrac{\partial^2 y}{\partial t^2}$, where y is the ordinate of an arbitrary point of the element. The time derivative is here written as a partial derivative because obviously y depends not only upon t but upon x as well. Applying Newton's law to the element, we thus can write

$$\frac{w(x)\Delta x}{g} \frac{\partial^2 y}{\partial t^2} = T \sin \alpha \Big|_{x+\Delta x} - T \sin \alpha \Big|_x$$

or, dividing by Δx and using (*f*),

$$\frac{w(x)}{g} \frac{\partial^2 y}{\partial t^2} = T \left(\frac{\tan \alpha \Big|_{x+\Delta x} - \tan \alpha \Big|_x}{\Delta x} \right)$$

The right-hand side of the last equation consists of the difference between tan α at $x + \Delta x$ and at x, divided by the difference Δx. In other words, it is precisely the difference quotient for the function tan α. Hence its limit as $\Delta x \to 0$ is the derivative of tan α with respect to x, that is, $\dfrac{\partial \tan \alpha}{\partial x}$. But since $\tan \alpha = \dfrac{\partial y}{\partial x}$, this can be written simply as

$\dfrac{\partial^2 y}{\partial x^2}$. Our final result, then, is that the deflection curve of the string, as a function of both x and t, satisfies the partial differential equation

(1)
$$\frac{\partial^2 y}{\partial t^2} = \frac{Tg}{w(x)} \frac{\partial^2 y}{\partial x^2}.$$

In most problems the weight of the string per unit length $w(x)$ is a constant, say ρ. When this is the case it is customary to write

$$\frac{Tg}{w(x)} = a^2$$

The dimensions of a^2 are

$$\frac{[\text{Force}][\text{acceleration}]}{[\text{Weight/unit length}]} = \frac{\dfrac{ML}{T^2} \dfrac{L}{T^2}}{\dfrac{ML}{T^2} \dfrac{1}{L}} = \frac{L^2}{T^2}$$

Thus a has the dimensions of velocity. The significance of this will become apparent when we discuss the solution of the **one-dimensional wave equation**

(2)
$$\frac{\partial^2 y}{\partial t^2} = a^2 \frac{\partial^2 y}{\partial x^2}$$

As a second important problem leading to a partial differential equation let us consider a shaft of length l vibrating torsionally. The material

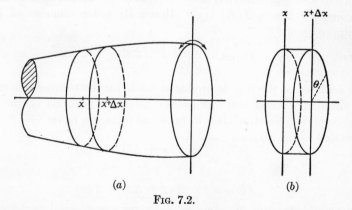

(a)   (b)

Fig. 7.2.

of the shaft we suppose to have a modulus of elasticity in shear of E, and to have weight per unit volume ρ. The area of cross section of the shaft at a distance x from one end is a known function $A(x)$. The polar moment of inertia of a general cross section about its center of gravity is likewise a known function of x, $J(x)$. We assume further that *a.* All cross sections of the shaft remain plane during rotation.

b. Each cross section rotates about its center of gravity.

c. The shape of a general cross section does not depart greatly from a circle.

d. The effect of friction can be neglected.

We begin by recalling from strength of materials the formula

$$\theta = \frac{Tl}{E_s J}$$

for the angle of twist θ produced in a uniform circular shaft of length l by a torque T. Applying this to an infinitesimal length of the shaft for which $l = \Delta x$, and for which θ is of course also infinitesimal, we have

$$T = E_s J \frac{\Delta\theta}{\Delta x}$$

Therefore in the limit as $\Delta x \to 0$, we find that the torque transmitted *through* a cross section of the shaft is $T = E_s J (d\theta/dx)$, or

$$(3) \qquad\qquad T = E_s J \frac{\partial\theta}{\partial x}$$

if, as in this problem, θ depends on both x and t.

Now consider as a free body an infinitesimal segment of the shaft bounded by two cross sections a distance Δx apart (Fig. 7.2*b*). The mass of such a disk is approximately $\Delta m = A(x)\Delta x\, \rho/g$. Its radius of gyration is approximately $k = \sqrt{J(x)/A(x)}$. Hence its polar moment of inertia ΔI is approximately

$$\Delta I = k^2\,\Delta m = \frac{J(x)}{A(x)} \frac{A(x)\Delta x\rho}{g} = \frac{J(x)\rho\,\Delta x}{g}$$

The rotation of the disk is produced solely by the torques transmitted to it through its end sections by the adjacent portions of the shaft. Hence, applying Newton's law in torsional form, we have

$$\frac{J(x)\rho\,\Delta x}{g} \frac{\partial^2\theta}{\partial t^2} = T(x + \Delta x) - T(x)$$

or

$$\frac{J(x)\rho}{g} \frac{\partial^2\theta}{\partial t^2} = \frac{T(x + \Delta x) - T(x)}{\Delta x}$$

As $\Delta x \to 0$, the right-hand member approaches $\dfrac{\partial T}{\partial x}$, and thus in the limit

$$\frac{J(x)\rho}{g} \frac{\partial^2\theta}{\partial t^2} = \frac{\partial T}{\partial x}$$

Using (3), this can be written

(4)
$$\frac{J(x)\rho}{g}\frac{\partial^2\theta}{\partial t^2} = \frac{\partial\left[E_sJ(x)\dfrac{\partial\theta}{\partial x}\right]}{\partial x} = E_s\frac{\partial\left[J(x)\dfrac{\partial\theta}{\partial x}\right]}{\partial x}$$

since E_s is a constant.

In the important special case in which the shaft is of uniform cross section, $J(x)$ is a constant. When this is true, it can be removed from the partial derivative on the right and then canceled from the equation, leaving

(5)
$$\frac{\rho}{g}\frac{\partial^2\theta}{\partial t^2} = E_s\frac{\partial^2\theta}{\partial x^2}$$

If, finally, we set $E_sg/\rho = a^2$, we see that the angular displacement θ of a uniform shaft vibrating torsionally satisfies precisely the same equation as does the displacement y of a uniform string vibrating transversely. In the present problem, as in the former, it is easy to verify that a has the dimensions of velocity.

Another vibration problem of great practical importance is that of the transverse vibrations of a beam. Let the beam be of length l, and let its weight per unit volume be ρ and its modulus of elasticity be E. The area of a general cross section at a distance x from one end we suppose to be a known function $A(x)$. Likewise the moment of inertia of such a cross section about its neutral axis we suppose known, say $I(x)$. We further assume that

  a. All particles of the beam move in a purely transverse direction, *i.e.*, the slight rotation of the cross sections during the vibration is negligible.

  b. Gravitational forces can be neglected.

  c. The effect of friction is negligible.

From Sec. 2.6 we recall the following formulas of beam flexure

(6)
$$M(x) = EI\frac{d^2y}{dx^2}, \qquad \frac{dM(x)}{dx} = -Q(x), \qquad \frac{dQ(x)}{dx} = w(x)$$

where $M(x) =$ bending moment at a general section
  $Q(x) =$ shear, or net vertical force, to the right of a general section
  $w(x) =$ load per unit length at a general section

During vibration, the unit loading on the beam is simply the distributed inertia force of the mass of the beam. The mass of a segment of the beam of length Δx is approximately $A(x)\Delta x(\rho/g)$, and the transverse acceleration of such a mass element is approximately $\dfrac{\partial^2y}{\partial t^2}$, where y is the displacement of an arbitrary particle of the segment. The inertia load per unit length is therefore

$$w(x) = \frac{\left[A(x)\Delta x \dfrac{\rho}{g}\right] \dfrac{\partial^2 y}{\partial t^2}}{\Delta x} = \frac{\rho A(x)}{g} \frac{\partial^2 y}{\partial t^2}$$

Substituting this into the chain of equations (6), and noting that the derivatives are now partial derivatives since all quantities change with t as well as with x, we find

$$\frac{\rho A(x)}{g} \frac{\partial^2 y}{\partial t^2} = w(x) = \frac{\partial Q(x)}{\partial x} = \frac{\partial \left[-\dfrac{\partial M(x)}{\partial x}\right]}{\partial x} = -\frac{\partial^2 \left[EI(x) \dfrac{\partial^2 y}{\partial x^2}\right]}{\partial x^2}$$

The deflection curve of the beam thus satisfies the partial differential equation

(7)
$$\frac{\partial^2 \left[EI(x) \dfrac{\partial^2 y}{\partial x^2}\right]}{\partial x^2} = -\frac{\rho A(x)}{g} \frac{\partial^2 y}{\partial t^2}$$

In many important applications the beam is of constant cross section. If this is the case both $A(x)$ and $I(x)$ are constant, and (7) reduces to

$$EI \frac{\partial^4 y}{\partial x^4} = -\frac{\rho A}{g} \frac{\partial^2 y}{\partial t^2}$$

or

(8)
$$a^2 \frac{\partial^4 y}{\partial x^4} = -\frac{\partial^2 y}{\partial t^2}$$

where $a^2 = (EIg/A\rho)$. In this case a does *not* have the dimensions of velocity.

As a final example from the field of vibrations, we consider the motion of a stretched, uniform, perfectly flexible membrane, such as a drumhead. Paralleling the analysis of the vibrating string, we assume that

  a. All particles of the membrane move in a purely transverse direction.

  b. The tension per unit length T in the membrane is the same at all points and in all directions, and does not change during the vibration.

  c. The membrane can transmit force only in the tangential direction.

  d. The effect of gravity can be neglected.

  e. The effect of friction can be neglected.

  f. The deflections are such that the approximation $\sin \alpha = \tan \alpha$ can be applied to all inclination angles.

Now the element of the membrane shown in Fig. 7.3 moves in the z-direction by virtue of the vertical components of the tensile forces which act across its edges. These components are obtained by multiplying the actual tensile forces, $T \Delta x$ or $T \Delta y$ as the case may be, by the sine of the angle at which they are inclined to the horizontal. Since these angles vary along the edges of the element, we evaluate the

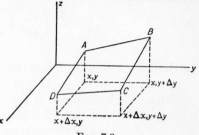

Fig. 7.3.

sines, or rather the tangents, $\dfrac{\partial z}{\partial x}$ and $\dfrac{\partial z}{\partial y}$, at the mid-points of the sides. Thus we have

$$F_z \text{ along } AB = (T\,\Delta y)\frac{\partial z}{\partial x}\bigg|_{\substack{x \\ y+\frac{1}{2}\Delta y}}$$

$$F_z \text{ along } DC = (T\,\Delta y)\frac{\partial z}{\partial x}\bigg|_{\substack{x+\Delta x \\ y+\frac{1}{2}\Delta y}}$$

$$F_z \text{ along } AD = (T\,\Delta x)\frac{\partial z}{\partial y}\bigg|_{\substack{x+\frac{1}{2}\Delta x \\ y}}$$

$$F_z \text{ along } BC = (T\,\Delta x)\frac{\partial z}{\partial y}\bigg|_{\substack{x+\frac{1}{2}\Delta x \\ y+\Delta y}}$$

If the weight of the membrane per unit area be ρ, the mass of the element is $(\rho/g)\Delta x\,\Delta y$. Applying Newton's law, we therefore can write

$$\left(\frac{\rho}{g}\Delta x\,\Delta y\right)\frac{\partial^2 z}{\partial t^2} = -T\,\Delta y\frac{\partial z}{\partial x}\bigg|_{\substack{x \\ y+\frac{1}{2}\Delta y}} + T\,\Delta y\frac{\partial z}{\partial x}\bigg|_{\substack{x+\Delta x \\ y+\frac{1}{2}\Delta y}} - T\,\Delta x\frac{\partial z}{\partial y}\bigg|_{\substack{x+\frac{1}{2}\Delta x \\ y}}$$

$$+ T\,\Delta x\frac{\partial z}{\partial y}\bigg|_{\substack{x+\frac{1}{2}\Delta x \\ y+\Delta y}}$$

The minus signs enter because as Δx and Δy approach zero the z-components of the tensile forces across parallel edges of the element necessarily act in opposite directions.

Dividing by Δx and Δy, we have

$$\frac{\rho}{g}\frac{\partial^2 z}{\partial t^2} = T\left(\frac{\dfrac{\partial z}{\partial x}\bigg|_{\substack{x+\Delta x \\ y+\frac{1}{2}\Delta y}} - \dfrac{\partial z}{\partial x}\bigg|_{\substack{x \\ y+\frac{1}{2}\Delta y}}}{\Delta x}\right) + T\left(\frac{\dfrac{\partial z}{\partial y}\bigg|_{\substack{x+\frac{1}{2}\Delta x \\ y+\Delta y}} - \dfrac{\partial z}{\partial y}\bigg|_{\substack{x+\frac{1}{2}\Delta x \\ y}}}{\Delta y}\right)$$

In the limit as Δx and Δy approach zero this yields the **two-dimensional wave equation,**

$$(9) \qquad \frac{\partial^2 z}{\partial t^2} = \frac{Tg}{\rho} \left(\frac{\partial^2 z}{\partial x^2} + \frac{\partial^2 z}{\partial y^2} \right) = a^2 \left(\frac{\partial^2 z}{\partial x^2} + \frac{\partial^2 z}{\partial y^2} \right)$$

In this case $a = \sqrt{Tg/\rho}$ has the dimensions of velocity.

An entirely different class of problems leading to partial differential equations is encountered in the study of the flow of heat in conducting solids. To obtain the differential equation governing this phenomenon, we must make use of the following experimental laws.

  a. Heat flows in the direction of decreasing temperature.

  b. The quantity of heat required to produce a given temperature change in a body is proportional to the mass of the body and to the temperature change.

  c. The rate at which heat flows through an area is proportional to the area and to the temperature gradient normal to the area.

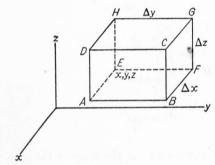

Fig. 7.4.

The proportionality constant in (b) is called the **specific heat** c of the material. The proportionality constant in (c) is called the **thermal conductivity** k.

Let us now consider the thermal conditions in an infinitesimal element of a conducting solid in which there are neither sources nor sinks of heat (Fig. 7.4). In general, heat will flow through all six faces of the element, and by computing the flow through each face we can obtain an expression for the rate at which the element is gaining heat. In particular, if $u(x,y,z,t)$ denote the temperature at any point at any instant, the amount of heat flowing into the element through the rear face $EFGH$ is by (c), approximately

$$-k \, \Delta y \, \Delta z \, \frac{\partial u}{\partial x} \bigg|_{\substack{x \\ y+\frac{1}{2}\Delta y \\ z+\frac{1}{2}\Delta z}}$$

where we have evaluated the normal temperature gradient $\dfrac{\partial u}{\partial x}$ at the mid-point of the face $(x, y + \frac{1}{2}\Delta y, z + \frac{1}{2}\Delta z)$. The minus sign is necessary because the element *gains* heat through the rear face if the normal temperature gradient is *negative*. Similarly the element gains heat through the front face at the approximate rate

$$k \, \Delta y \, \Delta z \, \frac{\partial u}{\partial x}\bigg|_{\substack{x+\Delta x \\ y+\frac{1}{2}\Delta y \\ z+\frac{1}{2}\Delta z}}$$

The sum of these two expressions is the net rate at which the element is gaining heat because of heat flow in the x-direction.

In the same way we find that the rates at which the element gains heat because of flow in the y- and z-directions are, respectively,

$$-k \, \Delta x \, \Delta z \, \frac{\partial u}{\partial y}\bigg|_{\substack{x+\frac{1}{2}\Delta x \\ y \\ z+\frac{1}{2}\Delta z}} + k \, \Delta x \, \Delta z \, \frac{\partial u}{\partial y}\bigg|_{\substack{x+\frac{1}{2}\Delta x \\ y+\Delta y \\ z+\frac{1}{2}\Delta z}}$$

and

$$-k \, \Delta x \, \Delta y \, \frac{\partial u}{\partial z}\bigg|_{\substack{x+\frac{1}{2}\Delta x \\ y+\frac{1}{2}\Delta y \\ z}} + k \, \Delta x \, \Delta y \, \frac{\partial u}{\partial z}\bigg|_{\substack{x+\frac{1}{2}\Delta x \\ y+\frac{1}{2}\Delta y \\ z+\Delta z}}$$

The sum of all these terms gives the net rate at which the element is gaining heat because of the flow of heat through its entire surface. If heat is neither created nor destroyed within the element (as we have assumed), this rate of increase of heat must be exactly measurable as a rate of increase of the temperature of the element. By (b), a quantity of heat ΔH flowing into the element in time Δt is related to the resulting change in temperature Δu by the equation

$$\Delta H = c \, \Delta m \, \Delta u = c\gamma \, \Delta x \, \Delta y \, \Delta z \, \Delta u$$

where γ is the density of the material in the element. Hence, dividing by Δt, we find as an alternative approximation for the rate of increase of heat in the element, the expression

$$c\gamma \, \Delta x \, \Delta y \, \Delta z \, \frac{\Delta u}{\Delta t}$$

Equating the two estimates which we now have for $\Delta H/\Delta t$, we obtain

$$c\gamma \, \Delta x \, \Delta y \, \Delta z \, \frac{\Delta u}{\Delta t} = k \, \Delta y \, \Delta z \left(\frac{\partial u}{\partial x}\bigg|_{\substack{x+\Delta x \\ y+\frac{1}{2}\Delta y \\ z+\frac{1}{2}\Delta z}} - \frac{\partial u}{\partial x}\bigg|_{\substack{x \\ y+\frac{1}{2}\Delta y \\ z+\frac{1}{2}\Delta z}} \right)$$

$$+ k \, \Delta x \, \Delta z \left(\frac{\partial u}{\partial y}\bigg|_{\substack{x+\frac{1}{2}\Delta x \\ y+\Delta y \\ z+\frac{1}{2}\Delta z}} - \frac{\partial u}{\partial y}\bigg|_{\substack{x+\frac{1}{2}\Delta x \\ y \\ z+\frac{1}{2}\Delta z}} \right) + k \, \Delta x \, \Delta y \left(\frac{\partial u}{\partial z}\bigg|_{\substack{x+\frac{1}{2}\Delta x \\ y+\frac{1}{2}\Delta y \\ z+\Delta z}} - \frac{\partial u}{\partial z}\bigg|_{\substack{x+\frac{1}{2}\Delta x \\ y+\frac{1}{2}\Delta y \\ z}} \right)$$

Dividing by $k \, \Delta x \, \Delta y \, \Delta z$ and letting $\Delta x, \Delta y, \Delta z, \Delta t \to 0$ we obtain finally the **equation of heat conduction**

$$(10) \qquad \frac{c\gamma}{k} \frac{\partial u}{\partial t} = \frac{\partial^2 u}{\partial x^2} + \frac{\partial^2 u}{\partial y^2} + \frac{\partial^2 u}{\partial z^2}$$

As a final example of the derivation of partial differential equations, we consider the flow of electricity in a long transmission line. We assume the cable to be imperfectly insulated so that there is both capacitance and current leakage to ground. Specifically, let

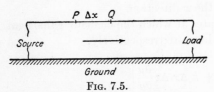

FIG. 7.5.

$\quad x$ = distance from sending end of the cable

$e(x,t)$ = potential at any point along the cable at any instant

$i(x,t)$ = current at any point along the cable at any instant

$\quad R$ = resistance of the cable per unit length

$\quad L$ = inductance of the cable per unit length

$\quad G$ = conductance to ground per unit length of the cable

$\quad C$ = capacitance to ground per unit length of the cable

Now the drop in potential along the element $PQ = \Delta x$ is the sum of the resistive and inductive drops, or

$$e(x + \Delta x,t) - e(x,t) = \Delta e = -(R \, \Delta x)i - (L \, \Delta x)\frac{\partial i}{\partial t}$$

Dividing by Δx and letting $\Delta x \to 0$, we obtain the first of the pair of partial differential equations governing the problem:

$$(11) \qquad \frac{\partial e}{\partial x} = -Ri - L \frac{\partial i}{\partial t}$$

Likewise, the change in current along the element PQ is the sum of the loss due to leakage to ground and the capacitative loss due to the varying charge resident on the element, or

$$i(x + \Delta x,t) - i(x,t) = \Delta i = -(G \, \Delta x)e - (C \, \Delta x)\frac{\partial e}{\partial t}$$

Dividing by Δx and letting $\Delta x \to 0$, we obtain the second of the transmission-line equations:

$$(12) \qquad \frac{\partial i}{\partial x} = -Ge - C \frac{\partial e}{\partial t}$$

If we differentiate the first of these equations with respect to x and the second with respect to t, we obtain

$$\frac{\partial^2 e}{\partial x^2} = -R \frac{\partial i}{\partial x} - L \frac{\partial^2 i}{\partial x \, \partial t}$$

$$\frac{\partial^2 i}{\partial t \, \partial x} = -G \frac{\partial e}{\partial t} - C \frac{\partial^2 e}{\partial t^2}$$

If we eliminate the term $\dfrac{\partial^2 i}{\partial t \, \partial x} \left(\equiv \dfrac{\partial^2 i}{\partial x \, \partial t} \right)$ between these two equations, and then substitute for $\dfrac{\partial i}{\partial x}$ from (12) we find that e satisfies the equation

$$(13) \qquad \frac{\partial^2 e}{\partial x^2} = LC \frac{\partial^2 e}{\partial t^2} + (RC + GL) \frac{\partial e}{\partial t} + RGe$$

By differentiating Eq. (11) with respect to t, and Eq. (12) with respect to x, and then eliminating the derivatives of e, we obtain a similar equation for i.

$$(14) \qquad \frac{\partial^2 i}{\partial x^2} = LC \frac{\partial^2 i}{\partial t^2} + (RC + GL) \frac{\partial i}{\partial t} + RGi$$

Equations (13) and (14) are known as the **telephone equations.**

Two special cases of the telephone equations are worthy of note.

a. If leakage and inductance are negligible, that is, if $G = L = 0$, we have

$$\frac{\partial^2 e}{\partial x^2} = RC \frac{\partial e}{\partial t}$$

$$\frac{\partial^2 i}{\partial x^2} = RC \frac{\partial i}{\partial t}$$

These are known as the **telegraph equations.**

b. At high frequencies the factor introduced by the time differentiation is large. Hence the terms involving i and $\partial i/\partial t$ are insignificant in comparison with the term containing $\partial^2 i/\partial t^2$. In this case the telephone equations reduce to

$$\frac{\partial^2 e}{\partial x^2} = LC \frac{\partial^2 e}{\partial t^2}$$

$$\frac{\partial^2 i}{\partial x^2} = LC \frac{\partial^2 i}{\partial t^2}$$

Each of these is an example of the one-dimensional wave equation, $1/\sqrt{LC}$ having in fact the dimensions of velocity. These equations are obtained at any frequency, of course, if $R = G = 0$.

It is interesting to note that nowhere in the derivation of any of the preceding equations was any use made of boundary conditions. In other words, the same differential equation is satisfied by a vibrating beam, for instance, whether the beam be built-in at one end and free at the other, built-in at both ends, or simply supported at both ends. Similarly the flow of heat in a body is described by the same differential equation whether the surface be maintained at a constant temperature, insulated against heat loss, or allowed to radiate freely. In general, as we shall soon see, the role of boundary conditions, for example permanent condition of constraint or of temperature, is to determine the *form* of those solutions of a partial differential equation which are relevant to a particular problem. Subsequent to this, the initial conditions of displacement, velocity, or temperature, say, determine specific values for the arbitrary constants appearing in these solutions.

EXERCISES

1. Derive the partial differential equation satisfied by the amplitude of the transverse vibrations of a beam of general cross section when an elastic restoring force proportional to the displacement acts along the entire length of the beam.

2. Consider the transmission-line equations in the case when $RC = LG$, and put $a^2 = RG$ and $v^2 = 1/LC$. Prove that if $e(x,t)$, or equally well $i(x,t)$, be written

$$e(x,t) = \epsilon^{-avt} y(x,t)$$

then the function y satisfies the wave equation

$$v^2 \frac{\partial^2 y}{\partial x^2} = \frac{\partial^2 y}{\partial t^2}$$

(Note: To avoid confusion, ϵ is used here instead of e to denote the base of natural logarithms.)

3. Derive the partial differential equation which describes the transverse vibrations of a uniform chain suspended from one end.

4. Derive the partial differential equation which describes the longitudinal vibrations of a shaft of general cross section.

$$Ans. \quad A(x) \frac{\partial^2 u}{\partial t^2} = \frac{Eg}{\rho} \frac{\partial \left(A(x) \frac{\partial u}{\partial x} \right)}{\partial x}$$

5. Derive the partial differential equation satisfied by the concentration of a liquid diffusing through a porous solid. (Hint: The rate at which liquid diffuses through an area is proportional to the area and to the concentration gradient perpendicular to the area.)

7.3 The D'Alembert* Solution of the Wave Equation.

Each of the partial differential equations we have so far encountered can be solved by an important method of considerable generality, known as separation of variables. The one-dimensional wave equation, however, can also be solved in a more special manner. In view of the importance of this

---

* Jean le Rond D'Alembert (1717–1783) was a great French mathematician.

equation it will be worth our while to examine this solution before proceeding to the more general process.

The whole matter is very simple. In fact, given the equation

(1)
$$a^2 \frac{\partial^2 y}{\partial x^2} = \frac{\partial^2 y}{\partial t^2}$$

it is evident by direct substitution that if f and g are any two functions possessing second derivatives, then

$$f(x - at) \qquad \text{and} \qquad g(x + at)$$

are solutions of (1), and so too is any linear combination of these functions.

This form of the solution of the wave equation is especially useful for revealing the significance of the parameter a, and its dimensions of velocity. Suppose specifically that we consider the vibrations of a uniform string* stretching from $-\infty$ to ∞. If its transverse displacement be given by

$$y(x,t) = f(x - at) + g(x + at)$$

we have in fact two waves traveling in opposite directions along the string, each with velocity a. For consider the function $f(x - at)$. At $t = 0$ it defines the curve $y = f(x)$, and at any later time, $t = t_1$, it defines the curve $y = f(x - at_1)$. But these two curves are identical except that the latter is translated to the right a distance at_1. Thus the entire configuration moves along the string without distortion a distance at_1 in t_1 units of time. The velocity of this progression is therefore

$$v = \frac{at_1}{t_1} = a$$

Similarly the function $g(x + at)$ defines a configuration which moves to the left along the string with constant velocity a. The total displacement of the string is, of course, the algebraic sum of these two traveling waves.

To carry the solution through in detail, let us suppose that the initial displacement of the string at any point is given by $\phi(x)$ and that the initial velocity of the string at any point is given by $\theta(x)$. Then as conditions to determine the form of f and g we have

$$y(x,0) = \phi(x) = f(x) + g(x)$$

$$\left. \frac{\partial y}{\partial t} \right|_{x,0} = \theta(x) = -af'(x) + ag'(x)$$

* The use of the string as an illustration is purely a matter of convenience, and any quantity satisfying the wave equation possesses the properties developed for the string.

Dividing the second of these equations by a and then integrating, we find

$$-f(x) + g(x) = \frac{1}{a} \int_{x_0}^{x} \theta(x) dx$$

Combining this with the first equation, $f(x) + g(x) = \phi(x)$, and introducing the dummy variable s in the integrals, we obtain

$$f(x) = \frac{1}{2} \left[\phi(x) - \frac{1}{a} \int_{x_0}^{x} \theta(s) ds \right]$$

$$g(x) = \frac{1}{2} \left[\phi(x) + \frac{1}{a} \int_{x_0}^{x} \theta(s) ds \right]$$

With the form of f and g known, we can now write

$$y \equiv f(x - at) + g(x + at) = \left[\frac{\phi(x - at)}{2} - \frac{1}{2a} \int_{x_0}^{x-at} \theta(s) ds \right]$$
$$+ \left[\frac{\phi(x + at)}{2} + \frac{1}{2a} \int_{x_0}^{x+at} \theta(s) ds \right]$$

or, combining the integrals,

$$(2) \qquad y(x,t) = \frac{\phi(x - at) + \phi(x + at)}{2} + \frac{1}{2a} \int_{x-at}^{x+at} \theta(s) ds$$

Example 1

A string stretching to infinity in both directions is given the initial displacement

$$\phi(x) = \frac{1}{1 + 8x^2}$$

and released from rest.   Determine its subsequent motion.

Since $\theta(x) \equiv 0$, we have simply

$$y(x,t) = \frac{\phi(x - at) + \phi(x + at)}{2} = \frac{1}{2} \left[\frac{1}{1 + 8(x - at)^2} + \frac{1}{1 + 8(x + at)^2} \right]$$

The deflection of the string when $(at) = 0, 0.5$, and 1.0 is shown in Fig. 7.6.

The motion of a semi-infinite string is completely equivalent to the motion of one-half of a two-way infinite string having a fixed point, or **node,** located at some finite point, say the origin.   To capitalize on this fact we need only imagine the actual string, stretching from 0 to ∞, to be extended in the opposite direction to $-\infty$.   The initial conditions of velocity and displacement for the new portion we define to be identical in value but opposite in sign to those given for the actual string.* The solution for the resulting two-way infinite string can be written down at once, using Eq. (2). In the nature of the extended initial conditions, the wave traveling to the right from the left portion of the string will, at the origin, always be equal but opposite in sign to the wave traveling to the left from the right-hand portion of the string. Hence the string will

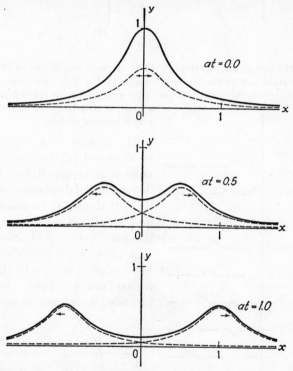

Fig. 7.6. Plot showing the propagation of a disturbance along a two-way infinite string.

always remain at rest at the origin, and the solution for the right half of the extended string will be precisely the solution of the original problem.

Example 2

A semi-infinite string is given the displacement shown in Fig. 7.7a and released from rest. Determine its subsequent motion.

We first imagine the string extended to $-\infty$ and released from rest in the extended initial configuration shown in Fig. 7.7b. Since $\theta(x) = 0$, we have from (2)

$$y(x,t) = \frac{\phi(x - at) + \phi(x + at)}{2}$$

* This method of extending the initial conditions is sufficient but not necessary (see Exercise 4, at the end of this section.)

where $\phi(x)$ is the displacement function shown in Fig. 7.7b. We thus have two displacement waves, each of shape defined by $\frac{1}{2}\phi(x)$, one traveling to the right and one

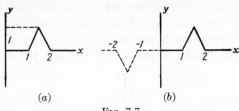

(a)   (b)

FIG. 7.7.

traveling to the left along the string. Plots of these waves and of their algebraic sum over the right half of the string are shown in Fig. 7.8. An inspection of these configurations reveals the important fact that a displacement wave is reflected from a fixed, or closed, end without distortion but with a reversal of sign.

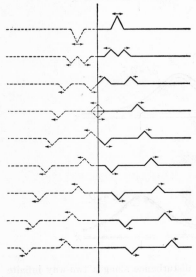

The motion of a finite string can be obtained as the motion of a segment of an infinite string with suitably defined initial displacement and velocity. If the string be given between 0 and l, say, it is first necessary to imagine it extended from 0 to $-l$ with initial conditions which are equal but opposite in sign to those for the actual string. Then the string is extended to infinity in each direction

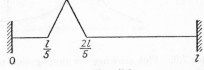

FIG. 7.8. Plot showing the propagation of a disturbance along a one-way infinite string.

FIG. 7.9.

subject to initial conditions which duplicate with period $2l$ the initial configuration between l and $-l$.

Example 3

A string of length l is given the displacement shown in Fig. 7.9 and released from rest. Determine its subsequent motion.

The necessary extension of the string and one half cycle of its motion are shown in Fig. 7.10.

An inspection of Fig. 7.10 shows that the period of the motion, *i.e.*, the least time for its return to its initial state, is just the time for either of the traveling waves to traverse a distance $2l$.   In other words, since the velocity of the waves is a, the period is $2l/a$.   The frequency of the vibrations is therefore $a/2l$.   We shall encounter this formula again when we solve the wave equation by the method of separation of variables.

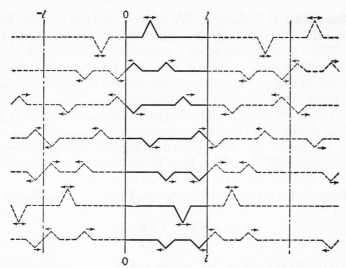

FIG. 7.10.   Plot showing one half cycle of the motion of a finite string.

EXERCISES

1. A uniform string stretching from $-\infty$ to ∞ is originally displaced into the curve

$$y = \begin{cases} \cos x, & x^2 < \left(\dfrac{\pi}{2}\right)^2 \\ 0, & x^2 > \left(\dfrac{\pi}{2}\right)^2 \end{cases}$$

Find the displacement of the string as a function of x and t, and plot the displacement curves for $(at) = 1$ and 2.

2. A uniform string stretching from $-\infty$ to ∞, while in its equilibrium position, is struck in such a way that the portion of the string between -1 and 1 is given a velocity of 1.   Find the displacement as a function of x and t, and plot the displacement curves for $(at) = 1$ and 2.

3. A uniform string stretching from 0 to ∞ is initially displaced into the curve $y = xe^{-x}$ and released from rest.   Find its displacement as a function of x and t.

4. A uniform string stretching from 0 to ∞ begins its motion with initial displacement $\phi(x)$ and initial velocity $\theta(x)$.   Show that its motion can be found as the motion of the right half of a two-way infinite string, provided merely that the initial displacement $\phi(-x)$ and the initial velocity $\theta(-x)$ for the negative extension of the string satisfy the condition

$$\phi(x) + \phi(-x) = -\frac{1}{a}\int_{-x}^{x}\theta(s)ds$$

5. If a semi-infinite string begins its motion with initial displacement $\phi(x) = (\sin x)/a$ and initial velocity $\theta(x) = 1$, and if the negative extension of the string is imagined to have initial displacement $\phi(-x) = 0$, find the necessary initial velocity for the extended portion of the string.

7.4 Separation of Variables.

We are now ready to consider the solution of partial differential equations by the method of separation of variables. While it is not universally applicable, it suffices for the great majority of the partial differential equations encountered in elementary applications in engineering and in physics, and it leads directly to the heart of the branch of mathematics which deals with boundary value problems.

The idea behind the process is the familiar mathematical strategem of reducing a new problem to dependence upon an old one. In this case we attempt to convert the given partial differential equation into several ordinary differential equations, hopeful that what we know about the latter will prove adequate for a successful continuation.

To illustrate the details of the procedure, let us again consider the wave equation

$$\frac{\partial^2 \theta}{\partial t^2} = a^2 \frac{\partial^2 \theta}{\partial x^2}$$

this time taking the torsionally vibrating shaft as a concrete representation. As a working hypothesis we assume that solutions for the angle of twist θ exist as products of a function of x alone and a function of t alone

$$\theta(x,t) = X(x)T(t)$$

If this be the case, then partial differentiation of θ amounts to total differentiation of one or the other of the factors of θ, and we have

$$\frac{\partial^2 \theta}{\partial x^2} = X''T$$

$$\frac{\partial^2 \theta}{\partial t^2} = XT''$$

Substituting these into the wave equation gives

$$XT'' = a^2 X''T$$

Dividing by XT then gives

$$\frac{T''}{T} = a^2 \frac{X''}{X}$$

as a necessary condition that $\theta(x,t) = X(x)T(t)$ should be a solution.

Now this condition requires that a function of t, namely, T''/T, be identically equal to a function of x, namely, X''/X. In general, this is impossible, for changing t will presumably change the left member but clearly cannot change the right member, which does not in any way depend on t. Similarly, changing x will presumably change the right member but cannot change the left. *The only way in which this paradoxical situation can be avoided is to suppose that each member is a constant,* say μ. Then we can write

$$\frac{T''}{T} = a^2 \frac{X''}{X} = \mu$$

Thus the determination of solutions of the original partial differential equation has been reduced to the determination of solutions of the two ordinary differential equations

$$T'' = \mu T \quad \text{and} \quad X'' = \frac{\mu}{a^2} X$$

Assuming that we need consider only real values of μ, there are three cases to investigate:

$$\mu > 0$$
$$\mu = 0$$
$$\mu < 0$$

If $\mu > 0$, we can write $\mu = \lambda^2$. In this case the differential equations and their solutions are

$$T'' = \lambda^2 T, \qquad\qquad X'' = \frac{\lambda^2}{a^2} X$$
$$T = Ae^{\lambda t} + Be^{-\lambda t}, \qquad X = Ce^{\lambda x/a} + De^{-(\lambda x/a)}$$

But a solution of the form

$$\theta(x,t) = X(x)T(t) = (Ce^{\lambda x/a} + De^{-(\lambda x/a)})(Ae^{\lambda t} + Be^{-\lambda t})$$

cannot describe the undamped vibrations of a system because it is not periodic, *i.e.*, does not repeat itself periodically as time increases. Hence although product solutions of the differential equation exist for $\mu > 0$, they have no significance in relation to the problem we are considering.

If $\mu = 0$, the equations and their solutions are

$$T'' = 0, \qquad\qquad X'' = 0$$
$$T = At + B, \qquad X = Cx + D$$

But, again a solution of the form

$$\theta(x,t) = X(x)T(t) = (Cx + D)(Ax + B)$$

cannot describe a periodic motion. Hence the alternative $\mu = 0$ must be rejected.

Finally, if $\mu < 0$, we can write $\mu = -\lambda^2$. Then the component differential equations and their solutions are

$$T'' = -\lambda^2 T, \qquad\qquad X'' = -\frac{\lambda^2}{a^2} X$$

$$T = A \cos \lambda t + B \sin \lambda t, \qquad X = C \cos \frac{\lambda}{a} x + D \sin \frac{\lambda}{a} x$$

In this case the solution

$$(1) \quad \theta(x,t) = X(x)T(t) = \left(C \cos \frac{\lambda}{a} x + D \sin \frac{\lambda}{a} x \right) (A \cos \lambda t + B \sin \lambda t)$$

is clearly periodic, repeating itself identically every time t increases by $2\pi/\lambda$. In other words, $\theta(x,t)$ represents a vibratory motion with period $2\pi/\lambda$ or frequency $\lambda/2\pi$. It remains now to find the value or values of λ and the constants A, B, C, and D. Since the admissible values of λ are determined by the boundary conditions of the problem, the continuation now varies in some respects, depending upon how the shaft is constrained at its ends. We shall discuss in turn the following simple cases (Fig. 7.11):

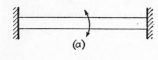

(a)

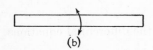

(b)

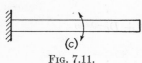

(c)

FIG. 7.11.

a. Both ends of the shaft are built-in, *i.e.*, are restrained so that no twisting can take place.

b. Both ends of the shaft are free to twist.

c. One end of the shaft is built-in, the other is free to twist.

If both ends of the shaft are held fixed, we have the following conditions to impose upon the general expression for $\theta(x,t)$,

$$\theta(0,t) = \theta(l,t) = 0 \qquad \text{identically in } t$$

Substituting $x = 0$ into the expression (1), we find

$$\theta(0,t) = C(A \cos \lambda t + B \sin \lambda t) = 0$$

This condition will be fulfilled for all values of t if both A and B are zero. In this case, however, $\theta(x,t)$ is identically zero at all times and the shaft remains motionless, a correct but trivial solution in which we have no interest. Hence we are driven to the other alternative, $C = 0$, which leaves

$$\theta(x,t) = \left(D \sin \frac{\lambda}{a} x \right) (A \cos \lambda t + B \sin \lambda t)$$

The second boundary condition, namely, that the right end of the shaft remains motionless at all times, requires that

$$\theta(l,t) = \left(D \sin \frac{\lambda l}{a}\right)(A \cos \lambda t + B \sin \lambda t) = 0$$

As before, we reject the possibility that $A = B = 0$, since it leads only to a trivial solution. Moreover, we cannot permit $D = 0$, since that too, with C already zero, leads to the trivial case. The only possibility which remains is that

$$\sin \frac{\lambda l}{a} = 0 \qquad \text{or} \qquad \frac{\lambda l}{a} = n\pi$$

From the continuous infinity of values of the parameter λ for which periodic solutions of the wave equation exist, we have thus been forced to reject all but the values

$$(2) \qquad\qquad \lambda_n = \frac{n\pi a}{l} \qquad n = 1, 2, 3, \ldots$$

These and only these values of λ (still infinite in number, however) yield solutions which, in addition to being periodic, will satisfy the end, or boundary, conditions of the problem at hand. With these solutions, one for each admissible value of λ, we must now attempt to construct a solution which will satisfy the remaining conditions of the problem, namely, that the shaft starts at $t = 0$ with a known angle of twist

$$\theta(x,0) = f(x)$$

and a known angular velocity

$$\left.\frac{\partial \theta}{\partial t}\right|_{x,0} = g(x)$$

at every section.

Now the wave equation is linear and thus, as it is easy to verify directly, if we have several solutions their sum is also a solution. Hence writing the solution associated with the nth value of λ in the form

$$\theta_n(x,t) = \sin \frac{\lambda_n}{a} x(A_n \cos \lambda_n t + B_n \sin \lambda_n t)$$

$$= \sin \frac{n\pi x}{l}\left(A_n \cos \frac{n\pi a t}{l} + B_n \sin \frac{n\pi a t}{l}\right)^{\dagger}$$

† The constants A and B now bear subscripts to indicate that they are not necessarily the same in the solutions associated with the different values of λ. The constant D can of course be absorbed into the constants A and B and need not be explicitly included.

it is natural enough (though perhaps optimistic, in view of the questions of convergence that are raised) to ask if an *infinite* series of *all* the θ_n's, say

$$(3)\quad \theta(x,t) = \sum_{n=1}^{\infty} \theta_n(x,t) = \sum_{n=1}^{\infty} \sin\frac{n\pi x}{l}\left(A_n \cos\frac{n\pi at}{l} + B_n \sin\frac{n\pi at}{l}\right)$$

can be made to yield a solution fitting the initial conditions of angular displacement and velocity.

This can be done, and in fact in this case the determination of the coefficients A_n and B_n requires nothing more than a simple application of Fourier series, as developed in Chap. 5. For if we set $t = 0$ in $\theta(x,t)$, we obtain

$$\theta(x,0) \equiv f(x) = \sum_{n=1}^{\infty} A_n \sin\frac{n\pi x}{l}$$

The problem of determining the A_n's so that this will be true is nothing but the problem of expanding a given function $f(x)$ in a half-range sine series over the interval $(0,l)$. Using Eq. (3), Sec. 5.4, we have explicitly

$$A_n = \frac{2}{l}\int_0^l f(x)\,\sin\frac{n\pi x}{l}\,dx$$

Also

$$\frac{\partial\theta}{\partial t} = \sum_{n=1}^{\infty} \sin\frac{n\pi x}{l}\left(-A_n \sin\frac{n\pi at}{l} + B_n \cos\frac{n\pi at}{l}\right)\left(\frac{n\pi a}{l}\right)$$

Hence, putting $t = 0$, we have the second condition

$$\left.\frac{\partial\theta}{\partial t}\right|_{x,0} \equiv g(x) = \sum_{n=1}^{\infty}\left(\frac{n\pi a}{l}B_n\right)\sin\frac{n\pi x}{l}$$

This, again, merely requires that the B_n's be determined so that the groups $[(n\pi a/l)B_n]$ will be the coefficients in the half-range sine expansion of the known function $g(x)$. Thus

$$\frac{n\pi a}{l}B_n = \frac{2}{l}\int_0^l g(x)\,\sin\frac{n\pi x}{l}\,dx \quad\text{or}\quad B_n = \frac{2}{n\pi a}\int_0^l g(x)\,\sin\frac{n\pi x}{l}\,dx$$

Our problem is now completely solved. We know that a shaft with both ends restrained against twisting can vibrate torsionally at any of an infinite number of natural frequencies,

$$f_n = \frac{\lambda_n}{2\pi} = \frac{na}{2l} \quad\text{cycles/unit time}\quad n = 1, 2, 3, \cdots$$

If and when the shaft vibrates at a single one of these frequencies, we know that the angular displacements along the shaft vary periodically between extreme values proportional to

$$\sin \frac{n\pi x}{l}$$

Finally, assuming any initial conditions of velocity and displacement we know how to construct the instantaneous deflection curve as an infinite series of the deflection curves associated with the respective natural frequencies, λ_n.

The treatment of the shaft with both ends free follows closely the above analysis, once we obtain the proper analytic formulation of the end conditions. To obtain this formulation, we observe that at a free end, although we have no knowledge of the amount of twist, we do know that there is no torque acting through the end section. Recalling the expression for the torque transmitted through a general cross section of a shaft [Eq. (3), Sec. 7.2], we thus find the free ends characterized by the requirement that

$$E_s J \frac{\partial \theta}{\partial x}\bigg|_{end} = 0$$

Since E_s is a nonzero constant of the material of the shaft, and since J cannot vanish for a shaft of uniform section such as we are considering, it follows that at a free end $\frac{\partial \theta}{\partial x} = 0$.

Returning to the original product solution (1), we find

$$\frac{\partial \theta}{\partial x} = \left(-C \frac{\lambda}{a} \sin \frac{\lambda}{a} x + D \frac{\lambda}{a} \cos \frac{\lambda}{a} x \right) (A \cos \lambda t + B \sin \lambda t)$$

Substituting $x = 0$ and equating the result to zero, we obtain the condition

$$\left(\frac{\lambda}{a} D \right) (A \cos \lambda t + B \sin \lambda t) = 0 \qquad \text{for all } t$$

From this we conclude that $D = 0$.

Substituting $x = l$ and again equating to zero, we find

$$\left(-C \frac{\lambda}{a} \sin \frac{\lambda l}{a} \right) (A \cos \lambda t + B \sin \lambda t) = 0$$

Since we cannot permit $C = 0$, we must have

$$\sin \frac{\lambda l}{a} = 0 \qquad \text{or} \qquad \frac{\lambda l}{a} = n\pi$$

Thus, as in the last example, to have the end conditions of the problem fulfilled, λ must be restricted to one of the discrete set of values

$$\lambda_n = \frac{n\pi a}{l}$$

Again, we construct the product solution for each λ

$$\theta_n(x,t) = \cos \frac{\lambda_n}{a} x (A_n \cos \lambda_n t + B_n \sin \lambda_n t)$$

$$= \cos \frac{n\pi x}{l} \left(A_n \cos \frac{n\pi a t}{l} + B_n \sin \frac{n\pi a t}{l} \right)$$

and attempt to form an infinite series of them

$$\theta(x,t) = \sum_{n=1}^{\infty} \theta_n(x,t) = \sum_{n=1}^{\infty} \cos \frac{n\pi x}{l} \left(A_n \cos \frac{n\pi a t}{l} + B_n \sin \frac{n\pi a t}{l} \right)$$

which will satisfy the initial displacement condition

$$\theta(x,0) = f(x)$$

and the initial velocity condition

$$\left. \frac{\partial \theta}{\partial t} \right|_{x,0} = g(x)$$

To satisfy the first condition, we must have

(4) $$\theta(x,0) \equiv f(x) = \sum_{n=1}^{\infty} A_n \cos \frac{n\pi x}{l}$$

which requires that the A_n's be the coefficients in the half-range cosine expansion of the known function $f(x)$, that is, that

$$A_n = \frac{2}{l} \int_0^l f(x) \cos \frac{n\pi x}{l} \, dx$$

To satisfy the second condition, we must have

(5) $$\left. \frac{\partial \theta}{\partial t} \right|_{x,0} \equiv g(x) = \sum_{n=1}^{\infty} \left(\frac{n\pi a}{l} B_n \right) \cos \frac{n\pi x}{l}$$

which requires that the groups $[(n\pi a/l)B_n]$ be the coefficients in the half-range cosine series for $g(x)$ over the interval $(0,l)$, that is, that

$$\frac{n\pi a}{l} B_n = \frac{2}{l} \int_0^l g(x) \cos \frac{n\pi x}{l} \, dx \qquad \text{or} \qquad B_n = \frac{2}{n\pi a} \int_0^l g(x) \cos \frac{n\pi x}{l} \, dx$$

We note in passing that since the admissible λ's are the same for the free-free shaft as for the fixed-fixed shaft, the natural frequencies of the two systems are the same. The amplitudes through which they vibrate are not the same, however. In fact, for the fixed-fixed shaft we found the distribution of amplitudes along the shaft given by the function $\sin(n\pi x/l)$, while for the free-free shaft the amplitudes are given by $\cos(n\pi x/l)$.

The case of the shaft with one end fixed and the other free can be disposed of quickly. Taking the fixed end at $x = 0$, we have the two conditions

$$\theta(0,t) = 0 \qquad \text{and} \qquad \frac{\partial \theta}{\partial x}\bigg|_{l,t} = 0 \qquad \text{for all } t.$$

Imposing these upon the general product solution

$$\theta(x,t) = \left(C \cos \frac{\lambda}{a} x + D \sin \frac{\lambda}{a} x \right) (A \cos \lambda t + B \sin \lambda t)$$

gives

$$(C)(A \cos \lambda t + B \sin \lambda t) = 0 \qquad \text{or} \qquad C = 0$$

and

$$\left(\frac{\lambda}{a} D \cos \frac{\lambda l}{a} \right) (A \cos \lambda t + B \sin \lambda t) = 0$$

from which

$$\cos \frac{\lambda l}{a} = 0, \qquad \frac{\lambda l}{a} = \frac{(2n-1)\pi}{2}, \qquad \lambda_n = \frac{(2n-1)a\pi}{2l}$$

The general solution of the problem, formed by adding together the product solutions corresponding to each λ, is therefore

$$\theta(x,t) = \sum_{n=1}^{\infty} \sin \frac{\lambda_n}{a} x (A_n \cos \lambda_n t + B_n \sin \lambda_n t)$$

$$= \sum_{n=1}^{\infty} \sin \left(\frac{2n-1}{2} \frac{\pi x}{l} \right)$$

$$\cdot \left[A_n \cos \left(\frac{2n-1}{2} \frac{\pi a t}{l} \right) + B_n \sin \left(\frac{2n-1}{2} \frac{\pi a t}{l} \right) \right]$$

To fit the initial displacement condition $\theta(x,0) = f(x)$, we must have

$$f(x) = \sum_{n=1}^{\infty} A_n \sin \left(\frac{2n-1}{2} \frac{\pi x}{l} \right)$$

This is not quite the usual half-range sine expansion problem, since arguments of the various terms are not integral multiples of the fundamental argument $\pi x/l$. It is, however, the special case of the half-range sine expansion over $(0,l)$ in which all even harmonics are absent. In Exercise 11, Sec. 5.4, it was shown that any function defined over $(0,l)$ could be given an expansion of this form by reflecting the function in the line $x = l$ and then expanding the extended function in a half-range sine series over the interval $(0,2l)$. The formula for the coefficients in such an expansion was shown to be

$$A_n = \frac{2}{l} \int_0^l f(x) \sin \left(\frac{2n-1}{2} \frac{\pi x}{l} \right) dx$$

Similarly, to fit the initial velocity condition $\dfrac{\partial \theta}{\partial t} \Big|_{x,0} = g(x)$, we must have

$$g(x) = \sum_{n=1}^{\infty} \left(\frac{2n-1}{2} \frac{\pi a}{l} B_n \right) \sin \left(\frac{2n-1}{2} \frac{\pi x}{l} \right)$$

which requires that

$$B_n = \frac{4}{(2n-1)a\pi} \int_0^l g(x) \sin \left(\frac{2n-1}{2} \frac{\pi x}{l} \right) dx$$

EXERCISES

1. Discuss the restrictions implicitly imposed on $f(x)$ and $g(x)$ by the absence of constant terms in the series in Eqs. (4) and (5). What is the physical meaning of these restrictions?

2. A uniform string stretched between two points a distance l apart is displaced into the shape $y = y_0 x(l - x)$ and released from rest. Find the resulting displacement as a function of x and t.

3. A uniform string of length l is struck in such a way that an initial velocity of v_0 is imparted to the portion of the string between $l/4$ and $3l/4$ while the string is in its equilibrium position. Find the subsequent displacement of the string as a function of x and t.

4. Work Exercise 3 if the uniform initial velocity is imparted to the string only over the middle 25 per cent of its length.

5. A uniform shaft, fixed at one end and free at the other, is twisted so that each cross section rotates through an angle proportional to the distance from the fixed end. If the shaft is released from rest in this position, find its subsequent angular displacement as a function of x and t.

6. Work Exercise 5 if the initial angular displacement of any cross section is proportional to the square of the distance from the fixed end.

7.5 Orthogonal Functions and the General Expansion Problem. The three examples which we considered in the last paragraph embody all the significant features of the general boundary value problem. However, they give an exaggerated picture of the role of Fourier series in the final expansion process that is required in order to fit the initial conditions. In general, a knowledge of Fourier series, as such, will not suffice to obtain the necessary expansions.

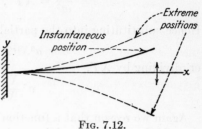

FIG. 7.12.

Hence before we attempt to summarize the major characteristics of boundary value problems, as illustrated in our examples, we shall consider a further example in which Fourier series play no part.

This time we shall consider a uniform cantilever beam, vibrating transversely (Fig. 7.12). The differential equation to be solved, as derived in Sec. 7.2, is

$$a^2 \frac{\partial^4 y}{\partial x^4} = - \frac{\partial^2 y}{\partial t^2}$$

Taking the origin at the built-in end of the beam, we have the boundary conditions

$a.$ $y(0,t) = 0$, that is, the displacement at the built-in end is zero.

$b.$ $\dfrac{\partial y}{\partial x}\bigg|_{0,t} = 0$, that is, the slope at the built-in end is zero.

$c.$ $\dfrac{\partial^2 y}{\partial x^2}\bigg|_{l,t} = 0$, that is, the moment $\equiv EI\dfrac{\partial^2 y}{\partial x^2}$ is zero at the free end.

Since E and I are different from zero, this requires that $\dfrac{\partial^2 y}{\partial x^2} = 0$.

$d.$ $\dfrac{\partial^3 y}{\partial x^3}\bigg|_{l,t} = 0$, that is, the shear $\equiv \dfrac{\partial\left(EI\dfrac{\partial^2 y}{\partial x^2}\right)}{\partial x}$ is zero at the free end.

Since E and I are constants different from zero, this requires that $\dfrac{\partial^3 y}{\partial x^3} = 0$.

Finally, we have the initial displacement condition

$$y(x,0) = f(x)$$

and the initial velocity condition

$$\frac{\partial y}{\partial t}\bigg|_{x,0} = g(x)$$

To begin with, we assume a product solution

$$y(x,t) = X(x)T(t)$$

in an attempt to separate the partial differential equation into several total differential equations. Then

$$\frac{\partial^2 y}{\partial t^2} = XT'', \qquad \frac{\partial^4 y}{\partial x^4} = X^{iv}T$$

Hence substituting into the partial differential equation, we find

$$a^2 X^{iv} T = -XT''$$

or, dividing by XT,

$$a^2 \frac{X^{iv}}{X} = -\frac{T''}{T}$$

Again we reason that a function of x can be identically equal to a function of t if and only if each is equal to the same constant. Hence we write

$$a^2 \frac{X^{iv}}{X} = -\frac{T''}{T} = \mu$$

or

$$T'' = -\mu T \qquad \text{and} \qquad X^{iv} = \frac{\mu}{a^2} X$$

Now if $\mu \leqq 0$ the solutions for T cannot be periodic, as we know they must be to represent undamped vibrations.* Hence we restrict μ to be positive, and write $\mu = \lambda^2$. Then the component differential equations and their solutions are

$$T'' = -\lambda^2 T$$
$$T = A \cos \lambda t + B \sin \lambda t$$

and

$$X^{iv} = \frac{\lambda^2}{a^2} X$$

$$X = C \cos \sqrt{\frac{\lambda}{a}}\, x + D \sin \sqrt{\frac{\lambda}{a}}\, x + E \cosh \sqrt{\frac{\lambda}{a}}\, x + F \sinh \sqrt{\frac{\lambda}{a}}\, x$$

* It is customary, especially among engineers, to impose this condition even earlier by assuming at the outset that

$$y(x,t) = X(x)(A \cos \lambda t + B \sin \lambda t)$$

If, as is often the case, only the natural frequencies λ_n and the associated amplitude functions $X_n(x)$ are required, y is simplified further to $y = X(x) \cos \lambda t$ or to

$$y = X(x) \sin \lambda t$$

Taking the latter, for instance, and substituting into the partial differential equation, we have

$$a^2 X^{iv} \sin \lambda t = -X(-\lambda^2 \sin \lambda t)$$

or, dividing by $a^2 \sin \lambda t$,

$$X^{iv} = \frac{\lambda^2}{a^2} X$$

as before. This procedure is correct only when damping is neglected.

Imposing the first boundary condition,

$$y(0,t) = X(0)T(t) = 0$$

we find

$$(C + E)(A \cos \lambda t + B \sin \lambda t) = 0$$

Since we cannot permit $A = B = 0$ without having the solution become trivial, we conclude that

$$C + E = 0$$

Imposing the second boundary condition,

$$\frac{\partial y}{\partial x}\bigg|_{0,t} = X'(0)T(t) = 0$$

we find

$$(D + F) \sqrt{\frac{\lambda}{a}} (A \cos \lambda t + B \sin \lambda t) = 0$$

Hence

$$D + F = 0$$

From the third and fourth boundary conditions,

$$\frac{\partial^2 y}{\partial x^2}\bigg|_{l,t} = X''(l)T(t) = 0 \qquad \text{and} \qquad \frac{\partial^3 y}{\partial x^3}\bigg|_{l,t} = X'''(l)T(t) = 0$$

we obtain, respectively,

$$\left(-C \cos \sqrt{\frac{\lambda}{a}} l - D \sin \sqrt{\frac{\lambda}{a}} l + E \cosh \sqrt{\frac{\lambda}{a}} l + F \sinh \sqrt{\frac{\lambda}{a}} l\right)\left(\frac{\lambda}{a}\right)$$
$$\cdot (A \cos \lambda t + B \sin \lambda t) = 0$$

$$\left(C \sin \sqrt{\frac{\lambda}{a}} l - D \cos \sqrt{\frac{\lambda}{a}} l + E \sinh \sqrt{\frac{\lambda}{a}} l + F \cosh \sqrt{\frac{\lambda}{a}} l\right)\left(\frac{\lambda}{a}\right)^{\frac{3}{2}}$$
$$\cdot (A \cos \lambda t + B \sin \lambda t) = 0$$

or, setting $z = \sqrt{\frac{\lambda}{a}} l$,

$$-C \cos z - D \sin z + E \cosh z + F \sinh z = 0$$
$$C \sin z - D \cos z + E \sinh z + F \cosh z = 0$$

If we eliminate C and D from these two equations by using the conditions

$$C + E = 0 \qquad \text{and} \qquad D + F = 0$$

we obtain the system

(1)
$$E(\cosh z + \cos z) + F(\sinh z + \sin z) = 0$$
$$E(\sinh z - \sin z) + F(\cosh z + \cos z) = 0$$

These equations have the obvious solution $E = F = 0$, and in general this will be their only solution. But if E and F vanish, so will C and D, and the resulting solution for y will be trivial. Hence the condition that the pair of equations (1) possess a unique solution, namely, that the determinant of their coefficients be different from zero, must be avoided. In other words, we require that

$$\begin{vmatrix} (\cosh z + \cos z) & (\sinh z + \sin z) \\ (\sinh z - \sin z) & (\cosh z + \cos z) \end{vmatrix} = 0$$

Expanding this, and recalling that $\cosh^2 z - \sinh^2 z = 1$, we obtain

$$\cosh z \cos z = -1$$

From the roots of this equation,* $z_1, z_2, z_3, \ldots$ we can find the values of λ at once:

$$\lambda_1 = \frac{a z_1^2}{l^2}, \qquad \lambda_2 = \frac{a z_2^2}{l^2}, \qquad \lambda_3 = \frac{a z_3^2}{l^2}, \ldots$$

When z has any one of the values $z_1, z_2, z_3, \ldots$, the equations (1) become dependent, and we can write either

$$\frac{E}{F} = -\frac{\sinh z + \sin z}{\cosh z + \cos z} \qquad \text{or} \qquad \frac{E}{F} = -\frac{\cosh z + \cos z}{\sinh z - \sin z}$$

as we choose.

Using the former, we have then

$$E_n = -C_n = -(\sinh z_n + \sin z_n)$$
$$F_n = -D_n = (\cosh z_n + \cos z_n)$$

Therefore

$$X_n(x) \equiv C_n \cos \sqrt{\frac{\lambda_n}{a}}\, x + D_n \sin \sqrt{\frac{\lambda_n}{a}}\, x + E_n \cosh \sqrt{\frac{\lambda_n}{a}}\, x + F_n \sinh \sqrt{\frac{\lambda_n}{a}}\, x$$

$$= (\sinh z_n + \sin z_n)\left(\cos \frac{z_n}{l} x - \cosh \frac{z_n}{l} x \right)$$

$$- (\cosh z_n + \cos z_n)\left(\sin \frac{z_n}{l} x - \sinh \frac{z_n}{l} x \right)$$

and, finally,

$$y(x,t) = \sum_{n=1}^{\infty} X_n(x) T_n(t) = \sum_{n=1}^{\infty} X_n(x)(A_n \cos \lambda_n t + B_n \sin \lambda_n t)$$

To satisfy the initial displacement condition, we must have

$$y(x,0) \equiv f(x) = \sum_{n=1}^{\infty} A_n X_n(x)$$

* The solution of this equation is discussed in Example 1, Sec. 16.1.

and to satisfy the initial velocity condition we must have

$$\left.\frac{\partial y}{\partial t}\right|_{x,0} \equiv g(x) = \sum_{n=1}^{\infty} (\lambda_n B_n) X_n(x)$$

Thus, as in the preceding examples, to satisfy the initial conditions we must be able to expand an arbitrary function in an infinite series of known functions. However, in this case the known functions $X_n(x)$ bear little or no resemblance to the terms of the general Fourier series or any of its special cases. Clearly something is involved which includes Fourier series as a special case but is itself more fundamental.

If we review thoughtfully the derivation of the formulas for the Fourier coefficients (Sec. 5.2), it should be apparent that the decisive property of the set of functions $\{\cos(n\pi x/l), \sin(n\pi x/l)\}$ which made the expansion possible was that the integral of the product of any two distinct functions of the set over a certain interval is zero. For it was this that enabled us to multiply the hypothetical expansion

$$f(x) = \frac{1}{2} a_0 + a_1 \cos \frac{\pi x}{l} + a_2 \cos \frac{2\pi x}{l} + \cdots$$
$$+ b_1 \sin \frac{\pi x}{l} + b_2 \sin \frac{2\pi x}{l} + \cdots$$

by $\cos(n\pi x/l)$ or $\sin(n\pi x/l)$ and eliminate all but one of the unknown coefficients simply by integrating from $-l$ to l.

Now sines and cosines are by no means the only systems of functions with the property that the integral between suitable limits of the product of two members of the set is zero. In fact, the trigonometric functions which appear in Fourier expansions are merely the simplest example of infinitely many such systems of orthogonal functions.

Definition 1. If a sequence of real functions $\{\phi_n(x)\}$, $n = 1, 2, 3, \ldots$ has the property that over some interval (a,b), finite or infinite,

$$\int_a^b \phi_m(x)\phi_n(x)dx \begin{cases} = 0, & m \neq n \\ \neq 0, & m = n \end{cases}$$

the functions are said to form an orthogonal set.

Definition 2. If in addition to being orthogonal the functions $\{\phi_n(x)\}$ have the property that the (necessarily positive) value of

$$\int_a^b \phi_n^2(x)dx$$

is one, then the functions are said to form an orthonormal set.

Any set of orthogonal functions can easily be converted into an ortho-normal set. In fact if k_n be the value of $\int_a^b \phi_n^2(x)dx$, the functions

$$\frac{\phi_1(x)}{\sqrt{k_1}}, \frac{\phi_2(x)}{\sqrt{k_2}}, \frac{\phi_3(x)}{\sqrt{k_3}}, \cdots$$

are clearly orthonormal, provided the ϕ's are orthogonal. It is therefore no specialization to assume that an orthogonal set of functions is also orthonormal.

Definition 3. If a sequence of real functions $\{\phi_n(x)\}$ has the property that over some interval (a,b), finite or infinite,

$$\int_a^b \rho(x)\phi_m(x)\phi_n(x)dx \begin{cases} = 0, & m \neq n \\ \neq 0, & m = n \end{cases}$$

the functions are said to be orthogonal with respect to the weight func-tion $\rho(x)$.

Any set of functions orthogonal with respect to a weight function $\rho(x)$ can be reduced to a system orthogonal in the first sense simply by multi-plying each member of the set by $\sqrt{\rho(x)}$, if, as we shall suppose, $\rho(x) \geqq 0$ for all values of x, under consideration.

Definition 4. If there exists no function $f(x)$, except the identically zero function, with the property that

$$\int_a^b f(x)\phi_n(x)dx = 0$$

for all members of an orthogonal system $\{\phi_n(x)\}$, then the set $\{\phi_n(x)\}$ is said to be complete.

Clearly, if even one of the ϕ's is omitted from the set $\{\phi_n(x)\}$ the result-ing set is not complete, for the omitted function, $\phi_i(x)$ obviously has the property that

$$\int_a^b \phi_i(x)\phi_n(x)dx = 0$$

for all functions $\phi_n(x)$ remaining in the set.

With respect to any complete orthogonal set of functions $\{\phi_n(x)\}$, an arbitrary function $f(x)$ has a formal expansion analogous to its Fourier expansion. For we can write

$$f(x) = a_1\phi_1(x) + a_2\phi_2(x) + \cdots + a_n\phi_n(x) + \cdots$$

Then multiplying by $\phi_n(x)$ and integrating between the appropriate limits, a and b, we have

$$\int_a^b f(x)\phi_n(x)dx = a_1 \int_a^b \phi_1(x)\phi_n(x)dx + a_2 \int_a^b \phi_2(x)\phi_n(x)dx + \cdots$$
$$+ a_n \int_a^b \phi_n^2(x)dx + \cdots$$

From the property of orthogonality, all integrals on the right are zero, except the one which contains a square in its integrand. Hence we can solve at once for a_n as the quotient of two known integrals

$$a_n = \frac{\int_a^b f(x)\phi_n(x)dx}{\int_a^b \phi_n^2(x)dx}$$

Since the system $\{\phi_n(x)\}$ is assumed to be complete, the coefficients a_n cannot all be zero. Hence a nontrivial function cannot have a trivial expansion, as it might if the system were not complete. If the set $\{\phi_n(x)\}$ is orthonormal, the integral in the denominator of the expression for a_n is 1, and we have the simpler formula

$$a_n = \int_a^b f(x)\phi_n(x)dx$$

A great deal of important advanced mathematics deals with the properties of special orthogonal systems and with the validity of the formal expansion we have just created. In our work we shall assume that all the expansions we obtain actually represent the functions which generate them.

Orthogonal functions arise naturally and inevitably in many types of problems in applied mathematics. Their existence in problems such as we have been considering is guaranteed by the following beautiful and important theorem.

Theorem 1.*   Given the differential equation

$$\frac{d[r(x)y']}{dx} + [q(x) + \lambda p(x)]y = 0$$

where $p(x)$ and $r(x)$ are continuous on the closed interval $a \leq x \leq b$ and $q(x)$ is continuous at least over the open interval $a < x < b$. If $\lambda_1, \lambda_2, \lambda_3,$ . . . are the values of the parameter λ for which there exist solutions of this equation possessing continuous first derivatives and satisfying the boundary conditions

$$a_1 y(a) - a_2 y'(a) = 0$$
$$b_1 y(b) - b_2 y'(b) = 0$$

where a_1, a_2, b_1, b_2 are any constants, and if $y_1, y_2, y_3,$ . . . are the solutions corresponding to these values of λ, then the functions $\{y_n(x)\}$ form a system orthogonal with respect to the weight function $p(x)$ over the interval (a,b).

---

* This theorem and the boundary value problem with which it deals are usually associated with the names of the Swiss mathematician J. C. F. Sturm (1803–1855) and the French mathematician Joseph Liouville (1809–1882).

Proof. Let y_m and y_n be the solutions associated with two distinct values of λ, λ_m and λ_n. This means that

$$\frac{d(ry_m')}{dx} + (q + \lambda_m p)y_m = 0$$

$$\frac{d(ry_n')}{dx} + (q + \lambda_n p)y_n = 0$$

Now multiply the first equation by y_n and the second by y_m, and subtract the second equation from the first. The result, after transposing, is

$$(\lambda_m - \lambda_n)py_m y_n = y_m \frac{d(ry_n')}{dx} - y_n \frac{d(ry_m')}{dx}$$

If we integrate this between a and b, we get

$$(\lambda_m - \lambda_n)\int_a^b py_m y_n \, dx = \int_a^b \left[y_m \frac{d(ry_n')}{dx} \right] dx - \int_a^b \left[y_n \frac{d(ry_m')}{dx} \right] dx$$

If we can prove that the integral on the left vanishes whenever m and n are different, we will have established the orthogonal property of the functions of the set $\{y_n(x)\}$. This we shall prove by showing that the right-hand side of the last equation is zero. To do this we begin by integrating the terms on the right by parts:

$$\int_a^b \left[y_m \frac{d(ry_n')}{dx} \right] dx \xrightarrow[\substack{u = y_m, \\ du = y_m' \, dx,}]{\substack{dv = \frac{d(ry_n')}{dx} dx \\ v = ry_n'}} ry_m y_n' \Big|_a^b - \int_a^b ry_n' y_m' \, dx$$

$$\int_a^b \left[y_n \frac{d(ry_m')}{dx} \right] dx \xrightarrow[\substack{u = y_n, \\ du = y_n' \, dx,}]{\substack{dv = \frac{d(ry_m')}{dx} dx \\ v = ry_m'}} ry_n y_m' \Big|_a^b - \int_a^b ry_m' y_n' \, dx$$

When we subtract these expressions, the integrals which remain on the right cancel, and we have

$$(2) \quad \int_a^b \left[y_m \frac{d(ry_n')}{dx} \right] dx - \int_a^b \left[y_n' \frac{d(ry_m')}{dx} \right] dx = r(y_m y_n' - y_m' y_n) \Big|_a^b$$
$$= r(b)[y_m(b)y_n'(b) - y_m'(b)y_n(b)] - r(a)[y_m(a)y_n'(a) - y_m'(a)y_n(a)]$$

Now y_m and y_n are not merely solutions of the given differential equation. For every m and n they also satisfy the boundary conditions

$$a_1 y(a) = a_2 y'(a), \qquad b_1 y(b) = b_2 y'(b)$$

Substituting for $y'(a)$ and $y'(b)$ from these expressions into the evaluated antiderivative in (2) we obtain

$$\int_a^b \left[y_m \frac{d(ry_n')}{dx} \right] dx - \int_a^b \left[y_n \frac{d(ry_m')}{dx} \right] dx$$

$$= r(b) \left[y_m(b) \frac{b_1}{b_2} y_n(b) - \frac{b_1}{b_2} y_m(b) y_n(b) \right]$$

$$- r(a) \left[y_m(a) \frac{a_1}{a_2} y_n(a) - \frac{a_1}{a_2} y_m(a) y_n(a) \right] \equiv 0$$

If a_2 or b_2, or both, should be zero, this result can still be established by substituting for $y(a)$ or $y(b)$, or both, instead of for their derivatives, since a_1 and a_2 cannot both vanish, nor can b_1 and b_2. Moreover, if $r(a) = 0$, then the first boundary condition becomes irrelevant. Likewise, if $r(b) = 0$, the second boundary condition is irrelevant.

We have thus shown that

$$(\lambda_m - \lambda_n) \int_a^b p y_m y_n \, dx = 0$$

Since λ_m and λ_n are two distinct values of λ, the difference $(\lambda_m - \lambda_n)$ cannot vanish. Hence

$$\int_a^b p y_m y_n \, dx = 0$$

Q.E.D.

In each of the torsional vibration problems which we considered, the functions in terms of which we had to expand the initial conditions satisfied a differential equation and a set of boundary conditions included under the last theorem. This, and not the coincidental fact that Fourier series were involved, explains why the final expansion could be carried out in each case.

Although many of the problems which we have yet to investigate will likewise appear as special cases of the last theorem, the vibrating cantilever is not included. Yet the fundamental property of orthogonality is present here, too, for the functions $X_n(x)$ satisfy the fourth-order differential equation

$$X^{iv} - \frac{\lambda^2}{a^2} X = 0$$

and the boundary conditions

$$X(0) = X'(0) = 0, \qquad X''(l) = X'''(l) = 0$$

and hence form an orthogonal system in virtue of the following analogous theorem.

Theorem 2. Given the differential equation

$$\frac{d^2[r(x)y'']}{dx^2} + [q(x) + \lambda p(x)]y = 0$$

where $p(x)$, $q(x)$, and $r(x)$ are continuous on the interval (a,b). If λ_1, λ_2, λ_3, . . . are the values of the parameter for which there exist solutions of this differential equation satisfying at both a and b boundary conditions of the form

$$c_1 y = d_1(ry'')'$$
$$c_2 y' = d_2(ry'')$$

and if y_1, y_2, y_3, . . . are the solutions corresponding to λ_1, λ_2, λ_3, . . . , then the set $\{y_n(x)\}$ is orthogonal with respect to the weight function $p(x)$ over the interval (a,b).

The main features of the process of solving a simple boundary value problem can now be summarized. By assuming that solutions for the dependent variable exist in the form of products of functions of the respective independent variables, the original differential equation is broken down into several ordinary differential equations, each of which involves a parameter λ which ranges over a continuous infinity of values.

When the boundary conditions of the problem are imposed upon the product solutions after the component total differential equations have been solved, it is necessary, in order to avoid solutions which are identically zero, that the parameter λ satisfy a certain equation. This equation is known as the **characteristic equation** of the problem, and its roots, in general infinite in number, are known as the **characteristic values** or **eigenvalues** or **eigenwerte*** of the problem. Only for them can solutions be found satisfying both the partial differential equation and the given boundary conditions. In a vibration problem, the characteristic values determine the natural frequencies of the system, and the characteristic equation is therefore usually called the **frequency equation.**

The solutions which correspond to the respective characteristic values are known as the **characteristic functions** or **eigenfunctions** of the problem. In a vibration problem, they are usually called the **normal modes** because they define the extreme positions between which the system oscillates when it is vibrating at a single natural frequency, *i.e.*, in a "normal" manner.

To satisfy the initial conditions of the problem it is necessary to be able to express an arbitrary function as an infinite series of the characteristic functions of the problem. This can be done in most cases of interest because under very general conditions the characteristic functions of a boundary value problem form an orthogonal set over the particular interval related to the problem.

---

* German for *characteristic values.*

EXERCISES

1. Prove that the general linear second-order differential equation

$$p_0(x)y'' + p_1(x)y' + p_2(x)y = \lambda y$$

can be reduced to an equation of the Sturm-Liouville type by multiplying it through by the factor

$$\frac{1}{p_0(x)} \, e^{\int_{x_0}^{x} [p_1(x)/p_0(x)]dx}$$

2. Prove Theorem 2.

Find the frequency equation and the normal modes for the transverse vibration of a uniform beam whose ends are

3. Free-free   *Ans.* $\cosh z \cos z = 1$
4. Fixed-fixed   *Ans.* $\cosh z \cos z = 1$
5. Hinged-hinged   *Ans.* $\sin z = 0$
6. Fixed-hinged
7. Hinged-free

8. Find the frequency equation for the transverse vibration of a uniform cantilever bearing a concentrated mass at the free end. Discuss any interesting limiting cases. (Hint: At the free end one boundary condition is that the shear, instead of being zero, is equal to the inertia force of the attached mass.)
9. Find the frequency equation for the transverse vibration of a hinged-hinged beam bearing a concentrated mass at its mid-point.
10. Find the frequency equation of a uniform torsional cantilever if a disk of polar moment of inertia I is attached to the free end of the shaft. (Hint: At the free end the boundary condition is that the torque, instead of being zero, is equal to the inertia torque of the disk.)
11. Show that the normal modes in Exercise 10 are not orthogonal.

7.6 Further Applications. Just as in the case of ordinary differential equations, so too in the field of partial differential equations, nonhomogeneous as well as homogeneous equations must sometimes be considered. The simplest problems leading to such equations concern the forced vibrations of continuous systems. Problems in the flow of heat in bodies in which heat is being generated, by electrical or chemical means, for instance, also lead to nonhomogeneous equations. We cannot investigate the matter at length, but it will be of interest to consider a typical example.

Suppose that a uniform cantilever is acted upon by a periodic, distributed, transverse force whose value per unit length is $F(x) \sin \omega t$. What is the forced response of the beam?

To find the nonhomogeneous partial differential equation which we must solve, we return to the derivation of the equation of the vibrating beam in Sec. 7.2 and add the distributed forcing load per unit length, $F(x) \sin \omega t$, to the inertia load per unit length. This gives the modified equation

$$\frac{\partial^2 \left[EI(x) \dfrac{\partial^2 y}{\partial x^2} \right]}{\partial x^2} = - \left[\frac{\rho A(x)}{g} \frac{\partial^2 y}{\partial t^2} + F(x) \sin \omega t \right]$$

or, for a uniform beam,

$$a^2 \frac{\partial^4 y}{\partial x^4} = - \frac{\partial^2 y}{\partial t^2} - \frac{g F(x)}{A \rho} \sin \omega t \qquad a^2 = \frac{EIg}{A\rho}$$

Assured by the physical nature of the problem that the effect of a periodic driving force on a linear, frictionless system will be to produce a displacement in phase with, and varying with the same frequency as the driving force, we attempt to find a particular integral of the form

$$Y = X(x) \sin \omega t$$

Substitution of this into the partial differential equation gives

$$a^2 X^{\mathrm{iv}} \sin \omega t = \omega^2 X \sin \omega t - \frac{g F(x)}{A \rho} \sin \omega t$$

Finally, dividing by $\sin \omega t$, we find that X must satisfy the nonhomogeneous ordinary differential equation

(1) $$X^{\mathrm{iv}} - \frac{\omega^2}{a^2} X = - \frac{g}{A \rho a^2} F(x)$$

Since $F(x)$ is a known function, this equation can easily be solved by the methods of Chap. 2. However, we must be careful to note that it is a particular integral of the partial differential equation and *not* of the X-equation which we need. We must in fact find the general solution of the X-equation and impose upon it the four end conditions which characterize a cantilever. This X-function, multiplied by $\sin \omega t$, will then be the required particular integral of the nonhomogeneous partial differential equation.

Example 1

Discuss the forced motion produced in a uniform cantilever by a distributed periodic load per unit length equal to $kx^2 \sin \omega t$.

Replacing $F(x)$ in Eq. (1) by the specific function kx^2, it appears that the amplitude function $X(x)$ of the particular integral $Y(x,t) = X(x) \sin \omega t$ must satisfy the differential equation

(2) $$X^{\mathrm{iv}} - \frac{\omega^2}{a^2} X = - \frac{kg}{A \rho a^2} x^2$$

subject to the conditions

$$X(0) = X'(0) = 0, \qquad X''(l) = X'''(l) = 0$$

The complementary function of the equation is

$$A \cos \sqrt{\frac{\omega}{a}}\, x + B \sin \sqrt{\frac{\omega}{a}}\, x + C \cosh \sqrt{\frac{\omega}{a}}\, x + D \sinh \sqrt{\frac{\omega}{a}}\, x$$

Moreover, it is easy to verify that a particular integral is

$$\frac{kg}{A\rho\omega^2}\, x^2$$

Hence the general solution of (2) is

$$X(x) = A \cos \sqrt{\frac{\omega}{a}}\, x + B \sin \sqrt{\frac{\omega}{a}}\, x + C \cosh \sqrt{\frac{\omega}{a}}\, x + D \sinh \sqrt{\frac{\omega}{a}}\, x + \frac{kg}{A\rho\omega^2}\, x^2$$

To satisfy the respective boundary conditions, we must have

$$A + C = 0$$
$$B + D = 0$$
$$\left(-A \cos \sqrt{\frac{\omega}{a}}\, l - B \sin \sqrt{\frac{\omega}{a}}\, l + C \cosh \sqrt{\frac{\omega}{a}}\, l + D \sinh \sqrt{\frac{\omega}{a}}\, l \right)\left(\frac{\omega}{a} \right) + \frac{2kg}{A\rho\omega^2} = 0$$
$$\left(A \sin \sqrt{\frac{\omega}{a}}\, l - B \cos \sqrt{\frac{\omega}{a}}\, l + C \sinh \sqrt{\frac{\omega}{a}}\, l + D \cosh \sqrt{\frac{\omega}{a}}\, l \right)\left(\frac{\omega}{a} \right)^{\frac{3}{2}} = 0$$

Writing $z = \sqrt{\omega/a}\, l$ and using the first two of these equations to simplify the last pair, we obtain

$$C(\cosh z + \cos z) + D(\sinh z + \sin z) = -\frac{2akg}{A\rho\omega^3}$$
$$C(\sinh z - \sin z) + D(\cosh z + \cos z) = 0$$

Hence

$$C = -A = -\frac{akg}{A\rho\omega^3}\left(\frac{\cosh z + \cos z}{\cosh z \cos z + 1} \right)$$
$$D = -B = \frac{akg}{A\rho\omega^3}\left(\frac{\sinh z - \sin z}{\cosh z \cos z + 1} \right)$$

Therefore

$$Y(x,t) = X(x) \sin \omega t$$
$$= \frac{akg}{A\rho\omega^3}\left[\frac{(\cosh z + \cos z)\left(\cos \frac{z}{l} x - \cosh \frac{z}{l} x \right) - (\sinh z - \sin z)\left(\sin \frac{z}{l} x - \sinh \frac{z}{l} x \right)}{\cosh z \cos z + 1} \right.$$
$$\left. + \frac{\omega}{a} x^2 \right] \sin \omega t$$

We note that the amplitude of the forced vibrations becomes infinite whenever $\cosh z \cos z + 1 = 0$, that is, for all values of ω which make $z = \sqrt{\omega/a}\, l$ a root of the frequency equation of the cantilever. In other words, because a continuous beam has infinitely many natural frequencies, infinitely many different resonant states are possible, one at each natural frequency.

Let us now examine the application of the ideas we have been developing to some typical problems in the flow of heat. A convenient system to use for illustration is a long slender rod of uniform cross section whose curved surface is perfectly insulated against the flow of heat. As a consequence of the assumptions that the radius of the rod is very small in comparison with its length and that insulation prevents any loss of heat from the lateral surface, the temperature u can be considered constant over any particular cross section of the bar. This means that the temperature depends only on the time t and the distance x from one end of the rod. We therefore have to solve the one-dimensional form of the heat equation [Eq. (10), Sec. 7.2]

$$a^2 \frac{\partial u}{\partial t} = \frac{\partial^2 u}{\partial x^2}, \qquad a^2 = \frac{c\gamma}{k}$$

subject to whatever thermal conditions exist at the ends of the rod.

Example 2

A long slender rod has its curved surface insulated against the flow of heat and has its left and right ends maintained at the respective temperatures

$$u(0,t) = 0, \qquad u(l,t) = u_0$$

Find the temperature u as a function of x and t if the initial temperature distribution along the bar is given by $u(x,0) = f(x)$.

We begin by assuming a product solution

$$u(x,t) = X(x)T(t)$$

and substituting it into the heat equation:

$$a^2 X T' = X'' T$$

Dividing by XT gives

$$a^2 \frac{T'}{T} = \frac{X''}{X}$$

from which we conclude, as usual, that

$$a^2 \frac{T'}{T} \qquad \text{and} \qquad \frac{X''}{X}$$

must equal the same constant, say μ.

Now if $\mu > 0$, say $\mu = \lambda^2$, we have

$$T' = \frac{\lambda^2}{a^2} T \qquad \text{and therefore} \qquad T = A e^{\lambda^2 t/a^2}$$

But this is absurd, since it indicates that the temperature increases beyond all bounds as t increases. Hence we reject the possibility that $\mu > 0$.

If $\mu = 0$, we have simply

$$T' = 0, \qquad X'' = 0$$
$$T = A, \qquad X = Bx + C$$

and
$$u = XT = A(Bx + C) = B'x + C'$$

For this to be applicable to our problem it must reduce to 0 when $x = 0$, and to u_0 when $x = l$.   Hence

$$C' = 0 \quad \text{and} \quad u_0 = B'l \quad \text{or} \quad B' = \frac{u_0}{l}$$

The corresponding solution is therefore

$$u = \frac{u_0 x}{l}$$

If, finally, $\mu < 0$, say $\mu = -\lambda^2$, the component differential equations and their solutions are

$$T' = -\frac{\lambda^2}{a^2} T, \qquad X'' = -\lambda^2 X$$

$$T = Ae^{-(\lambda^2 t/a^2)}, \qquad X = B \cos \lambda x + C \sin \lambda x$$

Hence in this case

$$u = Ae^{-(\lambda^2 t/a^2)}(B \cos \lambda x + C \sin \lambda x) = e^{-(\lambda^2 t/a^2)}(B' \cos \lambda x + C' \sin \lambda x)$$

To fit the left end condition, this must reduce to 0 for all t when $x = 0$.   Hence $B' = 0$ and there remains the solution

$$u = C'e^{-(\lambda^2 t/a^2)} \sin \lambda x$$

To fit the right end condition, we do *not* want this expression to reduce to u_0 when $x = l$.   For if more than *one* particular solution gives the value u_0 at $x = l$, then forming a sum of such solutions, as we will undoubtedly need to do to fit the initial conditions, will give a solution reducing not to u_0 but to some multiple of u_0.   Moreover, it is impossible for the last expression to equal a nonzero constant for all values of t, even if we wished to impose such a condition.   Since we have already found one particular solution which reduces to u_0 when $x = l$, namely, the one associated with $\mu = 0$, we therefore require all other solutions to vanish at $x = l$.   Hence for all values of t we must have

$$C'e^{-(\lambda^2 t/a^2)} \sin \lambda l = 0$$

Since we cannot permit C' to be zero, it follows that

$$\sin \lambda l = 0 \quad \text{and} \quad \lambda_n = \frac{n\pi}{l}, \qquad n = 1, 2, 3, \ldots$$

Thus we have the infinite set of particular solutions

$$u_n = C'_n e^{-(\lambda_n^2 t/a^2)} \sin \lambda_n x = C'_n e^{-(n^2 \pi^2 t/a^2 l^2)} \sin \frac{n\pi x}{l} \qquad n = 1, 2, 3, \ldots$$

Adding the particular solution $u_0 x/l$ to the infinite series constructed from the solutions of the last set, we obtain for u the expression

$$u(x,t) = \frac{u_0 x}{l} + \sum_{n=1}^{\infty} C'_n e^{-(n^2 \pi^2 t/a^2 l^2)} \sin \frac{n\pi x}{l}$$

The problem will be solved if we can determine values of C'_n such that $u(x,t)$ reduces to $f(x)$ when $t = 0$.

This requires that

$$f(x) = \frac{u_0 x}{l} + \sum_{n=1}^{\infty} C'_n \sin \frac{n\pi x}{l}$$

Hence the (C'_n)'s are simply the coefficients in the half-range sine expansion, not of $f(x)$, but of the function

$$f(x) - \frac{u_0 x}{l}$$

That is

$$C'_n = \frac{2}{l} \int_0^l \left[f(x) - \frac{u_0 x}{l} \right] \sin \frac{n\pi x}{l} \, dx$$

Example 3

A long slender rod has its curved surface insulated against the flow of heat. Its left end is maintained at the temperature $u(0,t) = 0$. The right end radiates freely into air of constant temperature 0. Find the temperature u as a function of x and t if the initial temperature distribution along the rod is given by $u(x,0) = f(x)$.

The first step in this problem is to determine the analytic formulation of the boundary condition at the right end. To do this, we must use **Newton's law of cooling**

$$\Delta Q = h(u - u_0)\Delta A \Delta t$$

where ΔQ = quantity of heat radiated from a surface

ΔA = area from which the radiation takes place

Δt = time in which the radiation takes place

u = surface temperature

u_0 = temperature of surrounding medium

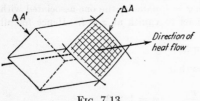

Fig. 7.13.

The proportionality constant h is sometimes called the **outer conductivity** of the material.

Next we observe that whatever heat leaves the surface of a body through an area ΔA must have passed through a parallel area $\Delta A'$ situated within the body an infinitesimal distance in the normal direction from ΔA (Fig. 7.13).

By Fourier's law of heat conduction, the amount of heat passing in time Δt through an area $\Delta A'$ within a body is

$$\Delta Q = -k \frac{\partial u}{\partial n} \Delta A' \Delta t$$

where $\dfrac{\partial u}{\partial n}$ is the temperature gradient in the direction of the normal to $\Delta A'$, drawn toward the surface element ΔA. Equating these two expressions for ΔQ we have in the limit as $\Delta A' \to \Delta A$,

$$-k \frac{\partial u}{\partial n} \bigg|_{\text{(surface)}} = h \left(u \bigg|_{\text{(surface)}} - u \bigg|_{\text{(surrounding medium)}} \right)$$

or in our case, since the x-axis is the normal to the right face in the outward direction, and since the temperature of the surrounding air is 0,

(3)
$$-k \frac{\partial u}{\partial x}\bigg|_{l,t} = hu(l,t)$$

Separating variables in the heat equation exactly as in Example 2, and rejecting the case $\mu > 0$, we find for $\mu = 0$ and $\mu < 0$ particular solutions of the respective forms

$$u = B + Cx, \qquad u = e^{-(\lambda^2 t/a^2)}(B \cos \lambda x + C \sin \lambda x)$$

Imposing the left end condition $u(0,t) = 0$, we find in each case that $B = 0$. Continuing with the right end condition (3), we have for the solution corresponding to $\mu = 0$

$$-k(C) = h(Cl)$$

Since k, h, and l are all positive quantities, this requires that $C = 0$, which shows that solutions of the first form do not enter into this problem.

For the solutions which correspond to $\mu < 0$, the right end condition becomes

$$-ke^{-(\lambda^2 t/a^2)}(\lambda C \cos \lambda l) = he^{-(\lambda^2 t/a^2)}(C \sin \lambda l)$$

or, dividing out the exponential and collecting terms,

$$C(h \sin \lambda l + \lambda k \cos \lambda l) = 0$$

If $C = 0$, the solution is trivial. Hence we must have

$$h \sin \lambda l + \lambda k \cos \lambda l = 0$$

or

$$\tan \lambda l = -\frac{\lambda k}{h} = -\frac{\lambda k l}{hl}$$

or finally

$$\tan z = -\alpha z$$

where $z = \lambda l$ and $\alpha = k/hl$.

The existence of roots of this equation and their general nature can be seen by considering the graphs of the functions

$$\tan z = y \qquad \text{and} \qquad y = -\alpha z$$

The abscissas of the points of intersection of these curves (Fig. 7.14) are the solutions of the equation $\tan z = -\alpha z$. There are obviously infinitely many roots, z_n. They are not spaced at regular intervals, although the interval between successive values approaches π as $n \to \infty$. From each value of z we obtain at once the corresponding value of λ,

$$\lambda_n = \frac{z_n}{l}$$

Combining the particular solutions corresponding to these characteristic values, we have

$$u(x,t) = \sum_{n=1}^{\infty} C_n e^{-(\lambda_n^2 t/a^2)} \sin \lambda_n x$$

To satisfy the initial temperature condition, we must have

(4)
$$u(x,0) \equiv f(x) = \sum_{n=1}^{\infty} C_n \sin \lambda_n x$$

From the fact that the values of λ are spaced at incommensurable intervals it is clear that the required expansion (4) is not a simple Fourier series. However, the characteristic functions

$$\sin \lambda_n x$$

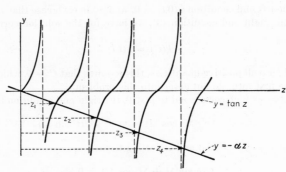

FIG. 7.14.   Plot showing the graphical solution of the equation $\tan z = -\alpha z$.

are orthogonal on the interval $(0,l)$ because they satisfy the differential equation

$$\frac{d^2X}{dx^2} + \lambda^2 X = 0$$

and the boundary conditions

$$X(0) = 0$$
$$hX(l) + kX'(l) = 0$$

which, for

$$p(x) = 1, \qquad q(x) = 0, \qquad r(x) = 1$$
$$a = 0, \qquad b = l$$
$$a_1 = 1, \qquad a_2 = 0, \qquad b_1 = h, \qquad b_2 = -k$$

is just a special case of the general problem covered by Theorem 1, Sec. 7.5.

Thus if we multiply both sides of (4) by $\sin(\lambda_n x)$ and integrate from 0 to l, all terms on the right drop out except the one involving the square of the characteristic function $\sin(\lambda_n x)$, and we have

$$\int_0^l f(x) \sin(\lambda_n x)dx = C_n \int_0^l \sin^2(\lambda_n x)dx$$

The value of the integral on the right is easy to work out. In fact,

$$\int_0^l \sin^2(\lambda_n x)dx = \frac{1}{2}\left[x - \frac{\sin(\lambda_n x)\cos(\lambda_n x)}{\lambda_n} \right]_0^l$$
$$= \frac{1}{2}\left[l - \frac{\sin(\lambda_n l)\cos(\lambda_n l)}{\lambda_n} \right]$$
$$= \frac{l}{2}\left(\frac{z_n - \sin z_n \cos z_n}{z_n} \right)$$

Therefore

$$C_n = \frac{2z_n}{(z_n - \sin z_n \cos z_n)l} \int_0^l f(x) \sin \lambda_n x \, dx$$

Since the numerical values of the characteristic values z_n are known, C_n is completely determined, and the problem is solved.

Example 4

A long, slender rod has its curved surface and right end perfectly insulated against the flow of heat. Heat is generated within the rod, the amount per unit volume per unit time being a known function of position, $\phi(x)$. Find the temperature as a function of x and t if the left end of the rod is maintained at the temperature $u(0,t) = 0$ and if the initial temperature distribution is given by $u(x,0) = f(x)$.

The nonhomogeneous partial differential equation which we must solve in this problem can be obtained easily by modifying the derivation of the heat equation in Sec. 7.2, noting that the temperature within an infinitestimal element now rises not only because of the influx of heat through its faces but also because of the internal generation of heat. If the rate of heat production per unit volume be $F(x,y,z,t)$, the resulting equation is

$$a^2 \frac{\partial u}{\partial t} = \frac{\partial^2 u}{\partial x^2} + \frac{\partial^2 u}{\partial y^2} + \frac{\partial^2 u}{\partial z^2} + \frac{F(x,y,z,t)}{k}$$

For the slender bar we are considering this reduces to

$$(5) \qquad\qquad a^2 \frac{\partial u}{\partial t} = \frac{\partial^2 u}{\partial x^2} + \frac{\phi(x)}{k}$$

Since we wish to find the temperature at any time, and not just the steady-state condition, we must first solve the homogeneous equation

$$a^2 \frac{\partial u}{\partial t} = \frac{\partial^2 u}{\partial x^2}$$

and then add to this solution a particular integral of the nonhomogeneous equation.

Separating variables in the homogeneous equation. rejecting the irrelevant cases, and imposing the left end condition is identical in every detail with the corresponding work in the last example, and, as before, we have to impose the right end condition on the solution

$$u = Ce^{-(\lambda^2 t/a^2)} \sin \lambda x$$

In this case since the right end is insulated and no heat flow takes place through it, the temperature gradient, $\dfrac{\partial u}{\partial x}$, at $x = l$ must be zero. This requires that

$$Ce^{-(\lambda^2 t/a^2)} \lambda \cos \lambda l = 0$$

Since C cannot vanish without the solution becoming trivial, it is necessary that

$$\cos \lambda l = 0 \qquad \text{and} \qquad \lambda_n = \frac{(2n-1)\pi}{2l}$$

The complete solution of the homogeneous equation is therefore

$$u = \sum_{n=1}^{\infty} C_n e^{-(\lambda_n^2 t/a^2)} \sin \lambda_n x = \sum_{n=1}^{\infty} C_n e^{-[(2n-1)^2 \pi^2/4a^2 l^2]t} \sin\left(\frac{2n-1}{2}\frac{\pi x}{l}\right)$$

In our search for a particular integral of the nonhomogeneous equation, we first observe that the continuous generation of heat within an imperfectly insulated body at a rate independent of time will ultimately lead to a steady-state condition of which the particular integral will necessarily be a description. Hence we try to find a solution independent of time, *i.e.*, of the form

$$u = X(x)$$

For this to be a solution of Eq.(5), it is necessary that

$$0 = X'' + \frac{\phi(x)}{k} \quad \text{or} \quad X'' = -\frac{\phi(x)}{k}$$

From this it is an easy matter to determine X by two integrations. Since X must also satisfy the end conditions of the problem, its derivative must vanish at $x = l$. Hence we perform the first integration between the limits of x and l, getting

$$X' = \frac{1}{k} \int_x^l \phi(s)ds$$

which is clearly zero when $x = l$. To satisfy the second condition, namely, that X vanish when $x = 0$, we integrate again, this time between the limits of 0 and x. This gives

$$X = \frac{1}{k} \int_0^x \int_r^l \phi(s)ds\, dr$$

which surely is zero when $x = 0$.

The complete solution for u can now be written

$$u(x,t) = \sum_{n=1}^\infty C_n e^{-[(2n-1)^2\pi^2/4a^2l^2]t} \sin\left(\frac{2n-1}{2}\frac{\pi x}{l}\right) + \frac{1}{k}\int_0^x \int_r^l \phi(s)ds\, dr$$

For this to reduce to the given initial temperature distribution when $t = 0$, it is necessary that

$$f(x) = \sum_{n=1}^\infty C_n \sin\left(\frac{2n-1}{2}\frac{\pi x}{l}\right) + \frac{1}{k}\int_0^x \int_r^l \phi(s)ds\, dr$$

Thus the C_n's are the coefficients in the expansion, not of $f(x)$, but of the function

$$f(x) - \frac{1}{k}\int_0^x \int_r^l \phi(s)ds\, dr = g(x), \text{ say.}$$

This is precisely the expansion discussed in Sec. 7.4 in connection with the torsional cantilever. Hence for C_n we have the explicit formula derived in that discussion,

$$C_n = \frac{2}{l}\int_0^l g(x) \sin\left(\frac{2n-1}{2}\frac{\pi x}{l}\right) dx$$

Example 5

A slender rod whose curved surface is perfectly insulated extends from $x = 0$ to $x = \infty$. Find the temperature along the rod as a function of x and t if the left end of the rod is maintained at the temperature $u(0,t) = 0$ and if the initial temperature distribution is given by $u(x,0) = f(x)$.

Exactly as in Examples 3 and 4 we find that the function

$$u = Ae^{-(\lambda^2 t/a^2)} \sin \lambda x$$

satisfies the heat equation and the one boundary condition. Lacking a second boundary condition, however, we have no further restrictions on λ. Therefore instead of having an infinite set of *discrete* characteristic values, λ_n, with corresponding solutions

$$u_n = A_n e^{-(\lambda_n^2 t/a^2)} \sin \lambda_n x$$

we have a continuous infinity of characteristic functions

$$u_\lambda = A(\lambda)e^{-(\lambda^2 t/a^2)} \sin \lambda x$$

where the arbitrary constant A is now associated, not with n, but with the *continuous* variable λ.

We cannot speak of an infinite series of particular solutions in this case. Instead of *adding* the solutions for each value of n, we therefore try *integrating* them over all values of λ,

$$(6) \qquad u(x,t) = \int_{-\infty}^{\infty} A(\lambda)e^{-(\lambda^2 t/a^2)} \sin \lambda x \, d\lambda$$

By direct substitution it is easily verified that this integral is a solution of the heat equation.

It is now necessary to impose the initial condition

$$u(x,0) = f(x)$$

on the solution $u(x,t)$. This requires that

$$f(x) = \int_{-\infty}^{\infty} A(\lambda) \sin \lambda x \, d\lambda$$

But this is just an instance of the Fourier integral which we considered in Sec. 5.7. There, in discussing what we called Fourier sine integrals, we saw [Eq. (7.1)] that if

$$f(x) = \int_{-\infty}^{\infty} A(\lambda) \sin \lambda x \, d\lambda$$

then

$$A(\lambda) = \frac{1}{\pi} \int_0^{\infty} f(x) \sin \lambda x \, dx$$

Introducing the dummy variable s for x in $A(\lambda)$, we can therefore write Eq. (6) in the form

$$u(x,t) = \int_{-\infty}^{\infty} e^{-(\lambda^2 t/a^2)} \left[\frac{1}{\pi} \int_0^{\infty} f(s) \sin \lambda s \, ds \right] \sin \lambda x \, d\lambda$$

$$= \frac{1}{\pi} \int_{-\infty}^{\infty} \int_0^{\infty} e^{-(\lambda^2 t/a^2)} f(s) \sin \lambda s \sin \lambda x \, ds \, d\lambda$$

Since the integrand is an even function of λ we can, if we choose, integrate with respect to λ only from 0 to ∞ and then multiply the result by 2, getting

$$u(x,t) = \frac{2}{\pi} \int_0^{\infty} \int_0^{\infty} e^{-(\lambda^2 t/a^2)} f(s) \sin \lambda s \sin \lambda x \, ds \, d\lambda$$

If we now write

$$2 \sin \lambda s \sin \lambda x = \cos \lambda (s - x) - \cos \lambda (s + x)$$

and interchange the order of integration we obtain

$$u(x,t) = \frac{1}{\pi} \int_0^\infty f(s) \int_0^\infty e^{-\lambda^2 t/a^2} [\cos \lambda (s - x) - \cos \lambda (s + x)] d\lambda \, ds$$

But (Example 2, Sec. A.6)

$$\int_0^\infty e^{-\alpha^2 v^2} \cos \beta v \, dv = \frac{\sqrt{\pi}}{2\alpha} e^{-(\beta^2/4\alpha^2)}$$

Hence applying this to the two inner integrals in $u(x,t)$, we have

$$u(x,t) = \frac{1}{\pi} \int_0^\infty f(s) \left[\frac{\sqrt{\pi}}{2\sqrt{t/a^2}} e^{-\frac{(s-x)^2}{4t/a^2}} - \frac{\sqrt{\pi}}{2\sqrt{t/a^2}} e^{-\frac{(s+x)^2}{4t/a^2}} \right] ds$$

$$= \frac{a}{2\sqrt{\pi t}} \int_0^\infty f(s) e^{-[(s-x)^2 a^2/4t]} \, ds - \frac{a}{2\sqrt{\pi t}} \int_0^\infty f(s) e^{-[(s+x)^2 a^2/4t]} \, ds$$

The evaluation of these integrals in a particular case may be difficult, but the problem is theoretically solved. For a given initial temperature distribution, numerical or graphical integration could be used to obtain a satisfactory approximation to u for any x and t.

EXERCISES

1. A thin sheet of metal bounded by the x-axis, the lines $x = 0$ and $x = 1$, and stretching to infinity in the y-direction, has its vertical edges maintained at the temperature 0. Over its base the temperature distribution $u(x,0) = u_0 x(1 - x)$ is maintained. Find the steady-state temperature at any point in the sheet. Assume the upper and lower faces of the sheet to be insulated so that the heat flow is purely two-dimensional.

$$Ans. \quad u(x,y) = \frac{8u_0}{\pi^3} \sum_{n=1}^\infty \frac{e^{-(2n-1)\pi y} \sin (2n - 1)\pi x}{(2n - 1)^3}$$

2. A thin square sheet of metal has three of its four edges maintained at the temperature 0. If an arbitrary temperature distribution is maintained along the fourth edge, find the steady-state temperature at any point within the sheet. How could the steady-state temperature be found if an arbitrary temperature distribution existed along each edge?

Ans. If the vertices of the square are $(0,0)$, $(l,0)$, $(0,l)$, (l,l), and if the upper edge of the square be the one maintained at the nonzero temperature $u(x,l) = f(x)$, then

$$u(x,y) = \sum_{n=1}^\infty A_n \sin \frac{n\pi x}{l} \sinh \frac{n\pi y}{l}$$

where

$$A_n = \frac{2}{l \sinh n\pi} \int_0^l f(x) \sin \frac{n\pi x}{l} \, dx$$

3. Work Exercise 1 if the boundary conditions are

$$u(0,y) = 0, \qquad u(1,y) = 100, \qquad u(x,0) = 100$$

4. Work Exercise 1 if the boundary conditions are

$$u(0,y) = 0 \qquad \frac{\partial u}{\partial x}\Big|_{1,y} = 0 \qquad u(x,0) = 100$$

5. Work Exercise 2 if the edge opposite the one on which the arbitrary temperature distribution is maintained is perfectly insulated instead of being kept at the temperature 0.

6. Work Exercise 2 if one of the edges adjacent to the one on which the arbitrary temperature distribution is maintained is perfectly insulated instead of being kept at the temperature 0.

7. Verify by direct substitution that the integral (6) for $u(x,t)$ in Example 5, Sec. 7.6, satisfies the heat equation.

8. A slender rod has its curved surface insulated against the flow of heat. At $t=0$, when the temperature throughout the bar is 0, each end is suddenly raised to the temperature 100 and maintained thereafter at that temperature. Find the temperature in the bar as a function of x and t.

9. A slender rod of length l has its curved surface and both ends insulated against the flow of heat. Initially the temperature distribution within the bar is given by $u(x,0) = u_0 (x/l)$. Find the temperature as a function of x and t.

10. A long, slender rod has its left end insulated against the flow of heat. Its right end radiates freely into air of temperature 70°. Initially the temperature throughout the bar is 100°. Find the temperature as a function of x and t. Compute the numerical values of the coefficients of the first two terms in the expansion of $u(x,t)$. (Hint: Make the preliminary change of dependent variable $U = u - 70$.)

11. Determine the natural frequencies and nodal lines of a square drumhead.

> *Ans.* The natural frequencies are $\dfrac{\sqrt{m^2 + n^2}\, a}{2l}$ $m, n = 1, 2, 3, \ldots$

12. Find the frequency equation of a circular shaft of length $2l$ vibrating torsionally, if between 0 and l the radius of the shaft is r_1 and between l and $2l$ the radius is r_2. (Hint: Set up and solve the appropriate differential equation for each section of the shaft, and make use of the fact that at $x = l$ both the angular displacement and the torque must be continuous.)

> *Ans.* The frequency equation is $\tan \dfrac{\lambda l}{a} = \left(\dfrac{r_1}{r_2}\right)^2$

13. A uniform circular shaft of length $2l$ is built-in at $x = 0$ and free at $x = 2l$. Between l and $2l$ a distributed torque equal to $T_0 \sin \omega t$ per unit length acts upon the shaft. Determine the forced torsional vibrations of the shaft.

> *Ans.* $\theta = \dfrac{a^2 T_0}{\omega^2 E_s J}\left[\dfrac{\sin \dfrac{\omega x}{a} \sin \dfrac{\omega l}{a}}{\cos \dfrac{2\omega l}{a}} - \left(1 - \cos \dfrac{\omega(x - l)}{a}\right) u(x - l)\right] \sin \omega t$

where $u(x)$ is the unit step function.

14. A hinged-hinged beam of uniform cross section and length l is acted upon by a distributed force equal to $F_0 x(l - x) \sin \omega t$ per unit length. Determine the forced vibration of the beam.

15. A long, slender rod stretching to infinity has its curved surface insulated against the flow of heat. At $t = 0$, when the temperature throughout this rod is 0, a second rod of unit length, whose curved surface is also insulated but whose temperature throughout is 100, is placed end to end against the infinite rod. The free end of the short rod is maintained thereafter at the temperature 0. Find the temperature in the composite rod as a function of x and t. Both rods are of the same material, and the contact between them is assumed to be perfect.

CHAPTER 8

BESSEL FUNCTIONS

8.1 Introduction. Many boundary value problems require for their solution functions which are not among those of elementary analysis. In this way many interesting and important new functions have entered mathematics. Chief among these are the Bessel* functions, a knowledge of which we shall find necessary for the solution of the following problem.

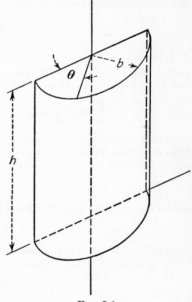

Example 1

A solid consists of one-half of a right circular cylinder of radius b and height h. The lower base, the curved surface, and the vertical plane face are maintained at the constant temperature 0. Over the upper base the temperature is a known function, $f(r,\theta)$. Assuming steady-state conditions, *i.e.*, assuming that the system has reached a state in which no further temperature changes take place with increasing time, find the temperature at any point in the solid.

Because of the nature of the boundaries of the solid it will be highly inconvenient

FIG. 8.1.

to use the heat equation in the cartesian form in which we derived it in Sec. 7.2, namely,

$$a^2 \frac{\partial u}{\partial t} = \frac{\partial^2 u}{\partial x^2} + \frac{\partial^2 u}{\partial y^2} + \frac{\partial^2 u}{\partial z^2}$$

or under steady-state conditions, for which $\frac{\partial u}{\partial t} = 0$,

$$\frac{\partial^2 u}{\partial x^2} + \frac{\partial^2 u}{\partial y^2} + \frac{\partial^2 y}{\partial z^2} = 0$$

---

* Named after the German mathematician and astronomer Friedrich Wilhelm Bessel (1784–1846), although special cases had been studied earlier by Jakob Bernoulli (1703), Daniel Bernoulli (1732), and Leonard Euler (1764).

Instead we use it as expressed in cylindrical coordinates (Sec. A.2)

$$\frac{\partial^2 u}{\partial r^2} + \frac{1}{r}\frac{\partial u}{\partial r} + \frac{1}{r^2}\frac{\partial^2 u}{\partial \theta^2} + \frac{\partial^2 u}{\partial z^2} = 0$$

As usual, we assume a product solution

$$u = R(r)\ \Theta(\theta)\ Z(z)$$

and substitute it into the partial differential equation. This gives

$$R''\Theta Z + \frac{1}{r}R'\Theta Z + \frac{1}{r^2}R\Theta''Z + R\Theta Z'' = 0$$

Multiplying by r^2, dividing by $R\Theta Z$, and transposing, we find

$$r^2\frac{R''}{R} + r\frac{R'}{R} + r^2\frac{Z''}{Z} = -\frac{\Theta''}{\Theta}$$

On the left we have a function of r and z. On the right we have a function of θ alone. The only way in which two such expressions can be identically equal is for each to be a constant. Hence we write

$$r^2\frac{R''}{R} + r\frac{R'}{R} + r^2\frac{Z''}{Z} = \mu \quad\text{and}\quad \frac{\Theta''}{\Theta} = -\mu \quad\text{or}\quad \Theta'' = -\mu\Theta$$

We first investigate the solution for Θ, keeping in mind the conditions that $u = 0$ when $\theta = 0$ and when $\theta = \pi$, for all values of r and z, which clearly can hold if and only if $\Theta(0) = \Theta(\pi) = 0$. If $\mu = 0$, we have

$$\Theta = A\theta + B$$

and for this to vanish when $\theta = 0$ and when $\theta = \pi$ it is necessary that

$$A = B = 0$$

Since this yields only a trivial solution, we must reject the possibility that $\mu = 0$.

If $\mu < 0$, say $\mu = -\lambda^2$, we have

$$\Theta = A\cosh \lambda\theta + B\sinh \lambda\theta$$

In order that $\Theta(0) = 0$ in this case, we must have $A = 0$. In order that $\Theta(\pi) = 0$, it is necessary that

$$B\sinh \lambda\pi = 0$$

This is possible only if $\lambda = 0$, which we have already rejected, or if $B = 0$, which again gives only a trivial solution. Thus μ cannot be negative.

If $\mu > 0$, say $\mu = \lambda^2$, we have

$$\Theta = A\cos \lambda\theta + B\sin \lambda\theta$$

For this to vanish when $\theta = 0$, we must have $A = 0$. For it to vanish at π, it is necessary that

$$B\sin \lambda\pi = 0$$

Since we cannot permit B to be zero, we must have $\sin \lambda\pi = 0$. Hence

$$\lambda = 1, 2, 3, 4, \ldots, n \ldots,$$

and thus for θ we have the family of special solutions

$$\Theta_n(\theta) = \sin n\theta$$

Since $\mu \equiv \lambda^2 = 1, 4, 9, 16 \ldots, n^2 \ldots$, the differential equation in R and Z now becomes

$$r^2 \frac{R''}{R} + r \frac{R'}{R} + r^2 \frac{Z''}{Z} = n^2$$

or dividing by r^2 and transposing,

$$\frac{Z''}{Z} = \frac{n^2}{r^2} - \frac{R''}{R} - \frac{R'}{rR}$$

Again we reason that these two functions of z and r, respectively, must have a common constant value, ν. Hence we have the two ordinary differential equations

$$Z'' = \nu Z, \qquad r^2 R'' + rR' + (\nu r^2 - n^2)R = 0$$

The solution of the Z-equation, whether ν be positive, negative, or zero, presents no difficulty. Which of these ranges is the appropriate one cannot be decided from the conditions of the problem applied solely to Z. Instead, the answer depends upon the properties of the solutions of the equation in R. We must therefore turn our attention to this equation and investigate the nature of its solutions. This is a major undertaking and a great deal of work must be done before we can return to the present heat-flow problem and complete its solution.

8.2 The Series Solution of the Bessel Equation. If we put $\nu = \lambda^2$ in the equation for R, we obtain

$$(1) \qquad r^2 R'' + rR' + (\lambda^2 r^2 - n^2)R = 0$$

This is known as **Bessel's equation of order n with a parameter λ.** Although in the problem we have been considering, n is known to be an integer, the general theory is developed without this restriction. Accordingly we shall take n to be any real number, until we return later to the problem we have left unfinished.

As a preliminary step in the solution for R, let us change the independent variable by the substitution

$$x = \lambda r$$

Then

$$R' \equiv \frac{dR}{dr} = \frac{dR}{dx}\frac{dx}{dr} = \lambda \frac{dR}{dx}$$

and similarly

$$R'' \equiv \frac{d^2R}{dr^2} = \lambda^2 \frac{d^2R}{dx^2}$$

Under these substitutions Eq. (1) becomes

$$(2) \qquad x^2 \frac{d^2R}{dx^2} + x \frac{dR}{dx} + (x^2 - n^2)R = 0$$

which is known simply as **Bessel's equation of order** n. If $R(x)$ is a solution of this equation, then of course $R(\lambda r)$ is a solution of the equation with a parameter (1).

As a tentative solution of (2), let us assume that

$$R(x) = x^c(a_0 + a_1 x + a_2 x^2 + \cdots)$$

where without loss of generality we may suppose that $a_0 \neq 0$. The exponent c is not necessarily a positive integer, so that we have *not* assumed a Maclaurin expansion for $R(x)$.*

Substituting this series into Eq. (2) and displaying the terms in a convenient array, we have

$$
\begin{aligned}
&[a_0 c(c-1)x^c + a_1(c+1)cx^{c+1} + a_2(c+2)(c+1)x^{c+2} + \cdots + a_k(c+k)(c+k-1)x^{c+k} + \cdots] \\
&+] \qquad a_0 c x^c + a_1(c+1)x^{c+1} + \qquad a_2(c+2)x^{c+2} + \cdots + \qquad a_k(c+k)x^{c+k} + \cdots] \\
&+[\qquad\qquad\qquad\qquad\qquad\qquad a_0 x^{c+2} + \cdots + \qquad a_{k-2}x^{c+k} + \cdots] \\
&+[\quad -n^2 a_0 x^c \quad - n^2 a_1 x^{c+1} - \qquad n^2 a_2 x^{c+2} - \cdots - \qquad n^2 a_k x^{c+k} - \cdots] = 0
\end{aligned}
$$

This will be identically true if and only if the coefficient of every power of x is zero:

$$a_0[c(c-1) + c - n^2] = 0$$
$$a_1[(c+1)c + (c+1) - n^2] = 0$$

and in general, for $k \geq 2$,

$$a_k[(c+k)(c+k-1) + (c+k) - n^2] + a_{k-2} = 0$$

Since $a_0 \neq 0$, the first condition requires that

$$c(c-1) + c - n^2 \equiv c^2 - n^2 = 0$$

Hence we must have $c = \pm n$. At present we shall suppose $c = +n$. Substituting $c = n$ into the equation containing a_1, we find

$$a_1[(c+1)c + (c+1) - n^2] \equiv a_1[(c+1)^2 - n^2] = a_1[(n+1)^2 - n^2]$$
$$= a_1(2n+1) = 0$$

In general, this will be true only if $a_1 = 0$. Even in the exceptional case in which $n = -\frac{1}{2}$, no essential generality is lost by supposing $a_1 = 0$.

Now for $c = n$ the general recurrence relation

$$a_k[(c+k)(c+k-1) + (c+k) - n^2] + a_{k-2}$$
$$\equiv a_k[(c+k)^2 - n^2] + a_{k-2} = 0$$

gives

$$a_k = -\frac{a_{k-2}}{(c+k)^2 - n^2} = -\frac{a_{k-2}}{(n+k)^2 - n^2} = -\frac{a_{k-2}}{k(2n+k)}$$

---

* This method of attack upon a differential equation is known as the **method of Frobenius** (1849–1917, German). It is of both practical and theoretical importance in connection with differential equations with variable coefficients.

From this it is clear that any coefficient a_k is proportional to the second preceding coefficient a_{k-2}. Hence, since $a_1 = 0$, a_3 must also vanish. Continuing in the same way, we conclude that every coefficient with an odd subscript must be zero.

On the other hand, starting with a_0, which is still perfectly arbitrary, and taking $k = 2, 4, 6 \ldots$ successively in the recurrence formula, we have

$$a_0 = a_0$$

$$a_2 = -\frac{a_0}{2(2n+2)} = -\frac{a_0}{2^2 \cdot 1!(n+1)}$$

$$a_4 = -\frac{a_2}{4(2n+4)} = -\frac{a_2}{2^2 \cdot 2 \cdot (n+2)} = \frac{a_0}{2^4 2!(n+1)(n+2)}$$

$$a_6 = -\frac{a_4}{6(2n+6)} = -\frac{a_4}{2^2 \cdot 3 \cdot (n+3)} = -\frac{a_0}{2^6 \cdot 3! \cdot (n+1)(n+2)(n+3)}$$

and in general

$$a_{2m} = \frac{(-1)^m a_0}{2^{2m} m!(n+1)(n+2)(n+3) \cdots (n+m)}$$

Now a_{2m} is the coefficient of $x^c x^{2m} \equiv x^{2m+n}$ in the expansion of R. Hence it would be convenient if a_{2m} contained the factor 2^{2m+n} in its denominator instead of just 2^{2m}. To achieve this, we write

$$a_{2m} = \frac{(-1)^m}{2^{2m+n} m!(n+1)(n+2) \cdots (n+m)} (2^n a_0)$$

Furthermore, the factors $(n+1) \cdots (n+m)$ suggest a factorial. In fact, if n were an integer, a factorial could be created by multiplying numerator and denominator by $n!$. However, since n is not necessarily an integer we must use not $n!$ but its generalization $\Gamma(n+1)$ (see Sec. A.6) for this purpose. Then

$$a_{2m} = \frac{(-1)^m}{2^{2m+n} m!(n+1) \cdots (n+m)\Gamma(n+1)} [2^n \Gamma(n+1) a_0]$$

Since the gamma function satisfies the recurrence formula

$$s\Gamma(s) = \Gamma(s+1)$$

this becomes finally

$$a_{2m} = \frac{(-1)^m}{2^{2m+n} m! \Gamma(n+m+1)} [2^n \Gamma(n+1) a_0]$$

Since a_0 is arbitrary, and since we are looking only for particular solutions, we choose

$$a_0 = \frac{1}{2^n \Gamma(n+1)}$$

so that

$$a_{2m} = \frac{(-1)^m}{2^{2m+n}m!\,\Gamma(n+m+1)}$$

Thus

$$R(x) = x^n\left[\frac{1}{2^n\Gamma(n+1)} - \frac{x^2}{2^{n+2}\Gamma(n+2)} + \frac{x^4}{2^{n+4}2!\,\Gamma(n+3)} - \cdots\right]$$

$$= \sum_{m=0}^{\infty} \frac{(-1)^m x^{n+2m}}{2^{2m+n}m!\,\Gamma(n+m+1)}$$

The function defined by this infinite series is known as the **Bessel function of the first kind of order** n, and is almost universally denoted by the symbol $J_n(x)$.

If we apply the ratio test to $J_n(x)$ to determine its region of convergence, we have

$$\left|\frac{u_{m+1}}{u_m}\right| = \left|\frac{(-1)^{m+1}x^{n+2m+2}}{2^{n+2m+2}(m+1)!\,\Gamma(n+m+2)} \cdot \frac{2^{n+2m}m!\,\Gamma(n+m+1)}{(-1)^m x^{n+2m}}\right|$$

$$= \left|\frac{x^2}{2^2 m(n+m+1)}\right|$$

Since the limit of this fraction as $m \to \infty$ is 0, we see that the series defining $J_n(x)$ converges for all values of x. The graphs of $J_0(x)$ and

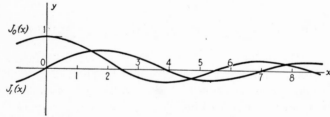

FIG. 8.2.   Plot showing the Bessel functions of the first kind, $J_0(x)$ and $J_1(x)$.

$J_1(x)$ are shown in Fig. 8.2. Their resemblance to the graphs of $\cos x$ and $\sin x$ is interesting.

Let us now return to the case $c = -n$. Since the gamma function is defined for all values of its argument except those which are nonpositive integers, it is evident that the function $J_{-n}(x)$, obtained from $J_n(x)$ by changing every n to $-n$, is a well-defined function of x for all x different from 0, when n is not an integer. At $x = 0, J_{-n}(x)$ becomes infinite because of the presence of negative powers of x in the early terms in the expansion. Moreover, since the Bessel equation of order n is left unchanged when n is replaced by $-n$, it follows that $J_{-n}(x)$ is also a solution wherever it is defined. Thus, if n is not an integer, we have found two solutions of the Bessel equation of order n, namely, $J_n(x)$ and $J_{-n}(x)$. And in this case since $J_{-n}(x)$ contains negative powers of x while $J_n(x)$ does not, it is obvious that the two cannot be proportional.   In other words, they are two *independent* solutions of the Bessel equation.   Since this is a linear second-order equation it follows from Theorem 2, Sec. 2.1, that its general solution is

$$R(x) = c_1 J_n(x) + c_2 J_{-n}(x)$$

If n is an integer, the situation is a little different.   In this case we have

$$J_{-n}(x) = \sum_{m=0}^{\infty} \frac{(-1)^m x^{-n+2m}}{2^{-n+2m} m!\, \Gamma(-n+m+1)}$$

The denominators of the first n terms now contain gamma functions which are infinite, since their arguments, $(-n+1)$, $(-n+2)$ . . . , -1, 0, are nonpositive integers.   This means that the first n terms of this series are actually not present, so that $J_{-n}(x)$ effectively starts with the term for which $m = n$:

$$J_{-n}(x) = \sum_{m=n}^{\infty} \frac{(-1)^m x^{-n+2m}}{2^{-n+2m} m!\, \Gamma(-n+m+1)}$$

Now let $m = j + n$ in the summation.   Then

$$J_{-n}(x) = \sum_{j=0}^{\infty} \frac{(-1)^{j+n} x^{-n+2(j+n)}}{2^{-n+2(j+n)} (j+n)!\, \Gamma(-n+j+n+1)}$$

$$= (-1)^n \sum_{j=0}^{\infty} \frac{(-1)^j x^{n+2j}}{2^{n+2j} \Gamma(j+n+1) j!}$$

$$= (-1)^n J_n(x)$$

This unpleasant result tells us that when n is an integer, $J_{-n}(x)$ is proportional to $J_n(x)$.   The two functions are therefore not independent, and the linear combination

$$c_1 J_n(x) + c_2 J_{-n}(x)$$

is no longer the general solution of Bessel's equation.   It is necessary then that we look for a second independent solution.

To do this, let us assume* that

$$R(x) = \phi(x) J_n(x)$$

* This method of obtaining a second solution of a linear second-order differential equation when one solution is known is a general one of considerable importance.   In particular, although we are concerned only with the case in which n is an integer, nothing in the procedure depends upon this fact.

where $\phi(x)$ is a function yet to be determined. Then

$$R' = \phi J'_n + \phi' J_n$$
$$R'' = \phi J''_n + 2\phi' J'_n + \phi'' J_n$$

and when we substitute into the differential equation (2), we have

$$x^2[\phi J''_n + 2\phi' J'_n + \phi'' J_n] + x[\phi J'_n + \phi' J_n] + (x^2 - n^2)\phi J_n = 0$$

or, rearranging,

$$x^2 J_n \phi'' + [2x^2 J'_n + x J_n]\phi' + [x^2 J''_n + x J'_n + (x^2 - n^2)J_n]\phi = 0$$

The last group of terms vanishes identically because J_n is a solution of Bessel's equation of order n. Hence to determine ϕ, we have merely to solve for ϕ' from the equation

$$x^2 J_n \phi'' + (2x^2 J'_n + x J_n)\phi' = 0$$

and then integrate. Separating variables in the last equation, we have

$$\frac{d\phi'}{\phi'} + \left(\frac{2J'_n}{J_n} + \frac{1}{x}\right) dx = 0$$

Then

$$\log \phi' + 2 \log J_n + \log x = \log C$$

or

$$\phi' = \frac{C}{x J_n^2}$$

Hence

$$\phi = C \int \frac{dx}{x J_n^2} + D$$

and thus the required second solution is

$$R(x) = \phi(x)J_n(x) = CJ_n \int \frac{dx}{x J_n^2} + DJ_n$$

Knowing the infinite series for $J_n(x)$ it is possible to express the entire integrand in $R(x)$ as a power series in x and hence ultimately to obtain an infinite series for $R(x)$. This would be a profitless task, however, since we have no real need of the series expansion for the second solution. It will be sufficient for our purposes to observe that because the denominator of the integrand contains the factor x^{2n+1}, the leading term in the expansion of the integrand is α_0/x^{2n+1}, where α_0 is a nonvanishing constant whose actual value is unimportant. If $n > 0$, this will integrate into the term $-(\alpha_0/2nx^{2n})$ which, even after multiplication by $J_n(x)$, will still become infinite at the origin. If $n = 0$, the leading term will integrate into $\alpha_0 \log x$ which will also become infinite as $x \to 0$ even after multiplication by $J_0(x)$. In any case, then, this second solution becomes infinite for $x = 0$. It is therefore independent of the first solution, $J_n(x)$ (which is finite at the origin when n is a positive integer), and will suffice for constructing the general solution in the troublesome case in which n is an integer.

Various standard forms, differing in the constants in the expression

$$R(x) = CJ_n \int \frac{dx}{xJ_n^2} + DJ_n$$

have been suggested for the second solution or **Bessel function of the second kind of order** n. The most common is denoted by the symbol $Y_n(x)$ in most texts, although in the important "Tables of Functions" of Jahnke-Emde it is called $N_n(x)$. Plots of $Y_0(x)$ and $Y_1(x)$ are shown in Fig. 8.3.

We can now summarize our discussion as follows. *Bessel's equation of order n has for its general solution, if n is not an integer, the expression*

$$c_1 J_n(x) + c_2 J_{-n}(x)$$

If n is an integer, the general solution is

$$c_1 J_n(x) + c_2 Y_n(x)$$

$J_n(x)$ *is finite at the origin, but both* $J_{-n}(x)$ *and* $Y_n(x)$ *become infinite as*

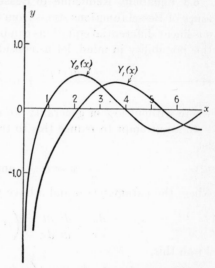

FIG. 8.3. Plot showing the Bessel functions of the second kind, $Y_0(x)$ and $Y_1(x)$.

$x \to 0$. *The solutions of Bessel's equation with a parameter, λ, in the respective cases are*

$$c_1 J_n(\lambda x) + c_2 J_{-n}(\lambda x)$$

and

$$c_1 J_n(\lambda x) + c_2 Y_n(\lambda x)$$

It can be shown that for all values of n both $J_n(x)$ and $Y_n(x)$ have infinitely many real zeros.

EXERCISES

Solve each of the following equations by the method of Frobenius. Where possible, determine the general term and the region of convergence of the solution(s).

1. $y'' + y = 0$

2. $y'' + xy' + y = 0$ *Ans.* $y_1 = \displaystyle\sum_{m=0}^{\infty} \frac{(-1)^m x^{2m}}{2^m m!}$, $\quad y_2 = \displaystyle\sum_{m=0}^{\infty} \frac{(-1)^m x^{2m+1} m! 2^m}{(2m + 1)!}$

3. $y'' + xy = 0$

4. $xy'' = y$

5. $y'' + xy' + x^2 y = 0$

6. $xy'' + xy' + y = 0$

Using the method of the text, find a second solution of each of the following equations:

7. $y'' + y = 0$ $y_1 = \sin x$

8. $(2x - x^2)y'' + 2(x - 1)y' - 2y = 0$ $y_1 = x - 1$ *Ans.* $y_2 = x^2 - 2x + 2$

9. $(x - 1)y'' - xy' + y = 0$ $y_1 = x$

10. $(1 - 2x)y'' + 2y' + (2x - 3)y = 0$ $y_1 = e^x$

8.3 Equations Reducible to Bessel's Equation. Much of the importance of Bessel functions stems from the fact that the solutions of numerous linear differential equations can be expressed in terms of them. With this possibility in mind, let us consider the differential equation

$$(1) \qquad \frac{d(x^p y')}{dx} + (ax^q + bx^r)y = 0$$

where without loss of generality we may suppose that $q > r$.

In an attempt to reduce this to the specific form of Bessel's equation, let

$$(2) \qquad x = t^\alpha \quad \text{and} \quad y = t^\beta z$$

where the parameters α and β have yet to be determined. Then

$$\frac{dy}{dx} = \frac{dy}{dt}\frac{dt}{dx} = \left(t^\beta \frac{dz}{dt} + \beta t^{\beta-1} z \right) \frac{1}{\alpha t^{\alpha-1}}$$

From this,

$$x^p \frac{dy}{dx} = t^{\alpha p} \left(t^\beta \frac{dz}{dt} + \beta t^{\beta-1} z \right) \frac{1}{\alpha t^{\alpha-1}}$$

$$= \frac{1}{\alpha} \left(t^{\alpha p+\beta-\alpha+1} \frac{dz}{dt} + \beta t^{\alpha p+\beta-\alpha} z \right)$$

Differentiating again, we find

$$\frac{d(x^p y')}{dx} = \frac{d(x^p y')}{dt}\frac{dt}{dx}$$

$$= \frac{1}{\alpha} \left[t^{\alpha p+\beta-\alpha+1} \frac{d^2 z}{dt^2} + (\alpha p + \beta - \alpha + 1)t^{\alpha p+\beta-\alpha} \frac{dz}{dt} \right.$$

$$\left. + \beta t^{\alpha p+\beta-\alpha} \frac{dz}{dt} + \beta(\alpha p + \beta - \alpha)t^{\alpha p+\beta-\alpha-1} z \right] \frac{1}{\alpha t^{\alpha-1}}$$

$$= \frac{1}{\alpha^2} \left[t^{\alpha p+\beta-2\alpha+2} \frac{d^2 z}{dt^2} + (\alpha p + 2\beta - \alpha + 1)t^{\alpha p+\beta-2\alpha+1} \frac{dz}{dt} \right.$$

$$\left. + \beta(\alpha p + \beta - \alpha)t^{\alpha p+\beta-2\alpha} z \right]$$

Substituting this, together with (2), into Eq. (1), we have

$$\frac{1}{\alpha^2}\left[t^{\alpha p+\beta-2\alpha+2}\frac{d^2z}{dt^2} + (\alpha p + 2\beta - \alpha + 1)t^{\alpha p+\beta-2\alpha+1}\frac{dz}{dt} \right.$$
$$\left. + \beta(\alpha p + \beta - \alpha)t^{\alpha p+\beta-2\alpha}z \right] + (at^{\alpha q+\beta} + bt^{\alpha r+\beta})z = 0$$

Multiplying this by α^2 and dividing by $t^{\alpha p+\beta-2\alpha+2}$ gives the simpler form

$$\frac{d^2z}{dt^2} + \frac{(\alpha p + 2\beta - \alpha + 1)}{t}\frac{dz}{dt}$$
$$+ \left[\frac{\beta(\alpha p + \beta - \alpha)}{t^2} + \alpha^2 a t^{\alpha q-\alpha p+2\alpha-2} + \alpha^2 b t^{\alpha r-\alpha p+2\alpha-2}\right]z = 0$$

For this to have the form of Bessel's equation, namely,

$$\frac{d^2z}{dt^2} + \frac{1}{t}\frac{dz}{dt} + \left(\lambda^2 - \frac{n^2}{t^2}\right)z = 0$$

it is necessary that the coefficient of $\frac{1}{t}\frac{dz}{dt}$ be 1, that the exponent of t in the fourth term be zero, and that the exponent of t in the last term be -2 (so that this term can be combined with the third). These conditions require that

$$\alpha p + 2\beta - \alpha + 1 = 1$$
$$\alpha q - \alpha p + 2\alpha - 2 = 0$$
$$\alpha r - \alpha p + 2\alpha - 2 = -2$$

The second of these equations fixes the value of α:

$$\alpha = \frac{2}{2 - p + q}$$

Substituting this into the first equation gives the value of β

$$\beta = \frac{\alpha(1 - p)}{2} = \frac{1 - p}{2 - p + q}$$

The third equation is simply

$$r = p - 2$$

This is a condition on the original equation which cannot be ensured by a disposition of the parameters α and β, which are now fixed. *If $r = p - 2$ or if $b = 0$* (which makes the condition $r = p - 2$ irrelevant), *then* the original equation can be reduced to the form of Bessel's equation:

$$\frac{d^2z}{dt^2} + \frac{1}{t}\frac{dz}{dt} + \left[a\alpha^2 + \frac{\beta(\alpha p + \beta - \alpha) + \alpha^2 b}{t^2}\right]z = 0$$

In this, the value of n^2 is $-\beta(\alpha p + \beta - \alpha) - \alpha^2 b$.   When the values of α and β are inserted, this gives

$$n = \frac{\sqrt{(1 - p)^2 - 4b}}{2 - p + q}$$

The value of the parameter λ is $\alpha \sqrt{a}$.   With these known, we can now write the general solution for z:

$$z = c_1 J_n(\lambda t) + c_2 J_{-n}(\lambda t) \qquad n \text{ not an integer}$$
$$z = c_1 J_n(\lambda t) + c_2 Y_n(\lambda t) \qquad n \text{ an integer}$$

The general solution for y can now be written down at once.   For, from (2),

$$t = x^{1/\alpha}$$

and thus

$$y = t^\beta z$$

(3.1)
$$= x^\mu [c_1 J_n(\lambda x^\nu) + c_2 J_{-n}(\lambda x^\nu)]$$

or, if n is an integer,

(3.2)
$$y = x^\mu [c_1 J_n(\lambda x^\nu) + c_2 Y_n(\lambda x^\nu)]$$

where

$$\lambda = \alpha \sqrt{a} = \frac{2\sqrt{a}}{2 - p + q}$$

$$\mu = \frac{\beta}{\alpha} = \frac{1 - p}{2}$$

$$\nu = \frac{1}{\alpha} = \frac{2 - p + q}{2}$$

$$n = \frac{\sqrt{(1 - p)^2 - 4b}}{2 - p + q} \qquad p \neq 2 + q$$

If $p = 2 + q$, the original equation instead of being reducible to Bessel's equation is reducible to the so-called Euler equation, discussed in Sec. 8.7.

Example 1

What is the general solution of the equation

$$\frac{d^2y}{dx^2} + \left(9x - \frac{20}{x^2}\right) y = 0$$

In this case $p = 0$, $q = 1$, $r = -2$, $a = 9$, $b = -20$, and since $r = p - 2$, the foregoing theory can be applied.   From these values we find at once

$$\lambda = 2, \qquad \mu = \tfrac{1}{2}, \qquad \nu = \tfrac{3}{2}, \qquad n = 3$$

and thus, from (3.2),

$$y = c_1 \sqrt{x}\, J_3(2x^{\frac{3}{2}}) + c_2 \sqrt{x}\, Y_3(2x^{\frac{3}{2}})$$

Example 2

What is the general solution of the equation $(d^2y/dx^2) + y = 0$?
In this equation $p = 0$, $q = 0$, $a = 1$, $b = 0$.　Hence

$$\lambda = 1, \qquad \mu = \tfrac{1}{2}, \qquad \nu = 1, \qquad n = \tfrac{1}{2}$$

and thus

$$y = c_1 \sqrt{x}\, J_{\frac{1}{2}}(x) + c_2 \sqrt{x}\, J_{-\frac{1}{2}}(x)$$

However, the general solution of this equation can also be written

$$y = d_1 \sin x + d_2 \cos x$$

Therefore for proper choice of the constants, the particular solutions

$$\sqrt{x}\, J_{\frac{1}{2}}(x) \qquad \text{and} \qquad \sqrt{x}\, J_{-\frac{1}{2}}(x)$$

must be expressible in the form $d_1 \sin x + d_2 \cos x$.

Now the series for $J_{\frac{1}{2}}(x)$ begins with the term

$$\frac{x^{\frac{1}{2}}}{2^{\frac{1}{2}}\, \Gamma\left(\tfrac{3}{2}\right)} = \sqrt{\frac{2}{\pi}}\, \sqrt{x}, \qquad \text{since } \Gamma\left(\frac{3}{2}\right) = \frac{1}{2}\, \Gamma\left(\frac{1}{2}\right) = \frac{1}{2}\, \sqrt{\pi}$$

Hence $\sqrt{x}\, J_{\frac{1}{2}}(x)$ begins with the term $\sqrt{2/\pi}\, x$.
Therefore if we write

$$\sqrt{x}\, J_{\frac{1}{2}}(x) = \sqrt{\frac{2}{\pi}}\, x - \cdots = d_1 \sin x + d_2 \cos x$$

and put $x = 0$, we find $d_2 = 0$.　Subsequently, equating the coefficients of x in the resulting identity, we find

$$d_1 = \sqrt{\frac{2}{\pi}}$$

This proves the interesting result

$$\sqrt{x}\, J_{\frac{1}{2}}(x) = \sqrt{\frac{2}{\pi}} \sin x$$

In a similar manner it can be shown that

$$\sqrt{x}\, J_{-\frac{1}{2}}(x) = \sqrt{\frac{2}{\pi}} \cos x$$

8.4 Modified Bessel Functions.　Certain equations closely resembling Bessel's equation occur so often in applications that their solutions, instead of being expressed in terms of the Bessel functions we have derived, are named and used as functions in their own right.　The most important of these equations is

$$(1) \qquad \frac{d^2y}{dx^2} + \frac{1}{x}\frac{dy}{dx} - \left(1 + \frac{n^2}{x^2}\right) y = 0$$

Since this can be written in the form

$$\frac{d^2y}{dx^2} + \frac{1}{x}\frac{dy}{dx} + \left(i^2 - \frac{n^2}{x^2}\right) y = 0$$

it is evident that this is nothing but Bessel's equation with the imaginary parameter i. However, to write the general solution as

$$y = c_1 J_n(ix) + c_2 J_{-n}(ix)$$

and retain the imaginaries in actual applications would be about as convenient as to write the solution of

$$\frac{d^2 y}{dx^2} - y = 0$$

in the form

$$y = c_1 \cos ix + c_2 \sin ix$$

and use this complex expression instead of resorting to real exponentials or to hyperbolic functions. Accordingly we seek modifications of $J_n(ix)$ and $J_{-n}(ix)$ that will be real functions of real variables. Now

$$J_n(ix) = \sum_{k=0}^{\infty} \frac{(-1)^k (ix)^{n+2k}}{2^{n+2k} k! \Gamma(n + k + 1)}$$

$$= i^n \sum_{k=0}^{\infty} \frac{x^{n+2k}}{2^{n+2k} k! \Gamma(n + k + 1)}$$

Of course $J_n(ix)$ multiplied by any constant will also be a solution of the equation we are considering. In particular, we can multiply it by i^{-n}, getting

$$i^{-n} J_n(ix) = \sum_{k=0}^{\infty} \frac{x^{n+2k}}{2^{n+2k} k! \Gamma(n + k + 1)}$$

This is a completely real function, identical with $J_n(x)$ except that its terms instead of alternating in sign are all positive. This new function, which is evidently related to $J_n(x)$ in the same way that $\sinh x$ and $\cosh x$ are related to $\sin x$ and $\cos x$, is known as the **modified Bessel function of the first kind of order** n, $I_n(x)$.* Unlike $J_n(x)$, which has infinitely many real roots, $I_0(x)$ has no real roots, while $I_n(x)$, $n \neq 0$, has only the one real root $x = 0$. If n is not an integer, $I_{-n}(x)$, obtained from $I_n(x)$ by replacing n by $-n$ throughout, is a second, independent solution of Eq. (1), whose general solution can therefore be written

$$y = c_1 I_n(x) + c_2 I_{-n}(x)$$

On the other hand, if n is an integer, we have the identity

$$J_{-n}(ix) = (-1)^n J_n(ix)$$

* In the "Tables of Functions" of Jahnke-Emde, $I_n(x)$ is written $i^{-n} J_n(ix)$.

or multiplying both sides by i^{-n}

$$i^{-n}J_{-n}(ix) = (-1)^n[i^{-n}J_n(ix)]$$
$$i^{-2n}[i^nJ_{-n}(ix)] = (-1)^nI_n(x)$$
$$i^{-2n}I_{-n}(x) = (-1)^nI_n(x)$$

and finally

$$I_{-n}(x) = I_n(x)$$

In this case, then, a second, independent solution remains to be found before the general solution can be written down.

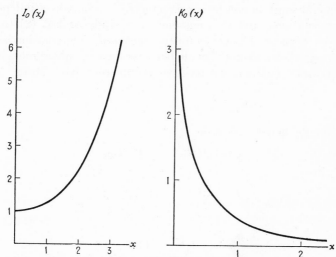

FIG. 8.4.   Plot showing the modified Bessel functions $I_0(x)$ and $K_0(x)$.

This may be done, as for the functions of the first kind, by determining $\phi(x)$ so that $\phi(x)I_n(x)$ will be a solution of the modified Bessel equation (1). The usual procedure, however, is to define the second solution as

$$\lim_{\nu \to n(=\text{integer})} \frac{\pi}{2} \frac{I_{-\nu}(x) - I_\nu(x)}{\sin \nu\pi}$$

The function thus defined is usually denoted by $K_n(x)$,* and is called the **modified Bessel function of the second kind of order** n. Its exact structure is of little concern to us. For our purposes it will be sufficient to know that both $I_{-n}(x)$ and $K_n(x)$ become infinite as $x \to 0$. Plots of $I_0(x)$ and $K_0(x)$ are shown in Fig. 8.4.

A second equation closely related to the Bessel equation is

(2) $$\frac{d^2y}{dx^2} + \frac{1}{x}\frac{dy}{dx} + \left(-i - \frac{n^2}{x^2}\right)y = 0 \qquad n \text{ an integer}$$

* In the "Table of Functions" of Jahnke-Emde, $i^{n+1}H_n{}^{(1)}(ix)$ is written for $\frac{2}{\pi}K_n(x)$.

This may be regarded either as Bessel's equation of order n with a parameter $\pm \sqrt{-i}$, or as the modified Bessel equation of order n with the parameter $\pm \sqrt{i}$. From the former point of view the general solution can be written

$$y = c_1 J_n(\pm \sqrt{-i}\, x) + c_2 Y_n(\pm \sqrt{-i}\, x)$$

From the second point of view the solution can be written

$$y = d_1 I_n(\pm \sqrt{i}\, x) + d_2 K_n(\pm \sqrt{i}\, x)$$

The general solution can be constructed from *any* pair of independent particular solutions, and it is customary in studying Eq. (2) to select $J_n(\pm \sqrt{-i}\, x)$ and $K_n(\pm \sqrt{i}\, x)$ for this purpose. The solution becomes unambiguous when a choice is made between the two square roots in each case. Naturally enough, the positive square roots are chosen. Then, since

$$\sqrt{-i} = \sqrt{-1}\, \sqrt{i} = i^{\frac{3}{2}}$$

we have for the general solution

$$y = c J_n(i^{\frac{3}{2}}x) + d K_n(i^{\frac{3}{2}}x)$$

Now

$$J_n(i^{\frac{3}{2}}x) = \sum_{k=0}^{\infty} \frac{(-1)^k (i^{\frac{3}{2}}x)^{n+2k}}{2^{n+2k} k!\, \Gamma(n+k+1)}$$

$$= i^{\frac{3n}{2}} \sum_{k=0}^{\infty} \frac{(-1)^k i^{3k} x^{n+2k}}{2^{n+2k} k!\, (n+k)!}$$

Moreover, i^{3k} can only take on one of the four values

$$
\begin{aligned}
1, &\qquad k = 0,\, 4,\, 8,\, \ldots \\
-i, &\qquad k = 1,\, 5,\, 9,\, \ldots \\
-1, &\qquad k = 2,\, 6,\, 10,\, \ldots \\
i, &\qquad k = 3,\, 7,\, 11,\, \ldots
\end{aligned}
$$

Hence the first, third, fifth, . . . terms in $J_n(i^{\frac{3}{2}}x)$ are real, while the second, fourth, sixth, . . . are imaginary. Separating the series into its real and imaginary parts, we obtain

$$J_n(i^{\frac{3}{2}}x) = i^{\frac{3n}{2}} \left[\sum_{j=0}^{\infty} \frac{(-1)^j x^{n+4j}}{2^{n+4j}(2j)!\,(n+2j)!} + i \sum_{j=0}^{\infty} \frac{(-1)^j x^{n+2+4j}}{2^{n+2+4j}(2j+1)!\,(n+2j+1)!} \right]$$

$$= i^{\frac{3n}{2}} \left(\sum_1 + i \sum_2 \right), \text{ say.}$$

Furthermore, using de Moivre's theorem (see Sec. 9.3), we can write

$$i^{\frac{3n}{2}} = \left(\cos \frac{1}{2} \pi + i \sin \frac{1}{2} \pi \right)^{\frac{3n}{2}} = \cos \frac{3n\pi}{4} + i \sin \frac{3n\pi}{4}$$

Thus

$$J_n(i^{\frac{3}{2}}x) = \left(\cos \frac{3n\pi}{4} + i \sin \frac{3n\pi}{4} \right) \left(\sum_1 + i \sum_2 \right)$$

$$= \left(\cos \frac{3n\pi}{4} \sum_1 - \sin \frac{3n\pi}{4} \sum_2 \right) + i \left(\cos \frac{3n\pi}{4} \sum_2 + \sin \frac{3n\pi}{4} \sum_1 \right)$$

$J_n(i^{\frac{3}{2}}x)$ thus consists of one purely real series plus i times a second purely real series. The series forming the real part of this expression is

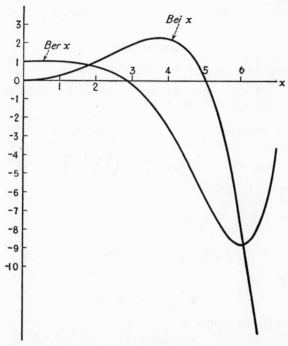

Fig. 8.5. Plot showing the functions ber x and bei x.

defined to be the function $\text{ber}_n\, x$. The series forming the imaginary part is defined to be the function $\text{bei}_n\, x$. The letters *be-* suggest the relation between these new functions and the Bessel functions themselves. The terminal letters, r and i, of course suggest the adjectives *real* and *imaginary*. For the important case $n = 0$, we have explicitly

$$\text{ber } x \equiv \text{ber}_0 \, x = \sum_{j=0}^{\infty} \frac{(-1)^j x^{4j}}{2^{4j}[(2j)\,!]^2}$$

$$\text{bei } x \equiv \text{bei}_0 \, x = \sum_{j=0}^{\infty} \frac{(-1)^j x^{4j+2}}{2^{4j+2}[(2j+1)\,!]^2}$$

Plots of ber x and bei x are shown in Fig. 8.5.

In a similar way the function $K_n(i^{\frac{1}{2}}x)$ can be expressed as a real series plus i times another real series. These series are taken as the definitions of the new functions $\text{ker}_n \, x$ and $\text{kei}_n \, x$, respectively. The general solution of Eq. (2) can thus be written

$$y = c(\text{ber}_n \, x + i \, \text{bei}_n \, x) + d(\text{ker}_n \, x + i \, \text{kei}_n \, x)$$

$\text{ber}_n \, x + i \, \text{bei}_n \, x$ is finite at the origin, but $\text{ker}_n \, x + i \, \text{kei}_n \, x$ becomes infinite as $x \to 0$.

EXERCISES

Find the general solution of each of the following equations:

1. $xy'' + 2y' + 4y = 0$.   (Hint: Multiply the equation by a factor which will make the first two terms the derivative of a product.)

$\qquad\qquad\qquad$ *Ans.* $\quad y = x^{-\frac{1}{2}}[c_1 J_1(4\sqrt{x}) + c_2 Y_1(4\sqrt{x})]$

2. $xy'' + 2y' - 4xy = 0$ $\qquad\qquad$ *Ans.* $\quad y = x^{-\frac{1}{2}}[c_1 I_{\frac{1}{2}}(2x) + c_2 I_{-\frac{1}{2}}(2x)]$

3. $x^2 y'' + 2xy' + (x^3 - 2)y = 0$ $\qquad$ *Ans.* $\quad y = x^{-\frac{1}{2}}[c_1 J_1(\frac{2}{3}x^{\frac{3}{2}}) + c_2 Y_1(\frac{2}{3}x^{\frac{3}{2}})]$

4. $xy'' - y' + 2x^2 y = x^2$ *Ans.* $\quad y = x\left[c_1 J_{\frac{2}{3}}\left(\frac{2\sqrt{2}}{3}x^{\frac{3}{2}}\right) + c_2 J_{-\frac{2}{3}}\left(\frac{2\sqrt{2}}{3}x^{\frac{3}{2}}\right)\right] + \frac{1}{2}$

5. $x^2 y'' + 3xy' + (1 + x)y = 0$

6. $y'' - x^4 y = 2x^5$

7. $x^2 y'' - 2xy' - 4(1 + x^2)y = 0$

8. Show that any solution of

$$\frac{d(x^{a-1}y')}{dx} = kx^{a-2}y \qquad \text{or} \qquad \frac{d(x^{a-1}y')}{dx} = -kx^{a-2}y$$

will satisfy

$$\frac{d^2(x^a y'')}{dx^2} = k^2 x^{a-2}y$$

9. What is the general solution of

$$\frac{d^2(x^2 y'')}{dx^2} = 9y$$

10. What is the general solution of

$$x^2 y^{\text{iv}} + 8xy''' + 12y'' - y = 0$$

8.5 Basic Identities. The Bessel functions are related by an amazing array of identities. Fundamental among these are the consequences of the following pair of theorems:

Theorem 1

$$\frac{d[x^{n+1}J_{n+1}(x)]}{dx} = x^{n+1}J_n(x)$$

Theorem 2

$$\frac{d[x^{-n}J_n(x)]}{dx} = -x^{-n}J_{n+1}(x)$$

To prove the first of these, take the series for $J_{n+1}(x)$, multiply it by x^{n+1}, and differentiate it term by term:

$$J_{n+1}(x) = \sum_{k=0}^{\infty} \frac{(-1)^k x^{n+1+2k}}{2^{n+1+2k}k!\,\Gamma(n+1+k+1)}$$

$$x^{n+1}J_{n+1}(x) = \sum_{k=0}^{\infty} \frac{(-1)^k x^{2n+2+2k}}{2^{n+1+2k}k!\,\Gamma(n+k+2)}$$

$$\frac{d[x^{n+1}J_{n+1}(x)]}{dx} = \sum_{k=0}^{\infty} \frac{(-1)^k 2(n+k+1)x^{2n+1+2k}}{2^{n+1+2k}k!(n+k+1)\Gamma(n+k+1)}$$

$$= \sum_{k=0}^{\infty} \frac{(-1)^k x^{n+1} x^{n+2k}}{2^{n+2k}k!\,\Gamma(n+k+1)}$$

$$= x^{n+1} \sum_{k=0}^{\infty} \frac{(-1)^k x^{n+2k}}{2^{n+2k}k!\,\Gamma(n+k+1)}$$

$$= x^{n+1}J_n(x)$$

Q.E.D.

To prove Theorem 2, we proceed in essentially the same manner:

$$J_n(x) = \sum_{k=0}^{\infty} \frac{(-1)^k x^{n+2k}}{2^{n+2k}k!\,\Gamma(n+k+1)}$$

$$x^{-n}J_n(x) = \sum_{k=0}^{\infty} \frac{(-1)^k x^{2k}}{2^{n+2k}k!\,\Gamma(n+k+1)}$$

$$\frac{d[x^{-n}J_n(x)]}{dx} = \sum_{k=1}^{\infty} \frac{(-1)^k 2k x^{2k-1}}{2^{n+2k}k!\,\Gamma(n+k+1)}$$

The sum now starts with $k = 1$ and not $k = 0$ because the first term in the series to be differentiated is a constant and hence differentiates to zero.   Now change the variable of summation by the substitution

$$k = j + 1$$

Then

$$\frac{d[x^{-n}J_n(x)]}{dx} = \sum_{j=0}^{\infty} \frac{(-1)^{j+1}2(j+1)x^{2\overline{j+1}-1}}{2^{n+2\overline{j+1}}(j+1)!\Gamma(n+\overline{j+1}+1)}$$

$$= -\sum_{j=0}^{\infty} \frac{(-1)^{i}x^{-n}x^{n+2j+1}}{2^{n+2j+1}j!\Gamma(n+1+j+1)}$$

$$= -x^{-n} \sum_{j=0}^{\infty} \frac{(-1)^{i}x^{\overline{n+1}+2j}}{2^{\overline{n+1}+2j}j!\Gamma(n+1+j+1)}$$

$$= -x^{-n}J_{n+1}(x)$$

Q.E.D.

From the basic identities

(1) $$\frac{d[x^{n+1}J_{n+1}(x)]}{dx} = x^{n+1}J_n(x)$$

(2) $$\frac{d[x^{-n}J_n(x)]}{dx} = -x^{-n}J_{n+1}(x)$$

we have, on performing the indicated differentiations,

$$x^{n+1}J'_{n+1}(x) + (n+1)x^nJ_{n+1}(x) = x^{n+1}J_n(x)$$
$$x^{-n}J'_n(x) - nx^{-n-1}J_n(x) = -x^{-n}J_{n+1}(x)$$

If we divide the first of these by x^{n+1} and multiply the second by x^n, we obtain

(3) $$J'_{n+1}(x) + \frac{n+1}{x}J_{n+1}(x) = J_n(x)$$

(4) $$J'_n(x) - \frac{n}{x}J_n(x) = -J_{n+1}(x)$$

In the first of these, which of course is an identity for all n, let $n+1$ be replaced by n.   Then, transposing, we obtain the important derivative formulas

→ (5) $$J'_n(x) = J_{n-1}(x) - \frac{n}{x}J_n(x)$$

→ (6) $$J'_n(x) = \frac{n}{x}J_n(x) - J_{n+1}(x)$$

Adding these and dividing by 2, we obtain a third formula for $J'_n(x)$:

(7) $$J'_n(x) = \frac{J_{n-1}(x) - J_{n+1}(x)}{2}$$

Subtracting (6) from (5) gives the highly important recurrence formula

$$(8) \qquad J_{n-1}(x) + J_{n+1}(x) = \frac{2n}{x} J_n(x)$$

Written as

$$(8.1) \qquad J_{n+1}(x) = \frac{2n}{x} J_n(x) - J_{n-1}(x) \qquad \longleftarrow$$

it serves to express Bessel functions of high orders in terms of functions of lower orders, frequently a useful manipulation.   Written as

$$(8.2) \qquad J_{n-1}(x) = \frac{2n}{x} J_n(x) - J_{n+1}(x) \qquad \longleftarrow$$

it serves similarly to express Bessel functions of large negative order (for instance) in terms of functions whose orders are numerically smaller.

Example 1

Express $J_4(x)$ in terms of $J_0(x)$ and $J_1(x)$.
Taking $n = 3$ in (8.1), we have first

$$J_4(x) = \frac{6}{x} J_3(x) - J_2(x)$$

Applying (8.1) again to $J_3(x)$ and $J_2(x)$, we have further

$$\begin{aligned} J_4(x) &= \frac{6}{x}\left[\frac{4}{x} J_2(x) - J_1(x)\right] - \left[\frac{2}{x} J_1(x) - J_0(x)\right] \\ &= \frac{24}{x^2} J_2(x) - \frac{8}{x} J_1(x) + J_0(x) \\ &= \frac{24}{x^2}\left[\frac{2}{x} J_1(x) - J_0(x)\right] - \frac{8}{x} J_1(x) + J_0(x) \\ &= \left(\frac{48}{x^3} - \frac{8}{x}\right) J_1(x) - \left(\frac{24}{x^2} - 1\right) J_0(x) \end{aligned}$$

Example 2

Show that

$$\frac{d[xJ_n(x)J_{n+1}(x)]}{dx} = x[J_n^2(x) - J_{n+1}^2(x)]$$

Performing the differentiation, we have

$$\frac{d[xJ_n(x)J_{n+1}(x)]}{dx} = J_n(x)J_{n+1}(x) + xJ_n'(x)J_{n+1}(x) + xJ_n(x)J_{n+1}'(x)$$

Substituting for $xJ_n'(x)$ from (4) and for $xJ_{n+1}'(x)$ from (3), we have

$$\frac{d[xJ_n(x)J_{n+1}(x)]}{dx} = J_n(x)J_{n+1}(x) + J_{n+1}(x)[nJ_n(x) - xJ_{n+1}(x)]$$
$$+ J_n(x)[xJ_n(x) - (n+1)J_{n+1}(x)]$$
$$= x[J_n^2(x) - J_{n+1}^2(x)]$$

The Bessel functions of the first kind are not the only ones which possess an extensive list of identities. The functions of the second kind as well as the modified functions and the ber, bei, ker, and kei functions are all connected by numerous important identities closely resembling and in some cases identical with those which we have established for $J_n(x)$. A few of these are indicated in the exercises at the end of this paragraph. The others can be found in larger and more advanced treatments than ours.

The basic differentiation identities (1) and (2) when written as integration formulas

(9) $$\int x^{n+1} J_n(x) dx = x^{n+1} J_{n+1}(x) + c$$
(10) $$\int x^{-n} J_{n+1}(x) dx = -x^{-n} J_n(x) + c$$

suffice for the integration of numerous simple expressions involving Bessel functions.

For example, taking $n = 0$ in (9), we find

$$\int x J_0(x) dx = x J_1(x) + c$$

Similarly, taking $n = 0$ in (10) gives

$$\int J_1(x) dx = -J_0(x) + c$$

Usually, however, integration by parts must be used in addition to (9) and (10).

Example 3

Integrate

$$\int J_3(x) dx$$

Now

$$\int J_3(x) dx = \int x^2 [x^{-2} J_3(x)] dx$$

and so, integrating by parts with

$$u = x^2, \qquad dv = x^{-2} J_3(x) dx$$
$$du = 2x\, dx, \qquad v = -x^{-2} J_2(x) \qquad \text{[by Eq. (10)]}$$

we have

$$\int J_3(x) dx = -J_2(x) + 2\int x^{-1} J_2(x) dx$$
$$= -J_2(x) + 2[-x^{-1} J_1(x)] + c$$
$$= -J_2(x) - \frac{2}{x} J_1(x) + c$$

Example 4

What is

$$\int \frac{J_2(x)}{x^2}\, dx$$

Multiply and divide the integrand by x^2, and then integrate by parts.   Then

$$\int \frac{J_2(x)}{x^2}\, dx = \int [x^2 J_2(x)]x^{-4}\, dx \longrightarrow - \frac{J_2(x)}{3x} + \frac{1}{3} \int J_1(x)\, \frac{dx}{x}$$

$$u = x^2 J_2(x) \qquad dv = \frac{dx}{x^4}$$

$$du = x^2 J_1(x)dx \quad v = -\frac{1}{3x^3}$$

$$= -\frac{J_2(x)}{3x} + \frac{1}{3} \int x J_1(x)\, \frac{dx}{x^2}$$

Again use integration by parts with

$$u = x J_1(x), \qquad dv = \frac{dx}{x^2}$$

$$du = x J_0(x)dx, \qquad v = -\frac{1}{x}$$

Then

$$\int J_2(x)\, \frac{dx}{x^2} = -\frac{J_2(x)}{3x} - \frac{1}{3} J_1(x) + \frac{1}{3} \int J_0(x)dx$$

The residual integral $\int J_0(x)dx$ cannot be evaluated in finite form.   In general, an integral of the form

$$\int x^n J_m(x)dx$$

where m and n are integers such that $m + n \geq 0$ can be completely integrated if $m + n$ is odd but will ultimately depend upon the residual integral $\int J_0(x)dx$ if $m + n$ is even.   For this reason $\int_0^x J_0(x)dx$ has recently been tabulated.[*]

Another class of identities of great usefulness can be derived by the following considerations.   If we take the function

$$e^{\frac{x}{2}\left(t - \frac{1}{t}\right)} = e^{\frac{xt}{2}} e^{-\frac{x}{2t}}$$

and expand each of the exponentials, we get, respectively,

$$1 + \left(\frac{xt}{2}\right) + \frac{1}{2!}\left(\frac{xt}{2}\right)^2 + \cdots + \frac{1}{n!}\left(\frac{xt}{2}\right)^n + \frac{1}{(n+1)!}\left(\frac{xt}{2}\right)^{n+1}$$
$$+ \frac{1}{(n+2)!}\left(\frac{xt}{2}\right)^{n+2} + \cdots$$

$$1 - \left(\frac{x}{2t}\right) + \frac{1}{2!}\left(\frac{x}{2t}\right)^2 - \cdots + \frac{(-1)^n}{n!}\left(\frac{x}{2t}\right)^n + \frac{(-1)^{n+1}}{(n+1)!}\left(\frac{x}{2t}\right)^{n+1}$$
$$+ \frac{(-1)^{n+2}}{(n+2)!}\left(\frac{x}{2t}\right)^{n+2} + \cdots$$

[*] A. N. Lowan and Milton Abramowitz, "Tables of Integrals of $\int_0^x J_0(t)dt$ and $\int_0^x Y_0(t)dt$" (MT 20), Superintendent of Documents, Government Printing Office, Washington, D.C.

If we multiply these two series, the coefficient of t^n will be obtained from the product of the term in t^n in the first series times the leading term in the second series and all the other products formed by advancing one term at a time in the respective series.   The result is

$$\left[\frac{1}{n!}\left(\frac{x}{2}\right)^n\right][1] + \left[\frac{1}{(n+1)!}\left(\frac{x}{2}\right)^{n+1}\right]\left[-\frac{x}{2}\right]$$

$$+ \left[\frac{1}{(n+2)!}\left(\frac{x}{2}\right)^{n+2}\right]\left[\frac{1}{2!}\left(\frac{x}{2}\right)^2\right] + \cdots$$

$$= \sum_{k=0}^{\infty} \frac{(-1)^k x^{n+2k}}{2^{n+2k}k!(n+k)!} = J_n(x)$$

In a similar way, to compute the coefficient of t^{-n} we begin with the product of the leading term in the first series times the term in t^{-n} in the second series and continue with the products of corresponding terms in the two series thereafter.   The result is

$$[1]\left[\frac{(-1)^n}{n!}\left(\frac{x}{2}\right)^n\right] + \left[\frac{x}{2}\right]\left[\frac{(-1)^{n+1}}{(n+1)!}\left(\frac{x}{2}\right)^{n+1}\right]$$

$$+ \left[\frac{1}{2!}\left(\frac{x}{2}\right)^2\right]\left[\frac{(-1)^{n+2}}{(n+2)!}\left(\frac{x}{2}\right)^{n+2}\right] + \cdots$$

$$= (-1)^n \sum_{k=0}^{\infty} \frac{(-1)^k x^{n+2k}}{2^{n+2k}k!(n+k)!} = (-1)^n J_n(x) = J_{-n}(x)$$

Thus

$$e^{\frac{x}{2}\left(t-\frac{1}{t}\right)} = \sum_{n=1}^{\infty} J_{-n}(x)t^{-n} + J_0(x) + \sum_{n=1}^{\infty} J_n(x)t^n$$

$$= J_0(x) + \sum_{n=1}^{\infty} J_n(x)\left[t^n + \frac{(-1)^n}{t^n}\right]$$

Now let $t = e^{i\phi}$, so that

$$\frac{1}{2}\left(t - \frac{1}{t}\right) = \frac{e^{i\phi} - e^{-i\phi}}{2} = i \sin \phi$$

and

$$e^{\frac{x}{2}\left(t-\frac{1}{t}\right)} = e^{ix\sin\phi} = \cos(x\sin\phi) + i\sin(x\sin\phi)$$

In the same way when n is even, say $n = 2k$,

$$t^n + \frac{(-1)^n}{t^n} = t^{2k} + \frac{1}{t^{2k}} = e^{2ki\phi} + e^{-2ki\phi} = 2\cos 2k\phi$$

and when n is odd, say $n = 2k - 1$,

$$t^n + \frac{(-1)^n}{t^n} = t^{2k-1} - \frac{1}{t^{2k-1}} = e^{(2k-1)i\phi} - e^{-(2k-1)i\phi} = 2i \sin (2k - 1)\phi$$

Therefore

$$e^{\frac{x}{2}\left(t-\frac{1}{t}\right)} = J_0(x) + \sum_{n=1}^{\infty} J_n(x) \left[t^n + \frac{(-1)^n}{t^n} \right]$$

may be written

$$e^{ix \sin \phi} \equiv \cos (x \sin \phi) + i \sin (x \sin \phi)$$
$$= J_0(x) + 2iJ_1(x) \sin \phi + 2J_2(x) \cos 2\phi + 2iJ_3(x) \sin 3\phi$$
$$+ 2J_4(x) \cos 4\phi \cdots$$
$$= J_0(x) + 2 \sum_{k=1}^{\infty} J_{2k}(x) \cos 2k\phi + 2i \sum_{k=1}^{\infty} J_{2k-1}(x) \sin (2k - 1)\phi$$

Equating real and imaginary parts, we obtain the identities

(11) $$\cos (x \sin \phi) = J_0(x) + 2 \sum_{k=1}^{\infty} J_{2k}(x) \cos 2k\phi$$

(12) $$\sin (x \sin \phi) = 2 \sum_{k=1}^{\infty} J_{2k-1}(x) \sin (2k - 1)\phi$$

Now multiply both sides of (11) by $\cos n\phi$ and both sides of (12) by $\sin n\phi$ and integrate each identity from 0 to π. Since

$$\int_0^{\pi} \cos m\phi \cos n\phi \, d\phi = \int_0^{\pi} \sin m\phi \sin n\phi \, d\phi = 0 \qquad m \neq n$$
$$\int_0^{\pi} \cos^2 n\phi \, d\phi = \int_0^{\pi} \sin^2 n\phi \, d\phi = \tfrac{1}{2}\pi \qquad m = n$$

this yields

(13) $$\int_0^{\pi} \cos n\phi \cos (x \sin \phi)d\phi = \begin{cases} \pi J_n(x) & n \text{ even} \\ 0 & n \text{ odd} \end{cases}$$

(14) $$\int_0^{\pi} \sin n\phi \sin (x \sin \phi)d\phi = \begin{cases} 0 & n \text{ even} \\ \pi J_n(x) & n \text{ odd} \end{cases}$$

If we add these two expressions and divide by π, we have for all integral values of n

$$J_n(x) = \frac{1}{\pi} \int_0^{\pi} [\cos n\phi \cos (x \sin \phi) + \sin n\phi \sin (x \sin \phi)]d\phi$$

since for every n, one or the other of the integrals vanishes while the remaining one gives $J_n(x)$. Finally, using the formula for the cosine of a difference, we have

$$(15) \qquad J_n(x) = \frac{1}{\pi} \int_0^\pi \cos{(n\phi - x \sin{\phi})}d\phi \qquad n \text{ an integer}$$

EXERCISES

1. Express $J_5(x)$ in terms of $J_0(x)$ and $J_1(x)$.
2. Express $J_3(2x)$ in terms of $J_0(2x)$ and $J_1(2x)$.
3. Express $J_{-\frac{3}{2}}(x)$ in terms of $\sin x$ and $\cos x$.
4. Show that $J_n''(x) = \left[\dfrac{n(n+1)}{x^2} - 1 \right] J_n(x) - \dfrac{J_{n-1}(x)}{x}.$
5. Show that
   (a) $4J_n'' = J_{n-2}(x) - 2J_n(x) + J_{n+2}(x)$
   (b) $8J_n'''(x) = J_{n-3}(x) - 3J_{n-1}(x) + 3J_{n+1}(x) - J_{n+3}(x)$
6. What is $\dfrac{d[x^2 J_3(2x)]}{dx}$?
7. What is $\dfrac{d[x J_0(x^2)]}{dx}$?
8. Write out $\text{ber}_1(x)$ and $\text{bei}_1(x)$.
9. Show that $J_0(x) = \dfrac{1}{\pi} \int_0^\pi \cos{(x \cos{\phi})}d\phi.$
10. Show that $\int J_0(x)dx = 2[J_1(x) + J_3(x) + J_5(x) + J_7(x) + \cdots]$
11. Show that

$$\int J_0(x)dx = J_1(x) + \int \frac{J_1(x)}{x}\,dx$$
$$= J_1(x) + \frac{J_2(x)}{x} + 1 \cdot 3 \int \frac{J_2(x)}{x^2}\,dx$$
$$= J_1(x) + \frac{J_2(x)}{x} + \frac{1 \cdot 3}{x^2} J_3(x) + 1 \cdot 3 \cdot 5 \int \frac{J_3(x)}{x^3}\,dx$$
$$= \cdots \cdots \cdots \cdots \cdots \cdots \cdots \cdots \cdots \cdots \cdots$$
$$= J_1(x) + \frac{J_2(x)}{x} + \frac{1 \cdot 3}{x^2} J_3(x) + \cdots \frac{(2n-2)!}{2^{n-1}(n-1)!} \frac{J_n(x)}{x^{n-1}} + \frac{(2n)!}{2^n n!} \int \frac{J_n(x)dx}{x^n}$$

12. Show that $\displaystyle \int x J_m^2(x)dx = x^2 \left[\dfrac{J_m^2(x) - J_{m-1}(x)J_{m+1}(x)}{2} \right] + c$
13. Show that $\int J_0(x) \cos x \, dx = x J_0(x) \cos x + x J_1(x) \sin x + c.$ (Hint: Verify by differentiation of the right-hand side.)
14. Show that $\int J_0(x) \sin x \, dx = x J_0(x) \sin x - x J_1(x) \cos x + c$
15. Show that $\int J_1(x) \cos x \, dx = x J_1(x) \cos x - J_0(x) (x \sin x + \cos x) + c$
16. Show that $\int J_1(x) \sin x \, dx = x J_1(x) \sin x + J_0(x) (x \cos x - \sin x) + c$
17. Determine
    (a) $\int x J_0(x) \cos x \, dx$ \qquad\qquad (b) $\int x J_1(x) \sin x \, dx$
18. Determine
    (a) $\int x J_0(x) \sin x \, dx$ \qquad\qquad (b) $\int x J_1(x) \cos x \, dx$
19. Show that
    (a) $\int x J_0(x)dx = x J_1(x) + c$
    (b) $\int x^2 J_0(x)dx = x^2 J_1(x) + x J_0(x) - \int J_0(x)dx + c$
    (c) $\int x^3 J_0(x)dx = (x^3 - 4x)J_1(x) + 2x^2 J_0(x) + c$

(d) $\int x^4 J_0(x)dx = (x^4 - 9x^2)J_1(x) + (3x^3 - 9x)J_0(x) + 9\int J_0(x)dx + c$

20. Show that

(a) $\int \dfrac{J_1(x)}{x} dx = -J_1(x) + \int J_0(x)dx + c$

(b) $\int J_1(x)dx = -J_0(x) + c$

(c) $\int xJ_1(x)dx = -xJ_0(x) + \int J_0(x)dx + c$

(d) $\int x^2 J_1(x)dx = 2xJ_1(x) - x^2 J_0(x) + c$

(e) $\int x^3 J_1(x)dx = 3x^2 J_1(x) - (x^3 - 3x)J_0(x) - 3\int J_0(x)dx + c$

(f) $\int x^4 J_1(x)dx = (4x^3 - 16x)J_1(x) - (x^4 - 8x^2)J_0(x) + c$

21. What is $\int x^2 J_1(2x)dx$?

22. What is $\int xJ_2(1 - x)dx$?

23. What is $\int J_0(\sqrt{x})dx$?

24. Prove

(a) $\dfrac{d[x^{m+1}I_{m+1}(x)]}{dx} = x^{m+1}I_m(x)$　　　　(b) $\int x^{m+1}I_m(x)dx = x^{m+1}I_{m+1}(x) + c$

25. Prove

(a) $\dfrac{d[x^{-m}I_m(x)]}{dx} = x^{-m}I_{m+1}(x)$　　　　(b) $\int x^{-m}I_{m+1}(x)dx = x^{-m}I_m(x) + c$

26. Prove

(a) $I_n'(x) = I_{n-1}(x) - \dfrac{n}{x} I_n(x)$　　　　(b) $I_n'(x) = \dfrac{n}{x} I_n(x) + I_{n+1}(x)$

(c) $I_n'(x) = \dfrac{I_{n-1}(x) + I_{n+1}(x)}{2}$　　　　(d) $I_{n-1}(x) - I_{n+1}(x) = \dfrac{2n}{x} I_n(x)$

27. What is

(a) $\int xI_0(x)dx$

(b) $\int x^2 I_0(x)dx$

(c) $\int x^3 I_0(x)dx$

28. What is

(a) $\int I_1(x)dx$　　　(c) $\int x^2 I_1(x)dx$

(b) $\int xI_1(x)dx$　　(d) $\int x^3 I_1(x)dx$

29. What is $\int I_0(a\sqrt{x})dx$?

30. What is $\int xI_2(2x)dx$?

8.6 Orthogonality of the Bessel Functions.

If we write Bessel's equation of order k in the form

$$x \frac{d^2y}{dx^2} + \frac{dy}{dx} + \left(\lambda^2 x - \frac{k^2}{x} \right) y = \frac{d(xy')}{dx} + \left(-\frac{k^2}{x} + \lambda^2 x \right) y = 0$$

it is clear that it is a special case [with $p(x) = x$, $q(x) = -(k^2/x)$, $r(x) = x$, and λ^2 written in place of λ] of the general equation covered by Theorem 1, Sec. 7.5. If the solutions of Bessel's equation satisfy suitable boundary conditions, they must therefore be orthogonal over any finite interval. In particular, if the interval is $(0,b)$, then $r(x) \equiv x$ vanishes at $x = 0$, and no boundary condition is required at that end of the interval. At the other end, $x = b$, the boundary condition must be of the form

$$Ay(b) - B \frac{dy}{dx}\bigg|_b = 0$$

or, more explicitly, for the particular solution $y = J_k(\lambda x)$,

$$AJ_k(\lambda b) - B \left. \frac{dJ_k(\lambda x)}{dx} \right|_b = AJ_k(\lambda b) - B\lambda J'_k(\lambda b) = 0$$

where the prime now indicates differentiation not with respect to x but with respect to the entire argument.

For practical purposes it is not enough, however, to know that the characteristic functions of a problem are orthogonal. In order to carry out the required expansions of initial conditions, it is necessary, in addition, to know the value of the integral of the square of the general characteristic function. To determine this result for the Bessel functions, we first recall, from Eq. (2), Sec. 7.5, that in general

$$(\lambda_m - \lambda_n) \int p(x) y_m(x) y_n(x) dx = r(x) \left[y_m(x) \frac{dy_n(x)}{dx} - y_n(x) \frac{dy_m(x)}{dx} \right]$$

Applied to Bessel's equation, this becomes

$$\int x J_k(\lambda_m x) J_k(\lambda_n x) dx = \frac{x \left[J_k(\lambda_m x) \dfrac{dJ_k(\lambda_n x)}{dx} - J_k(\lambda_n x) \dfrac{dJ_k(\lambda_m x)}{dx} \right]}{\lambda_m^2 - \lambda_n^2}$$

$$= \frac{J_k(\lambda_m x) \lambda_n x J'_k(\lambda_n x) - J_k(\lambda_n x) \lambda_m x J'_k(\lambda_m x)}{\lambda_m^2 - \lambda_n^2}$$

If $\lambda_m = \lambda_n$, the integral on the left becomes the integral of the square of the general characteristic function, but the expression on the right assumes the indeterminate form $0/0$. Hence we must apply l'Hospital's rule and differentiate numerator and denominator with respect to λ_m before setting $\lambda_m = \lambda_n$. However, to avoid second derivatives, it will be convenient, before differentiating, to eliminate the products

$$\lambda_m x J'_k(\lambda_m x) \qquad \text{and} \qquad \lambda_n x J'_k(\lambda_n x)$$

by means of the identity [Eq. (6), Sec. 8.5]

$$x J'_n(x) = n J_n(x) - x J_{n+1}(x)$$

This gives for the above antiderivative

$$\frac{J_k(\lambda_m x)[k J_k(\lambda_n x) - \lambda_n x J_{k+1}(\lambda_n x)] - J_k(\lambda_n x)[k J_k(\lambda_m x) - \lambda_m x J_{k+1}(\lambda_m x)]}{\lambda_m^2 - \lambda_n^2}$$

$$= \frac{x[\lambda_m J_k(\lambda_n x) J_{k+1}(\lambda_m x) - \lambda_n J_k(\lambda_m x) J_{k+1}(\lambda_n x)]}{\lambda_m^2 - \lambda_n^2}$$

Now differentiating numerator and denominator with respect to λ_m, we have

$$\frac{x[J_k(\lambda_n x) J_{k+1}(\lambda_m x) + \lambda_m J_k(\lambda_n x) x J'_{k+1}(\lambda_m x) - \lambda_n x J'_k(\lambda_m x) J_{k+1}(\lambda_n x)]}{2\lambda_m}$$

Next, letting $\lambda_m \to \lambda_n$, and evaluating between the limits of 0 and b, we obtain

$$\int_0^b xJ_k^2(\lambda_n x)dx$$

$$= \frac{b[J_k(\lambda_n b)J_{k+1}(\lambda_n b) + \lambda_n J_k(\lambda_n b)bJ'_{k+1}(\lambda_n b) - \lambda_n bJ'_k(\lambda_n b)J_{k+1}(\lambda_n b)]}{2\lambda_n}$$

Finally, we may substitute for the product $\lambda_n bJ'_{k+1}(\lambda_n b)$ the value [Eq. (3), Sec. 8.5]

$$\lambda_n bJ_k(\lambda_n b) - (k + 1)J_{k+1}(\lambda_n b)$$

getting

$$\int_0^b xJ_k^2(\lambda_n x)dx$$

$$= \frac{b}{2\lambda_n} [J_k(\lambda_n b)J_{k+1}(\lambda_n b) + J_k(\lambda_n b)\{\lambda_n bJ_k(\lambda_n b) - (k + 1)J_{k+1}(\lambda_n b)\}$$

$$- \lambda_n bJ'_k(\lambda_n b)J_{k+1}(\lambda_n b)]$$

$$(1) \quad = \frac{b}{2\lambda_n} [\lambda_n bJ_k^2(\lambda_n b) - kJ_k(\lambda_n b)J_{k+1}(\lambda_n b) - \lambda_n bJ'_k(\lambda_n b)J_{k+1}(\lambda_n b)]$$

Into this expression we must now substitute the boundary condition

$$AJ_k(\lambda_n b) - B\lambda_n J'_k(\lambda_n b) = 0$$

This gives $(B \neq 0)$

$$\int_0^b xJ_k^2(\lambda_n x)dx$$

$$= \frac{b}{2\lambda_n} \left[\lambda_n bJ_k^2(\lambda_n b) - kJ_k(\lambda_n b)J_{k+1}(\lambda_n b) - b\left\{\frac{A}{B}J_k(\lambda_n b)\right\} J_{k+1}(\lambda_n b) \right]$$

$$(2) \quad = \frac{b}{2\lambda_n} \left[\lambda_n bJ_k^2(\lambda_n b) - J_k(\lambda_n b)J_{k+1}(\lambda_n b) \left\{k + \frac{bA}{B}\right\} \right]$$

Now [Eq. (6), Sec. 8.5]

$$J_{k+1}(\lambda_n b) = \frac{k}{\lambda_n b} J_k(\lambda_n b) - J'_k(\lambda_n b)$$

and thus, substituting for $J'_k(\lambda_n b)$ from the boundary condition, we have

$$J_{k+1}(\lambda_n b) = \frac{k}{\lambda_n b} J_k(\lambda_n b) - \frac{A}{\lambda_n B} J_k(\lambda_n b)$$

$$= J_k(\lambda_n b) \left(\frac{k}{\lambda_n b} - \frac{A}{\lambda_n B} \right)$$

Substituting this into the expression (2), we have

$$\int_0^b xJ_k^2(\lambda_n x)dx = \frac{b^2}{2} J_k^2(\lambda_n b) - \frac{b}{2\lambda_n} J_k^2(\lambda_n b)\left(\frac{k}{\lambda_n b} - \frac{A}{\lambda_n B}\right)\left(k + \frac{bA}{B}\right)$$

$$= \frac{J_k^2(\lambda_n b)}{2\lambda_n^2}\left[(\lambda_n b)^2 - k^2 + \left(\frac{bA}{B}\right)^2\right] \qquad B \neq 0$$

If $B = 0$, that is, if the boundary condition at $x = b$ is of the simpler form

$$J_k(\lambda x) \Big|_b = 0$$

the last expression is meaningless. In this case, the correct result can be obtained almost at once by setting $J_k(\lambda_n b) = 0$ in (1). This gives

$$\int_0^b xJ_k^2(\lambda_n x)dx = -\frac{b^2}{2} J_k'(\lambda_n b)J_{k+1}(\lambda_n b)$$

Now [Eq. (6), Sec. 8.5]

$$J_k'(\lambda_n b) = \frac{k}{\lambda_n b} J_k(\lambda_n b) - J_{k+1}(\lambda_n b)$$

which reduces to

$$J_k'(\lambda_n b) = -J_{k+1}(\lambda_n b)$$

when the boundary condition $J_k(\lambda_n b) = 0$ is substituted into it. Therefore

$$\int_0^b xJ_k^2(\lambda_n x)dx = \frac{b^2}{2} J_{k+1}^2(\lambda_n b) \qquad B = 0$$

The results of this analysis may be summarized in the following theorem,

Theorem 1. The Bessel functions of the first kind of order k which satisfy the condition

$$AJ_k(\lambda b) - B\frac{dJ_k(\lambda x)}{dx}\Big|_b = 0$$

form an orthogonal system with respect to the weight function x, over the interval $(0,b)$. The integral of the square of any function of the set is

$$\int_0^b xJ_k^2(\lambda_n x)\,dx = \begin{cases} \dfrac{J_k^2(\lambda_n b)}{2\lambda_n^2}\left[(\lambda_n b)^2 - k^2 + \left(\dfrac{bA}{B}\right)^2\right], & B \neq 0 \\ \dfrac{b^2}{2} J_{k+1}^2(\lambda_n b), & B = 0 \end{cases}$$

Example 1

Expand $f(x) = 4x - x^3$ over the interval $(0,2)$ in terms of the Bessel functions of the first kind of order 1 which satisfy the boundary condition

$$J_1(\lambda x)\Big|_2 = 0$$

In this case the characteristic values are the values of λ determined by the roots of the equation

$$J_1(2\lambda) = 0$$

The roots of the equation $J_1(z) = 0$ as given in the "Tables of Functions" of Jahnke-Emde, are

$$z_0 = 0, \qquad z_1 = 3.832, \qquad z_2 = 7.016, \qquad z_3 = 10.174, \qquad z_4 = 13.324 \ldots$$

Hence

$$\lambda_0 = 0, \qquad \lambda_1 = 1.916, \qquad \lambda_2 = 3.508, \qquad \lambda_3 = 5.087, \qquad \lambda_4 = 6.662 \ldots$$

The characteristic functions in terms of which the expansion is to be carried out are therefore [since $J_1(\lambda_0 x) = J_1(0) \equiv 0$]

$$J_1(\lambda_1 x), \; J_1(\lambda_2 x), \; J_1(\lambda_3 x), \; J_1(\lambda_4 x), \; \ldots$$

As in the simpler case of Fourier expansions, we begin by writing

$$f(x) \equiv 4x - x^3 = A_1 J_1(\lambda_1 x) + A_2 J_1(\lambda_2 x) + \cdots + A_n J_1(\lambda_n x) + \cdots$$

Multiplying both sides of this expression by $x J_1(\lambda_n x)$, integrating from 0 to 2, and using the results of Theorem 1 gives

$$\int_0^2 (4x - x^3) x J_1(\lambda_n x) dx = A_n \int_0^2 x J_1^2(\lambda_n x) dx = 2 A_n J_2^2(2\lambda_n)$$

Hence

$$A_n = \frac{\displaystyle\int_0^2 (4x^2 - x^4) J_1(\lambda_n x) dx}{2 J_2^2(2\lambda_n)}$$

For the integral

$$4 \int_0^2 x^2 J_1(\lambda_n x) dx = \frac{4}{\lambda_n^3} \int_0^2 (\lambda_n x)^2 J_1(\lambda_n x) d(\lambda_n x)$$

we have immediately the result [Eq. (9), Sec. 8.5]

$$\frac{4}{\lambda_n^3} (\lambda_n x)^2 J_2(\lambda_n x)\Big|_0^2 = \frac{16}{\lambda_n} J_2(2\lambda_n)$$

To integrate

$$\int_0^2 x^4 J_1(\lambda_n x) dx = \frac{1}{\lambda_n^5} \int_0^2 (\lambda_n x)^4 J_1(\lambda_n x) d(\lambda_n x) = \frac{1}{\lambda_n^5} \int_0^{2\lambda_n} z^4 J_1(z) dz$$

we must use integration by parts, with

$$u = z^2, \qquad dv = z^2 J_1(z) dz$$
$$du = 2z \, dz, \qquad v = z^2 J_2(z)$$

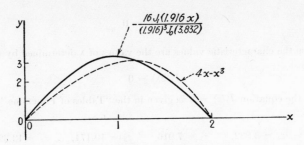

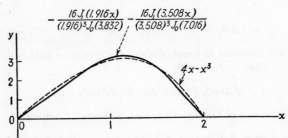

FIG. 8.6. Plot showing the approximation of a function by the first two terms of a Bessel function expansion.

This gives

$$\int_0^2 x^4 J_1(\lambda_n x)dx = \frac{1}{\lambda_n^5}\left[z^4 J_2(z)\Big|_0^{2\lambda_n} - 2\int_0^{2\lambda_n} z^3 J_2(z)dz \right]$$

$$= \frac{1}{\lambda_n^5}\left[z^4 J_2(z) - 2z^3 J_3(z) \right]_0^{2\lambda_n}$$

$$= \frac{16}{\lambda_n^2}\left[\lambda_n J_2(2\lambda_n) - J_3(2\lambda_n) \right]$$

Thus

$$A_n = \frac{1}{2J_2^2(2\lambda_n)}\left[\frac{16}{\lambda_n}J_2(2\lambda_n) - \frac{16}{\lambda_n^2}\{\lambda_n J_2(2\lambda_n) - J_3(2\lambda_n)\} \right]$$

$$= \frac{8J_3(2\lambda_n)}{\lambda_n^2 J_2^2(2\lambda_n)}$$

But

$$J_3(2\lambda_n) = \frac{4}{2\lambda_n}J_2(2\lambda_n) - J_1(2\lambda_n) = \frac{2J_2(2\lambda_n)}{\lambda_n}$$

since the $\{\lambda_n\}$ are such that $J_1(2\lambda_n) = 0$.   Therefore A_n can be further simplified to

$$A_n = \frac{16}{\lambda_n^3 J_2(2\lambda_n)}$$

The same reduction can be repeated for $J_2(2\lambda_n)$, since

$$J_2(2\lambda_n) = \frac{2}{2\lambda_n}J_1(2\lambda_n) - J_0(2\lambda_n) = -J_0(2\lambda_n)$$

Hence, finally,

$$A_n = -\frac{16}{\lambda_n^3 J_0(2\lambda_n)}$$

The required expansion is therefore

$$4x - x^3 = -16 \sum_{n=1}^{\infty} \frac{J_1(\lambda_n x)}{\lambda_n^3 J_0(2\lambda_n)}$$

Plots showing the degree to which the first term and the first pair of terms of this series approximate $4x - x^3$ are shown in Fig. 8.6.

EXERCISES

1. Expand $f(x) = 1$ over the interval $0 < x < 3$ in terms of the functions $J_0(\lambda_n x)$ where the $\{\lambda_n\}$ are determined by $J_0(3\lambda) = 0$.   *Ans.* $A_n = \dfrac{2}{3\lambda_n J_1(3\lambda_n)}$

2. Expand $f(x) = x^2$ over the interval $0 < x < 3$ in terms of the functions $J_0(\lambda_n x)$ where the $\{\lambda_n\}$ are determined by $J_1(3\lambda) = 0$.

$$\text{\textit{Ans.}} \quad A_0 = \frac{9}{2}, \; A_n = \frac{4}{\lambda_n^2 J_0(3\lambda_n)} \qquad n = 1, 2, 3, \ldots$$

3. Expand $f(x) = 1$ over the interval $0 < x < 3$ in terms of the functions $J_0(\lambda_n x)$ where the $\{\lambda_n\}$ are determined from the equation $J_0(3\lambda) + \lambda J_1(3\lambda) = 0$.

4. Expand $f(x) = \begin{cases} x & 0 < x < 1 \\ 0 & 1 < x < 2 \end{cases}$ in terms of the functions $J_1(\lambda_n x)$ where the $\{\lambda_n\}$ are determined by $J_1'(2\lambda) = 0$.

5. Expand $f(x) = x^2$ over the interval $0 < x < 1$ in terms of the functions $J_2(\lambda_n x)$ where the $\{\lambda_n\}$ are determined by $J_2(\lambda) = 0$.

8.7 Further Applications. We are now in a position to complete the heat-flow problem of Sec. 8.1, which introduced us to Bessel functions. To recall briefly, we were concerned with the partial differential equation

$$\frac{\partial^2 u}{\partial r^2} + \frac{1}{r} \frac{\partial u}{\partial r} + \frac{1}{r^2} \frac{\partial^2 u}{\partial \theta^2} + \frac{\partial^2 u}{\partial z^2} = 0$$

and the conditions

$$\begin{aligned}
&u = 0 \text{ when } z = 0 && \text{for all } r \text{ and } \theta \\
&u = 0 \text{ when } r = b && \text{for all } \theta \text{ and } z \\
&u = 0 \text{ when } \theta = 0 \text{ or } \pi && \text{for all } r \text{ and } z \\
&u = f(r,\theta) \text{ when } z = h
\end{aligned}$$

Assuming a product solution,

$$u(r,\theta,z) = R(r)\Theta(\theta)Z(z)$$

we found that

$$\Theta(\theta) = \sin n\theta \qquad n = 1, 2, 3, \ldots$$

and that R and Z had to satisfy the ordinary differential equations

$$r^2 R'' + r R' + (\nu r^2 - n^2)R = 0, \qquad Z'' = \nu Z$$

If $\nu < 0$, say $\nu = -\lambda^2$, the equation for R is just the modified Bessel equation of order n. Its solution is therefore

$$R(r) = AI_n(\lambda r) + BK_n(\lambda r)$$

Since $K_n(\lambda r)$ becomes infinite as r approaches 0, it is necessary that $B = 0$. To ensure that $u = 0$ on the curved surface of the cylinder for all values of θ and z, it is necessary that $R(b) = 0$, that is, that

$$AI_n(\lambda b) = 0$$

But the function $I_n(x)$ never vanishes unless its argument is zero. Hence A must be zero, which leads only to a trivial solution. This forces us to abandon the possibility that $\nu < 0$.

If $\nu = 0$, R must satisfy the equation

$$r^2 R'' + r R' - n^2 R = 0$$

This is not a form of Bessel's equation, but is instead an example of the so-called **Euler equation**

$$a_0 x^n y^{(n)} + a_1 x^{n-1} y^{(n-1)} + \cdots + a_{n-1} x y' + a_n y = 0$$

where the coefficient of each derivative is a constant times the corresponding power of the independent variable. By the change of independent variable

$$x = e^v \qquad \text{or} \qquad v = \log x$$

the general Euler equation can always be transformed into a linear equation with constant coefficients. In our case

$$v = \log r$$

and thus

$$\frac{dR}{dr} = \frac{dR}{dv}\frac{dv}{dr} = \frac{1}{r}\frac{dR}{dv}$$

$$\frac{d^2R}{dr^2} = \frac{d\left(\frac{1}{r}\frac{dR}{dv}\right)}{dr} = -\frac{1}{r^2}\frac{dR}{dv} + \frac{1}{r}\frac{d(dR/dv)}{dr} = -\frac{1}{r^2}\frac{dR}{dv} + \frac{1}{r^2}\frac{d^2R}{dv^2}$$

Under these substitutions the differential equation for R becomes

$$r^2\left(\frac{1}{r^2}\frac{d^2R}{dv^2} - \frac{1}{r^2}\frac{dR}{dv}\right) + r\left(\frac{1}{r}\frac{dR}{dv}\right) - n^2 R \equiv \frac{d^2R}{dv^2} - n^2 R = 0$$

The general solution of this is

$$R = Ae^{nv} + Be^{-nv}$$

or in terms of r,

$$R = Ae^{n\log r} + Be^{-n\log r}$$
$$= Ar^n + \frac{B}{r^n}$$

Clearly we must have $B = 0$ in order to prevent R, and hence the temperature u, becoming infinite on the axis of the cylinder. For u to be zero when $r = b$ requires further that

$$R(b) \equiv Ab^n = 0$$

which is possible if and only if $A = 0$. Thus $\nu = 0$ leads also to a trivial solution.

Finally suppose that $\nu > 0$, say $\nu = \lambda^2$. Then R must satisfy Bessel's equation of order n with a parameter, and thus we have

$$R(r) = AJ_n(\lambda r) + BY_n(\lambda r)$$

Now $Y_n(\lambda r)$ becomes infinite as $r \to 0$. Hence B must be zero. The condition that $u = 0$ on the curved surface requires then that

$$AJ_n(\lambda b) = 0$$

The characteristic values of the problem are thus

$$\lambda_{nm} = \frac{\rho_{nm}}{b}$$

where ρ_{nm} is the mth root of the equation $J_n(x) = 0$. Thus for every value of n there are infinitely many particular solutions for R, namely,

$$R_{nm}(r) = J_n(\lambda_{nm}r)$$

Now that it is known that $\nu = \lambda^2$, the Z-equation can be solved at once, giving

$$Z(z) = C \cosh \lambda z + D \sinh \lambda z$$

Since $u = 0$ when $z = 0$, it is necessary that $C = 0$. The solution for Z associated with $R_{nm}(r)$ is therefore

$$Z_{nm}(z) = \sinh \lambda_{nm}z$$

For *each* n, we therefore have infinitely many product solutions, each consisting of the same Θ factor, $\Theta_n(\theta) = \sin n\theta$, multiplied by the product of any pair of corresponding R's and Z's:

$$u_{nm} = B_{nm}J_n(\lambda_{nm}r) \sinh \lambda_{nm}z \sin n\theta$$

To build up a series solution for u, it is thus necessary first to add up all the product solutions associated with a particular value of n, getting

$$u_n = \sum_{m=1}^{\infty} u_{nm} = \sin n\theta \sum_{m=1}^{\infty} B_{nm}J_n(\lambda_{nm}r) \sinh \lambda_{nm}z$$

Then we must add up all these series for every value of n:

$$u(r,\theta,z) = \sum_{n=1}^{\infty} u_n = \sum_{n=1}^{\infty} \sin n\theta \sum_{m=1}^{\infty} B_{nm}J_n(\lambda_{nm}r) \sinh \lambda_{nm}z$$

The final step in the problem is to satisfy the temperature distribution over the upper base of the cylinder. This requires that the double series for u should reduce to the known function $f(r,\theta)$ when $z = h$:

$$f(r,\theta) = \sum_{n=1}^{\infty} \sin n\theta \sum_{m=1}^{\infty} B_{nm}J_n(\lambda_{nm}r) \sinh \lambda_{nm}h$$

To carry out this expansion, let us imagine that r is held constant and that θ is allowed to vary over the range of the problem $(0,\pi)$. Under these conditions the inner sum is effectively a constant depending on n, say G_n, or more explicitly $G_n(r)$. That is,

$$f(r,\theta) = \sum_{n=1}^{\infty} G_n \sin n\theta$$

But this is a familiar problem! In fact it is nothing but the Fourier sine expansion problem, and we can write immediately

$$G_n = G_n(r) = \frac{2}{\pi} \int_0^{\pi} f(r,\theta) \sin n\theta \, d\theta$$

Thus $G_n(r)$ is a *known* function of r. But, by definition,

$$G_n(r) = \sum_{m=1}^{\infty} (B_{nm} \sinh \lambda_{nm}h) J_n(\lambda_{nm}r)$$

and thus it is evident that the coefficients B_{nm} must be such that the products

$$B_{nm} \sinh \lambda_{nm}h$$

are the coefficients in a Bessel function expansion of $G_n(r)$. Hence from the theory of the last section, recalling that the $\{\lambda_{nm}\}$ are determined by the condition

$$J_n(\lambda b) = 0$$

we can write

$$B_{nm} \sinh \lambda_{nm}h = \frac{\int_0^b r G_n(r) J_n(\lambda_{nm}r) dr}{\dfrac{b^2}{2} J_{n+1}^2(\lambda_{nm}b)}$$

Therefore

$$B_{nm} = \frac{\int_0^b r G_n(r) J_n(\lambda_{nm}r) dr}{\dfrac{b^2}{2} \sinh \lambda_{nm}h J_{n+1}^2(\lambda_{nm}b)}$$

where

$$G_n(r) = \frac{2}{\pi} \int_0^{\pi} f(r,\theta) \sin n\theta \, d\theta$$

This completes the solution of the problem.

Example 1

A metal fin of triangular cross section is attached to a plane surface to help carry off heat from the latter. Assuming dimensions and coordinates as shown in the accompanying figure, find the steady-state temperature distribution along the fin if the root (*i.e.*, wall) temperature is u_w and if the fin radiates freely into air of constant temperature u_a.

We shall base our analysis upon a unit length of the fin, and shall assume that the fin is so thin that temperature variations parallel to the base can be neglected. We also assume that θ is so small that $\cos \theta$ may be replaced by 1.

Now consider the heat balance in the element of the fin between x and $x + \Delta x$. This element gains heat by internal flow through its right face and loses heat by internal flow through its left face and by radiation through its upper and lower

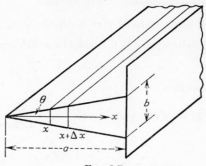

FIG. 8.7.

surfaces.   Through the right face the gain of heat per unit time is

Area $\times$ thermal conductivity $\times$ temperature gradient

$$= \left[\left(1 \times \frac{bx}{a} \right) (k) \left(\frac{du}{dx} \right) \right]_{x+\Delta x} = \left[\frac{bkx}{a} \frac{du}{dx} \right]_{x+\Delta x}$$

Through the left face the element loses heat at the rate

$$\left[\frac{bkx}{a} \frac{du}{dx} \right]_{x}$$

Through the surfaces exposed to the air the element loses heat at the rate

Area $\times$ outer conductivity $\times$ (surface temperature $-$ air temperature)

$$= \left(2 \times 1 \frac{\Delta x}{\cos \theta} \right) (h)(u - u_a) = 2h(u - u_a)\Delta x$$

Under steady-state conditions the rate of gain of heat must equal the rate of loss, and thus we have

$$\left[\frac{bkx}{a} \frac{du}{dx} \right]_{x+\Delta x} = \left[\frac{bkx}{a} \frac{du}{dx} \right]_{x} + 2h(u - u_a)\Delta x$$

Writing this as

$$\frac{x \dfrac{du}{dx}\Big|_{x+\Delta x} - x \dfrac{du}{dx}\Big|_{x}}{\Delta x} - \frac{2ah}{bk}(u - u_a) = 0$$

and letting $\Delta x \to 0$, we obtain the differential equation

$$\frac{d(xu')}{dx} - \frac{2ah}{bk}(u - u_a) = 0$$

If we set

$$U = u - u_a \qquad \text{and} \qquad \alpha^2 = \frac{2ah}{bk}$$

this becomes

$$\frac{d(xU')}{dx} - \alpha^2 U = 0$$

The general solution of this, according to the theory of Sec. 8.3, is

$$U = u - u_a = c_1 J_0(2\alpha i \sqrt{x}) + c_2 Y_0(2\alpha i \sqrt{x})$$

or, using the modified Bessel functions,

$$u - u_a = c_3 I_0(2\alpha \sqrt{x}) + c_4 K_0(2\alpha \sqrt{x})$$

Since $K_0(2\alpha \sqrt{x})$ is infinite when $x = 0$, c_4 must be zero, leaving

$$u - u_a = c_3 I_0(2\alpha \sqrt{x})$$

When $x = a$, $u = u_w$, and thus

$$u_w - u_a = c_3 I_0(2\alpha \sqrt{a}) \qquad \text{or} \qquad c_3 = \frac{u_w - u_a}{I_0(2\alpha \sqrt{a})}$$

Therefore

$$u = u_a + (u_w - u_a) \frac{I_0(2\alpha \sqrt{x})}{I_0(2\alpha \sqrt{a})}$$

Example 2

Find the first two natural frequencies of a steel shaft 20 in. long vibrating torsionally if the shaft is built-in at one end and free at the other, and if the radius of the shaft at a distance x from the free end is

$$r(x) = \left(\frac{x}{20}\right)^{\frac{1}{4}}$$

Steel weighs 0.285 lb/in.³, and its modulus of elasticity in shear is $E_s = 12 \times 10^6$ lb/in.².
    In Sec. 7.2, we obtained

$$E_s \frac{\partial \left[J(x) \dfrac{\partial \theta}{\partial x} \right]}{\partial x} = J(x) \frac{\rho}{g} \frac{\partial^2 \theta}{\partial t^2}\dagger$$

as the differential equation satisfied by the angular displacement $\theta(x,t)$ of a shaft vibrating torsionally.   As a first step we must therefore compute the polar moment of inertia of the shaft, $J(x)$:

$$J(x) = \text{cross-section area} \times \frac{1}{2} \text{radius}^2 = \pi r^2 \times \frac{1}{2} r^2 = \frac{\pi r^4}{2} = \frac{\pi x}{40}$$

The partial differential equation we must solve is now (dividing out $\pi/40$)

$$a^2 \frac{\partial \left[x \dfrac{\partial \theta}{\partial x} \right]}{\partial x} = x \frac{\partial^2 \theta}{\partial t^2} \qquad a^2 = \frac{E_s g}{\rho}$$

Knowing that the solution for θ must be periodic, we may as well assume at the outset that

$$\theta(x,t) = X(x) \sin \omega t$$

where ω is a frequency yet to be determined.   Substituting this into the differential

_____

† Note that $J(x)$ without a subscript denotes the polar moment of inertia of the general cross section of the shaft, and *not* a Bessel function.

equation and dividing out sin ωt, we find

$$a^2 \frac{d(xX')}{dx} = -\omega^2 xX$$

or, expanding, dividing by x, and transposing,

$$X'' + \frac{X'}{x} + \frac{\omega^2}{a^2} X = 0$$

This is precisely Bessel's equation of order zero, with the parameter ω/a. Its general solution is

$$X(x) = AJ_0\left(\frac{\omega}{a} x\right) + BY_0\left(\frac{\omega}{a} x\right)$$

Since $Y_0[(\omega/a)x]$ is infinite when $x = 0$, it is necessary that $B = 0$, leaving

$$X(x) = AJ_0\left(\frac{\omega}{a} x\right)$$

At the free end the usual "zero-torque" condition

$$E_s J(x) \left.\frac{\partial \theta}{\partial x}\right|_{x=0} = 0$$

must be fulfilled. However, since $J(x) = \pi x/40$ vanishes when $x = 0$, this condition is automatically satisfied without further restriction on θ.

At the built-in end, θ must be zero at all times. Hence

$$J_0\left(20\frac{\omega}{a}\right) = 0$$

which is the frequency equation of the problem. From the tables in Jahnke-Emde we find that the first two roots of $J_0(z) = 0$ are

$$z_1 = 2.405 \quad \text{and} \quad z_2 = 5.520$$

Hence

$$\frac{20\omega_1}{a} = 2.405, \quad \frac{20\omega_2}{a} = 5.520$$

Since

$$a = \sqrt{\frac{E_s g}{\rho}} = \sqrt{\frac{(12 \times 10^6)(384)}{0.285}} = 127{,}000$$

we have

$$\omega_1 = 15{,}300 \text{ rad/sec} = 2{,}400 \text{ cycles/sec}$$
$$\omega_2 = 35{,}200 \text{ rad/sec} = 5{,}600 \text{ cycles/sec}$$

Example 3

If the Laplace transform of a function is

$$\frac{1}{\sqrt{s^2 + a^2}}$$

what is the function?

To find the function, expand $1/\sqrt{s^2 + a^2}$ into an infinite series by means of the binomial expansion, and proceed on the assumption that the inverse of the series can be found term by term:

$$\frac{1}{\sqrt{s^2 + a^2}} = \frac{1}{s[1 + (a^2/s^2)]^{\frac{1}{2}}}$$

$$= \frac{1}{s}\left[1 - \frac{1}{2}\frac{a^2}{s^2} + \frac{1}{2}\frac{3}{2}\frac{1}{2!}\frac{a^4}{s^4} - \frac{1}{2}\frac{3}{2}\frac{5}{2}\frac{1}{3!}\frac{a^6}{s^6} + \cdots\right]$$

Therefore

$$\mathcal{L}^{-1}\left(\frac{1}{\sqrt{s^2 + a^2}}\right) = \mathcal{L}^{-1}\left(\frac{1}{s}\right) - \mathcal{L}^{-1}\left(\frac{a^2}{2s^3}\right) + \mathcal{L}^{-1}\left(\frac{1 \cdot 3a^4}{2^2 2! s^5}\right) - \mathcal{L}^{-1}\left(\frac{1 \cdot 3 \cdot 5a^6}{2^3 3! s^7}\right) + \cdots$$

$$= 1 - \frac{a^2}{2 \cdot 1!}\left(\frac{t^2}{2!}\right) + \frac{1 \cdot 3a^4}{2^2 2!}\left(\frac{t^4}{4!}\right) - \frac{1 \cdot 3 \cdot 5a^6}{2^3 3!}\left(\frac{t^6}{6!}\right) + \cdots$$

$$= 1 - \frac{1}{(1!)^2}\left(\frac{at}{2}\right)^2 + \frac{1}{(2!)^2}\left(\frac{at}{2}\right)^4 - \frac{1}{(3!)^2}\left(\frac{at}{2}\right)^6 + \cdots$$

$$= J_0(at)$$

EXERCISES

1. (a) In Example 1, Sec. 8.7, verify that all the heat that enters the fin is radiated from its surface.

(b) What fraction of the heat entering the fin is radiated from the section of the fin between $x = 0$ and $x = a/2$?

2. A very thin fin of rectangular cross section is attached to a flat wall. Heat conducted from the wall to the fin is lost from the latter by radiation into air of temperature u_a. Find the temperature distribution along the fin in the direction perpendicular to the wall if the temperature of the wall is u_w and if the dimensions of the cross section of the fin are a and w.

3. (a) Derive the differential equation for the radial temperature distribution in a thin fin of rectangular cross section which completely encircles a heated cylinder.

(b) Derive the differential equation for the radial temperature distribution in a thin fin of triangular cross section which completely encircles a heated cylinder.

   Ans.   (b) $\dfrac{d[r(R - r)u']}{dr} = \dfrac{2ha}{bk}(R - r)(u - u_a)$ where r is measured radially

inward from the tip of the fin, R is the radial distance out to the tip of the fin, and a, b, h, k, u_a have the same significance as in Example 1, Sec. 8.7.

4. A thin circular plate has its upper and lower faces insulated against the flow of heat. One half of its circumference is maintained at the constant temperature u_0; the other half is maintained at the temperature 0. Find the steady-state temperature distribution in the disk.

   Ans.   If the radius of the disk be b, and if θ be measured from the radius to the mid-point of the arc on which $u = u_0$, then

$$u(r,\theta) = u_0\left[\frac{a_0}{2} + \sum_{n=1}^{\infty} a_n\left(\frac{r}{b}\right)^n \cos n\theta\right] \text{ where } a_0 = 1, \ a_n = \frac{2}{\pi n}\sin\frac{n\pi}{2}$$

5. A right circular cylinder of height h and radius b has its upper and lower bases maintained at the temperature 0. The curved surface of the cylinder is main-

tained at the temperature distribution $u(b,z) = f(z)$. Determine the steady-state temperature distribution throughout the cylinder.

$$Ans. \ u(r,z) = \sum_{n=1}^{\infty} A_n I_0 \left(\frac{n\pi r}{h}\right) \sin \frac{n\pi z}{h} \text{ where } A_n I_0 \left(\frac{n\pi b}{h}\right) = \frac{2}{h} \int_0^h f(z) \sin \frac{n\pi z}{h} \, dz$$

6. A right circular cylinder of radius b and height h has its base maintained at the constant temperature 0. Over its upper face the temperature distribution $u(h,r) = f(r)$ is maintained. If the curved surface radiates freely into air of temperature 0, find the steady-state temperature distribution within the cylinder.

7. A cantilever beam of length l and breadth b has its upper surface horizontal. The depth of the beam varies directly as the cube root of the distance from the free end. An oblique tensile force F, whose direction makes an angle θ with the horizontal, acts at the free end of the beam. Find the equation of the deflection curve of the beam.

   Ans. Taking the origin at the free end of the beam,

$$y = \tan \theta \left[x - \frac{\sqrt{x} \, I_1(2a \sqrt{x})}{a I_0(2a \sqrt{l})} \right]$$

where $a^2 = \dfrac{12F \cos \theta}{Ebk^3}$ and b is the constant width of the beam.

8. Work Exercise 7 if the force is an oblique compressive force.

9. A cantilever beam of breadth b and length l has its upper surface horizontal. The depth of the beam varies directly as the two-thirds power of the distance from the free end. If the beam bears a uniform load of w lb per unit length and is acted on by a pure tensile force at its free end, find the equation of the deflection curve of the beam.

10. Work Exercise 9 if the force is a pure compressive force.

11. An elastic string whose weight per unit length is $w_0(1 + \alpha x)$, where x is the distance from one end of the string, is stretched under tension T between two points a distance l apart. Find the equation giving the natural frequencies of the string.

$$Ans. \ J_{\frac{1}{3}}\left(\frac{2\omega}{3\alpha a}\right) J_{-\frac{1}{3}}\left(\frac{2\omega s^{\frac{3}{2}}}{3\alpha a}\right) - J_{\frac{1}{3}}\left(\frac{2\omega s^{\frac{3}{2}}}{3\alpha a}\right) J_{-\frac{1}{3}}\left(\frac{2\omega}{3\alpha a}\right) = 0$$

where

$$a = \sqrt{\frac{Tg}{w_0}} \qquad \text{and} \qquad s = (1 + \alpha l)$$

12. The lower end of a thin uniform rod is clamped so that the rod is initially vertical. If the upper end of the rod is displaced slightly, determine the position into which it will bend under its own weight.

13. A body whose mass varies according to the law $m = m_0(1 + \alpha t)^{-1}$ moves along the x-axis under the influence of a force of attraction which varies directly as the distance from the origin. Determine the equation of motion of the body if it starts from rest at the point $x = x_0$.

14. Work Exercise 13 if the force is directed away from the origin.

15. A bar has the shape of a truncated right circular cone of length l, the radii of its bases being R and r. Find the frequency equation for the longitudinal vibrations of the bar, assuming both ends of the bar free. (Hint: The partial differential equation to be solved was derived in Exercise 4, Sec. 7.2.)

Ans. $\quad J_{\frac{3}{2}}\left(\dfrac{\omega R}{a}\right) J_{-\frac{3}{2}}\left(\dfrac{\omega r}{a}\right) - J_{\frac{3}{2}}\left(\dfrac{\omega r}{a}\right) J_{-\frac{3}{2}}\left(\dfrac{\omega R}{a}\right) = 0$

where

$$a^2 = \frac{Eg}{\rho}\left(\frac{R-r}{l}\right)^2$$

16. Determine the limiting form of the frequency equation in Exercise 15 when $r \to R$. Check by deriving the frequency equation for the longitudinal vibrations of a uniform bar with both ends free. (Hint: Express the Bessel functions in terms of sines and cosines.)

17. Work Exercise 15 if the big end of the bar is built-in.

18. Find the frequency equation for the torsional vibrations of the bar of Exercise 15 if the big end is built-in.

19. Determine the limiting form of the frequency equation in Exercise 18 as $r \to R$. Does this check the frequency equation as derived for a uniform bar?

20. Determine the frequency equation for the transverse vibrations of a flexible cable suspended from one end.

21. Show that $\mathcal{L}[tJ_0(at)] = \dfrac{s}{(a^2+s^2)^{\frac{3}{2}}}$

22. Show that $\mathcal{L}[tJ_1(at)] = \dfrac{a}{(a^2+s^2)^{\frac{3}{2}}}$

23. What is $\mathcal{L}[t^n J_n(at)]$?

24. Show that $\displaystyle\int_0^\infty J_0(at)dt = \frac{1}{a}$

What is $\displaystyle\int_0^\infty tJ_0(at)dt$? $\qquad \displaystyle\int_0^\infty tJ_1(at)dt$?

25. Show that

$$\mathcal{L}[J_1(at)] = \frac{a}{\sqrt{s^2+a^2}\,(\sqrt{s^2+a^2}+s)}$$

$$\mathcal{L}[J_2(at)] = \frac{a^2}{\sqrt{s^2+a^2}\,(\sqrt{s^2+a^2}+s)^2}$$

26. What is $\mathcal{L}[J_n(at)]$?

27. Show that

$$\mathcal{L}^{-1}\left[\frac{1}{(a^2+s^2)^m}\right] = \left(\frac{2t}{a}\right)^{\frac{2m-1}{2}}\frac{\Gamma\left(\dfrac{2m+1}{2}\right)}{\Gamma(2m)}J_{\frac{2m-1}{2}}(at)$$

28. Determine the natural frequencies of a uniform circular drumhead.

    Ans. The frequency equation is $J_n(\omega b/a)$, $n = 0, 1, 2, \ldots$, where b is the radius of the drumhead and $a = \sqrt{Tg/\rho}$.

29. Find the frequency equation for the transverse vibrations of a cantilever if the beam is a solid of revolution whose radius varies directly as the distance from the free end. (Hint: Use the results of Exercise 8, Sec. 8.4.)

    Ans. $\quad J_1(2\sqrt{\omega a l})I_2(2\sqrt{\omega a l}) - J_2(2\sqrt{\omega a l})I_1(2\sqrt{\omega a l}) = 0$

where $a^2 = \dfrac{4\rho}{Egk^2}$.

30. Find the frequency equation for the transverse vibrations of a cantilever whose width is constant but whose depth, *i.e.*, dimension in the direction of the motion, varies directly as the distance from the free end.

CHAPTER 9

ANALYTIC FUNCTIONS OF A COMPLEX VARIABLE

9.1 Introduction. In our work up to this point we have frequently found the use of complex numbers either necessary, or at least convenient. For instance, we encountered them in the solution of linear differential equations with constant coefficients in Chap. 2. In Chap. 4 they appeared as the complex impedance, which was of considerable utility in the determination of the steady-state behavior of electric circuits. Then in Chap. 5 their use led to the important complex exponential form of Fourier series, and ultimately to the inversion integral of Laplace transform theory. Finally, in Chap. 8 we found that certain important physical problems required the consideration of Bessel functions of complex arguments.

None of these applications (with the exception of the inversion integral, for which, fortunately, we had no immediate need) required any knowledge of the properties of complex numbers, or of functions of a complex variable, beyond what is ordinarily acquired in courses in college algebra and calculus. There are, however, large areas of applied mathematics in which familiarity with the theory of functions of a complex variable beyond this minimum is indispensable. In this and the next five chapters we shall develop the major features of this theory, and illustrate some of its more striking applications.

9.2 Algebraic Preliminaries. By a **complex number** we mean a number of the form

$$z = x + iy$$

where x and y are real numbers and i is the **imaginary unit** defined by

$$i = \sqrt{-1}$$

The real number x is called the **real component** or **real part** of z. The real number y is called the **imaginary component** or **imaginary part** of z. The real and imaginary parts of a complex number or expression z are often denoted by the respective symbols

$$\Re(z) \quad \text{and} \quad \Im(z)$$

It is important to keep in mind that $\Im(z)$, as here defined, is a real quantity.

291

Two complex numbers $a + ib$ and $c + id$ are said to be **equal** if and only if the real and imaginary parts of the first are, respectively, equal to the real and imaginary parts of the second. In particular, the vanishing of a complex number implies not one but *two* conditions, namely, that both the real part and the imaginary part of the given number are zero.

Example 1

If $(x + y + 2) + (x^2 + y)i = 0 = 0 + 0i$, then

$$x + y + 2 = 0$$

and also

$$x^2 + y = 0$$

From this pair of simultaneous equations it follows necessarily that

$$x = 2 \text{ and } y = -4 \qquad \text{or} \qquad x = -1 \text{ and } y = -1$$

Addition, subtraction, and **multiplication** of complex numbers follow the familiar rules for real quantities, with the additional provision that in multiplication, all powers of i are to be reduced as far as possible by applying the definitive property of i and its obvious extensions:

$$i^2 = -1$$
$$i^3 = i^2 i = -i$$
$$i^4 = i^2 i^2 = 1$$
$$i^5 = i^4 i = i$$
$$\cdots \cdots \cdots$$

Example 2

$$(a + ib) + (c + id) - (e + if) = (a + c - e) + (b + d - f)i$$

Example 3

$$(a + ib)(c + id) = (ac - bd) + i(bc + ad)$$

Since $i \equiv \sqrt{-1}$ is an irrational quantity, the division of complex numbers is just a special case of the division of radical expressions, and is performed as usual by the process of rationalizing the denominator.

Example 4

$$(a + ib) \div (c + id) = \frac{a + ib}{c + id}$$
$$= \frac{a + ib}{c + id}\frac{c - id}{c - id}$$
$$= \left(\frac{ac + bd}{c^2 + d^2}\right) + \left(\frac{bc - ad}{c^2 + d^2}\right)i$$

If two complex numbers differ only in the sign of their imaginary parts, either one is said to be the **conjugate** of the other. The conjugate of a complex number, z, is usually written $\bar{z}$, or less frequently z^*. Conjugate complex numbers have various simple, though important, properties. For instance, if $z = x + iy$, then

$$(1) \qquad z\bar{z} = (x + iy)(x - iy) = x^2 + y^2$$

which is a purely real quantity. This is the basis for the use of conjugates in division, as illustrated in Example 4. Also

$$z + \bar{z} = (x + iy) + (x - iy) = 2x = 2\Re(z)$$

or

$$(2) \qquad \Re(z) = \frac{z + \bar{z}}{2}$$

and

$$z - \bar{z} = (x + iy) - (x - iy) = 2iy = 2i\Im(z)$$

or

$$(3) \qquad \Im(z) = \frac{z - \bar{z}}{2i}$$

In taking the conjugate of a complicated expression, the following results are of great utility.

$$(4) \qquad \overline{z_1 \pm z_2} = \bar{z}_1 \pm \bar{z}_2$$

$$(5) \qquad \overline{z_1 z_2} = \bar{z}_1 \bar{z}_2$$

$$(6) \qquad \overline{\left(\frac{z_1}{z_2}\right)} = \frac{\bar{z}_1}{\bar{z}_2}$$

The proofs of these all follow immediately from the four laws of operation and the definition of conjugates.

EXERCISES

1. Prove that if a number is equal to its conjugate it is necessarily real.
2. Prove that any number is equal to the conjugate of its conjugate.
3. Prove that if the product of two complex numbers is zero, at least one of the numbers must be zero.

Reduce each of the following expressions to the form $a + ib$.

4. $(1 + i)^2 + (2 - i)^2$ 5. $i(2 + 3i)^4$ *Ans.* $120 - 119i$

6. $(1 + 2i)(3 - 2i)^2$ 7. $\dfrac{1 + i}{1 - i} - \dfrac{1 - i}{1 + i}$ *Ans.* $2i$

8. $\dfrac{1 + 2i}{3 - i}$ 9. $\dfrac{(1 - i)^3}{(2 + i)(1 + 2i)}$ *Ans.* $\dfrac{-2 + 2i}{5}$

10. Verify that $z = \dfrac{1 \pm i\sqrt{3}}{2}$ satisfies the equation $z^2 - z + 1 = 0$.

11. Show that for all combinations of signs, $\dfrac{\pm 1 \pm i}{\sqrt{2}}$ satisfies the equation $z^4 = -1$.

12. If $z = x + iy$, what is $\Re(z^3 - 2z)$? $\Im(z^3 - 2z)$?

13. If $F(z)$ is a polynomial in z with real coefficients and if $F(2 + 3i) = 1 - i$, what is $F(2 - 3i)$? Is $F(2 - 3i)$ determined by a knowledge of $F(2 + 3i)$ if the coefficients of $F(z)$ are complex numbers?

14. Show that the equation $(A + \bar{A})z\bar{z} + Bz + \bar{B}\bar{z} + (C + \bar{C}) = 0$ represents a real circle if $B\bar{B} > (A + \bar{A})(C + \bar{C})$, and find its center and radius.

15. Solve for x and y if $(x^2y - 2) + i(x + 2xy - 5) = 0$.

9.3 The Geometric Representation of Complex Numbers.

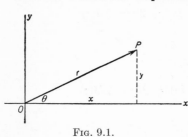

FIG. 9.1.

A complex number is represented geometrically either by the point, P, whose abscissa and ordinate are, respectively, the real and imaginary components of the given number, or by the directed line segment, or vector, which joins the origin to this point. When used in this fashion for representing complex numbers, the cartesian plane is referred to as the **argand diagram,** * or the **complex plane,** or simply as the **z-plane.**

The vector OP which represents the complex number $x + iy$ possesses two important attributes besides its components, x and y. These are its length

$$(1) \qquad r = \sqrt{x^2 + y^2}$$

and its direction angle

$$(2) \qquad \theta = \tan^{-1}\frac{y}{x}$$

Since

$$x = r\cos\theta \qquad \text{and} \qquad y = r\sin\theta$$

it is evident that $z = x + iy$ can be written in the equivalent form

$$(3) \qquad z = r\cos\theta + ir\sin\theta = r(\cos\theta + i\sin\theta) \; = \gamma e^{i\theta} \quad (p.31\text{?})$$

This is known as the **polar** or **trigonometric form** of a complex number, and is sometimes abbreviated to

$$r \text{ cis } \theta$$

in which only the initial letters of *cosine* and *sine* are retained. The length r is called the **absolute value** or **modulus** of z (written mod z). The angle θ is called the **amplitude** or **argument** of z (written arg z).

The various combinations of complex numbers which we have thus far discussed can easily be interpreted geometrically. For instance, Fig. 9.2*a* shows that the negative of a complex number is the reflection of that

* Named for the French mathematician J. R. Argand (1768–1822), although the Norwegian Caspar Wessel (1745–1818) published a discussion of this method of representation 9 years before Argand did.

number in the origin, while Fig. 9.2b shows that the conjugate of a complex number is the reflection of that number in the real axis.   The geometrical addition of complex numbers is shown in Fig. 9.3a.   By drawing one complex number from the terminus of the other and completing the triangle thus formed, a third complex number* is obtained whose components are precisely those of the sum, $z_1 + z_2$.   Figure 9.3b shows the

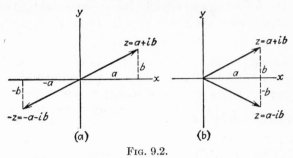

FIG. 9.2.

construction for the difference of two complex numbers, *i.e.*, for the sum $z_1 + (-z_2)$.   Evidently $z_1 - z_2$ is identical in length and direction with the vector drawn from the end of z_2 to the end of z_1.

Both the sum and the difference of two complex numbers can be described in terms of the parallelogram formed on the two numbers as adjacent sides.   For the sum is simply the diagonal of the parallelogram

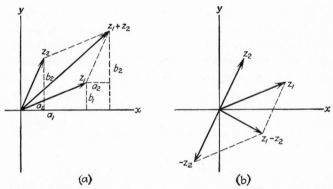

FIG. 9.3.   Plot illustrating the graphical addition and subtraction of complex numbers.

which passes through the common origin of the two vectors, while the difference is just the other diagonal, properly directed.   Much of the utility of complex numbers in elementary engineering applications stems from the fact that they add according to this so-called **parallelogram law.**

* For conciseness of expression, we shall often speak of a complex number and its geometric image as though they were the same thing.

Since this is the experimentally established law for the addition of such things as forces, velocities, currents, and voltages, it is evident that complex numbers can conveniently be used to represent such physical quantities.

Although we shall have no occasion to use it, a graphic process for multiplying and dividing complex numbers can also be devised. It is based upon the following exceedingly important considerations. If we have two complex numbers given in polar form, their product can be written

$$z_1 z_2 = [r_1(\cos \theta_1 + i \sin \theta_1)][r_2(\cos \theta_2 + i \sin \theta_2)]$$
$$= r_1 r_2[(\cos \theta_1 \cos \theta_2 - \sin \theta_1 \sin \theta_2) + i(\sin \theta_1 \cos \theta_2 + \cos \theta_1 \sin \theta_2)]$$
$$(4) \qquad = r_1 r_2[\cos (\theta_1 + \theta_2) + i \sin (\theta_1 + \theta_2)]$$

and their quotient can be written

$$\frac{z_1}{z_2} = \frac{r_1(\cos \theta_1 + i \sin \theta_1)}{r_2(\cos \theta_2 + i \sin \theta_2)}$$
$$= \frac{r_1(\cos \theta_1 + i \sin \theta_1)}{r_2(\cos \theta_2 + i \sin \theta_2)} \frac{(\cos \theta_2 - i \sin \theta_2)}{(\cos \theta_2 - i \sin \theta_2)}$$
$$= \frac{r_1}{r_2} \left[\frac{(\cos \theta_1 \cos \theta_2 + \sin \theta_1 \sin \theta_2) + i(\sin \theta_1 \cos \theta_2 - \cos \theta_1 \sin \theta_2)}{\cos^2 \theta_2 + \sin^2 \theta_2} \right]$$
$$(5) \qquad = \frac{r_1}{r_2}[\cos (\theta_1 - \theta_2) + i \sin (\theta_1 - \theta_2)]$$

In words, then, *the product of two complex numbers is a complex number whose absolute value is the product of the absolute values of the two factors and whose amplitude is the sum of the amplitudes of the two factors,* and *the quotient of two complex numbers is a complex number whose absolute value is the quotient of the absolute values of the numbers and whose amplitude is the difference of their amplitudes.* The behavior of angles when complex numbers are multiplied or divided is concisely expressed in the formulas

$$(6) \qquad \arg (z_1 z_2) = \arg z_1 + \arg z_2$$

$$(7) \qquad \arg \left(\frac{z_1}{z_2} \right) = \arg z_1 - \arg z_2$$

In a later section when we succeed in writing a general complex number as an exponential, the reason for the striking resemblance of these results to the corresponding logarithmic formulas will be apparent.

The extension of these ideas to products of more than two factors is obvious, and we can write at once

$$z_1 z_2 \cdots z_n$$
$$= r_1 r_2 \cdots r_n[\cos (\theta_1 + \theta_2 + \cdots \theta_n) + i \sin (\theta_1 + \theta_2 + \cdots \theta_n)]$$

In particular, if all the z's are the same, we have the important result

$$(8) \qquad z^n = r^n(\cos n\theta + i \sin n\theta)$$

if $r = 1$; this is known as **de Moivre's theorem.*** Since the law of division in polar form gives

$$\frac{1}{z} = \frac{1}{r} [\cos (0 - \theta) + i \sin (0 - \theta)] = \frac{1}{r} [\cos (-\theta) + i \sin (-\theta)]$$

which is just the content of Eq. (8) for $n = -1$, it is clear that this formula is valid for all integral values of n, both positive and negative.

The extension of Eq. (8) to integral roots is an easy matter. In fact the nth root of $z = r(\cos \theta + i \sin \theta)$ is defined to be a number

$$w = R(\cos \phi + i \sin \phi)$$

such that

$$w^n \equiv R^n(\cos n\phi + i \sin n\phi) = z \equiv r(\cos \theta + i \sin \theta)$$

Since two complex numbers which are equal must have the same modulus, it follows that

$$R^n = r \qquad \text{or} \qquad R = r^{1/n}$$

which involves only a purely real calculation. Also the angles of equal complex numbers must either be equal or differ at most by an integral multiple of 2π. Hence

$$n\phi = \theta + 2k\pi \qquad \text{or} \qquad \phi = \frac{\theta + 2k\pi}{n}$$

Distinct values of ϕ are obtained for $k = 0, 1, 2, \ldots, (n - 1)$, following which these values repeat themselves with an irrelevant factor of 2π. Hence there are exactly n distinct values of $w = z^{1/n}$:

$$(9) \qquad w = z^{1/n} = r^{1/n} \left(\cos \frac{\theta + 2k\pi}{n} + i \sin \frac{\theta + 2k\pi}{n} \right)$$
$$k = 0, 1, 2, \ldots, (n - 1)$$

In the argand diagram these are represented by radii of the circle with center at the origin and radius $r^{1/n}$, spaced at equal intervals of $2\pi/n$ from the radius whose angle is θ/n.

With integral powers and roots defined, the general rational power of a complex number can be defined at once. In fact

---

* Named for the French mathematician Abraham de Moivre (1667–1754), although an equivalent form had been obtained earlier by the Englishman Roger Cotes (1682–1716).

$$z^{p/q} = (z^{1/q})^p = \left[r^{1/q} \left(\cos \frac{\theta + 2k\pi}{q} + i \sin \frac{\theta + 2k\pi}{q} \right) \right]^p$$

$$(10) \qquad = r^{p/q} \left[\cos \frac{p}{q}(\theta + 2k\pi) + i \sin \frac{p}{q}(\theta + 2k\pi) \right]$$

$$k = 0, 1, 2, \ldots, (q-1)$$

However, the definition of z^α when α is not a rational number must be postponed to Sec. 9.7.

Example 1

Find the four fourth roots of $-8i$.

To do this, we must first write $-8i$ in the standard polar form:

$$-8i = 8 \left(\cos \frac{3\pi}{2} + i \sin \frac{3\pi}{2} \right)$$

Then applying Eq. (9) to this expression, we have

$$(-8i)^{\frac{1}{4}} = 8^{\frac{1}{4}} \left[\cos \frac{1}{4} \left(\frac{3\pi}{2} + 2k\pi \right) + i \sin \frac{1}{4} \left(\frac{3\pi}{2} + 2k\pi \right) \right] \qquad k = 0, 1, 2, 3$$

$$= 8^{\frac{1}{4}} \left(\cos \frac{3\pi}{8} + i \sin \frac{3\pi}{8} \right) \qquad\qquad (k = 0)$$

$$= 8^{\frac{1}{4}} \left(\cos \frac{7\pi}{8} + i \sin \frac{7\pi}{8} \right) \qquad\qquad (k = 1)$$

$$= 8^{\frac{1}{4}} \left(\cos \frac{11\pi}{8} + i \sin \frac{11\pi}{8} \right) \qquad\qquad (k = 2)$$

$$= 8^{\frac{1}{4}} \left(\cos \frac{15\pi}{8} + i \sin \frac{15\pi}{8} \right) \qquad\qquad (k = 3)$$

The coefficient $8^{\frac{1}{4}}$ is, of course, the *real* fourth root of 8, the value of which is found by a simple logarithmic calculation to be 1.682.

Example 2

Using de Moivre's theorem and the binomial expansion, express $\cos 4\theta$ and $\sin 4\theta$ in terms of powers of functions of the angle θ itself.

To do this we consider $(\cos \theta + i \sin \theta)^4$, and expand it first by de Moivre's theorem and then by the binomial theorem. This gives the identity

$$\cos 4\theta + i \sin 4\theta = \cos^4 \theta + 4i \cos^3 \theta \sin \theta + 6i^2 \cos^2 \theta \sin^2 \theta + 4i^3 \cos \theta \sin^3 \theta + i^4 \sin^4 \theta$$
$$= (\cos^4 \theta - 6 \cos^2 \theta \sin^2 \theta + \sin^4 \theta) + i(4 \cos^3 \theta \sin \theta - 4 \cos \theta \sin^3 \theta)$$

Equating real and imaginary parts of these two equal complex expressions, we obtain the required formulas:

$$\cos 4\theta = \cos^4 \theta - 6 \cos^2 \theta \sin^2 \theta + \sin^4 \theta$$
$$\sin 4\theta = 4 (\sin \theta \cos^3 \theta - \cos \theta \sin^3 \theta)$$

EXERCISES

1. Show that multiplying a complex number by i rotates it through 90° without changing its length. What is the effect of multiplying a complex number by $-i$? by $\sqrt{i}$?

2. Find all the fifth roots of 32.

3. Express the complex number $8 - 8\sqrt{3}i$ in polar form, and find its fourth roots.

4. Find the three cube roots of $1 + i$, and reduce each to the form $a + ib$, where a and b are decimal fractions.

5. Find all the distinct values of $i^{\frac{2}{3}}$.

6. A square lies entirely in the second quadrant. If one of its sides joins the points -2 and $2i$, find the coordinates of the other two vertices.

7. Using de Moivre's theorem, express $\cos 5\theta$ and $\sin 5\theta$ in terms of powers of $\cos \theta$ and $\sin \theta$.

8. Prove that the centroid of a system of three equal particles situated at the points z_1, z_2, z_3 is the point $\dfrac{z_1 + z_2 + z_3}{3}$. What point is represented by $\dfrac{z_1 + z_2}{2}$? What is the locus of the points $\lambda z_1 + \mu z_2$, where λ and μ are real parameters?

9. If $z = \cos \dfrac{2\pi}{5} + i \sin \dfrac{2\pi}{5}$, prove that $(z^2 - z^3)(z^4 - z) = \sqrt{5}$.

10. Using the polar form of the multiplication law, devise a geometric process for multiplying two complex numbers.

9.4 Absolute Values. We have already defined the absolute value of a complex number z to be the length of its representative vector

$$|z| = \sqrt{x^2 + y^2} = \sqrt{\Re^2(z) + \mathscr{I}^2(z)}$$

From this it is evident that a complex number is zero if and only if its absolute value is zero. Since $\Re^2(z)$ and $\mathscr{I}^2(z)$ are both nonnegative real numbers, it is also clear, by neglecting first one and then the other of these quantities, that*

(1) $$|z| \geqq \Re(z)$$
(2) $$|z| \geqq \mathscr{I}(z)$$

Moreover, from the definition of conjugate complex numbers, it follows that

(3) $$z\bar{z} = |z|^2$$

and

(4) $$|z| = |\bar{z}|$$

Also, from Eqs. (4) and (5), Sec. 9.3, giving the products and quotients of complex numbers expressed in polar form, it is clear that

(5) $$|z_1 z_2| = |z_1| \cdot |z_2|$$

and

(6) $$\left| \frac{z_1}{z_2} \right| = \frac{|z_1|}{|z_2|}$$

---

* We must be careful to keep in mind that we have not defined an order relation for complex numbers and that *greater than* and *less than* have meaning only when applied to real numbers.

Since any side of a triangle must be equal to or less than the sum of the other two sides, it follows from the geometric addition of complex numbers (Fig. 9.4a) that

$$(7) \qquad |z_1 + z_2| \leqq |z_1| + |z_2|$$

This can readily be extended to three terms, for

$$\begin{aligned} |z_1 + z_2 + z_3| &= |z_1 + (z_2 + z_3)| \\ &\leqq |z_1| + |z_2 + z_3| \\ &\leqq |z_1| + \{|z_2| + |z_3|\} = |z_1| + |z_2| + |z_3| \end{aligned}$$

The important extension to n terms is obvious:

$$(8) \qquad \left| \sum_{k=1}^{n} z_k \right| \leqq \sum_{k=1}^{n} |z_k|$$

It is also geometrically evident that any side of a triangle must be at least as long as the difference of the other two sides. Hence, from

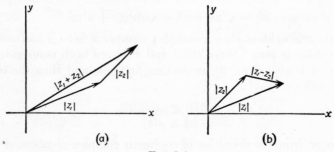

FIG. 9.4.

Fig. 9.4b, it is apparent that

$$(9) \qquad |z_1 - z_2| \geqq ||z_1| - |z_2||$$

If the notation has been chosen so that $|z_1|$ is greater than $|z_2|$, the outer absolute value signs on the right in (9) are unnecessary.

Example 1

Describe the region in the z-plane defined by the inequality $\Re(z) > 1$.

If the real part of z is greater than 1, the image of z must be a point to the right of the line $x = 1$. Since the equality sign is not included in the definition of the region, points actually on the line $x = 1$ do *not* belong to the region.

Example 2

What region in the z-plane is defined by $|z - z_0| \leqq 9$?

In words, the given inequality asserts that the distance between the image point of z and the fixed point which is the image of z_0 is equal to or less than 9. This clearly defines the set of all points within and on the boundary of the circle of radius 9 which has the image of z_0 as its center. In the work that lies ahead, we will frequently have to consider regions of this type.

Example 3

If $w = (z + i)/(iz + 1)$, show that the restriction $\mathcal{I}(z) \leqq 0$ implies the restriction $|w| \leqq 1$.

Since we are asked to establish a certain property of $|w|$, our first step is to compute this quantity. This we do by constructing the product

$$w\bar{w} = |w|^2 = \left(\frac{z + i}{iz + 1}\right)\overline{\left(\frac{z + i}{iz + 1}\right)}$$

Since the conjugate of a quotient is the quotient of the conjugates, this can be written as

$$|w|^2 = \left(\frac{z + i}{iz + 1}\right)\left(\frac{\overline{z + i}}{\overline{iz + 1}}\right)$$

But the conjugate of a sum is the sum of the conjugates; hence we have further

$$|w|^2 = \left(\frac{z + i}{iz + 1}\right)\left(\frac{\bar{z} + \bar{i}}{\overline{iz} + 1}\right)$$

Finally, since $\bar{i} = -i$ and $\overline{iz} = \bar{i}\bar{z} = -i\bar{z}$, we have

$$\begin{aligned} |w|^2 &= \left(\frac{z + i}{iz + 1}\right)\left(\frac{\bar{z} - i}{-i\bar{z} + 1}\right) \\ &= \frac{(z\bar{z} + 1) - i(z - \bar{z})}{(z\bar{z} + 1) + i(z - \bar{z})} \\ &= \frac{(z\bar{z} + 1) + 2\mathcal{I}(z)}{(z\bar{z} + 1) - 2\mathcal{I}(z)} \end{aligned}$$

All terms here are entirely real, and it is clear that if $\mathcal{I}(z) \leqq 0$, as given, then the numerator of the fraction is equal to or less than the denominator. Thus $|w|^2$, and hence $|w|$, is at most equal to 1 under the given conditions.

EXERCISES

1. Show that $\left|\dfrac{a + ib}{b + ia}\right| = 1$.

2. Find $|z|$, $\mathcal{R}(z)$, and $\mathcal{I}(z)$ if $z = \dfrac{(3 + 4i)(12 - 5i)}{2i}$.

3. Under what conditions will $|z_1 + z_2| = |z_1| + |z_2|$?

4. What region in the z-plane is defined by the inequalities

$$0 < \mathcal{R}(z) \leqq \mathcal{I}(z)$$

5. What region in the z-plane is defined by the inequality

$$|z - 1| \leqq \mathcal{R}(z)$$

6. Prove that the locus of points for which $\left|\dfrac{z - 1}{z + 1}\right| = k$, where k is a real constant different from 1, is a circle. What is the locus if $k = 1$?

7. Prove that $|z| \geqq \dfrac{|x| + |y|}{\sqrt{2}}$.

8. Prove that $\left|\dfrac{z_1}{z_1 + z_2}\right| \leqq \dfrac{|z_1|}{||z_1| - |z_2||}$. Under what conditions will the equality sign hold?

9. Prove that $|z_1 - z_2|^2 + |z_1 + z_2|^2 = 2|z_1|^2 + 2|z_2|^2$.

10. If $w = i\dfrac{(1 - z)}{(1 + z)}$, prove that $|z| < 1$ implies $\mathscr{I}(w) > 0$.

9.5 Functions of a Complex Variable. If $z = x + iy$ and $w = u + iv$ are two complex variables, and if for each value of z in some portion of the complex plane one or more values of w are defined, then w is said to be a **function of** z, and we write

$$w = f(z)$$

If a unique value of w exists for each value of z, then w is called a **single-valued function of** z. If more than one value of w corresponds to a given value of z, then w is called a **multiple-valued function.**

Any function, $w = f(z)$, can be thought of as eventually reducible to an expression of the form

$$(1) \qquad\qquad w = u(x,y) + iv(x,y)$$

where $u(x,y)$ and $v(x,y)$ are real functions of the real variables x and y. Clearly, whenever a value of z is given, values of x and y are thereby provided, and thus one or more values of w are determined by (1). For example, if

$$f(z) = (x^2 - y) + (x + y^2)i$$

and if

$$z = 1 + 2i$$

then

$$x = 1 \qquad \text{and} \qquad y = 2$$

and thus

$$f(1 + 2i) = (1^2 - 2) + (1 + 2^2)i = -1 + 5i$$

It may be possible by suitable manipulations to rearrange w so that x and y occur only in the binomial combination $x + iy$. For instance,

$$w = (x^2 - y^2) + 2ixy$$

is immediately recognizable as

$$w = (x + iy)^2 = z^2$$

and

$$w = \frac{x}{x^2 + y^2} - i\frac{y}{x^2 + y^2}$$

is nothing but the rationalized form of

$$w = \frac{1}{x + iy} = \frac{1}{z}$$

On the other hand, it may be impossible to reduce w to dependence upon the explicit combination $x + iy = z$, except in some artificial sense, as, for instance,

$$w = x - iy = \bar{z}$$

or

$$w = 2x + iy = \Re(z) + z$$

In our work, and in fact in almost all applications of complex variable theory, the only functions of interest will be those which can be written as formulas in z itself, of familiar, *i.e.*, "nonartificial," structure.

Frequently our interest in a function will be restricted to its behavior over some part or region of the z-plane. If there exists a circle with

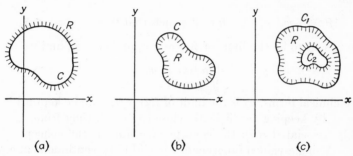

(a)   (b)   (c)

Fig. 9.5.   Plot showing typical regions in the complex plane.

center at the origin enclosing all the points of a region, R, then R is said to be **bounded.** Analytically this means that a region, R, is bounded if and only if there exists a positive number d such that

$$|z| < d \qquad \text{for all } z \text{ in } R$$

The regions with which we shall have to deal will usually be defined by one or more **simple closed curves.*** Figure 9.5 shows various possibilities. In (*a*) the region R is the *unbounded* part of the z-plane exterior to the simple closed curve C. In (*b*), R is the *bounded* region interior to the curve C. In (*c*), R is the *bounded* region inside C_1 and outside C_2. If a region R is defined to include all the points on its various boundary curves it is said to be **closed.** If R contains none of its boundary points, it is said to be **open.**

The regions shown in Fig. 9.5*b* and *c*, although both are bounded, differ in one significant respect. In Fig. 9.5*b any* simple closed curve which

* For our purposes it will be sufficient to "let sleeping dogs lie" and consider a simple closed curve as adequately defined by intuition. How unsatisfactory this is for a pure mathematician, whose business it is to explore exceptional, nonintuitive cases, can be inferred from the article "What Is a Curve?" by G. T. Whyburn in the *American Mathematical Monthly*, Vol. 49, p. 493, October, 1942.

can be drawn in R can enclose only points of R. This is not the case in Fig. 9.5c, for although some closed curves can be drawn whose interiors contain only points of R, others, namely, any of those encircling C_2, will enclose points not in R. Regions like that shown in Fig. 9.5b are called **simply connected**. Regions with the property of the one shown in Fig. 9.5c are called **multiply connected**.

It will often be necessary for us to consider the limit of a function of z as z approaches some particular value, z_0. The basis for this is the following definition.

Definition 1. If $f(z)$ is a single-valued function of z, and w_0 is a complex constant, and if for every $\epsilon > 0$ there exists a positive number $\delta(\epsilon)$ such that

$$|f(z) - w_0| < \epsilon \quad \text{for all } z \text{ such that } 0 < |z - z_0| < \delta$$

then w_0 is said to be the limit of $f(z)$ as z approaches z_0, and we write

$$\lim_{z \to z_0} f(z) = w_0$$

In less technical terms, w_0 is the limit of $f(z)$ if $f(z)$ can be kept arbitrarily close to w_0 by keeping z sufficiently close to, but distinct from, z_0.

Closely associated with the concept of a limit is the concept of continuity. A single-valued function of z is said to be **continuous at a point,** z_0, provided each of the following conditions is satisfied:

a. $f(z_0)$ exists.

b. $\lim_{z \to z_0} f(z)$ exists.

c. $\lim_{z \to z_0} f(z) = f(z_0)$.

If $f(z)$ is continuous at every point of a region R, it is said to be **continuous throughout** R.

There are various theorems on continuous functions which we shall need from time to time. For the most part they appear almost self-evident, although the proofs of some of them are by no means easy. We shall merely list them here, and refer to standard texts on advanced calculus for their proof.

Theorem 1. A necessary and sufficient condition that

$$f(z) = u(x,y) + iv(x,y)$$

be continuous is that the real functions $u(x,y)$ and $v(x,y)$ should be continuous.

Theorem 2. Sums, differences, products, and quotients of continuous functions are continuous, provided in the case of quotients that the divisor function is different from zero.

Theorem 3.   If $f(z)$ is continuous at the point z_0, and if $f(z_0) \neq 0$, then there exists a region containing z_0 in its interior throughout which $f(z)$ is different from 0.

Theorem 4.   If $f(z)$ is continuous over a bounded, closed region R, then there exists a positive constant M such that $|f(z)| < M$ for all values of z in R.

EXERCISES

1. If $f(z) = xy + i(x^2 - y^2)$, what is $f(-1 + 2i)$?

2. If $f(z) = z + (\bar{z})^2 + \mathcal{I}(z\bar{z})$, what is $f(2 + i)$?

3. Express $(2xy + 2x - 1) - i(x^2 - y^2 - 2y)$ as a function of the binomial argument $z = x + iy$.

4. Express $x^2 + iy^2$ in terms of z and $\bar{z}$.

5. Describe each of the following regions, telling whether it is bounded or unbounded, open or closed, and simply or multiply connected.

(a) $\mathcal{I}(z) > 0$ (d) $\left|z^2 - 1\right| \leq \tfrac{5}{4}$

(b) $2 \leq |z| \leq 3$ (e) $0 \leq \mathcal{R}(z) \leq 1$

(c) $|z - 1| > 4$ (f) $0 \leq \mathcal{I}(z) \leq 1$

9.6 Analytic Functions.   The **derivative of a function of a complex variable,** $w = f(z)$, is defined to be

$$(1) \qquad \frac{dw}{dz} \equiv w' \equiv f'(z) = \lim_{\Delta z \to 0} \frac{f(z + \Delta z) - f(z)}{\Delta z}$$

This definition is formally identical with that for the derivative of a function of a real variable.   Moreover, the general theory of limits is valid for complex variables as well as for real variables.   Hence it is clear that formulas for the differentiation of functions of a real variable will have identical counterparts in the domain of complex numbers, when the corresponding functions of a complex variable are suitably defined. In particular, such familiar formulas as

$$\frac{d(w_1 \pm w_2)}{dz} = \frac{dw_1}{dz} \pm \frac{dw_2}{dz}$$

$$\frac{d(w_1 w_2)}{dz} = w_1 \frac{dw_2}{dz} + w_2 \frac{dw_1}{dz}$$

$$\frac{d(w_1/w_2)}{dz} = \frac{w_2(dw_1/dz) - w_1(dw_2/dz)}{w_2^2}$$

$$\frac{d(w^n)}{dz} = nw^{n-1} \frac{dw}{dz}$$

are valid when w_1, w_2, and w are functions of a complex variable z.   However, $\Delta z = \Delta x + i\,\Delta y$ is itself a complex variable, and in some cases the question of just how it is to approach zero involves difficulties which have no counterpart in the differentiation of functions of a real variable.

In Fig. 9.6, it is clear that Δz can approach zero, *i.e.*, the point

$$P = z + \Delta z$$

can approach the point $Q = z$, along infinitely many paths. In particular, P can approach Q along the rectilinear path PAQ on which first Δx and then Δy approaches zero, or along the rectilinear path PBQ on which first Δy and then Δx approaches zero. *In order for the derivative of*

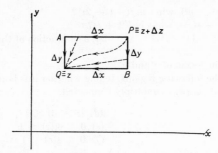

FIG. 9.6. Plot showing various ways in which Δz can approach zero.

$f(z)$ to exist, it is necessary that the limit of the difference quotient (1) *be the same no matter how Δz approaches zero.* How severe a restriction this is can be seen by considering the simple function

$$w = f(z) = \bar{z} = x - iy$$

Giving to z the increment $\Delta z = \Delta x + i\,\Delta y$ means that x changes by the amount Δx and y changes by the amount Δy. Hence

$$\frac{f(z + \Delta z) - f(z)}{\Delta z} = \frac{[(x + \Delta x) - i(y + \Delta y)] - [x - iy]}{\Delta x + i\,\Delta y}$$

$$= \frac{\Delta x - i\,\Delta y}{\Delta x + i\,\Delta y}$$

Now if $\Delta z \to 0$ in such a way that first Δx and then Δy approaches zero, we have

$$\lim_{\Delta z \to 0} \frac{\Delta x - i\,\Delta y}{\Delta x + i\,\Delta y} = \lim_{\Delta y \to 0} \frac{-i\,\Delta y}{i\,\Delta y} = -1$$

On the other hand, if $\Delta z \to 0$ in such a way that first Δy and then Δx approaches zero, we have

$$\lim_{\Delta z \to 0} \frac{\Delta x - i\,\Delta y}{\Delta x + i\,\Delta y} = \lim_{\Delta x \to 0} \frac{\Delta x}{\Delta x} = 1$$

More generally, if we let $\Delta z \to 0$ in such a way that $\Delta y = k\,\Delta x$, that is, if we let $z + \Delta z$ approach z along a line of slope k, we have

$$\lim_{\Delta z \to 0} \frac{\Delta x - i \, \Delta y}{\Delta x + i \, \Delta y} = \lim_{\Delta x \to 0} \frac{\Delta x - ik \, \Delta x}{\Delta x + ik \, \Delta x} = \frac{1 - ik}{1 + ik} = \frac{(1 - k^2) - 2ik}{1 + k^2}$$

Thus there are infinitely many complex values which the difference quotient for $f(z) = x - iy$ can be made to approach by choosing properly the manner in which Δz shall approach zero. It is therefore apparent that $f(z) = x - iy$ possesses no derivative.

That a function as simple as $f(z) = x - iy$ should have no derivative seems at first glance a discouraging state of affairs. However, there are many functions of z which do have derivatives, and in applications it is these functions which are of importance. Our immediate task is to identify these functions by obtaining conditions for the existence of a derivative of a function of a complex variable.

To do this, consider

$$w = f(z) = u(x,y) + iv(x,y)$$

By definition

$$(2) \quad \frac{dw}{dz} = \lim_{\Delta z \to 0} \frac{\Delta w}{\Delta z}$$

$$= \lim_{\substack{\Delta x \to 0 \\ \Delta y \to 0}} \frac{[u(x + \Delta x, y + \Delta y) + iv(x + \Delta x, y + \Delta y)] - [u(x,y) + iv(x,y)]}{\Delta x + i \, \Delta y}$$

Now if we let $\Delta y \to 0$ and then $\Delta x \to 0$, we obtain

$$\frac{dw}{dz} = \lim_{\Delta x \to 0} \frac{[u(x + \Delta x, y) + iv(x + \Delta x, y)] - [u(x,y) + iv(x,y)]}{\Delta x}$$

$$= \lim_{\Delta x \to 0} \left[\frac{u(x + \Delta x, y) - u(x,y)}{\Delta x} + i \frac{v(x + \Delta x, y) - v(x,y)}{\Delta x} \right]$$

The two difference quotients which appear in this expression are precisely those which define the partial derivatives of u and v with respect to x. Hence it appears that

$$(3) \qquad \frac{dw}{dz} = \frac{\partial u}{\partial x} + i \frac{\partial v}{\partial x}$$

On the other hand, if we let $\Delta x \to 0$ and then $\Delta y \to 0$, we find from (2) that

$$\frac{dw}{dz} = \lim_{\Delta y \to 0} \frac{[u(x, y + \Delta y) + iv(x, y + \Delta y)] - [u(x,y) + iv(x,y)]}{i \, \Delta y}$$

$$= \lim_{\Delta y \to 0} \left[\frac{u(x, y + \Delta y) - u(x,y)}{i \, \Delta y} + i \frac{v(x, y + \Delta y) - v(x,y)}{i \, \Delta y} \right]$$

$$= \frac{1}{i} \frac{\partial u}{\partial y} + \frac{\partial v}{\partial y}$$

or, finally,

(4)
$$\frac{dw}{dz} = \frac{\partial v}{\partial y} - i\frac{\partial u}{\partial y}$$

If the derivative dw/dz is to exist, it is thus necessary that the two expressions which we have just derived for it should be the same. Hence, from (3) and (4),

$$\frac{\partial u}{\partial x} + i\frac{\partial v}{\partial x} = \frac{\partial v}{\partial y} - i\frac{\partial u}{\partial y}$$

which requires that

(5.1)
$$\frac{\partial u}{\partial x} = \frac{\partial v}{\partial y}$$

(5.2)
$$\frac{\partial u}{\partial y} = -\frac{\partial v}{\partial x}$$

These two extremely important conditions, which are known as the **Cauchy-Riemann equations,*** have arisen here from a consideration of only two of the infinitely many ways in which Δz can approach zero. It is therefore natural to expect that severe additional conditions will be necessary to ensure that along each of these paths $\Delta w/\Delta z$ also approaches the same limit, dw/dz. Such is not the case, however, and it can be proved without great difficulty† that if u and v, together with their first partial derivatives, $\frac{\partial u}{\partial x}, \frac{\partial u}{\partial y}, \frac{\partial v}{\partial x}, \frac{\partial v}{\partial y}$, are continuous in some neighborhood of the point z_0, then the Cauchy-Riemann equations are not only necessary, but also sufficient conditions for the existence of a derivative of $w = u(x,y) + iv(x,y)$ at $z = z_0$. If $w = f(z)$ possesses a derivative at $z = z_0$ and at every point in some neighborhood of z_0, then $f(z)$ is said to be **analytic at** $z = z_0$, and z_0 is called a **regular point** of the function. If $f(z)$ is not analytic at z_0 but if every neighborhood of z_0 contains points at which $f(z)$ is analytic, then z_0 is called a **singular point** of $f(z)$. A function which is analytic at all points of a region R we shall call **analytic in** R. Although most writers use this term, a few substitute such adjectives as **regular, holomorphic,** and **monogenic.** As a summary of our discussion we have the following theorem.

Theorem 1. If u and v are real single-valued functions of x and y which, with their four first partial derivatives, are continuous throughout a region R, then the Cauchy-Riemann equations,

* After Augustin Louis Cauchy (1789–1857), one of the greatest French mathematicians, and George Friedrich Bernhard Riemann (1826–1866), one of the greatest German mathematicians.

† See, for instance, R. S. Burington and C. C. Torrance, "Higher Mathematics," p. 575, McGraw-Hill Book Company, Inc., New York, 1939.

$$\frac{\partial u}{\partial x} = \frac{\partial v}{\partial y} \quad \text{and} \quad \frac{\partial u}{\partial y} = -\frac{\partial v}{\partial x}$$

are both necessary and sufficient conditions that $f(z) = u(x,y) + iv(x,y)$ be analytic in R. In this case, the derivative of $f(z)$ is given by either of the expressions

$$f'(z) = \frac{\partial u}{\partial x} + i\frac{\partial v}{\partial x} \quad \text{or} \quad f'(z) = \frac{\partial v}{\partial y} - i\frac{\partial u}{\partial y}$$

Example 1

For $w = \bar{z} = x - iy$, we have $u = x$ and $v = -y$. In this case

$$\frac{\partial u}{\partial x} = 1, \qquad \frac{\partial u}{\partial y} = 0, \qquad \frac{\partial v}{\partial x} = 0, \qquad \frac{\partial v}{\partial y} = -1$$

and although the second of the Cauchy-Riemann equations is satisfied everywhere, the first is nowhere satisfied. Hence there is no point in the z-plane where dw/dz exists, which, of course, confirms our earlier investigation of the function.

Example 2

For $w = z\bar{z} = x^2 + y^2$, we have $u = x^2 + y^2$ and $v = 0$. In this case, the partial derivatives

$$\frac{\partial u}{\partial x} = 2x, \qquad \frac{\partial u}{\partial y} = 2y, \qquad \frac{\partial v}{\partial x} = 0, \qquad \frac{\partial v}{\partial y} = 0$$

are continuous everywhere. However, the Cauchy-Riemann equations, which in this case are, respectively,

$$2x = 0 \quad \text{and} \quad 2y = 0$$

are satisfied only at the origin. Hence $z = 0$ is the only point at which dw/dz exists, and thus $w = z\bar{z}$ is nowhere analytic.

Example 3

For $w = z^2 = (x^2 - y^2) + 2ixy$, we have

$$\frac{\partial u}{\partial x} = 2x, \qquad \frac{\partial u}{\partial y} = -2y, \qquad \frac{\partial v}{\partial x} = 2y, \qquad \frac{\partial v}{\partial y} = 2x$$

and the Cauchy-Riemann equations are identically satisfied. Moreover, the partial derivatives of u and v are continuous everywhere. Hence the derivative dw/dz exists at all points of the z-plane, and its value, either from (3) or from (4), is

$$\frac{dw}{dz} = 2x + 2iy = 2z$$

This, of course, is exactly what formal differentiation according to the power rule would give.

Analytic functions have a great many important properties, many of which we shall investigate in later paragraphs. At this point we note only the following.

Property 1.   Both the real part and the imaginary part of any analytic function satisfy Laplace's equation

$$\frac{\partial^2 \phi}{\partial x^2} + \frac{\partial^2 \phi}{\partial y^2} = 0$$

To prove that u is a solution of Laplace's equation, differentiate the first of the Cauchy-Riemann equations (which of course u and v must satisfy if $u + iv$ is analytic) with respect to x and the second with respect to y and add the results:

$$\frac{\partial^2 u}{\partial x^2} = \frac{\partial^2 v}{\partial x\, \partial y}$$

$$\frac{\partial^2 u}{\partial y^2} = -\frac{\partial^2 v}{\partial y\, \partial x}$$

$$\overline{\frac{\partial^2 u}{\partial x^2} + \frac{\partial^2 u}{\partial y^2} = 0}$$

The existence of the second partial derivatives and their continuity, which makes the order of differentiation immaterial, must here be assumed. Later we shall show that an analytic function possesses not only a first derivative, but derivatives of *all* orders, which implies the existence and continuity of all the partial derivatives of u and v.   In exactly the same manner it can be shown that $\dfrac{\partial^2 v}{\partial x^2} + \dfrac{\partial^2 v}{\partial y^2} = 0$.

A function which possesses continuous second partial derivatives and satisfies Laplace's equation is usually called a **harmonic function.**   Two harmonic functions, u and v, so related that $u + iv$ is an analytic function are called **conjugate harmonic functions.**   This use of the word *conjugate* must not be confused with its use in describing $\bar{z}$, the complex number conjugate to z.

Property 2.   If $w = u + iv$ is an analytic function, the curves of the family $u(x,y) = c$ are the orthogonal trajectories of the curves of the family $v(x,y) = k$, and vice versa.

To prove this we compute the slope of the general curve of each family by implicit differentiation, getting, respectively,

$$\frac{dy}{dx} = -\frac{\partial u/\partial x}{\partial u/\partial y} \qquad \text{and} \qquad \frac{dy}{dx} = -\frac{\partial v/\partial x}{\partial v/\partial y}$$

Since w is an analytic function, by hypothesis, it follows that u and v satisfy the Cauchy-Riemann equations.   Hence the slope of the general curve of the family $v(x,y) = k$ can be written

$$\frac{dy}{dx} = \frac{\partial u/\partial y}{\partial u/\partial x}$$

which, at any common point, is just the negative reciprocal of the slope of the general curve of the family $u(x,y) = c$, as computed above.

Property 3. If in any analytic function, $w = u + iv$, the variables x and y are replaced by their equivalents in terms of z and $\bar{z}$, namely,

$$x = \frac{z + \bar{z}}{2} \qquad y = \frac{z - \bar{z}}{2i}$$

w will appear as a function of z alone.

To prove this, let us regard w, by virtue of the above substitutions, as a function of the new independent variables z and $\bar{z}$. To show that w depends only on z and does not involve $\bar{z}$, it is sufficient to compute $\dfrac{\partial w}{\partial \bar{z}}$ and to verify that it is identically zero. Now

$$\frac{\partial w}{\partial \bar{z}} = \frac{\partial (u + iv)}{\partial \bar{z}} = \frac{\partial u}{\partial \bar{z}} + i \frac{\partial v}{\partial \bar{z}}$$

$$= \left[\frac{\partial u}{\partial x} \frac{\partial x}{\partial \bar{z}} + \frac{\partial u}{\partial y} \frac{\partial y}{\partial \bar{z}} \right] + i \left[\frac{\partial v}{\partial x} \frac{\partial x}{\partial \bar{z}} + \frac{\partial v}{\partial y} \frac{\partial y}{\partial \bar{z}} \right]$$

From the substitution equations we have

$$\frac{\partial x}{\partial \bar{z}} = \frac{1}{2} \qquad \frac{\partial y}{\partial \bar{z}} = \frac{-1}{2i} = \frac{i}{2}$$

Hence we can write

$$\frac{\partial w}{\partial \bar{z}} = \left[\frac{1}{2} \frac{\partial u}{\partial x} + \frac{i}{2} \frac{\partial u}{\partial y} \right] + i \left[\frac{1}{2} \frac{\partial v}{\partial x} + \frac{i}{2} \frac{\partial v}{\partial y} \right]$$

$$= \frac{1}{2} \left[\frac{\partial u}{\partial x} - \frac{\partial v}{\partial y} \right] + \frac{i}{2} \left[\frac{\partial u}{\partial y} + \frac{\partial v}{\partial x} \right]$$

Since w, by hypothesis, is an analytic function, u and v satisfy the Cauchy-Riemann equations, and thus each of the bracketed quantities in the last expression vanishes. Thus $\dfrac{\partial w}{\partial \bar{z}} \equiv 0$, and thus w is independent of $\bar{z}$, that is, is a function of x and y only through the combination $z = x + iy$.

EXERCISES

1. At what points does $\dfrac{z - 2}{(z + 1)(z^2 + 1)}$ fail to be analytic?

2. Verify by direct substitution that $\Re(z^3)$ and $\mathcal{I}(z^3)$ satisfy Laplace's equation.

3. Where are the Cauchy-Riemann equations satisfied for the function

$$f(z) = xy^2 + iyx^2?$$

Where does $f'(z)$ exist? Where is $f(z)$ analytic?

4. Show that the various values approached by the difference quotient of $f(z) = \bar{z}$ as $\Delta z \to 0$ along the lines $y = kx$, all lie on a circle.

5. If $f(z)$ is an analytic function of z, show that

$$\left[\frac{\partial^2}{\partial x^2} + \frac{\partial^2}{\partial y^2} \right] |f(z)|^2 = 4|f'(z)|^2$$

9.7 The Elementary Functions of z.   The exponential function e^z is of fundamental importance, not only for its own sake, but also as a basis for defining all the other elementary functions.   In its definition we seek to preserve as many of the characteristic properties of the real exponential function e^x as possible.   Specifically, we desire that

a. e^z shall be single-valued and analytic.

b. $\dfrac{de^z}{dz} = e^z$.

c. e^z shall reduce to e^x when $\mathscr{I}(z) = 0$.

If we let

(1) $e^z = u + iv$

and recall that the derivative of an analytic function can be written

$$f'(z) = \frac{\partial u}{\partial x} + i\, \frac{\partial v}{\partial x}$$

then to satisfy (*b*) we must have

$$\frac{\partial u}{\partial x} + i\, \frac{\partial v}{\partial x} = u + iv$$

Hence, equating real and imaginary parts,

(2) $\dfrac{\partial u}{\partial x} = u$

(3) $\dfrac{\partial v}{\partial x} = v$

Equation (2) will be satisfied if we write

(4) $u = e^x \phi(y)$

where $\phi(y)$ is any function of y.   Since e^z is to be analytic, u and v must satisfy the Cauchy-Riemann equations; hence (3) can be written

(5) $-\dfrac{\partial u}{\partial y} = v$

Differentiating this with respect to y, we obtain

$$\frac{\partial^2 u}{\partial y^2} = -\frac{\partial v}{\partial y}$$

or, replacing $\dfrac{\partial v}{\partial y}$ by $\dfrac{\partial u}{\partial x}$ according to the first of the Cauchy-Riemann equations,

$$\frac{\partial^2 u}{\partial y^2} = -\frac{\partial u}{\partial x}$$

Finally, using (2), this becomes

$$\frac{\partial^2 u}{\partial y^2} = -u$$

which, on substituting $u = e^x \phi(y)$ from (4), reduces to

$$e^x \phi''(y) = -e^x \phi(y) \qquad \text{or} \qquad \phi''(y) = -\phi(y)$$

This is a simple linear differential equation whose solution can be written down at once:

$$\phi(y) = A \cos y + B \sin y$$

Hence from (4)

$$u = e^x \phi(y) = e^x(A \cos y + B \sin y)$$

and from (5)

$$v = -\frac{\partial u}{\partial y} = -e^x(-A \sin y + B \cos y)$$

Therefore

$$e^z = u + iv = e^x[(A \cos y + B \sin y) + ie^x(A \sin y - B \cos y)]$$

If this is to reduce to e^x when $y = 0$, according to requirement (c), we must have

$$e^x = e^x[A - iB]$$

which will be true if and only if

$$A = 1 \qquad \text{and} \qquad B = 0$$

Thus we have been led inevitably to the definition

(6) $$e^z = e^{x+iy} = e^x(\cos y + i \sin y)$$

It is important to note that the right-hand side of (6) is in standard polar form.   Hence

$$\operatorname{mod} e^z = |e^z| = e^x$$
$$\arg e^z = y$$

The possibility of writing any complex number in exponential form is now apparent, for applying (6), with $x = 0$ and $y = \theta$, we have

(7) $$\cos \theta + i \sin \theta = e^{i\theta}$$

and thus

(8) $$r(\cos \theta + i \sin \theta) = re^{i\theta}$$

The fact that the angle or argument of a complex number is actually an exponent explains why the angles of complex numbers are added when the numbers are multiplied, and subtracted when the numbers are divided, as we found to be the case in Sec. 9.3.

From the relation

$$e^{i\theta} = \cos \theta + i \sin \theta$$

and its obvious companion

$$e^{-i\theta} = \cos (-\theta) + i \sin (-\theta) = \cos \theta - i \sin \theta$$

we obtain, by addition and subtraction, the familiar formulas

$$\cos \theta = \frac{e^{i\theta} + e^{-i\theta}}{2}$$

$$\sin \theta = \frac{e^{i\theta} - e^{-i\theta}}{2i}$$

$2 \sin\theta = -je^{i\theta} + je^{-i\theta}$

On the basis of these equations, we extend the definitions of the sine and cosine into the complex domain by the formulas

(9)
$$\cos z = \frac{e^{iz} + e^{-iz}}{2}$$

(10)
$$\sin z = \frac{e^{iz} - e^{-iz}}{2i}$$

From these definitions it is easy to establish the validity of such familiar formulas as

$$\cos^2 z + \sin^2 z = 1$$

$$\cos (z_1 \pm z_2) = \cos z_1 \cos z_2 \mp \sin z_1 \sin z_2$$

$$\sin (z_1 \pm z_2) = \sin z_1 \cos z_2 \pm \cos z_1 \sin z_2$$

$$\frac{d(\cos z)}{dz} = - \sin z$$

$$\frac{d(\sin z)}{dz} = \cos z$$

If we expand the exponentials in (9), we find

$$\cos z = \frac{e^{i(x+iy)} + e^{-i(x+iy)}}{2}$$

$$= \frac{e^{-y}e^{ix} + e^{y}e^{-ix}}{2}$$

$$= \frac{e^{-y}(\cos x + i \sin x) + e^{y}(\cos x - i \sin x)}{2}$$

$$= \cos x \left(\frac{e^{y} + e^{-y}}{2}\right) - i \sin x \left(\frac{e^{y} - e^{-y}}{2}\right)$$

or, using the usual definitions of the hyperbolic functions of real variables,

$$(11) \qquad\qquad \cos z = \cos x \cosh y - i \sin x \sinh y$$

Similarly it is easy to show that

$$(12) \qquad\qquad \sin z = \sin x \cosh y + i \cos x \sinh y$$

In particular, taking $x = 0$ in (11) and (12), we obtain

$$(13) \qquad\qquad\qquad \cos iy = \cosh y$$
$$(14) \qquad\qquad\qquad \sin iy = i \sinh y$$

The remaining trigonometric functions of z are defined in terms of $\cos z$ and $\sin z$ by means of the identities

$$\tan z = \frac{\sin z}{\cos z}$$

$$\cot z = \frac{\cos z}{\sin z}$$

$$\sec z = \frac{1}{\cos z}$$

$$\csc z = \frac{1}{\sin z}$$

Example 1

What is $\cos (1 + 2i)$?
By direct use of (11) we have

$$\begin{aligned}
\cos (1 + 2i) &= \cos 1 \cosh 2 - i \sin 1 \sinh 2 \\
&= (0.54030)(3.7622) - i(0.84147)(3.6269) \\
&= 2.033 - i\, 3.052
\end{aligned}$$

Example 2

Prove that the only values of z for which $\sin z = 0$, are the familiar real values $z = 0,\ \pm\pi,\ \pm 2\pi,\ \ldots$.
Since

$$\sin z = \sin x \cosh y + i \cos x \sinh y$$

it is necessary, if $\sin z$ is to vanish, that simultaneously

$$\sin x \cosh y = 0$$
$$\cos x \sinh y = 0$$

Since y is a real number it follows from familiar properties of the hyperbolic cosine that $\cosh y \geqq 1$. Hence the first of these equations can hold only if $\sin x = 0$; that is, if

$$x = 0,\ \pm\pi,\ \pm 2\pi,\ \ldots$$

But for these values of x, $\cos x$, being either 1 or -1, can never vanish. For the second equation to hold, it is therefore necessary that $\sinh y = 0$. Since y is real, the familiar properties of the hyperbolic sine can be invoked, leading to the conclusion that

$$y = 0$$

Hence the only values of z for which $\sin z = 0$ are of the form

$$z = n\pi + 0i = n\pi \qquad n = 0, \pm 1, \pm 2, \ldots$$

The hyperbolic functions of z we define simply by extending the familiar definitions into the complex number field:

$$(15) \qquad \cosh z = \frac{e^z + e^{-z}}{2}$$

$$(16) \qquad \sinh z = \frac{e^z - e^{-z}}{2}$$

By expanding the exponentials and regrouping, as we did in deriving (11), we obtain without difficulty the formulas

$$(17) \qquad \cosh z = \cosh x \cos y + i \sinh x \sin y$$
$$(18) \qquad \sinh z = \sinh x \cos y + i \cosh x \sin y$$

In particular, by setting $x = 0$, we find

$$(19) \qquad \cosh iy = \cos y$$
$$(20) \qquad \sinh iy = i \sin y$$

The remaining hyperbolic functions are defined from $\cosh z$ and $\sinh z$ via the usual identities.

The logarithm of z we define implicitly as the function

$$w = \log z$$

which satisfies the equation

$$(21) \qquad e^w = z$$

If we let

$$w = u + iv \qquad \text{and} \qquad z = re^{i\theta}$$

Eq. (21) becomes

$$e^{u+iv} = e^u e^{iv} = re^{i\theta}$$

Hence

$$e^u = r \qquad \text{or} \qquad u = \log r$$

and

$$v = \theta$$

Thus

$$w = u + iv = \log r + i\theta$$
$$(22) \qquad \qquad = \log |z| + i \arg z$$

If we let θ_1 be the **principal argument** of z, that is, the particular argument of z which lies in the interval $0 \leq \theta < 2\pi$, Eq. (22) can be written

$$(22.1) \qquad \log z = \log |z| + i(\theta_1 + 2n\pi) \qquad n = 0, \pm 1, \ldots$$

which shows that the logarithmic function is infinitely many-valued. For any particular value of n, a unique branch of the function is determined, and the logarithm becomes effectively single-valued. If $n = 0$, the resulting branch of $\log z$ is called the **principal value.** Any particular branch of the logarithmic function is analytic, for we have from the definitive relation, $z = e^w$, by differentiation,

$$\frac{dz}{dw} = e^w = z$$

or

$$\frac{dw}{dz} = \frac{d(\log z)}{dz} = \frac{1}{z}$$

For a particular value of n, the derivative of $\log z$ thus exists for all $z \neq 0$.

By means of (22.1) the familiar laws of logarithms which hold for real variables can be established for complex variables as well. For example, to show that

$$\log \left(\frac{z_1}{z_2} \right) = \log z_1 - \log z_2$$

let

$$z_1 = r_1 e^{i\theta_1} \qquad \text{and} \qquad z_2 = r_2 e^{i\theta_2}$$

where θ_1 and θ_2 are the principal arguments of z_1 and z_2, respectively. Then

$$
\begin{aligned}
\log z_1 - \log z_2 &= [\log r_1 + i(\theta_1 + 2n_1\pi)] - [\log r_2 + i(\theta_2 + 2n_2\pi)] \\
&= [\log r_1 - \log r_2] + i[(\theta_1 - \theta_2) + 2(n_1 - n_2)\pi] \\
&= \log \left(\frac{r_1}{r_2} \right) + i[(\theta_1 - \theta_2) + 2n_3\pi] \\
&= \log \left| \frac{z_1}{z_2} \right| + i \arg \left(\frac{z_1}{z_2} \right) \\
&= \log \left(\frac{z_1}{z_2} \right)
\end{aligned}
$$

General powers of z are defined by the formula

$$(23) \qquad z^a = e^{a \log z}$$

which generalizes a familiar result for real variables which we frequently found useful in solving linear first-order differential equations. Since log z is infinitely many-valued, so too is z^a, in general. For

$$z^a = e^{a \log z} = e^{a[\log |z| + i(\theta_1 + 2n\pi)]}$$
$$= e^{a \log |z|} e^{ia\theta_1} e^{i2na\pi}$$

The last factor in this product clearly involves infinitely many different values unless a is a rational number, say p/q, in which case, as we saw in our discussion of de Moivre's theorem in Sec. 9.3, there are only q distinct values.

Example 3

What is the principal value of $(1 + i)^{(2-i)}$?
By definition

$$(1 + i)^{(2-i)} = e^{(2-i) \log (1+i)}$$
$$= e^{(2-i)[\log \sqrt{2} + i(\pi/4 + 2n\pi)]}$$

The principal value of this, obtained by taking $n = 0$, is

$$e^{(2-i)(\log \sqrt{2} + i\pi/4)} = e^{(2 \log \sqrt{2} + \pi/4) + i(-\log \sqrt{2} + \pi/2)}$$
$$= e^{(\log 2 + \pi/4)} \left[\cos \left(\frac{\pi}{2} - \log \sqrt{2} \right) + i \sin \left(\frac{\pi}{2} - \log \sqrt{2} \right) \right]$$
$$= e^{(\log 2 + \pi/4)} [\sin (\log \sqrt{2}) + i \cos (\log \sqrt{2})]$$
$$= e^{1.4785} [\sin (0.3466) + i \cos (0.3466)]$$
$$= 1.490 + i4.126$$

The inverse trigonometric and hyperbolic functions we define implicitly. For instance,

$$w = \cos^{-1} z$$

we define as the value, or values, of w which satisfies the equation

$$z = \cos w = \frac{e^{iw} + e^{-iw}}{2}$$

From this by obvious steps we obtain successively

$$e^{2iw} - 2ze^{iw} + 1 = 0$$
$$e^{iw} = z \pm \sqrt{z^2 - 1}$$

and finally by taking logarithms and solving for w,

(24) $$w = \cos^{-1} z = -i \log (z \pm \sqrt{z^2 - 1})$$

Since the logarithm is infinitely many-valued, so too is $\cos^{-1} z$.
Similarly we may obtain the formulas

(25) $$\sin^{-1} z = -i \log (iz \pm \sqrt{1 - z^2})$$

(26) $$\tan^{-1} z = \frac{i}{2} \log \left(\frac{i + z}{i - z} \right)$$

$$(27) \qquad\qquad \cosh^{-1} z = \log (z \pm \sqrt{z^2 - 1})$$

$$(28) \qquad\qquad \sinh^{-1} z = \log (z \pm \sqrt{z^2 + 1})$$

$$(29) \qquad\qquad \tanh^{-1} z = \frac{1}{2} \log \left(\frac{1 + z}{1 - z} \right)$$

From these, after their principal values have been suitably defined, the usual differentiation formulas may be obtained without difficulty.

EXERCISES

Prove the following identities:

1. $\cos^2 z + \sin^2 z = 1$

2. $\cos (z_1 \pm z_2) = \cos z_1 \cos z_2 \mp \sin z_1 \sin z_2$

3. $\sin (z_1 \pm z_2) = \sin z_1 \cos z_2 \pm \cos z_1 \sin z_2$

4. $\dfrac{d(\cos z)}{dz} = -\sin z$ \qquad\qquad **5.** $\dfrac{d(\sin z)}{dz} = \cos z$

6 to 10. State and prove the formulas for the hyperbolic functions of z which correspond, respectively, to the formulas of Exercises 1 to 5.

11. Prove that the only zeros of $\cos z$ are $\pm \dfrac{\pi}{2}, \pm \dfrac{3\pi}{2}, \pm \dfrac{5\pi}{2}, \cdots$.

12. What is $|e^{if(x,y)}|$, where $f(x,y)$ is a real function of the real variables x and y?

Express each of the following quantities in the form $a + ib$, where a and b are decimal fractions:

13. $\sin (2 - i)$ \qquad\qquad **14.** $\cosh (1 + i)$ \qquad\qquad **15.** $\sinh (2 + 3i)$

16. Show by direct substitution that $\Re(\cos z)$ and $\mathscr{I}(\cos z)$ satisfy Laplace's equation.

17. Show that all the values of $(1 + i)^{(1-i)}$ have the same argument, and find its value.

18. What is the principal value of $\log (3 + 4i)$?

19. What is the principal value of $(1 - i)^{(2-3i)}$?

20. Prove that the arguments of the successive values of $(1 + 2i)^{(\frac{1}{4}-i)}$ differ by a constant amount.

21. Prove that $\overline{e^z} = e^{\bar{z}}$. What is the conjugate of $re^{i\theta}$?

22. Prove that $\overline{\cos z} = \cos \bar{z}$

23. Is $\overline{\sin z} = \sin \bar{z}$?

24. Find all solutions of the equation $\sin z = 3$.

25. Find all solutions of the equation $e^z = -2$.

FIG. 10.12   A FUNCTION OF A COMPLEX VARIABLE   310

$$\tanh z = \log \frac{1+z}{1-z} \qquad (29)$$

$$\sinh^{-1} z = \log (z + \sqrt{z^2 + 1}) \qquad (30)$$

$$\tanh^{-1} z = \frac{1}{2} \log \frac{1+z}{1-z} \qquad (31)$$

From these illustrations principal values have been suitably defined. The ...

EXERCISES

CHAPTER 10

INTEGRATION IN THE COMPLEX PLANE

10.1 Line Integration.   In much of our work with complex variables, and in vector analysis as well, a simple extension of the familiar process of integration known as line integration will be of fundamental importance.   Because the line integrals which occur in vector analysis are entirely real and because line integrals in the complex plane can easily be reduced to real integrals, we shall begin by developing the concept of a line integral in the real cartesian plane.

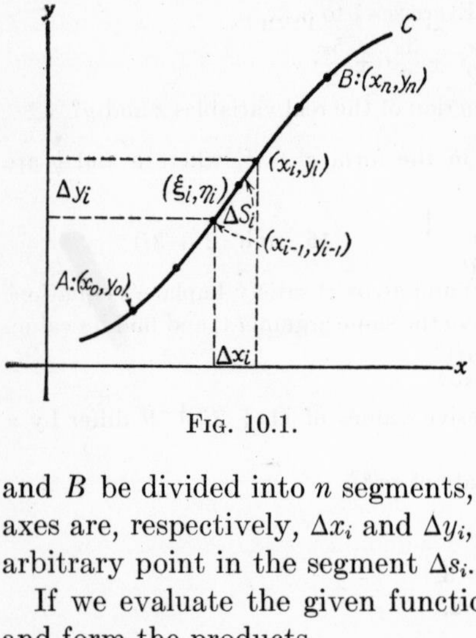

Fig. 10.1.

Let $F(x,y)$ be a real function of the real variables x and y, continuous in both x and y, and let C be a continuous curve of finite length joining the points A and B. $F(x,y)$ bears no relation to the equation of C, and is merely a function defined at every point in some region of the xy-plane containing the portion of the curve C under consideration.   Further, let the arc of C between A and B be divided into n segments, Δs_i, whose projections on the x and y axes are, respectively, Δx_i and Δy_i, and let (ξ_i, η_i) be the coordinates of an arbitrary point in the segment Δs_i.

If we evaluate the given function $F(x,y)$ at each of the points (ξ_i, η_i) and form the products

$$F(\xi_i, \eta_i)\Delta s_i, \qquad F(\xi_i, \eta_i)\Delta x_i, \qquad F(\xi_i, \eta_i)\Delta y_i$$

we have, on summing over all the subdivisions of the arc AB, the three sums

$$\sum_{i=1}^{n} F(\xi_i, \eta_i)\Delta s_i, \qquad \sum_{i=1}^{n} F(\xi_i, \eta_i)\Delta x_i, \qquad \sum_{i=1}^{n} F(\xi_i, \eta_i)\Delta y_i$$

The limits of these sums as n approaches infinity in such a way that every Δs_i approaches zero are known as **line integrals,** and are written,

320

respectively,

$$\int_C F(x,y)ds, \qquad \int_C F(x,y)dx, \qquad \int_C F(x,y)dy$$

From these definitions it follows that such familiar properties of ordinary definite integrals as

$$\int_A^B c\phi\, dt = c \int_A^B \phi\, dt$$

$$\int_A^B (\phi_1 + \phi_2)dt = \int_A^B \phi_1\, dt + \int_A^B \phi_2\, dt$$

$$\int_A^B \phi\, dt = - \int_B^A \phi\, dt$$

$$\int_A^B \phi\, dt = \int_A^C \phi\, dt + \int_C^B \phi\, dt$$

are equally valid for line integrals, provided that the curve joining A and B remains the same.

Much of the initial strangeness of line integrals will disappear if we observe that the ordinary definite integrals of elementary calculus are just line integrals in which the curve C is the x-axis, and the integrand is a function of x alone. Moreover, the evaluation of line integrals can be reduced to the evaluation of ordinary definite integrals, as the following example shows.

Example 1

What is the value of $\int_{0,0}^{1,\frac{1}{2}} xy\, ds$ along each of the paths shown in Fig. 10.2?

Along the curved path OP we can write

$$ds = \sqrt{1 + (y')^2}\, dx = \sqrt{1 + x^2}\, dx$$

This fixes x as the variable in terms of which the integration is actually to be performed, and gives the integral

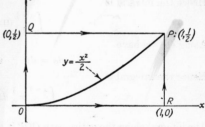

FIG. 10.2.

$$\int_{x=0}^{x=1} (xy)\, (\sqrt{1 + x^2}\, dx)$$

Before this can be evaluated, it is necessary that y be expressed in terms of x. To do this, we recall from the definition of a line integral that the integrand is always to be evaluated *along the path*, which means in this case that for each value of x, y is equal to $x^2/2$. This gives the definite integral

$$\int_0^1 \frac{x^3}{2} \sqrt{1 + x^2}\, dx$$

An easy integration by parts with $u = x^2/2$ and $dv = x\,\sqrt{1 + x^2}\, dx$ yields the result

$$\left[\frac{x^2}{2}\frac{(1 + x^2)^{\frac{3}{2}}}{3} - \frac{(1 + x^2)^{\frac{5}{2}}}{15}\right]_0^1 = \frac{1 + \sqrt{2}}{15}$$

$$\int x^4 dx = \frac{x^5}{5}$$

$$d(1+x^2) = 2x\,dx$$

$$v = \frac{1}{\frac{3}{2}}(1+x^2)^{\frac{3}{2}}$$

$$du = 2x\,dx$$

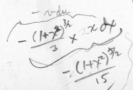

On the other hand, we could have written

$$ds = \sqrt{1 + (x')^2}\, dy = \sqrt{1 + \left(\frac{1}{\sqrt{2y}}\right)^2}\, dy = \sqrt{\frac{1 + 2y}{2y}}\, dy$$

which establishes y as the variable of integration and yields the integral

$$\int_{y=0}^{y=\frac{1}{2}} (xy) \left(\sqrt{\frac{1 + 2y}{2y}}\, dy\right)$$

This time we must replace x by its equivalent in terms of y along the path, namely, $x = \sqrt{2y}$, which gives the definite integral

$$\int_0^{\frac{1}{2}} \sqrt{2y}\, y\, \sqrt{\frac{1 + 2y}{2y}}\, dy = \int_0^{\frac{1}{2}} y\, \sqrt{1 + 2y}\, dy$$

In this case the substitution $t = 1 + 2y$ leads easily to the result

$$\frac{1}{4}\left(\frac{2t^{\frac{5}{2}}}{5} - \frac{2t^{\frac{3}{2}}}{3}\right) \Bigg|_{t=1}^{t=2} = \frac{1 + \sqrt{2}}{15}$$

as before.

For the rectilinear path OQP, it is necessary to perform the integration in two stages.   Along OQ we have

$$ds = dy \qquad \text{and} \qquad x = 0$$

Hence the integral is

$$\int_{y=0}^{y=\frac{1}{2}} (0)(y)dy = 0$$

Along QP we have

$$ds = dx \qquad \text{and} \qquad y = \frac{1}{2}$$

Hence the integral is

$$\int_{x=0}^{x=1} x\, \frac{1}{2}\, dx = \frac{x^2}{4}\Bigg|_0^1 = \frac{1}{4}$$

The integral along the entire path OQP is therefore $0 + \frac{1}{4} = \frac{1}{4}$.

For the rectilinear path ORP, it is also necessary to perform the integration in two stages.   Along OR, we have $y = 0$, and thus the integral vanishes identically.   Along RP, $ds = dy$ and $x = 1$.   Hence the integral is

$$\int_{y=0}^{y=\frac{1}{2}} (1)(y)dy = \frac{y^2}{2}\Bigg|_0^{\frac{1}{2}} = \frac{1}{8}$$

This example not only illustrates the computational details of line integration but also shows that in general a line integral depends not only on the end points of the integration but also upon the particular path which joins them.

It is possible, as in the case of ordinary integration, to interpret a line integral as an area.   For if we think of the integrand function $F(x,y)$ as defining a surface over the xy-plane, then the vertical cylindrical surface standing on the arc AB as base, or directrix, will cut the surface $z = F(x,y)$ in some curve such as DC in Fig. 10.3.   This curve is clearly the upper boundary of the portion, $ABCD$, of the cylindrical surface which lies above the xy-plane, below the surface $z = F(x,y)$, and between the generators AD and BC. Moreover, the product $F(\xi_i,\eta_i)\Delta s_i$ is approximately the area of the vertical strip of this portion of the surface which stands above the infinitesimal base, Δs_i. Hence the sum

$$\sum_{i=1}^{n} F(\xi_i,\eta_i)\Delta s_i$$

is approximately equal to the curved area $ABCD$, and in the limit the integral

$$\int_C F(x,y)ds$$

gives this area exactly.

In a similar fashion the product $F(\xi_i,\eta_i)\Delta x_i$ is approximately the area of the projection on the xz-plane of the vertical strip standing on Δs_i; the sum

$$\sum_{i=1}^{n} F(\xi_i,\eta_i)\Delta x_i$$

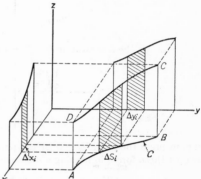

Fig. 10.3. Plot showing the interpretation of a line integral as an area.

represents approximately the area of the projection on the xz-plane of the entire curved area $ABCD$; and in the limit the integral

$$\int_C F(x,y)dx$$

gives the projected area exactly. In the same way

$$\int_C F(x,y)dy$$

represents the area of the projection of $ABCD$ on the yz-plane.

Although this geometrical interpretation of line integrals as areas is vivid and easily grasped, it is dangerous too, for it obscures the fact that more often than not in physical applications the function $F(x,y)$ has its existence in the xy-plane itself, and not in some associated space of three dimensions.

Example 2

If a particle in the xy-plane is attracted toward the origin by a force which is proportional to the distance from the origin, how much work is done when the particle is moved from the point $(0,1)$ to the point $(1,2)$ along the path $y = x^2 + 1$ (Fig. 10.4), assuming a coefficient of friction of μ between the particle and the path?

In moving the particle an infinitesimal distance, Δs, along the path, work must be done against two forces, namely, the tangential component of the central force

$$F_t = F \cos \alpha = kd \cos \alpha$$

and the frictional force

$$F_f = \mu F_n = \mu F \sin \alpha = \mu kd \sin \alpha$$

arising from the component of the central force which is normal to the path and which

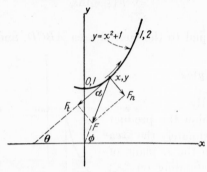

FIG. 10.4.

acts to press the particle against the path.   The infinitesimal amount of work done against these forces in moving a distance Δs is approximately

$$\Delta W = F_t \, \Delta s + F_f \, \Delta s = (kd \cos \alpha + \mu kd \sin \alpha)\Delta s$$

Hence, summing and passing to the limit, we have

$$W = k \int_{0,1}^{1,2} (d \cos \alpha + \mu d \sin \alpha)ds$$

Now from the exterior angle theorem of plane geometry, $\alpha = \phi - \theta$.   Hence

$$W = k \int_{0,1}^{1,2} d \cos (\phi - \theta)ds + \mu k \int_{0,1}^{1,2} d \sin (\phi - \theta)ds$$

$$= k \int_{0,1}^{1,2} d(\cos \phi \cos \theta + \sin \phi \sin \theta)ds + \mu k \int_{0,1}^{1,2} d(\sin \phi \cos \theta - \cos \phi \sin \theta)ds$$

But

$$d \cos \phi = x, \qquad d \sin \phi = y$$

and

$$\cos \theta \, ds = dx, \qquad \sin \theta \, ds = dy$$

Substituting these into the last expression for W, we have

$$W = k \int_{0,1}^{1,2} (x \, dx + y \, dy) + \mu k \int_{0,1}^{1,2} (y \, dx - x \, dy)$$

The first of these integrals can be written very simply as

$$\frac{k}{2} \int_{0,1}^{1,2} d(x^2 + y^2)$$

which, *independently of the path*, is just

$$\frac{k}{2}(x^2 + y^2)\Big|_{0,1}^{1,2} = 2k$$

The second integral is not an exact differential, and thus, as usual, due account must be taken of the path. Now along the path,

$$y = x^2 + 1 \qquad \text{and} \qquad x = \sqrt{y - 1}$$

Hence

$$\mu k \int_{0,1}^{1,2} (y\,dx - x\,dy) = \mu k \int_0^1 (x^2 + 1)dx - \mu k \int_1^2 \sqrt{y - 1}\,dy$$

$$= \mu k \left(\frac{x^3}{3} + x\right)\Big|_0^1 - \mu k \frac{2}{3}(y - 1)^{\frac{3}{2}}\Big|_1^2$$

$$= \frac{2\mu k}{3}$$

The total amount of work done in the course of the motion is therefore

$$2k + \frac{2\mu k}{3}$$

The first term represents recoverable work stored as potential energy; the second term represents irrecoverable work dissipated as heat through friction.

EXERCISES

1. Evaluate $\int_{0,2}^{4,0} (x^2 + y^2)dx$ along the path $y = \sqrt{4 - x}$.   *Ans.* $\frac{88}{3}$

2. Evaluate $\int x^2 y\,ds$ completely around the square whose vertices are $(0,0)$, $(1,0)$, $(1,1)$, $(0,1)$. Is $\int_{a,b}^{a,b} f(x,y)ds$ always zero?

3. Evaluate $\int_{0,0}^{1,1} x\,ds$ along the paths $y = x$, $y = x^{\frac{3}{2}}$, and $y = x^2$.

4. Evaluate $\int_{-1,0}^{1,0} y(1 + x)dy$ along the x-axis, and along the parabola $y = 1 - x^2$.

5. Evaluate $\int x^2 y^2\,ds$ around the circle $x^2 + y^2 = 1$. (Hint: Use polar coordinates.)

Ans. $\frac{\pi}{4}$

6. Evaluate $\int_{0,1}^{2,3} (2xy - 1)dx + (x^2 + 1)dy$ along the paths $y = x + 1$ and $y = \frac{x^2}{2} + 1$.

7. Evaluate $\int_{1,\frac{1}{4}}^{2,1-\log\sqrt{2}} (x + y)ds$ along the path $y = \frac{x^2}{4} - \frac{\log x}{2}$.

8. Along what curve of the family $y = kx(1 - x)$ does the integral $\int_{0,0}^{1,0} y(x - y)dx$ have the largest value?

9. If a particle is attracted toward the origin by a force proportional to the nth power of the distance from the origin, show that the work done against this force in moving the particle from the point (x_0, y_0) to the point (x_1, y_1) is independent of the path, and find its amount.

10. A particle is attracted toward the origin by a force proportional to the cube of the distance from the origin. How much work is done in moving the particle from the origin to the point $(1,1)$ if motion takes place (a) along the path $y = x$, (b) along the path $y = x^2$, and (c) along the x-axis to $(1,0)$ and then vertically to $(1,1)$ and if the coefficient of friction between the particle and the path is μ?

10.2 Green's Lemma. Many important results stem from the relation between a line integral around a closed curve and the double integral of an associated function taken over the area bounded by the curve. Specifically we have the following theorem.

Theorem 1. If $P(x,y)$, $Q(x,y)$, and the partial derivatives $\dfrac{\partial P}{\partial y}$ and $\dfrac{\partial Q}{\partial x}$ are continuous single-valued functions over the closed region R bounded by the curve C, then

$$\int_C (P\,dx + Q\,dy) = \int\int_R \left(\frac{\partial Q}{\partial x} - \frac{\partial P}{\partial y}\right) dx\,dy$$

This is ordinarily known as **Green's theorem in two dimensions** or **Green's lemma.***

To prove this, let us imagine first that C has the property that it is intersected at most twice by any vertical or horizontal line, and let us draw the horizontal and vertical lines which circumscribe C. The arcs

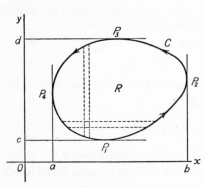

FIG. 10.5.

$P_4P_1P_2$ and $P_4P_3P_2$, which are single-valued functions of x, we shall call $f_1(x)$ and $f_2(x)$, respectively. The arcs $P_1P_4P_3$ and $P_1P_2P_3$, which are single-valued functions of y, we shall call $g_1(y)$ and $g_2(y)$, respectively.

Now consider

$$I_1 = \int\int_R \frac{\partial Q}{\partial x} dx\,dy$$

To cover the region R, it is necessary to integrate with respect to x from the arc $P_1P_4P_3$ to the arc $P_1P_2P_3$, and then to integrate with respect to y from c to d. Hence

$$I_1 = \int_c^d \int_{g_1(y)}^{g_2(y)} \frac{\partial Q}{\partial x} dx\,dy$$

The inner integration can easily be performed, and we find

$$I_1 = \int_c^d Q(x,y) \Big|_{g_1(y)}^{g_2(y)} dy$$
$$= \int_c^d Q[g_2(y),y]dy - \int_c^d Q[g_1(y),y]dy$$
$$= \int_c^d Q[g_2(y),y]dy + \int_d^c Q[g_1(y),y]dy$$

* After the English mathematical physicist George Green (1793–1841).

Now the first of these integrals is precisely the line integral

$$\int_c^d Q(x,y)dy$$

taken along the path $x = g_2(y)$, from P_1 to P_3, and the second is just the same line integral taken along the path $x = g_1(y)$ *in the direction from P_3, through P_4, to P_1.* Together, then, they constitute the line integral of $Q(x,y)$ around the entire closed curve C, or

$$(1) \qquad \int\int_R \frac{\partial Q}{\partial x}\, dx\, dy = \int_C Q(x,y)dy$$

Similarly, if we consider

$$I_2 = \int\int_R \frac{\partial P}{\partial y}\, dx\, dy = \int\int_R \frac{\partial P}{\partial y}\, dy\, dx$$

we can write more specifically

$$I_2 = \int_a^b \int_{f_1(x)}^{f_2(x)} \frac{\partial P}{\partial y}\, dy\, dx$$

Performing the inner integration, we have

$$
\begin{aligned}
I_2 &= \int_a^b P(x,y)\, \Big|_{f_1(x)}^{f_2(x)}\, dx \\
&= \int_a^b P[x,f_2(x)]dx - \int_a^b P[x,f_1(x)]dx \\
&= -\int_b^a P[x,f_2(x)]dx - \int_a^b P[x,f_1(x)]dx
\end{aligned}
$$

The first of these integrals is just the negative of the line integral of $P(x,y)$ along $y = f_2(x)$ in the direction from P_2 to P_4. The second is the negative of the integral of $P(x,y)$ along $y = f_1(x)$ from P_4 to P_2. Together they constitute the negative of the line integral of $P(x,y)$ entirely around C, *in the same direction in which we integrated in* (1):

$$(2) \qquad \int\int_R \frac{\partial P}{\partial y}\, dx\, dy = -\int_C P(x,y)dy$$

If we subtract (2) from (1) and combine the integrals on each side, we have the desired result

$$(3) \qquad \int_C P\, dx + Q\, dy = \int\int_R \left(\frac{\partial Q}{\partial x} - \frac{\partial P}{\partial y}\right) dx\, dy$$

The direction in which it is necessary to integrate around C, in order for Green's lemma to be correct as we have stated it, is characterized by the fact that an observer moving along C in this direction always has the region R *on his left*. This direction is called the **positive direction** of traversing C.

It is a simple matter now to extend Green's lemma to regions bounded by more complicated curves. Suppose first that the boundary curve does not satisfy the condition that every vertical and every horizontal line meets it in at most two points. In this case we merely subdivide R into regions whose boundaries are of this type, apply Green's lemma to each subregion, and add the results. Referring to Fig. 10.6 as an illustration, we see that the integrals over R_1 and R_2 add to give precisely the integral over $R \equiv R_1 + R_2$. The line integrals around R_1 and R_2 add to give the line integral around the entire boundary C, *plus* two line integrals

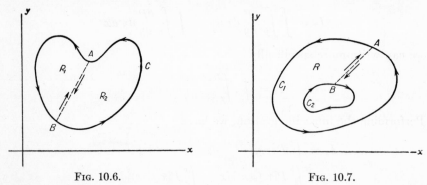

FIG. 10.6.   FIG. 10.7.

taken along AB in opposite directions, which of course just cancel each other.

The introduction of an auxiliary boundary segment also permits Green's lemma to be applied when R is a multiply connected region, bounded by not one but several simple closed curves. Consider, for instance, the region R shown in Fig. 10.7. After the crosscut AB has been drawn, R becomes simply connected and Green's lemma can surely be applied. The double integral over R is unaffected by the segment AB, while the line integral around the boundary consists of the integral around C_1 plus the integral around C_2, plus two integrals along AB, taken in opposite directions. These cancel each other, leaving

$$\int_{C_1} P\,dx + Q\,dy + \int_{C_2} P\,dx + Q\,dy = \int_{C_1+C_2} P\,dx + Q\,dy$$

$$= \int\int_R \left(\frac{\partial Q}{\partial x} - \frac{\partial P}{\partial y}\right) dx\,dy$$

We must keep in mind, of course, that the integrations around C_1 and C_2 are to be performed in the positive sense, that is, in such a way that an observer moving in the direction of integration would always have the area of R on his left.   This explains the superficially contradictory situation in which the curve C_1 is traversed in the counterclockwise direction while the inner curve C_2 is traversed in the clockwise direction.

Several important theorems follow immediately as corollaries of Green's lemma.   In each, of course, we retain the hypothesis that P, Q, $\dfrac{\partial P}{\partial y}$, $\dfrac{\partial Q}{\partial x}$ are continuous.

Theorem 2.   If R is a simply connected region and if

$$\frac{\partial Q}{\partial x} = \frac{\partial P}{\partial y}$$

at all points of R, then the line integral

$$\int_C P \, dx + Q \, dy$$

around every closed curve in R is zero.

To prove this, it is only necessary to apply Green's lemma to R_1, the subregion of R which is bounded by the particular closed curve, C_1, in question:

$$\int_{C_1} P \, dx + Q \, dy = \int\int_{R_1} \left(\frac{\partial Q}{\partial x} - \frac{\partial P}{\partial y} \right) dx \, dy$$

The condition that $\dfrac{\partial Q}{\partial x} = \dfrac{\partial P}{\partial y}$ at all points of R, and hence, perforce, at all points of R_1, makes the double integral, and therefore the line integral, vanish, as asserted.   If R is a multiply connected region, the theorem is not necessarily true, for in a multiply connected region, closed curves can be drawn which will enclose points not in the region.   At such points we have no knowledge of whether

$$\frac{\partial Q}{\partial x} = \frac{\partial P}{\partial y}$$

or not, and thus we cannot conclude that the integrand of

$$\int\int_{R_1} \left(\frac{\partial Q}{\partial x} - \frac{\partial P}{\partial y} \right) dx \, dy$$

vanishes identically, as required in our proof.

Theorem 3.   If R is a simply connected region and if

$$\frac{\partial Q}{\partial x} = \frac{\partial P}{\partial y}$$

at all points of R, then the line integral

$$\int_{x_1,y_1}^{x_2,y_2} P\,dx + Q\,dy$$

is independent of the path joining the points (x_1,y_1) and (x_2,y_2), or in other words is a function of the end points alone.

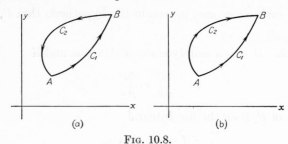

FIG. 10.8.

To prove this, we merely consider an arbitrary pair of paths in R which join $A \equiv (x_1,y_1)$ and $B \equiv (x_2,y_2)$ (Fig.10.8).   Together they form a simple closed curve in R, to which the last theorem may be applied, giving

$$\int_{C_1+C_2} P\,dx + Q\,dy = 0$$

or

$$\int_A^B P\,dx + Q\,dy + \int_B^A P\,dx + Q\,dy = 0$$
$$\text{(along } C_1)\qquad\qquad\qquad \text{(along } C_2)$$

Transposing the second integral, and absorbing the resulting minus sign by reversing the direction in which C_2 is traversed, we have

$$\int_A^B P\,dx + Q\,dy = \int_A^B P\,dx + Q\,dy$$
$$\text{(along } C_1)\qquad\qquad\qquad \text{(along } C_2)$$

Since C_1 and C_2 are any two curves joining P and Q, this establishes the theorem.

Theorem 4.   If R is a simply connected region and if

$$\frac{\partial Q}{\partial x} = \frac{\partial P}{\partial y}$$

at all points of R, so that the integral

$$I = \int_{a,b}^{x,y} P\,dx + Q\,dy$$

is independent of the path, and hence a function of x and y alone, then

$$\frac{\partial I}{\partial x} = P(x,y)\qquad \text{and}\qquad \frac{\partial I}{\partial y} = Q(x,y)$$

To prove the first assertion of the theorem, we have by definition

$$\frac{\partial I}{\partial x} = \lim_{\Delta x \to 0} \frac{\int_{a,b}^{x+\Delta x, y} (P\,dx + Q\,dy) - \int_{a,b}^{x,y} (P\,dx + Q\,dy)}{\Delta x}$$

where the paths of integration may be chosen arbitrarily since each integral is independent of the path which joins its end points. For convenience, let the path of the first integration consist of any curve

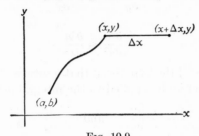

FIG. 10.9.

joining (a,b) and (x,y), plus the horizontal segment joining (x,y) and $(x + \Delta x, y)$ (Fig. 10.9).   Then

$$\frac{\partial I}{\partial x} = \lim_{\Delta x \to 0} \frac{\left(\int_{a,b}^{x,y} P\,dx + Q\,dy + \int_{x,y}^{x+\Delta x, y} P\,dx + Q\,dy \right) - \int_{a,b}^{x,y} P\,dx + Q\,dy}{\Delta x}$$

$$= \lim_{\Delta x \to 0} \frac{1}{\Delta x} \int_{x,y}^{x+\Delta x, y} P\,dx + Q\,dy$$

since the first and last integrals cancel.

Now $dy \equiv 0$ along the horizontal path which joins (x,y) and $(x + \Delta x, y)$, and thus the last expression becomes simply

$$\frac{\partial I}{\partial x} = \lim_{\Delta x \to 0} \frac{1}{\Delta x} \int_{x}^{x+\Delta x} P\,dx$$

Since $P(x,y)$ is assumed to be continuous, the law of the mean for integrals can be applied, and we have

$$\frac{\partial I}{\partial x} = \lim_{\Delta x \to 0} \frac{1}{\Delta x} [P(x + \theta \Delta x, y)\Delta x] \qquad 0 \leq \theta \leq 1$$

$$= P(x,y)$$

A similar discussion establishes the second half of the theorem.

Theorem 5.   If $u(x,y)$ is any solution of Laplace's equation, then the analytic function whose real part is u is $u + iv$, where

$$v = \int_{a,b}^{x,y} \left(-\frac{\partial u}{\partial y}\,dx + \frac{\partial u}{\partial x}\,dy \right)$$

To prove this, we note first that v is independent of the path between the fixed point (a,b) and the variable point (x,y), since the condition for independence, namely,

$$\frac{\partial P}{\partial y} = \frac{\partial Q}{\partial x}$$

is in this case

$$\frac{\partial\left(-\dfrac{\partial u}{\partial y}\right)}{\partial y} = \frac{\partial\left(\dfrac{\partial u}{\partial x}\right)}{\partial x}$$

or

$$-\frac{\partial^2 u}{\partial y^2} = \frac{\partial^2 u}{\partial x^2}$$

which is true because of the hypothesis that u satisfies Laplace's equation. Theorem 4 can therefore be applied to the integral defining v, giving

$$\frac{\partial v}{\partial x} = -\frac{\partial u}{\partial y} \quad \text{and} \quad \frac{\partial v}{\partial y} = \frac{\partial u}{\partial x}$$

These are precisely the Cauchy-Riemann equations, which, if these derivatives are continuous, are the conditions that $u + iv$ be an analytic function. But $\dfrac{\partial u}{\partial x}$ and $\dfrac{\partial u}{\partial y}$, and hence $\dfrac{\partial v}{\partial y}$ and $-\dfrac{\partial v}{\partial x}$, to which these are, respectively, equal, must be continuous, since the second partial derivatives $\dfrac{\partial^2 u}{\partial x^2}$ and $\dfrac{\partial^2 u}{\partial y^2}$ are known to exist. This completes the proof of the theorem.

Example 3

Verify Green's lemma for the integral $\int (x + y)dx + x^2y\, dy$ taken around the boundary shown in Fig. 10.10.

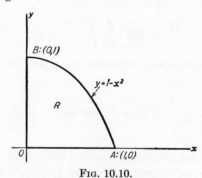

$B: (0,1)$

$y = 1 - x^2$

R

O

$A: (1,0)$

FIG. 10.10.

According to Green's lemma we should have

$$\int_C (x + y)dx + x^2y\, dy = \int\int_R (2xy - 1)dx\, dy$$

The line integral must be evaluated as three integrals, corresponding to the segments OA, AB, and BO.

$$OA: \int_0^1 (x + 0)dx + \int_0^0 (x^2)(0)dy = \tfrac{1}{2}$$

$$AB: \int_1^0 (x + 1 - x^2)dx + \int_0^1 (1 - y)y \, dy = -1$$

$$BO: \int_0^0 y \, dx + \int_1^0 (0)(y)dy = 0$$

The value of the entire line integral is therefore $-\tfrac{1}{2}$.

For the double integral, we have

$$\int \int_R (2xy - 1)dx \, dy = \int_0^1 \int_0^{\sqrt{1-y}} (2xy - 1)dx \, dy$$
$$= \int_0^1 (x^2y - x) \Big|_0^{\sqrt{1-y}} dy$$
$$= \int_0^1 [(1 - y)y - \sqrt{1 - y}]dy$$
$$= -\tfrac{1}{2}$$

Example 4

If $u = 2xy + 2x$, determine v so that $u + iv$ will be an analytic function.

The first step here is to verify that u is a solution of Laplace's equation, for if this is not the case it is impossible to proceed. Since $\dfrac{\partial^2 u}{\partial x^2}$ and $\dfrac{\partial^2 u}{\partial y^2}$ are both identically zero for the given expression, u, it is clear that u satisfies Laplace's equation, as required. By the last theorem we can now write

$$v = \int_{a,b}^{x,y} \left[-\frac{\partial u}{\partial y} dx + \frac{\partial u}{\partial x} dy \right] = \int_{a,b}^{x,y} [-2x \, dx + (2y + 2)dy]$$
$$= \left[-x^2 + (y^2 + 2y) \right]_{a,b}^{x,y}$$
$$= -x^2 + y^2 + 2y + k$$

where $k = a^2 - b^2 - 2b$. The required analytic function is therefore

$$u + iv = (2xy + 2x) + i(-x^2 + y^2 + 2y + k)$$

This can be further simplified to

$$-i(x + iy)^2 + 2(x + iy) + ik$$

or finally

$$-iz^2 + 2z + ik$$

EXERCISES

1. Verify Green's lemma for the integral $\int (x^2 + y)dx - xy^2 \, dy$, taken around the boundary of the square whose vertices are $(0,0)$, $(1,0)$, $(1,1)$, $(0,1)$.
2. Verify Green's lemma for the integral $\int (x - y)dx + (x + y)dy$ taken around the boundary of the area in the first quadrant between the curves $y = x^2$ and $y^2 = x$.
3. Verify Green's lemma for the integral $\int (x - 2y)dx + x \, dy$ taken around the unit circle, $x^2 + y^2 = 1$.

4. Use Green's lemma to evaluate $\int(2xy + y^2)dx + (x^2 + xy)dy$ taken around the boundary of the region cut off from the first quadrant by the curve $y^2 = 1 - x^3$.

5. If $u = x^3 - 3xy^2 + y + 1$, determine v so that $u + iv$ will be an analytic function.

10.3 Complex Integration. Line integration in the complex plane is defined as follows.   Let $f(z)$ be any function of z, analytic or not, and let

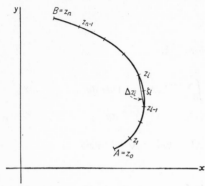

C be an arc of finite length connecting the points A and B.   Subdivide C by the points z_i, $i = 1, 2, 3, \ldots$, and set

$$\Delta z_i = z_i - z_{i-1} \quad .$$

Finally, let ζ_i be an arbitrary point of the arc $z_{i-1}z_i$.   Then the limit of the sum

$$(1) \qquad \sum_{i=1}^{n} f(\zeta_i)\Delta z_i$$

FIG. 10.11.

as $n \to \infty$ in such a way that the length of every chord, Δz_i, approaches zero, is called the **line integral of** $f(z)$ along C,

$$\int_C f(z)dz$$

We note in passing that this definition differs from the definition of a real line integral in that it does not involve the infinitesimal increments of arc, Δs_i, but is based rather on the infinitesimal directed chords, Δz_i.

In working with complex line integrals, it is frequently necessary to establish bounds on their absolute values.   To do this, let us return to the definitive sum (1) and apply to it the fundamental fact that the absolute value of a sum of complex numbers is equal to or less than the sum of their absolute values [Eq. (8), Sec. 9.4].   Then

$$\left| \sum_{i=1}^{n} f(\zeta_i)\Delta z_i \right| \leqq \sum_{i=1}^{n} \left| f(\zeta_i)\Delta z_i \right| = \sum_{i=1}^{n} |f(\zeta_i)||\Delta z_i|$$

the last equality following from the fact that the absolute value of a product is *equal* to the product of the absolute values.   As $n \to \infty$, this yields a corresponding inequality for the integrals which are the limits of the respective sums:

$$(2) \qquad \left| \int_C f(z)dz \right| \leqq \int_C |f(z)||dz|$$

The integral on the right-hand side is the real line integral

$$\int_C \sqrt{u^2 + v^2}\, \sqrt{dx^2 + dy^2} = \int_C \sqrt{u^2 + v^2}\, ds$$

In particular, if $f(z) \equiv 1$, we have the simple but important result

(3) $$\int_C |dz| = \int_C ds = L$$

where L is the length of the path of integration.

If it should happen that $f(z)$ is a bounded function on the path of integration, that is, if $|f(z)| \leq M$ for all z's on C, then we have from (2)

$$\left| \int_C f(z)dz \right| \leq \int_C |f(z)||dz| \leq \int_C M|dz| = M \int_C |dz|$$

Hence, using (3), we have the very important inequality

(4) $$\left| \int_C f(z)dz \right| \leq ML$$

where M is the maximum value of $|f(z)|$ on C and L is the length of C.

Complex line integrals can readily be expressed in terms of real integrals. For we can write

$$\int_C f(z)dz = \int_C (u + iv)(dx + i\,dy)$$

(5) $$\int_C f(z)dz = \int_C u\,dx - v\,dy + i \int_C v\,dx + u\,dy$$

and clearly each line integral on the right is entirely real. From this fact and the known properties of real integrals, or directly from the original definition, it is easy to see that when the same path of integration is used in each integral we have

(6) $$\int_A^B f(z)dz = - \int_B^A f(z)dz$$

(7) $$\int_A^B kf(z)dz = k \int_A^B f(z)dz$$

(8) $$\int_A^B [f(z) \pm g(z)]dz = \int_A^B f(z)dz \pm \int_A^B g(z)dz$$

If A, B, and C are three points on the path C, we also have

(9) $$\int_A^B f(z)dz = \int_A^C f(z)dz + \int_C^B f(z)dz$$

Example 1

If C is a circle of radius r and center z_0, and if n is an integer, what is the value of

$$\int_C \frac{dz}{(z - z_0)^{n+1}}$$

For convenience, let us make the substitution $z - z_0 = re^{i\theta}$. Then $dz = rie^{i\theta}d\theta$ and the integral becomes

$$\int_0^{2\pi} \frac{rie^{i\theta}\,d\theta}{r^{n+1}e^{i(n+1)\theta}} = \frac{i}{r^n} \int_0^{2\pi} e^{-in\theta}\,d\theta$$

If $n = 0$, this becomes simply

$$i \int_0^{2\pi} d\theta = 2\pi i$$

If $n \neq 0$, we have

$$\frac{i}{r^n} \int_0^{2\pi} (\cos n\theta - i \sin n\theta)d\theta = 0$$

This is an important example, to which we shall have occasion to refer from time to time.

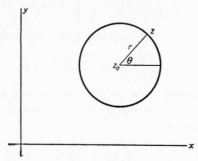

FIG. 10.12.

EXERCISES

1. Evaluate $\int_0^{3+i} z^2 \, dz$

   (a) Along $y = \dfrac{x}{3}$

   (b) Along the real axis to 3 and then vertically to $3 + i$
   (c) Along the imaginary axis to i and then horizontally to $3 + i$

2. Evaluate $\int_0^{3+i} (\bar{z})^2 \, dz$ along each of the paths used in Exercise 1.

3. Evaluate $\int_0^{1+i} (x^2 + iy)dz$ along the paths $y = x$ and $y = x^2$.

4. Obtain an upper bound for the absolute value of the integral

$$\int_0^{1+2i} e^{-z^2} \, dz$$

   along the path $y = 2x$.

5. Obtain an upper bound for the absolute value of the integral

$$\frac{1}{2\pi i} \int \frac{e^{2z}}{z + i} \, dz$$

   taken around the circle $|z| = 3$.

10.4 Cauchy's Theorem. We are now in a position to prove very simply the famous theorem of Cauchy, perhaps the most fundamental and far-reaching result in the theory of analytic functions.

Theorem 1. If $f(z)$ is analytic at all points within and on a closed curve, C, and if $f'(z)$ is continuous throughout this closed region, R, then

$$\int_C f(z)dz = 0$$

To prove this, we recall from Eq. (5), Sec. 10.3, that

$$\int_C f(z)dz = \int_C (u\,dx - v\,dy) + i\int_C (v\,dx + u\,dy)$$

The hypotheses that $f(z)$ is analytic and that $f'(z)$ is continuous guarantee that the partial derivatives

$$\frac{\partial u}{\partial x},\ \frac{\partial u}{\partial y},\ \frac{\partial v}{\partial x},\ \frac{\partial v}{\partial y}$$

exist and are continuous. Hence Green's lemma can be applied to each of the above line integrals, giving

$$\int_C f(z)dz = \int\int_R \left(-\frac{\partial v}{\partial x} - \frac{\partial u}{\partial y}\right) dx\,dy + i\int\int_R \left(\frac{\partial u}{\partial x} - \frac{\partial v}{\partial y}\right) dx\,dy$$

But u and v necessarily satisfy the Cauchy-Riemann equations, and thus the integrand of each of these double integrals vanishes identically, leaving

$$\int_C f(z)dz = 0$$

as asserted.

This theorem can be proved without making use of the hypothesis that $f'(z)$ is continuous. The French mathematician E. Goursat (1850–1936) was the first to do this, and in his honor the more general form of the result is usually known as the **Cauchy-Goursat theorem.**

Various of the corollaries of Green's lemma can also be applied to

$$\int_C f(z)dz$$

For instance, the Cauchy-Riemann equations are precisely the conditions that the two real line integrals upon which $\int_C f(z)dz$ depends should be independent of the path. Hence it is evident that *if $f(z)$ is analytic within a simply connected region R, then the line integral of $f(z)$ between any two points of R is independent of the path.*

If R is a multiply connected region whose complete boundary C consists of several simple closed curves, C_1, C_2, . . . , the extension of Green's lemma to such regions can be applied to $\int_C f(z)dz$, leading to the conclusion that *if $f(z)$ is analytic over a multiply connected region R, then the integral of $f(z)$ around the complete boundary of R is zero, provided that each portion of the boundary is traversed in the positive sense.* Line integrals around the complete boundary of a region are frequently called **contour integrals.**

In particular, if $f(z)$ is analytic in the region R between two simple closed curves, C_1 and C_2, we have

$$\int_{C_1} f(z)dz + \int_{C_2} f(z)dz = 0$$

provided that each curve is traversed in the positive direction as shown in Fig. 10.13a. On the other hand, if we reverse the direction of integration around C_2 and transpose this integral, we obtain

$$\int_{C_1} f(z)dz = \int_{C_2} f(z)dz$$

each integration being now performed in the counterclockwise sense, as shown in Fig. 10.13b. Since there may be points in the interior of C_2

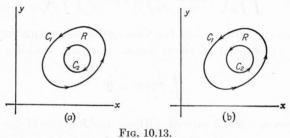

FIG. 10.13.

(which of course is not a part of R) where $f(z)$ is not analytic, we cannot assert that either of these integrals has the value zero. However, we have shown that both have the same value. This result may be summarized in the highly important **principle of the deformation of contours:** *The line integral of an analytic function around any closed curve, C, is equal to the line integral of the same function around any other closed curve into which the first can be continuously deformed without passing over a point where $f(z)$ is nonanalytic.*

One of the most important consequences of Cauchy's theorem is what is known as **Cauchy's integral formula.**

Theorem 2. If $f(z)$ is analytic within and on the boundary C of a simply connected region R and if z_0 is any point in the interior of R, then

$$f(z_0) = \frac{1}{2\pi i} \int_C \frac{f(z)}{z - z_0} \, dz$$

where the integration around C is in the positive sense.

To prove this, let C_0 be a circle with center at z_0 whose radius ρ is sufficiently small that C_0 lies entirely in R (Fig. 10.14). Now by hypothesis, $f(z)$ is analytic everywhere within R.   Hence the function

$$\frac{f(z)}{z - z_0}$$

is analytic everywhere within R except at the one point $z = z_0$.   In particular, it is analytic everywhere in the region R' between C and C_0.

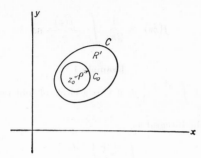

Fig. 10.14.

Therefore the contour C may be deformed into C_0 without altering the value of the integral under consideration.   That is,

$$\int_C \frac{f(z)}{z - z_0}\, dz = \int_{C_0} \frac{f(z)}{z - z_0}\, dz$$

$$= \int_{C_0} \frac{f(z_0) + f(z) - f(z_0)}{z - z_0}\, dz$$

$$(1) \qquad\qquad = f(z_0) \int_{C_0} \frac{dz}{z - z_0} + \int_{C_0} \frac{f(z) - f(z_0)}{z - z_0}\, dz$$

By Example 1, Sec. 10.3, the first integral on the right is equal to $2\pi i$. Hence the assertion of the theorem will be established if we can show that the last integral vanishes.

   To do this we observe that

$$\left| \int_{C_0} \frac{f(z) - f(z_0)}{z - z_0}\, dz \right| \leqq \int_{C_0} \frac{|f(z) - f(z_0)|}{|z - z_0|}\, |dz|$$

On C_0, $z - z_0 = \rho$.   Moreover, since $f(z)$ is analytic, and hence continuous, it follows that for any $\epsilon > 0$ there exists a δ such that

$$|f(z) - f(z_0)| < \epsilon \qquad \text{provided } |z - z_0| \equiv \rho < \delta$$

Choosing the radius ρ to be less than δ, we can therefore write

$$\left| \int_{C_0} \frac{f(z) - f(z_0)}{z - z_0}\, dz \right| < \int_{C_0} \frac{\epsilon}{\rho}\, |dz| = \frac{\epsilon}{\rho} \int_{C_0} |dz| = \frac{\epsilon}{\rho}\, 2\pi\rho = 2\pi\epsilon$$

Since the integral on the left is independent of ϵ, yet cannot exceed $2\pi\epsilon$, which can be made arbitrarily small, it follows that the absolute value of the integral, and hence the integral itself, is zero. Thus (1) reduces to

$$\int_C \frac{f(z)}{z - z_0} \, dz = f(z_0)2\pi i + 0$$

whence

$$f(z_0) = \frac{1}{2\pi i} \int_C \frac{f(z)}{z - z_0} \, dz$$

as asserted.

Example 1

What is the value of $\int_C \frac{z^2 + 1}{z^2 - 1} \, dz$ if C is a circle of unit radius with center at (a) $z = 1$ and (b) $z = -1$?

In (a) we think of the integral as

$$\int_C \frac{z^2 + 1}{z + 1} \frac{dz}{z - 1}$$

and identify $f(z)$ as $(z^2 + 1)/(z + 1)$ and z_0 as 1. The function $f(z)$ is analytic everywhere within a circle of unit radius around $z_0 = 1$. (In fact, it is analytic everywhere except at $z = -1$.) Therefore we can apply Cauchy's integral formula, getting

$$\int_C \frac{z^2 + 1}{z + 1} \frac{dz}{z - 1} = 2\pi i f(1) = 2\pi i \frac{1^2 + 1}{1 + 1} = 2\pi i$$

In (b) we identify $f(z)$ as $(z^2 + 1)/(z - 1)$, and z_0 as -1. Then Cauchy's integral formula gives immediately

$$\int_C \frac{z^2 + 1}{z - 1} \frac{dz}{z + 1} = 2\pi i f(-1) = 2\pi i \frac{(-1)^2 + 1}{-1 - 1} = -2\pi i$$

From Cauchy's integral formula, which expresses the value of an analytic function at an interior point of a region R in terms of its values on the boundary of the region, we can readily obtain an expression for the derivative of a function at an interior point of R in terms of the boundary values of the function. In fact, we have

$$f'(z_0) = \lim_{\Delta z_0 \to 0} \frac{f(z_0 + \Delta z_0) - f(z_0)}{\Delta z_0}$$

$$= \lim_{\Delta z_0 \to 0} \frac{1}{\Delta z_0} \left[\frac{1}{2\pi i} \int_C \frac{f(z)dz}{z - (z_0 + \Delta z_0)} - \frac{1}{2\pi i} \int_C \frac{f(z)dz}{z - z_0} \right]$$

$$= \lim_{\Delta z_0 \to 0} \frac{1}{\Delta z_0} \left[\frac{1}{2\pi i} \int_C f(z) \left\{ \frac{1}{z - (z_0 + \Delta z_0)} - \frac{1}{z - z_0} \right\} dz \right]$$

$$= \lim_{\Delta z_0 \to 0} \frac{1}{2\pi i} \int_C \frac{f(z)dz}{(z - z_0 - \Delta z_0)(z - z_0)}$$

Taking for granted that the limit of the integral is equal to the integral of the limit, and letting $\Delta z_0 \to 0$ in the integrand, we obtain the desired result

$$(2) \qquad f'(z_0) = \frac{1}{2\pi i} \int_C \frac{f(z)dz}{(z - z_0)^2}$$

That the limiting procedure is legitimate in this case can easily be established by showing that the absolute value of the difference

$$\frac{1}{2\pi i} \int_C \frac{f(z)dz}{(z - z_0 - \Delta z_0)(z - z_0)} - \frac{1}{2\pi i} \int_C \frac{f(z)dz}{(z - z_0)^2}$$

approaches zero as $\Delta z_0 \to 0$.

Continuing in the same way, we obtain the additional formulas

$$(3) \qquad f''(z_0) = \frac{2!}{2\pi i} \int_C \frac{f(z)dz}{(z - z_0)^3}$$

$$(4) \qquad f'''(z_0) = \frac{3!}{2\pi i} \int_C \frac{f(z)dz}{(z - z_0)^4}$$

$$\cdot\ \cdot\ \cdot\ \cdot\ \cdot\ \cdot\ \cdot\ \cdot\ \cdot\ \cdot\ \cdot\ \cdot$$

$$(5) \qquad f^{(n)}(z_0) = \frac{n!}{2\pi i} \int_C \frac{f(z)dz}{(z - z_0)^{n+1}}$$

All these results could have been obtained formally by repeated differentiation of Cauchy's integral formula with respect to the parameter z_0.

We have thus established the remarkable fact that *analytic functions possess derivatives of all orders.* Moreover, since this is the case, *every derivative of an analytic function possesses a derivative, and thus is analytic,* by definition.

This observation allows us to prove the converse of Cauchy's theorem, which is known as **Morera's Theorem.**

Theorem 3.   If $f(z)$ is continuous in a simply connected region R and if

$$\int_C f(z)dz = 0$$

for every simple closed curve C which can be drawn in R, then $f(z)$ is analytic in R.

To prove this, we observe as in the proof of Theorem 3, Sec. 10.2, that if the line integral of $f(z)$ around every closed curve in R is zero, then the line integral of $f(z)$ between a fixed point, z_0, and a variable point, z, in R is independent of the path, and hence is a function of z alone, say $F(z)$:

$$F(z) = \int_{z_0}^{z} f(z)dz$$

If we let $f(z) = u + iv$ and $F(z) = U + iV$, this can be written

$$F(z) = U + iV = \int_{x_0, y_0}^{x, y} u\, dx - v\, dy + i \int_{x_0, y_0}^{x, y} v\, dx + u\, dy$$

By Theorem 4, Sec. 10.2, each of these integrals can be differentiated partially with respect to x and y, and it is easy to verify that

$$\frac{\partial U}{\partial x} = u, \qquad \frac{\partial U}{\partial y} = -v, \qquad \frac{\partial V}{\partial x} = v, \qquad \frac{\partial V}{\partial y} = u$$

Since u and v are continuous, because of the hypothesis that $f(z) = u + iv$ is continuous, it follows that $\dfrac{\partial U}{\partial x}, \dfrac{\partial U}{\partial y}, \dfrac{\partial V}{\partial x}, \dfrac{\partial V}{\partial y}$ are continuous.

Moreover

$$\frac{\partial U}{\partial x} = \frac{\partial V}{\partial y} \quad \text{and} \quad \frac{\partial U}{\partial y} = -\frac{\partial V}{\partial x}$$

and thus $F(z) = U + iV$ is an analytic function whose derivative, in fact, is

$$F'(z) = \frac{\partial U}{\partial x} + i\frac{\partial V}{\partial x} = u + iv = f(z)$$

Being the derivative of an analytic function, $f(z)$ is therefore analytic, as asserted.

If in the formula for the general derivative of $f(z)$, namely,

$$f^{(n)}(z_0) = \frac{n!}{2\pi i} \int_C \frac{f(z)\,dz}{(z - z_0)^{n+1}}$$

we choose C to be a circle of radius r with center at z_0, we readily obtain the important result known as **Cauchy's inequality,**

$$|f^{(n)}(z_0)| \leq \frac{n!M}{r^n}$$

where M is the maximum value of $|f(z)|$ on the path of the integration C. For we have

$$|f^{(n)}(z_0)| = \left| \frac{n!}{2\pi i} \int_C \frac{f(z)\,dz}{(z - z_0)^{n+1}} \right|$$
$$\leq \frac{n!}{2\pi} \int_C \frac{|f(z)|\,|dz|}{|z - z_0|^{n+1}}$$
$$\leq \frac{n!}{2\pi} \frac{M}{r^{n+1}} \int_C |dz|$$
$$= \frac{n!}{2\pi} \frac{M}{r^{n+1}} 2\pi r$$
$$= \frac{n!M}{r^n}$$

For the special case $n = 0$, we have

$$|f(z_0)| \leqq M$$

Since this bound does not involve r (except through M), this shows that *the absolute value of a function $f(z)$ cannot have a maximum at any point, z_0, where the function is analytic,* for on every circle around z_0, no matter how small, there will always be one or more points where $|f(z)|$ is at least as great as $|f(z_0)|$.

If we consider the case $n = 1$, and assume that $f(z)$ is bounded for all values of z, we have

$$|f'(z_0)| \leqq \frac{M}{r}$$

where M, now, does not depend upon the radius r of the particular circle C. Since r can be taken arbitrarily large, it follows that $|f'(z_0)|$ must be zero at all points in the complex plane. But if $|f'(z)|$ vanishes, so too does $f'(z)$ itself, and hence

$$f(z) = \text{constant}$$

This establishes the simple but important **theorem of Liouville.***

Theorem 4. If $f(z)$ is analytic, and if $f(z)$ is bounded for all values of z, then $f(z)$ is a constant.

EXERCISES

1. What is the value of the integral $\int (z^3 + e^{z^2})dz$ taken around the circle $|z - 1| = 2$?

2. What is the value of $\dfrac{1}{2\pi i} \displaystyle\int_C \dfrac{3z^2 + 7z + 1}{z + 1}\,dz$ where C is the circle $|z + 1| = 1$?
   What is the value of this integral if C is the circle $|z| = \frac{1}{2}$?

3. What is the value of $\displaystyle\int_C \dfrac{dz}{z^3}$, where C is the ellipse $\dfrac{x^2}{9} + \dfrac{y^2}{4} = 1$?

4. What is the value of $\displaystyle\int_C \dfrac{z + 4}{z^2 + 2z + 5}\,dz$ if C is
   (a) The circle $|z| = 1$
   (b) The circle $|z + 1 - i| = 2$
   (c) The circle $|z + 1 + i| = 2$

5. What is the value of $\displaystyle\int_C \dfrac{e^{iz}}{z^2 + 1}\,dz$, if C is the circle $|z - 2i| = \dfrac{3}{2}$?

* Actually due to Cauchy.

CHAPTER 11

INFINITE SERIES IN THE COMPLEX PLANE

11.1 Series of Complex Terms. Most of the definitions and theorems relating to infinite series of real terms (Secs. A.3 and A.4) can be applied without change to series whose terms are complex. To recall these briefly, let

$$(1) \qquad f_1(z) + f_2(z) + f_3(z) + \cdots + f_n(z) + \cdots$$

be a series whose terms are functions of the complex variable z. Then the partial sums of this series are defined to be the finite sums

$$S_1(z) = f_1(z)$$
$$S_2(z) = f_1(z) + f_2(z)$$
$$\cdots \cdots \cdots \cdots$$
$$S_n(z) = f_1(z) + f_2(z) + \cdots + f_n(z)$$

The series (1) is said to **converge to the limit function** $S(z)$, or to **have the sum** $S(z)$, provided that for all values of z in some region, R, $S(z)$ is the limit of the nth partial sum, as n becomes infinite. According to the technical definition of a limit, this requires that for any $\epsilon > 0$ there should exist an integer, N, depending in general on ϵ and on the particular value of z under consideration, such that

$$|S(z) - S_n(z)| < \epsilon \qquad \text{for all } n > N$$

The difference $S(z) - S_n(z)$ is evidently just the **remainder after n terms of the series,** $R_n(z)$, and thus the definition of convergence requires that the limit of $|R_n(z)|$, as n becomes infinite, should be zero. A series which has a sum, as just defined, is said to be **convergent,** and R is called the **region of convergence** of the series. A series which is not convergent is said to **diverge,** or to be **divergent.** If the absolute values of the terms in (1) form a convergent series

$$|f_1(z)| + |f_2(z)| + \cdots + |f_n(z)| + \cdots$$

then (1) is said to be **absolutely convergent.** If (1) converges but is not absolutely convergent, it is said to be **conditionally convergent.** Absolute convergence is a sufficient, though not a necessary condition for ordinary convergence. From the definition of convergence it is easy to prove the following theorem.

344

Theorem 1.   A necessary and sufficient condition that the series of complex terms

$$f_1(z) + f_2(z) + \cdots + f_n(z) + \cdots$$

should converge is that the series of the real parts and the series of the imaginary parts of these terms should each converge.   If

$$\sum_{n=1}^{\infty} \Re(f_n) \quad \text{and} \quad \sum_{n=1}^{\infty} \mathscr{I}(f_n)$$

converge to the functions $R(z)$ and $I(z)$, respectively, then the given series converges to $R(z) + iI(z)$.

Of all the tests for the convergence of infinite series the most useful is probably the familiar **ratio test,** which applies to series whose terms are complex as well as to series whose terms are real.

Theorem 2.   For the series

$$f_1 + f_2 + \cdots + f_n + \cdots$$

whose terms may be either real or complex, let

$$\lim_{n \to \infty} \left| \frac{f_{n+1}}{f_n} \right| = |r|$$

Then the series converges absolutely wherever $0 \leq |r| < 1$ and diverges wherever $|r| > 1$.   When $|r| = 1$, the test gives no information about the series.

Example 1

What is the region of convergence of the series

$$1 + \frac{1}{2^2}\left(\frac{z+1}{z-1}\right) + \frac{1}{3^2}\left(\frac{z+1}{z-1}\right)^2 + \frac{1}{4^2}\left(\frac{z+1}{z-1}\right)^3 + \cdots$$

Applying the ratio test, we find

$$\left| \frac{f_{n+1}}{f_n} \right| = \left| \frac{\dfrac{1}{(n+1)^2}\left(\dfrac{z+1}{z-1}\right)^n}{\dfrac{1}{n^2}\left(\dfrac{z+1}{z-1}\right)^{n-1}} \right| = \left| \frac{n^2}{(n+1)^2} \frac{z+1}{z-1} \right|$$

As n approaches infinity, this ratio approaches $\left|\dfrac{z+1}{z-1}\right|$.   Hence the values of z for which the series surely converges are those in the region defined by the inequality

$$\left| \frac{z+1}{z-1} \right| < 1$$

or by

$$|z+1| < |z-1|$$

Now $|z + 1|$ is just the distance from z to the point -1, and $|z - 1|$ is just the distance from z to the point 1. Hence z is restricted to be nearer to the point -1 than to the point 1. In other words, z must lie in the left half of the complex plane. The borderline cases for which the test fails are the values of z on the imaginary axis, which is the locus of points equidistant from -1 and 1. For these points, the related series of absolute values is the convergent real series

$$1 + \frac{1}{2^2} + \frac{1}{3^2} + \frac{1}{4^2} + \cdots$$

Hence for all values of z on the imaginary axis the given series, being absolutely convergent, is convergent, and these points are properly a part of the region of convergence.

The theorems which govern such manipulations of series as addition, subtraction, multiplication, and division are the same whether the terms of the series are real or complex, and may be found in Sec. A.4. To establish conditions under which series may legitimately be integrated or differentiated term by term, the concept of uniform convergence is required.

Definition 1. A series of functions is said to converge uniformly to the function $S(z)$ in a given region, R, either open or closed, if corresponding to an arbitrary $\epsilon > 0$ there exists a positive integer N, depending on ϵ *but not on z*, such that for every value of z in R

$$|S(z) - S_n(z)| < \epsilon \qquad \text{for all } n > N$$

In other words, if a series converges uniformly, a given accuracy of approximation (measured by ϵ) can be obtained *anywhere* in the given region by using *no more than* a fixed number, N, of terms. It may well be that fewer than N terms will suffice at most of the points of the region, but *nowhere* will more than N be required. This is in sharp contrast with ordinary convergence where in the neighborhood of certain points it may be necessary to take arbitrarily many terms to secure a prescribed degree of accuracy.

Example 2

Discuss the convergence of the series

$$z^2 + \frac{z^2}{(1 + z^2)} + \frac{z^2}{(1 + z^2)^2} + \frac{z^2}{(1 + z^2)^3} + \cdots$$

in the 90° sector bounded by the right halves of the lines $y = \pm x$ (Fig. 11.1a).

The given series is a geometric progression whose common ratio, r, is

$$\frac{1}{(1 + z^2)}$$

Since the angle of z is restricted to lie between $-\pi/4$ and $\pi/4$, the angle of z^2 must lie between $-\pi/2$ and $\pi/2$. Hence the length of the complex number $1 + z^2$ is at least 1,

$\rightarrow$ p.625

Sum: $S = a \dfrac{r^m - 1}{r - 1} = a \dfrac{r^\alpha - 1}{r - 1} = \dfrac{a}{1 - r}$ for $r^\alpha = 0$ as $r < 1$

$n \equiv$ no. of terms $r \equiv$ common ratio

$a \equiv$ first term of the progression

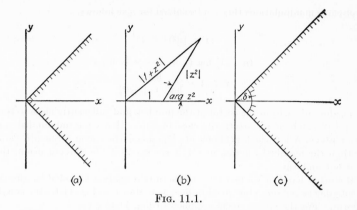

FIG. 11.1.

and thus throughout the region of the problem, with the exception of the point $z = 0$, the absolute value of the common ratio is less than 1. Therefore the series converges and its sum is

$$S = \begin{cases} \dfrac{a}{1-r} = \dfrac{z^2}{1 - [1/(1 + z^2)]} = 1 + z^2, & z \neq 0 \\ 0 + 0 + 0 + \cdots = 0, & z = 0 \end{cases}$$

Now let an arbitrary $\epsilon > 0$ be given, and let us determine how many terms of the series must be taken in order that

$$|S - S_n| < \epsilon$$

This difference, *i.e.*, the remainder after n terms of the series, is just the geometric progression

$$\frac{z^2}{(1 + z^2)^n} + \frac{z^2}{(1 + z^2)^{n+1}} + \frac{z^2}{(1 + z^2)^{n+2}} + \cdots$$

whose sum is

$$R_n = \begin{cases} \dfrac{1}{(1 + z^2)^{n-1}}, & z \neq 0 \\ 0, & z = 0 \end{cases}$$

Hence our task is to find a value of N such that

$$|R_n| = \frac{1}{|1 + z^2|^{n-1}} < \epsilon \qquad \text{for all } n > N.$$

If we overestimate the denominator of $|R_n|$, we reduce the fraction itself. Therefore, observing that

$$|1 + z^2| \leq 1 + |z^2| = 1 + |z|^2$$

we write

$$\frac{1}{(1 + |z|^2)^{n-1}} \leq \frac{1}{|1 + z^2|^{n-1}} = |R_n|$$

and consider the easier problem of finding an N such that

(2) $$\frac{1}{(1 + |z|^2)^{n-1}} < \epsilon \qquad \text{for all } n > N$$

By obvious manipulations this can be solved for n as follows,

$$(1 + |z|^2)^{n-1} > \frac{1}{\epsilon}$$

$$(n - 1) \log (1 + |z|^2) > - \log \epsilon$$

$$n > 1 - \frac{\log \epsilon}{\log (1 + |z|^2)}$$

But for values of z within the sector of the problem and sufficiently close to the origin, $\log (1 + |z|^2)$ can be made arbitrarily close to zero. Hence n is unbounded, and there exists no integer N for which (2) holds at *all* points of the region. Since $|R_n|$ is actually larger than the modified fraction in (2), it is clear that the convergence of the given series is not uniform.

On the other hand, if we restrict z to the infinite region bounded by the two rays and a circular arc of small but fixed radius, δ, as shown in Fig. 11.1c, the convergence is uniform. For the law of cosines applied to Fig. 11.1b gives

$$|1 + z^2|^2 = 1 + |z^2|^2 + 2|z^2| \cos (\arg z^2)$$

or, since $-\pi/2 \leqq \arg z^2 \leqq \pi/2$ so that $\cos (\arg z^2) \geqq 0$,

$$|1 + z^2|^2 \geqq 1 + |z^2|^2 = 1 + |z|^4$$

Hence, underestimating the denominator of $|R_n|$, we can write the required condition as

$$(3) \qquad |R_n| = \left| \frac{1}{(1 + z^2)^{n-1}} \right| \leqq \frac{1}{(1 + |z|^4)^{(n-1)/2}} < \epsilon$$

The most unfavorable case for the last inequality occurs when $|z|$ is as small as possible. But for the modified region we are now considering, the smallest possible value for $|z|$ is δ. Hence, solving for n under the worst conditions, we find

$$\frac{1}{(1 + \delta^4)^{(n-1)/2}} < \epsilon$$

$$(1 + \delta^4)^{\frac{n-1}{2}} > \frac{1}{\epsilon}$$

$$\frac{n-1}{2} \log (1 + \delta^4) > - \log \epsilon$$

$$n > 1 - \frac{2 \log \epsilon}{\log (1 + \delta^4)}$$

If we choose N as the first integer equal to or greater than the expression on the right of the last inequality, the chain of inequalities (3) will hold regardless of what the value of z may be. Hence in the modified region the convergence is uniform.

Usually uniform convergence is established not by a direct application of the definition, as in the example we have just worked, but by the so-called **Weierstrass M test.** *

Theorem 3. If a sequence of positive constants $\{M_n\}$ exists such that $|f_n(z)| \leqq M_n$ for all positive integers, n, and for all values of z in a given

---

* Karl Weierstrass (1815–1897), often called the "father of modern rigor," was one of the greatest of German mathematicians.

region, R, and if the series

$$M_1 + M_2 + M_3 + \cdots + M_n + \cdots$$

is convergent, then the series

$$f_1(z) + f_2(z) + f_3(z) + \cdots + f_n(z) + \cdots$$

converges uniformly in R.

To prove this, we must show that for any $\epsilon > 0$ there exists an N, independent of z, such that the absolute value of the remainder after n terms in the series of the f's is less than ϵ whenever n exceeds N. To do this, we note that

$$\begin{aligned} |R_n(z)| &= |f_{n+1}(z) + f_{n+2}(z) + \cdots| \\ &\leq |f_{n+1}(z)| + |f_{n+2}(z)| + \cdots \\ &\leq M_{n+1} + M_{n+2} + \cdots \end{aligned}$$

The last expression is just the remainder after n terms of the series of the M's. Since this series is convergent, by hypothesis, it follows that for every $\epsilon > 0$ there exists an N such that this remainder is less than ϵ for all $n > N$. This value of N, arising as it does from a series of constants, is obviously independent of z. Moreover, from the above inequalities it is clear that whenever n exceeds this N, $|R_n(z)| < \epsilon$ for all values of z under consideration. Hence the series of the f's is uniformly convergent, as asserted. Incidentally, this theorem implies a comparison test which proves that the series of the f's is also absolutely convergent.

The Weierstrass M test is merely a sufficient test, that is, there exist uniformly convergent series whose terms cannot be dominated by the respective terms of any convergent series of positive constants. The M test suffices for almost all applications, however.

It is important to note that *if the terms of a uniformly convergent series are multiplied by any bounded function of z, the resulting series will also converge uniformly.* To see this, suppose that $|g(z)| < M$ throughout R, the region of uniform convergence of the series

$$f_1(z) + f_2(z) + \cdots + f_n(z) + \cdots$$

Then corresponding to the infinitesimal ϵ/M there exists an integer N such that

$$|f_{n+1}(z) + f_{n+2}(z) + \cdots | < \frac{\epsilon}{M} \qquad \text{for all } n > N$$

and for all values of z in R. Now

$$\begin{aligned} |g(z)f_{n+1}(z) + g(z)f_{n+2}(z) + \cdots | &= |g(z)||f_{n+1}(z) + f_{n+2}(z) + \cdots | \\ &\leq M|f_{n+1}(z) + f_{n+2}(z) + \cdots | \\ &\leq M \frac{\epsilon}{M} \\ &= \epsilon \qquad n > N, z \text{ in } R \end{aligned}$$

But this is precisely the condition that the product series,

$$g(z)f_1(z) + g(z)f_2(z) + \cdots + g(z)f_n(z) + \cdots$$

should be uniformly convergent.

One important consequence of uniform convergence is embodied in the following theorem.

Theorem 4. The sum of a uniformly convergent series of continuous functions is a continuous function.

To prove this, let

$$f(z) = f_1(z) + f_2(z) + \cdots + f_n(z) + \cdots = S_n(z) + R_n(z)$$

be a uniformly convergent series in which each f is a continuous function of z, and choose any infinitesimal $\epsilon/3$. Then since the series converges uniformly, an integer N exists such that

$$|R_n(z)| < \frac{\epsilon}{3} \qquad \text{for all } n > N$$

and for all z's in the region of uniform convergence. In particular, if $\Delta_1 z$ is any increment such that $z + \Delta_1 z$ is still in the region of uniform convergence, we also have

$$|R_n(z + \Delta_1 z)| < \frac{\epsilon}{3} \qquad n > N$$

Moreover, since each term of the given series is a continuous function, and since any *finite* sum of continuous functions is necessarily continuous, it follows that there exists an increment $\Delta_2 z$, such that

$$|S_n(z + \Delta z) - S_n(z)| < \frac{\epsilon}{3} \qquad \text{for all } |\Delta z| < |\Delta_2 z|$$

Now

$$
\begin{aligned}
|f(z + \Delta z) - f(z)| &= |\{S_n(z + \Delta z) + R_n(z + \Delta z)\} - \{S_n(z) + R_n(z)\}| \\
&\leqq |S_n(z + \Delta z) - S_n(z)| + |R_n(z + \Delta z)| + |R_n(z)|
\end{aligned}
$$

Hence for all values of Δz less than the smaller of the increments $\Delta_1 z$ and $\Delta_2 z$, it follows that

$$|f(z + \Delta z) - f(z)| < \frac{\epsilon}{3} + \frac{\epsilon}{3} + \frac{\epsilon}{3} = \epsilon$$

which is precisely what we mean by saying that $f(z)$ is continuous.

In a negative sense this theorem tells us that *the sum of an infinite series of continuous functions is not necessarily continuous.* For instance, the first part of Example 2, in which we found the sum of the series to be

$$f(z) = \begin{cases} 1 + z^2, & z \neq 0 \\ 0, & z = 0 \end{cases}$$

proves that the limit of a sum of continuous functions may be discontinuous if the convergence is nonuniform. In fact around $z = 0$, where the convergence is nonuniform, the sum function jumps abruptly from 1 to 0, even though every term of the series is a continuous function of z.

One of the most important properties of uniformly convergent series is given by the following theorem.

Theorem 5. The integral of the sum of a uniformly convergent series of continuous functions along any curve C can be found by termwise integration of the series. Moreover, if each of the terms of the series is analytic, so too is the sum.

Let the given series be

$$f(z) = f_1(z) + f_2(z) + \cdots + f_n(z) + \cdots$$

Then the question we have to answer in order to establish the theorem is this: Does the series

$$\int_C f_1(z)dz + \int_C f_2(z)dz + \cdots + \int_C f_n(z)dz + \cdots$$

converge to

$$\int_C f(z)dz \equiv \int_C [\lim_{n \to \infty} S_n(z)]dz$$

To show that this is the case, we must demonstrate, as usual, that $\int_C f(z)dz$ is the limit of the partial sums of the series resulting from the termwise integration. In other words, we must prove that for any $\epsilon > 0$ there exists an integer N such that

$$\left| \int_C f(z)dz - \sum_{i=1}^{n} \int_C f_i(z)dz \right| < \epsilon \qquad \text{for all } n > N$$

Now for any *finite* sum it is true that the integral of a sum is equal to the sum of the integrals. Hence the last inequality can be written

$$\left| \int_C f(z)dz - \int_C \sum_{i=1}^{n} f_i(z)dz \right| < \epsilon$$

or

$$\left| \int_C \left[f(z) - \sum_{i=1}^{n} f_i(z) \right] dz \right| < \epsilon$$

or, finally,

$$\left| \int_C R_n(z)dz \right| < \epsilon$$

Let L be the length of the path of integration. Then from the uniform convergence of the given series, there exists an integer N such that

$$|R_n(z)| < \frac{\epsilon}{L} \qquad \text{for all } n > N$$

and for all z in the region of uniform convergence, in particular for all values of z on the path of integration. If $n > N$, we can therefore write

$$\left| \int_C R_n(z)dz \right| \leqq \int_C |R_n(z)||dz| < \frac{\epsilon}{L} \int_C |dz| = \frac{\epsilon}{L} L = \epsilon$$

which establishes the first part of the theorem.

If each term, $f_i(z)$, is analytic in R, then by Cauchy's theorem the integral of each term around any closed curve in R is zero. Hence the integral of the sum, $f(z)$, around any closed curve is zero, and thus by Morera's theorem, $f(z)$ is analytic. This completes the proof of the theorem.

The companion result on the termwise differentiation of series is the following.

Theorem 6. If $f(z)$ is the sum of a uniformly convergent series of analytic functions, then the derivative of $f(z)$ at any point in the region of uniform convergence can be found by termwise differentiation.

To prove this, let z be a general point of R and let C be a simple closed curve drawn around z in R. If we write the given series as

$$f(t) = f_1(t) + f_2(t) + \cdots + f_n(t) + \cdots$$

where t stands for any of the values of z on C, we can multiply by the bounded function

$$\frac{1}{2\pi i(t - z)^2}$$

and the resulting series

$$\frac{f(t)}{2\pi i(t - z)^2} = \frac{f_1(t)}{2\pi i(t - z)^2} + \frac{f_2(t)}{2\pi i(t - z)^2} + \cdots + \frac{f_n(t)}{2\pi i(t - z)^2} + \cdots$$

will also converge uniformly. It can therefore be integrated termwise around C, giving

$$\frac{1}{2\pi i} \int_C \frac{f(t)dt}{(t - z)^2} = \frac{1}{2\pi i} \int_C \frac{f_1(t)dt}{(t - z)^2} + \frac{1}{2\pi i} \int_C \frac{f_2(t)dt}{(t - z)^2} + \cdots$$

But these integrals, by the first generalization of Cauchy's integral formula, are precisely the derivatives of the respective terms of the given series.   Hence

$$f'(z) = f_1'(z) + f_2'(z) + \cdots + f_n'(z) + \cdots$$

which establishes the theorem.

EXERCISES

What is the region of convergence of each of the following series?

1. $\dfrac{1}{1 \cdot 2} + \dfrac{(z - i)}{2 \cdot 3} + \dfrac{(z - i)^2}{3 \cdot 4} + \cdots$

2. $\dfrac{1}{2(z + i)} + \dfrac{1}{2^2(z + i)^2} + \dfrac{1}{2^3(z + i)^3} + \cdots$

3. $1 + \dfrac{1}{2^2}\left(\dfrac{\Re(z)}{z + 1}\right) + \dfrac{1}{3^2}\left(\dfrac{\Re(z)}{z + 1}\right)^2 + \cdots$

4. Show that the series $x + x(1 - x) + x(1 - x)^2 + \cdots$ converges for $0 \leqq x < 2$ but that the convergence is nonuniform in any subinterval which includes the origin.

5. Show that the series

$$\frac{1}{1 + x^2} - \frac{1}{2 + x^2} + \frac{1}{3 + x^2} - \frac{1}{4 + x^2} + \cdots$$

converges uniformly over any interval of the x-axis. Can this be established by the M test?

11.2 Taylor's Expansion.   Very often the series with which one has to deal in applications are those which are studied formally in elementary calculus under the name of Taylor's series. Their systematic study begins with the following theorem.

Theorem 1.   If $f(z)$ is analytic throughout the region R bounded by a simple closed curve C and if z and a are both interior to C, then

$$f(z) = f(a) + f'(a)(z - a) + f''(a)\frac{(z - a)^2}{2!} + \cdots$$

$$+ f^{(n-1)}(a)\frac{(z - a)^{n-1}}{(n - 1)!} + R_n$$

where $\qquad R_n = (z - a)^n \dfrac{1}{2\pi i}\displaystyle\int_C \dfrac{f(w)dw}{(w - a)^n(w - z)}$

To prove this, we first note that Cauchy's integral formula can be written

$$f(z) = \frac{1}{2\pi i}\int_C \frac{f(w)dw}{w - z} = \frac{1}{2\pi i}\int_C \frac{f(w)}{(w - a)}\left[\frac{1}{1 - [(z - a)/(w - a)]}\right]dw$$

Moreover, from the identity

$$\frac{1 - u^n}{1 - u} = 1 + u + u^2 + \cdots + u^{n-1}$$

we have at once

$$\frac{1}{1-u} = 1 + u + u^2 + \cdots + u^{n-1} + \frac{u^n}{1-u}$$

Applying this to the factor,

$$\frac{1}{1 - (z-a)/(w-a)}$$

in the last integral, we can write

$$f(z) = \frac{1}{2\pi i} \int_C \frac{f(w)}{w-a} \left[1 + \frac{z-a}{w-a} + \left(\frac{z-a}{w-a}\right)^2 + \cdots + \left(\frac{z-a}{w-a}\right)^{n-1} \right.$$
$$\left. + \frac{[(z-a)/(w-a)]^n}{1 - (z-a)/(w-a)} \right] dw$$

$$= \frac{1}{2\pi i} \int_C \frac{f(w)dw}{w-a} + \frac{z-a}{2\pi i} \int_C \frac{f(w)dw}{(w-a)^2} + \cdots$$
$$+ \frac{(z-a)^{n-1}}{2\pi i} \int_C \frac{f(w)dw}{(w-a)^n}$$
$$+ \frac{(z-a)^n}{2\pi i} \int_C \frac{f(w)dw}{(w-a)^n(w-z)}$$

From the generalizations of Cauchy's integral formula it is evident that except for the necessary factorials, the first n integrals in the last expression are precisely the corresponding derivatives of $f(z)$ evaluated at $z = a$. Hence

$$f(z) = f(a) + f'(a)(z-a) + \cdots$$
$$+ f^{(n-1)}(a) \frac{(z-a)^{n-1}}{(n-1)!} + \frac{(z-a)^n}{2\pi i} \int_C \frac{f(w)dw}{(w-a)^n(w-z)}$$

which establishes **Taylor's theorem**.

By **Taylor's series** we mean the infinite expansion suggested by the last theorem, namely,

$$f(z) = f(a) + f'(a)(z-a) + f''(a)\frac{(z-a)^2}{2!} + \cdots + f^{(n-1)}(a)\frac{(z-a)^{n-1}}{(n-1)!} + \cdots$$

To show that this series actually converges to $f(z)$, we must show, as usual, that the absolute value of the difference between $f(z)$ and the sum of the first n terms approaches zero as n approaches infinity. From Taylor's theorem it is evident that this difference is

$$R_n(z) = \frac{(z-a)^n}{2\pi i} \int_C \frac{f(w)dw}{(w-a)^n(w-z)}$$

Accordingly we must determine the values of z for which the absolute value of this integral approaches zero as n becomes infinite.

To do this, let r_1 and r_2 be the radii of two circles, C_1 and C_2, lying entirely within R and having their centers at a (Fig. 11.2). Since $f(z)$ is analytic throughout the interior of C, the entire integrand of $R_n(z)$ is analytic in the region between C and C_2, provided that z, like a, lies in the interior of C_2. Under these conditions the integral around C may be replaced by the

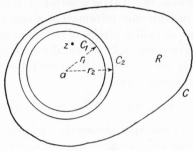

Fig. 11.2.

integral around C_2. If in addition z is interior to C_1, then for all values of w on C_2 (the w's now involved in the integration) we have

$$|w - a| = r_2$$
$$|z - a| < r_1$$
$$|w - z| > r_2 - r_1$$

and

$$|f(w)| \leqq M$$

where M is the maximum of $|f(z)|$ on C_2. Hence

$$|R_n(z)| = \left| \frac{(z - a)^n}{2\pi i} \int_C \frac{f(w)dw}{(w - a)^n(w - z)} \right|$$

$$\leqq \frac{|z - a|^n}{|2\pi i|} \int_C \frac{|f(w)||dw|}{|w - a|^n|w - z|}$$

$$< \frac{r_1^n}{2\pi} \int_C \frac{M|dw|}{r_2^n(r_2 - r_1)}$$

$$= \frac{r_1^n M}{2\pi r_2^n(r_2 - r_1)} 2\pi r_2$$

$$= M \left(\frac{r_1}{r_2} \right)^n \frac{r_2}{r_2 - r_1}$$

Since $r_1 < r_2$, the fraction $(r_1/r_2)^n$ approaches zero as n approaches infinity, and thus the limit of $R_n(z)$ is zero. Thus *Taylor's series is a valid representation of a function at all points interior to any circle having its center at a, and within which the function is analytic.* The largest circle which can be drawn around $z = a$, such that $f(z)$ is analytic throughout its interior, is called the **circle of convergence** of the Taylor's series of $f(z)$. The radius of this circle is called the **radius of convergence** of the series. Of course this entire discussion applies without change to the case $a = 0$, which is usually called **Maclaurin's series.**

The preceding discussion established a circular region around the point $z = a$ within which the Taylor's series of $f(z)$ converges to $f(z)$. However, it did not provide any information about the behavior of the series outside of the so-called circle of convergence. Actually, the Taylor's series of $f(z)$ converges only within the circle of convergence, and diverges everywhere outside of this circle, as the following theorem shows.

Theorem 2. If the power series

$$a_0 + a_1(z - a) + a_2(z - a)^2 + a_3(z - a)^3 + \cdots$$

converges for $z = z_1$, it converges absolutely and uniformly for all values of z such that $|z - a| < |z_1 - a|$. Moreover, the sum to which it converges is analytic.

To prove this, we note that since the given series converges when $z = z_1$, it is necessary that the terms of the series for this value of z should be bounded. That is, there must exist a positive constant M such that

$$|a_n(z_1 - a)^n| = |a_n||z_1 - a|^n < M \qquad \text{for } n = 0, 1, 2, 3, \cdots$$

Now let z_0 be any value of z such that

$$|z_0 - a| < |z_1 - a|$$

that is, let z_0 be any point nearer to a than z_1. Then, for the general term of the series when $z = z_0$, we have

$$|a_n(z_0 - a)^n| = |a_n||z_0 - a|^n = |a_n||z_1 - a|^n \frac{|z_0 - a|^n}{|z_1 - a|^n} < M \left|\frac{z_0 - a}{z_1 - a}\right|^n$$

If we set

$$\left|\frac{z_0 - a}{z_1 - a}\right| = k$$

where k is obviously less than 1, this shows that the terms of the series

$$a_0 + a_1(z_0 - a) + a_2(z_0 - a)^2 + a_3(z_0 - a)^3 + \cdots$$

are dominated, respectively, by the terms of the series of positive constants

$$M + Mk + Mk^2 + Mk^3 + \cdots$$

This is a geometric series whose common ratio k is numerically less than 1. The series therefore converges, and thus provides a test series which can be used in applying the Weierstrass M test to the series

$$\sum_{n=1}^{\infty} a_n(z - a)^n$$

for values of z in the region where $|z - a| < |z_1 - a|$. The latter series therefore converges absolutely and uniformly in this region. Moreover, since every term $a_n(z - a)^n$ is an analytic function, it follows from the second part of Theorem 5, Sec. 11.1, that within the region of convergence of the series its sum is analytic.

Now let z_0 be the singular point of $f(z)$ which is nearest to the point $z = a$ and suppose that the Taylor's series for $f(z)$ converges for some value, $z = z_1$, further from a than z_0. By the last theorem, the series must converge for all points nearer to a than z_1, and, moreover, the sum function must be analytic at any such point. This clearly contradicts the hypothesis that z_0 is a singular point of $f(z)$. Hence *it is impossible for the Taylor's series of a function to converge outside of the circle whose center is at the point of expansion, $z = a$, and whose radius is the distance from a to the nearest singular point of $f(z)$.*

The notion of the circle of convergence is often useful in determining the interval of convergence of a series arising as the expansion of a function of a real variable. To illustrate, consider

$$f(z) = \frac{1}{1 + z^2} = 1 - z^2 + z^4 - z^6 + \cdots$$

This will converge throughout the interior of the largest circle which can be drawn around the origin and in which $f(z)$ is analytic. Now by inspection, $f(z)$ is undefined at $z = \pm i$, and even though one may be concerned solely with real values of z [for which $1/(1 + x^2)$ is everywhere well behaved] these singularities in the complex plane set an inescapable limit to the interval of convergence along the x-axis. We can, in fact, have convergence around $a = 0$ on the real axis only over the horizontal diameter of the circle of convergence.

EXERCISES

1. Expand $f(z) = \dfrac{z - 1}{z + 1}$ in a Taylor's series about (a) the point $z = 0$ and (b) the point $z = 1$. Determine the region of convergence in each case.
2. Expand $f(z) = \cosh z$ in a Taylor's series about the point $z = i\pi$. What is the region of convergence of the resulting series?

Without computing the series, determine the radius of convergence of each of the following expansions:

3. Tan z about $z = 0$

4. $\text{Tan}^{-1} z$ about $z = 1$

5. $\dfrac{1}{e^z - 1}$ about $z = 4i$

11.3 Laurent's Expansion. In many applications it is necessary to expand functions around points where, or in the neighborhood of which, the functions are not analytic. The method of Taylor's series is obviously inapplicable in such cases, and a new type of series known as **Laurent's expansion** is necessary. This furnishes us with a representation which is valid in the annular ring bounded by two concentric circles, provided that the function which is being expanded is analytic everywhere between the two circles. As in the case of Taylor's series, the function may have singular points outside the larger circle, and, as the

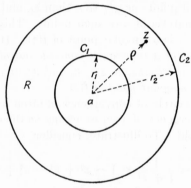

Fig. 11.3.

essentially new feature, it may also have singular points within the inner circle. The price we pay for this is that negative as well as positive powers of $(z - a)$ now appear in the expansion. The precise result is given by the following theorem.

Theorem 1. If $f(z)$ is analytic throughout the closed region, R, bounded by two concentric circles, C_1 and C_2, then at any point in the annular ring bounded by the circles, $f(z)$ can be represented by the series

$$f(z) = \sum_{n = -\infty}^{\infty} a_n (z - a)^n$$

where a is the common center of the circles, and

$$a_n = \frac{1}{2\pi i} \int_C \frac{f(w)\,dw}{(w - a)^{n+1}}$$

each integral being taken in the counterclockwise sense around any curve, C, lying within the annulus and encircling its inner boundary.

To prove this, let z be an arbitrary point of the annulus. Then according to Cauchy's integral formula we can write

$$f(z) = \frac{1}{2\pi i} \int_{C_2+C_1} \frac{f(w)dw}{(w-z)} = \frac{1}{2\pi i} \int_{C_2} \frac{f(w)dw}{(w-z)} + \frac{1}{2\pi i} \int_{C_1} \frac{f(w)dw}{(w-z)}$$

where C_2 is traversed in the counterclockwise direction and C_1 is traversed in the clockwise direction, in order that the entire integration shall be in the positive direction (Fig. 11.3). Reversing the sign of the second integral and also changing the direction of integration from clockwise to counterclockwise, we can write

$$f(z) = \frac{1}{2\pi i} \int_{C_2} \frac{f(w)dw}{w-z} - \frac{1}{2\pi i} \int_{C_1} \frac{f(w)dw}{w-z}$$

$$= \frac{1}{2\pi i} \int_{C_2} \frac{f(w)}{w-a} \left[\frac{1}{1-(z-a)/(w-a)} \right] dw$$

$$+ \frac{1}{2\pi i} \int_{C_1} \frac{f(w)}{z-a} \left[\frac{1}{1-(w-a)/(z-a)} \right] dw$$

Now in each of these integrals let us apply the expansion

$$\frac{1}{1-u} = 1 + u + u^2 + \cdots + u^{n-1} + \frac{u^n}{1-u}$$

which we used in deriving Taylor's theorem in the last section. Then

$$f(z) = \frac{1}{2\pi i} \int_{C_2} \frac{f(w)}{w-a} \left[1 + \left(\frac{z-a}{w-a}\right) + \cdots + \left(\frac{z-a}{w-a}\right)^{n-1} \right.$$

$$\left. + \frac{[(z-a)/(w-a)]^n}{1-(z-a)/(w-a)} \right] dw + \frac{1}{2\pi i} \int_{C_1} \frac{f(w)}{z-a} \left[1 + \left(\frac{w-a}{z-a}\right) \right.$$

$$\left. + \cdots + \left(\frac{w-a}{z-a}\right)^{n-1} + \frac{[(w-a)/(z-a)]^n}{1-(w-a)/(z-a)} \right] dw$$

$$= \frac{1}{2\pi i} \int_{C_2} \frac{f(w)dw}{w-a} + \frac{z-a}{2\pi i} \int_{C_2} \frac{f(w)dw}{(w-a)^2} + \cdots$$

$$+ \frac{(z-a)^{n-1}}{2\pi i} \int_{C_2} \frac{f(w)dw}{(w-a)^n} + R_{n2} + \frac{1}{2\pi i(z-a)} \int_{C_1} f(w)dw$$

$$+ \frac{1}{2\pi i(z-a)^2} \int_{C_1} (w-a)f(w)dw + \cdots$$

$$+ \frac{1}{2\pi i(z-a)^n} \int_{C_1} (w-a)^{n-1}f(w)dw + R_{n1}$$

where

$$R_{n2} = \frac{(z-a)^n}{2\pi i} \int_{C_2} \frac{f(w)dw}{(w-a)^n(w-z)}$$

$$R_{n1} = \frac{1}{2\pi i(z-a)^n} \int_{C_1} \frac{(w-a)^n f(w)}{z-w} dw$$

The truth of the theorem will be established if we can show that

$$\lim_{n \to \infty} R_{n2} = 0 \qquad \text{and} \qquad \lim_{n \to \infty} R_{n1} = 0$$

The proof of the first of these we can pass over without comment because it was given in complete detail in the derivation of Taylor's series. To prove the second, we note that for values of w on C_1 (Fig. 11.3)

$$|w - a| = r_1$$
$$|z - a| = \rho, \text{ say, where } \rho > r_1$$
$$|z - w| = |(z - a) - (w - a)| \geqq \rho - r_1$$

and

$$|f(w)| \leqq M$$

where M is the maximum of $|f(z)|$ on C_1. Then

$$\begin{aligned}
|R_{n1}| &= \left| \frac{1}{2\pi i (z-a)^n} \int_{C_1} \frac{(w-a)^n f(w)}{z-w} \, dw \right| \\
&\leqq \frac{1}{|2\pi i||z-a|^n} \int_{C_1} \frac{|w-a|^n |f(w)|}{|z-w|} \, |dw| \\
&\leqq \frac{1}{2\pi \rho^n} \frac{r_1^n M}{\rho - r_1} \int_{C_1} |dw| \\
&= \frac{M}{2\pi} \left(\frac{r_1}{\rho} \right)^n \frac{2\pi r_1}{\rho - r_1} \\
&= M \left(\frac{r_1}{\rho} \right)^n \frac{r_1}{\rho - r_1}
\end{aligned}$$

Since $\dfrac{r_1}{\rho} < 1$, the last expression approaches zero as n approaches infinity. Hence $\lim\limits_{n \to \infty} R_{n1} = 0$, and thus we have

$$\begin{aligned}
f(z) = {}& \frac{1}{2\pi i} \int_{C_2} \frac{f(w)dw}{w-a} + \frac{1}{2\pi i} \int_{C_2} \frac{f(w)dw}{(w-a)^2} (z-a) \\
& + \frac{1}{2\pi i} \int_{C_2} \frac{f(w)dw}{(w-a)^3} (z-a)^2 + \cdots \\
& + \frac{1}{2\pi i} \int_{C_1} f(w)dw \frac{1}{z-a} + \frac{1}{2\pi i} \int_{C_1} f(w)(w-a)dw \frac{1}{(z-a)^2} + \cdots
\end{aligned}$$

Since $f(z)$ is analytic throughout the region between C_1 and C_2, the paths of integration C_1 and C_2 can be replaced by any other curve C within this region and encircling C_1. This completes the proof of the theorem.

It should be noted that the coefficients, a_n, for $n \geqq 0$, namely,

$$\frac{1}{2\pi i} \int_{C_2} \frac{f(w)dw}{(w-a)^{n+1}}$$

cannot be replaced by the derivative expressions

$$\frac{f^{(n)}(a)}{n!}$$

as they were in the derivation of Taylor's series, since $f(z)$ is not analytic throughout the interior of C_2, and hence Cauchy's generalized integral formula cannot be applied. Specifically, $f(z)$ may have many points of nonanalyticity within C_1, and therefore within C_2.

Ordinarily the Laurent expansion of a function is not found through the use of the last theorem. Instead, various algebraic manipulations suggested by the nature of the function are employed. That this is a correct procedure follows from the fact that *the Laurent expansion of a function over a given annulus is unique.* In other words, if an expansion of the Laurent type is found by any process, it must be *the* Laurent expansion.

Example 1

Find the Laurent expansion of

$$f(z) = \frac{1}{z(1 - z)^2}$$

in each of the annuli shown in Fig. 11.4.

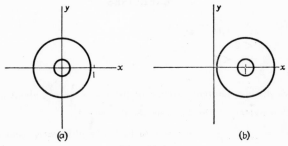

(a)   (b)

FIG. 11.4.

To obtain the expansion of $f(z)$ over the first annular region we write

$$f(z) = \frac{1}{z}(1 - z)^{-2}$$

and expand the second factor by the binomial expansion, getting

$$f(z) = \frac{1}{z}(1 + 2z + 3z^2 + 4z^3 + \cdots) \checkmark$$

$$= \frac{1}{z} + 2 + 3z + 4z^2 + \cdots$$

Over the second annulus we write

$$f(z) = \frac{1}{(z - 1)^2}\left[\frac{1}{1 + (z - 1)}\right] = \frac{1}{(z - 1)^2}[1 + (z - 1)]^{-1}$$

and expand the second factor by the binomial expansion:

$$f(z) = \frac{1}{(z-1)^2} [1 - (z-1) + (z-1)^2 - (z-1)^3 + \cdots]$$

$$= \frac{1}{(z-1)^2} - \frac{1}{z-1} + 1 - (z-1) + (z-1)^2 - \cdots$$

Incidentally, the fact that we have obtained the Laurent expansion without using the general theory means that we can evaluate the integrals in the coefficient formulas by comparing them with the numerical values of the coefficients which we have found independently. For instance, in the second of the expansions, the coefficient of $(z-1)^{-1}$ is -1. According to the theory of Laurent's expansion, the coefficient of this term is

$$a_{-1} = \frac{1}{2\pi i} \int_C f(z) dz = \frac{1}{2\pi i} \int_C \frac{dz}{z(1-z)^2}$$

where C is any curve in the second annulus which encircles the point $z = 1$. Thus although we have done nothing resembling an integration, we have nonetheless shown that

$$\frac{1}{2\pi i} \int_C \frac{dz}{z(1-z)^2} = -1 \quad \text{or} \quad \int_C \frac{dz}{z(1-z)^2} = -2\pi i$$

In the next chapter we shall endeavor to capitalize systematically on this possibility.

EXERCISES

1. Expand $f(z) = \dfrac{1}{(z-1)(z-2)}$

(a) For $1 < |z| < 2$

(b) For $0 < |z-1| < 1$

(c) For $|z| > 2$

2. Obtain two distinct Laurent expansions for $f(z) = \dfrac{1+2z}{1-z^2}$ about $z = 1$, and tell where each converges. Do the same about $z = -1$.

3. Expand $f(z) = \dfrac{1}{z^2(z-i)}$ about $z = i$, and tell where the expansions converge.

4. Construct all the Laurent expansions in powers of z associated with

$$f(z) = \frac{1}{z(z-1)(z-2)}$$

and tell where each converges.

5. If k is a real number such that $k^2 < 1$, prove that

$$\sum_{n=0}^{\infty} k^n \sin [(n+1)\theta] = \frac{\sin \theta}{1+k^2-2k\cos\theta}$$

$$\sum_{n=0}^{\infty} k^n \cos [(n+1)\theta] = \frac{\cos \theta - k}{1+k^2-2k\cos\theta}$$

[Hint: Expand $(z-k)^{-1}$ for $|z| > k$, set $z = e^{i\theta}$, and equate real and imaginary components of the resulting expression.]

CHAPTER 12

THE THEORY OF RESIDUES

12.1 The Residue Theorem. We have already defined a singular point of a function as one at which the function fails to be analytic. If $z = a$ is a singular point of the function $f(z)$, but if there exists a circle with center at a in which there are no other singular points of $f(z)$, then $z = a$ is called an **isolated singular point.** If $z = a$ is an isolated singularity of $f(z)$, then $f(z)$ can be expanded in a Laurent series around $z = a$. Moreover, because the singularity is isolated, the inner radius of the annulus can be made as small as we please.

If in the expansion of $f(z)$ around an isolated singular point, all negative powers of $(z - a)$ after the mth are missing, $f(z)$ is said to have a **pole of order** m **at** $z = a$, and the sum of the negative powers

$$\frac{a_{-m}}{(z - a)^m} + \cdots + \frac{a_{-2}}{(z - a)^2} + \frac{a_{-1}}{(z - a)}$$

is called the **principal part of** $f(z)$ at $z = a$. If the Laurent expansion of $f(z)$ contains an infinite number of negative powers of $(z - a)$, then $z = a$ is called an **essential singularity** of the function. For instance, the function

$$\frac{1}{z(1 - z)^2} = \frac{1}{(z - 1)^2} - \frac{1}{z - 1} + 1 - (z - 1) + (z - 1)^2 - \cdots$$

which we considered in Example 1, Sec. 11.3, has a pole of order 2 at $z = 1$, and the principal part of $f(z)$ at $z = 1$ is

$$\frac{1}{(z - 1)^2} - \frac{1}{z - 1}$$

On the other hand,

$$e^{1/z} = 1 + \frac{1}{z} + \frac{1}{2!z^2} + \frac{1}{3!z^3} + \frac{1}{4!z^4} + \cdots$$

has an essential singularity at $z = 0$.

As we suggested at the end of the last chapter, the coefficient, a_{-1}, of the term $(z - a)^{-1}$ in the Laurent expansion of a function, $f(z)$, is of great importance because of its connection with the integral of the function, through the formula

363

Def. ✓ Residue

$$a_{-1} = \frac{1}{2\pi i} \int_C f(z)dz$$

In particular, the coefficient of $(z - a)^{-1}$ in the expansion of $f(z)$ *around an isolated singular point* is called the **residue** of $f(z)$ at that point.

Now consider a simple closed curve C containing in its interior a number of isolated singularities of a function $f(z)$ (Fig. 12.1). If around each singular point we draw a circle so small that it encloses no other singular points, these circles, together with the curve C, form the boundary of a

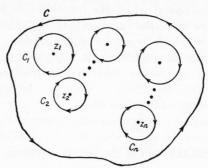

Fig. 12.1.

multiply connected region in which $f(z)$ is everywhere analytic and to which Cauchy's theorem can therefore be applied. This gives

$$\frac{1}{2\pi i} \int_C f(z)dz + \frac{1}{2\pi i} \int_{C_1} f(z)dz + \cdots + \frac{1}{2\pi i} \int_{C_n} f(z)dz = 0$$

If we reverse the direction of integration around each of the circles and change the sign of each of the integrals to compensate, this can be written

$$\frac{1}{2\pi i} \int_C f(z)dz = \frac{1}{2\pi i} \int_{C_1} f(z)dz + \cdots + \frac{1}{2\pi i} \int_{C_n} f(z)dz$$

where all integrals are now to be taken in the counterclockwise sense. But the integrals on the right are, by definition, just the residues of $f(z)$ at the various isolated singularities within C. Hence we have established the important residue theorem.

Theorem 1. If C is a closed curve and if $f(z)$ is analytic within and on C except at a finite number of singular points in the interior of C, then

$$\int_C f(z)dz = 2\pi i[r_1 + r_2 + r_3 + \cdots + r_n]$$

where $r_1, r_2, \ldots, r_n$ are the residues of $f(z)$ at the singular points within C.

Example 1

What is the integral of

$$f(z) = \frac{-3z + 4}{z(z - 1)(z - 2)}$$

around the circle $|z| = \frac{3}{2}$?

In this case although there are three singular points of the function, namely, the three first order poles at $z = 0$, $z = 1$, and $z = 2$, only $z = 0$ and $z = 1$ lie within the contour of integration. Hence the core of the problem is to find the residues of $f(z)$ at these two points:

At $z = 0$, we have

$$f(z) = \frac{(-3z + 4)(1 - z)^{-1}(2 - z)^{-1}}{z}$$

$$= \frac{1}{z} (-3z + 4)(1 + z + z^2 + \cdots) \left(\frac{1}{2} + \frac{z}{4} + \frac{z^2}{8} + \cdots \right)$$

$$= \frac{2}{z} + \frac{3}{2} + \frac{5z}{4} + \cdots$$

The residue of $f(z)$ at $z = 0$ is therefore 2.

At $z = 1$, we have

$$f(z) = \frac{[-3(z - 1) + 1][1 + (z - 1)]^{-1}[-1 + (z - 1)]^{-1}}{z - 1}$$

$$= \frac{[-3(z - 1) + 1][1 - (z - 1) + (z - 1)^2 \cdots \cdot][-1 - (z - 1) - (z - 1)^2 \cdots \cdot]}{z - 1}$$

$$= \frac{-1}{z - 1} + 3 - (z - 1) + \cdots$$

The residue at $z = 1$ is therefore -1. Hence, according to the residue theorem,

$$\int_C \frac{-3z + 4}{z(z - 1)(z - 2)} \, dz = 2\pi i[(2) + (-1)] = 2\pi i$$

The determination of residues by the use of series expansions, as we have just illustrated, is often quite tedious. Hence it is desirable to have a simpler alternative procedure. Such a process is provided by the following considerations. Suppose first that $f(z)$ has a simple or first-order pole at $z = a$. We can then write

$$f(z) = \frac{a_{-1}}{z - a} + a_0 + a_1(z - a) + \cdots$$

If we multiply this identity by $(z - a)$, we get

$$(z - a)f(z) = a_{-1} + a_0(z - a) + a_1(z - a)^2 + \cdots$$

Now if we let $z \to a$, we obtain for the residue

(1) $$a_{-1} = \lim_{z \to a} [(z - a)f(z)]$$

If $f(z)$ has a second-order pole at $z = a$, we have

$$f(z) = \frac{a_{-2}}{(z - a)^2} + \frac{a_{-1}}{(z - a)} + a_0 + a_1(z - a) + \cdots$$

This time, to obtain a_{-1}, we must multiply this identity by $(z - a)^2$ and then differentiate with respect to z before we let $z \to a$. Then

(2) $$a_{-1} = \lim_{z \to a} \frac{d}{dz} [(z - a)^2 f(z)]$$

The same procedure can be extended to poles of higher order, giving the general formula for the residue at a pole of order m,

(3) $$(m - 1)!\, a_{-1} = \lim_{z \to a} \frac{d^{m-1}}{dz^{m-1}} [(z - a)^m f(z)]$$

The process evidently fails if $z = a$ is an essential singularity of $f(z)$.

Example 1 (continued)

Reconsidering Example 1 in the light of this new technique, we have at $z = 0$,

$$a_{-1} = \lim_{z \to 0} \left[z \left\{ \frac{-3z + 4}{z(z - 1)(z - 2)} \right\} \right] = \lim_{z \to 0} \left[\frac{-3z + 4}{(z - 1)(z - 2)} \right] = 2$$

and at $z = 1$,

$$a_{-1} = \lim_{z \to 1} \left[(z - 1) \left\{ \frac{-3z + 4}{z(z - 1)(z - 2)} \right\} \right] = \lim_{z \to 1} \left[\frac{-3z + 4}{z(z - 2)} \right] = -1$$

These values for the residues are of course the same as those we found before.

EXERCISES

1. Find the residue of $f(z) = \dfrac{z}{z^2 + 1}$ at $z = i$ and at $z = -i$.

2. Find the residue of $f(z) = \dfrac{z + 1}{z^2(z - 2)}$ at $z = 0$ and at $z = 2$.

3. What is the residue of $f(z) = \dfrac{1}{(z + 1)^3}$ at $z = -1$?

4. What is the residue of $f(z) = \tan z$ at $z = \pi/2$?

5. Find the residue of $f(z) = \dfrac{z}{z^2 + 2z + 5}$ at each of its poles.

12.2 The Evaluation of Real Definite Integrals.   There are several large and important classes of real definite integrals to which the application of the theory of residues can be made a routine matter.   The results in question are contained in the next three theorems.

Theorem 1.   If $R(\cos \theta, \sin \theta)$ is a rational function of $\cos \theta$ and $\sin \theta$ which is finite on the closed interval $0 \leqq \theta \leqq 2\pi$, and if $f(z)$ is the function of z obtained from R by the substitutions

$$\cos \theta = \frac{z + z^{-1}}{2} \qquad \text{and} \qquad \sin \theta = \frac{z - z^{-1}}{2i}$$

then $\int_0^{2\pi} R(\cos\theta, \sin\theta)d\theta$ is equal to $2\pi i$ times the sum of the residues of the function

$$\frac{f(z)}{iz}$$

at such of its poles as lie within the unit circle, $|z| = 1$.

To prove this, let us transform the given integral by means of the substitution

$$z = e^{i\theta}$$

according to which

$$\cos\theta = \frac{e^{i\theta} + e^{-i\theta}}{2} = \frac{z + z^{-1}}{2}, \qquad \sin\theta = \frac{e^{i\theta} - e^{-i\theta}}{2i} = \frac{z - z^{-1}}{2i}, \qquad d\theta = \frac{dz}{iz}$$

Under this transformation the original integrand becomes a rational function of z which we call $f(z)$. Furthermore, as θ ranges from 0 to 2π, the relation $z = e^{i\theta}$ shows that z ranges around the unit circle, $|z| = 1$. Hence the transformed integral is

$$\int_C f(z)\frac{dz}{iz}$$

where C is the unit circle. By the residue theorem, the value of this integral is $2\pi i$ times the sum of the residues at those poles of its integrand, namely, $f(z)/iz$, which lie within the unit circle. Since this integral is exactly equal to the original one, the theorem is established.

Example 1

What is the value of $\int_0^{2\pi} \dfrac{\cos 2\theta\, d\theta}{1 - 2p\cos\theta + p^2}$ $0 < p < 1$

Since the denominator of the integrand can be written

$$1 - 2p\cos\theta + p^2 = 1 - 2p + p^2 + 2p - 2p\cos\theta = (1 - p)^2 + 2p(1 - \cos\theta)$$

it is clear that it can never vanish for $0 \leqq \theta \leqq 2\pi$ if $0 < p < 1$. Hence the preceding theory is applicable. Now

$$\cos 2\theta = \frac{e^{2i\theta} + e^{-2i\theta}}{2} = \frac{z^2 + z^{-2}}{2}$$

and thus the integral becomes

$$\int_C \frac{z^2 + z^{-2}}{2}\, \frac{1}{1 - 2p\left(\dfrac{z + z^{-1}}{2}\right) + p^2}\, \frac{dz}{iz} = \int_C \frac{z^4 + 1}{2z^2}\, \frac{z}{z - pz^2 - p + p^2 z}\, \frac{dz}{iz}$$

$$= \int_C \frac{(1 + z^4)dz}{2iz^2(1 - pz)(z - p)}$$

Of the three poles of the integrand, only the first-order pole at $z = p$ and the second-order pole at $z = 0$ lie within the unit circle. For the residue at the former, we have

$$\lim_{z \to p} \left[(z - p) \frac{1 + z^4}{2iz^2(1 - pz)(z - p)} \right] = \frac{1 + p^4}{2ip^2(1 - p^2)}$$

For the residue at $z = 0$, we have

$$\lim_{z \to 0} \frac{d}{dz} \left[z^2 \frac{1 + z^4}{2iz^2(z - pz^2 - p + p^2z)} \right]$$

$$= \lim_{z \to 0} \frac{(z - pz^2 - p + p^2z)(4z^3) - (1 + z^4)(1 - 2pz + p^2)}{2i(z - pz^2 - p + p^2z)^2}$$

$$= -\frac{1 + p^2}{2ip^2}$$

The value of the integral is therefore

$$2\pi i \left[\frac{1 + p^4}{2ip^2(1 - p^2)} - \frac{1 + p^2}{2ip^2} \right] = \frac{2\pi p^2}{1 - p^2}$$

Theorem 2. If $Q(z)$ is a function which is analytic in the upper half of the z-plane except at a finite number of poles, none of which lies on the real axis, and if $|zQ(z)|$ converges uniformly to zero when $z \to \infty$ through values for which $0 \leq \arg z \leq \pi$, then $\int_{-\infty}^{\infty} Q(x)dx$ is equal to $2\pi i$ times the sum of the residues at the poles of $Q(z)$ which lie in the upper half plane.

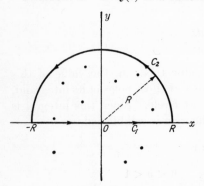

FIG. 12.2.

To prove this, we consider a semi-circular contour with center at $z = 0$ and with radius R large enough to include all the poles of $Q(z)$ which lie in the upper half plane (Fig. 12.2). Then by the residue theorem

$$\int_{C_1 + C_2} Q(z)dz = 2\pi i \sum \text{residues of } Q(z) \text{ at all poles within } C_1 + C_2$$

or

$$\int_{-R}^{R} Q(x)dx + \int_{C_2} Q(z)dz = 2\pi i \sum \text{residues}$$

Hence

(1)
$$\left| \int_{-R}^{R} Q(x)dx - 2\pi i \sum \text{residues} \right| = \left| \int_{C_2} Q(z)dz \right|$$

In the integral on the right, let $z = Re^{i\theta}$, so that

$$dz = Rie^{i\theta} d\theta = iz d\theta$$

Then

$$\left| \int_{C_2} Q(z)dz \right| = \left| \int_0^\pi Q(z)iz\, d\theta \right| \leqq \int_0^\pi |zQ(z)||d\theta|$$

But by the hypothesis that $zQ(z)$ converges *uniformly* to zero when $z \to \infty$ and $0 \leqq \arg z \leqq \pi$, it follows that for any arbitrarily small positive quantity, say ϵ/π, there exists a radius R_0 such that

$$|zQ(z)| < \frac{\epsilon}{\pi}$$

for all values of z on C_2 whenever $R > R_0$. Thus for $R > R_0$

$$\int_0^\pi |zQ(z)||d\theta| < \frac{\epsilon}{\pi} \int_0^\pi |d\theta| = \epsilon$$

This coupled with (1) proves that

$$\lim_{R \to \infty} \int_{-R}^R Q(x)dx = 2\pi i \sum \text{residues}$$

Since the limit on the left is what we mean by $\int_{-\infty}^\infty Q(x)dx$,* the theorem is established.

In particular, the quotient of two polynomials, $p(z)/q(z)$, automatically satisfies all the hypotheses of the last theorem whenever the order of the denominator exceeds the order of the numerator by at least two. Hence we can state the highly important corollary.

Corollary 1.   If $p(x)$ and $q(x)$ are real polynomials, such that the order of $q(x)$ is at least two more than the order of $p(x)$, and if $q(x) = 0$ has no real roots, then

$$\int_{-\infty}^\infty \frac{p(x)}{q(x)}\, dx = 2\pi i \sum \text{residues of } \frac{p(z)}{q(z)} \text{ at its poles in the upper half plane}$$

* Actually,

$$\lim_{R \to \infty} \int_{-R}^R Q(x)dx$$

is only the **principal value** of the integral $\int_{-\infty}^\infty Q(x)dx$, whose correct definition is

$$\lim_{R \to \infty} \int_{-R}^0 Q(x)dx + \lim_{S \to \infty} \int_0^S Q(x)dx$$

where R and S approach infinity independently of each other. As the simple function $Q(x) \equiv x$ shows, the principal value of an integral may exist when the integral itself is undefined.

Example 2

Evaluate

$$\int_{-\infty}^{\infty} \frac{x^2\,dx}{(x^2+a^2)(x^2+b^2)}$$

This is an integral to which the corollary of Theorem 2 can surely be applied. The only poles of

$$\frac{z^2}{(z^2+a^2)(z^2+b^2)}$$

are at $z = \pm ai,\ \pm bi$. Of these, only $z = ai$ and $z = bi$ lie in the upper half plane. At $z = ai$, the residue is

$$\lim_{z\to ai}\left[(z-ai)\frac{z^2}{(z-ai)(z+ai)(z^2+b^2)}\right] = \frac{-a^2}{2ai(b^2-a^2)} = \frac{a}{2i(a^2-b^2)}$$

From symmetry, the residue at $z = ib$ is obviously $b/2i(b^2-a^2)$. Hence the value of the integral is

$$2\pi i\left[\frac{a}{2i(a^2-b^2)}+\frac{b}{2i(b^2-a^2)}\right] = \frac{\pi}{a+b}$$

If $Q(z)$ satisfies all the hypotheses of the last theorem, then so does $e^{imz}Q(z)$, provided $m > 0$. For e^{imz} is analytic everywhere, and under the assumption that $m > 0$, its absolute value is

$$\left|e^{imz}\right| = \left|e^{im(x+iy)}\right| = \left|e^{imx}e^{-my}\right| = e^{-my}$$

which is less than one for all values of y in the upper half plane.

Therefore

$$\left|e^{imz}zQ(z)\right| \leqq \left|zQ(z)\right|$$

and thus if the latter converges uniformly to zero when $|z| \to \infty$ and $0 \leqq \arg z \leqq \pi$, so will the former. Hence the conclusions of the last theorem can be applied equally well to $e^{imz}Q(z)$, and we can write

$$(2)\quad \int_{-\infty}^{\infty} e^{imx}Q(x)\,dx = 2\pi i \sum \text{residues of } e^{imz}Q(z) \text{ at its poles in the upper half plane}$$

Separating the last integral into its real and its imaginary parts, and equating these to the corresponding terms on the right of (2), we find

$$(3)\quad \int_{-\infty}^{\infty} \cos mx\, Q(x)dx = -2\pi \sum \text{imaginary parts of the residues}$$

$$(4)\quad \int_{-\infty}^{\infty} \sin mx\, Q(x)dx = 2\pi \sum \text{real parts of the residues}$$

Example 3

Evaluate

$$\int_{-\infty}^{\infty} \frac{\cos mx}{1+x^2}\,dx$$

To do this, we consider the related integral

$$\int_{-\infty}^{\infty} \frac{e^{imx}\,dx}{1+x^2}$$

The only pole of $e^{imz}/(1 + z^2)$ in the upper half plane is at $z = i$, and the residue there is

$$\lim_{z\to i}\left[(z-i)\frac{e^{imz}}{(z-i)(z+i)}\right] = \frac{e^{-m}}{2i} = \frac{-ie^{-m}}{2}$$

Hence by (3)

$$\int_{-\infty}^{\infty} \frac{\cos\,mx\,dx}{1+x^2} = -2\pi\mathcal{I}\left(\frac{-ie^{-m}}{2}\right) = \pi e^{-m}$$

Theorem 3. If $Q(z)$ is analytic everywhere in the z-plane except at a finite number of poles, none of which lies on the positive half of the real

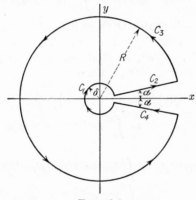

FIG. 12.3.

axis, and if $z^aQ(z)$ converges uniformly to zero when z approaches either zero or infinity, then

$$\int_0^{\infty} x^{a-1}Q(x)dx = \frac{\pi}{\sin a\pi} \sum \text{residues of } (-z)^{a-1}Q(z) \text{ at all its poles}$$

To prove this, consider the integral of $(-z)^{a-1}Q(z)$ around the contour shown in Fig. 12.3. If a is not an integer, $(-z)^{a-1}$ is a multiple-valued function which is to be interpreted as

$$(-z)^{a-1} = e^{(a-1)\log(-z)} = e^{(a-1)[\log|z|+i\,\text{arg}(-z)]}, \qquad -\pi \leqq \text{arg } z \leqq \pi$$

With this agreement, $(-z)^{a-1}Q(z)$ is single-valued and analytic everywhere except on the positive real axis and at the poles of $Q(z)$.* Now by the residue theorem

---

* The seemingly more natural function $z^{a-1}Q(z)$ could also have been used, subject to the agreement that $0 \leqq \text{arg } z \leqq 2\pi$. The final expression for the integral is not quite so convenient in this case, however.

$$\int_{C_1+C_2+C_3+C_4} (-z)^{a-1}Q(z)dz = \int_{C_1} (-z)^{a-1}Q(z)dz + \int_{C_2} (-z)^{a-1}Q(z)dz$$
$$+ \int_{C_3} (-z)^{a-1}Q(z)dz + \int_{C_4} (-z)^{a-1}Q(z)dz$$
$$= 2\pi i\Sigma \text{ residues of } (-z)^{a-1}Q(z) \text{ at the poles within } C$$

On the small circle, let $-z = \delta e^{i\theta}$ and $dz = -iz\, d\theta$. Then*

$$\int_{C_1} (-z)^{a-1}Q(z)dz = \int_{\pi}^{-\pi} i(-z)^a Q(z)d\theta$$

and from the hypothesis that $|z^a Q(z)| \to 0$ as $|z| \to 0$, it is clear that the last integral approaches zero as $|z| \equiv \delta \to 0$.

On the large circle, let $-z = Re^{i\theta}$ and $dz = -iz\, d\theta$. Then

$$\int_{C_3} (-z)^{a-1}Q(z)dz = \int_{-\pi}^{\pi} i(-z)^a Q(z)d\theta$$

and from the hypothesis that $|z^a Q(z)| \to 0$ as $|z| \to \infty$, it is clear that this integral approaches zero as $|z| \equiv R \to \infty$.

Now on C_2 write $z = re^{i\alpha}$, so that $-z = re^{i(\alpha-\pi)}$; and on C_4 write $z = re^{-i\alpha}$, so that $-z = re^{-i(\alpha-\pi)}$. Then

$$\int_{C_2} (-z)^{a-1}Q(z)dz = \int_{\delta}^{R} [re^{i(\alpha-\pi)}]^{a-1}Q(re^{i\alpha})(e^{i\alpha}\, dr)$$
$$= \int_{\delta}^{R} r^{a-1}e^{i(\alpha-\pi)(a-1)}Q(re^{i\alpha})(e^{i\alpha}\, dr)$$

and

$$\int_{C_4} (-z)^{a-1}Q(z)dz = \int_{R}^{\delta} [re^{-i(\alpha-\pi)}]^{a-1}Q(re^{-i\alpha})(e^{-i\alpha}\, dr)$$
$$= \int_{R}^{\delta} r^{a-1}e^{-i(\alpha-\pi)(a-1)}Q(re^{-i\alpha})(e^{-i\alpha}\, dr)$$

When $\delta \to 0$, and $R \to \infty$, as before, and when $\alpha \to 0$, so that $r \to x$, these integrals become, respectively,

$$\int_0^\infty x^{a-1}e^{-i\pi(a-1)}Q(x)dx = e^{i\pi}e^{-i\pi a}\int_0^\infty x^{a-1}Q(x)dx = -e^{-i\pi a}\int_0^\infty x^{a-1}Q(x)dx$$

and

$$\int_\infty^0 x^{a-1}e^{i\pi(a-1)}Q(x)dx = -e^{-i\pi}e^{i\pi a}\int_0^\infty x^{a-1}Q(x)dx = e^{i\pi a}\int_\infty^\infty x^{a-1}Q(x)dx$$

Therefore, as δ and α approach zero, and as R approaches ∞, we have

$$\int_{C_1} (-z)^{a-1}Q(z)dz + \int_{C_2} (-z)^{a-1}Q(z)dz + \int_{C_3} (-z)^{a-1}Q(z)dz$$
$$+ \int_{C_4} (-z)^{a-1}Q(z)dz = 0 - e^{-i\pi a}\int_0^\infty x^{a-1}Q(x)dx + 0$$
$$+ e^{i\pi a}\int_0^\infty x^{a-1}Q(x)dx = 2\pi i\sum \text{residues}$$

---

* The infinitesimal angular gap at $\theta = 0$ which is neglected in the second integral obviously has no effect on the final result.

or, collecting terms and solving for the integral in question,

$$(e^{i\pi a} - e^{-i\pi a}) \int_0^\infty x^{a-1} Q(x) dx = 2\pi i \sum \text{residues}$$

$$\int_0^\infty x^{a-1} Q(x) dx = \frac{\pi}{(e^{i\pi a} - e^{-i\pi a})/2i} \sum \text{residues} = \frac{\pi}{\sin a\pi} \sum \text{residues}$$

as asserted.

Example 4

Evaluate

$$\int_0^\infty \frac{x^{a-1}}{1 + x^2} dx \qquad 0 < a < 2$$

For a within the specified range, the conditions of the last theorem are fulfilled; hence the given integral is equal to $\pi/\sin a\pi$ times the sum of the residues of $\dfrac{(-z)^{a-1}}{1 + z^2}$ at $z = \pm i$.

At $z = i$, we have for the residue

$$\lim_{z \to i} \left[(z - i) \frac{(-z)^{a-1}}{(z - i)(z + i)} \right] = \frac{(-i)^{a-1}}{2i} = \frac{(e^{-(i\pi/2)})^{a-1}}{2i} = \frac{e^{-[i\pi(a-1)/2]}}{2i}$$

At $z = -i$, we have for the residue

$$\lim_{z \to -i} \left[(z + i) \frac{(-z)^{a-1}}{(z - i)(z + i)} \right] = \frac{i^{a-1}}{-2i} = \frac{(e^{i\pi/2})^{a-1}}{-2i} = \frac{e^{[i\pi(a-1)/2]}}{-2i}$$

The value of the integral is therefore

$$\int_0^\infty \frac{x^{a-1} dx}{1 + x^2} = \frac{\pi}{\sin a\pi} \left[\frac{e^{[i\pi(a-1)/2]} - e^{-[i\pi(a-1)/2]}}{-2i} \right] = -\frac{\pi}{\sin a\pi} \sin \frac{(a - 1)\pi}{2}$$

For definite integrals not covered by the last three theorems, evaluation by the method of residues, when possible at all, is usually a matter of considerable ingenuity, which only the skills acquired through practice can supply. As a final example of this sort, we consider the following integral.

Example 5

Evaluate

$$\int_{-\infty}^\infty \frac{\cos mx \, dx}{e^x + e^{-x}}$$

To do this, consider $\displaystyle\int_C \frac{e^{imz} dz}{e^z + e^{-z}}$, where C is the rectangular contour shown in Fig. 12.4. The integrand has a simple pole at $z = i\pi/2$, since

$$e^{i\pi/2} + e^{-(i\pi/2)} = 2 \cos\left(\frac{\pi}{2}\right) = 0;$$

and for all values of R this is the only pole within C. Therefore by the residue theorem

$$\int_C \frac{e^{imz} dz}{e^z + e^{-z}} = 2\pi i \left(\text{residue of } \frac{e^{imz}}{e^z + e^{-z}} \text{ at } z = \frac{i\pi}{2} \right)$$

To compute the residue at this point, we have as usual

$$\lim_{z \to \frac{i\pi}{2}} \left[\left(z - \frac{i\pi}{2} \right) \frac{e^{imz}}{e^z + e^{-z}} \right]$$

However, the denominator does not factor readily in this case, and as a consequence the indeterminate form arising when $z \to \dfrac{i\pi}{2}$ cannot be evaluated simply by canceling

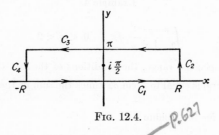

P.627

Fig. 12.4.

the factor $[z - (i\pi/2)]$ from numerator and denominator before letting z approach $i\pi/2$. The formal application of L'Hospital's rule is perhaps the easiest procedure here. This gives

$$\lim_{z \to \frac{i\pi}{2}} (e^{imz}) \cdot \lim_{z \to \frac{i\pi}{2}} \left[\frac{z - (i\pi/2)}{e^z + e^{-z}} \right] = e^{-m(\pi/2)} \left[\frac{1}{e^{i\pi/2} - e^{-(i\pi/2)}} \right] = \frac{e^{-m(\pi/2)}}{2i}$$

Hence

(5) $$\int_C \frac{e^{imz}\, dz}{e^z + e^{-z}} = 2i\pi \left[\frac{e^{-m(\pi/2)}}{2i} \right] = \pi e^{-(m\pi/2)}$$

Now

$$\int_C \frac{e^{imz}\, dz}{e^z + e^{-z}} = \int_{C_1} \frac{e^{imz}\, dz}{e^z + e^{-z}} + \int_{C_2} \frac{e^{imz}\, dz}{e^z + e^{-z}} + \int_{C_3} \frac{e^{imz}\, dz}{e^z + e^{-z}} + \int_{C_4} \frac{e^{imz}\, dz}{e^z + e^{-z}}$$

$$= \int_{-R}^{R} \frac{e^{imx}\, dx}{e^x + e^{-x}} + \int_0^{\pi} \frac{e^{im(R+iy)}i\, dy}{e^{R+iy} + e^{-(R+iy)}} + \int_R^{-R} \frac{e^{im(x+i\pi)}\, dx}{e^{x+i\pi} + e^{-(x+i\pi)}}$$
$$+ \int_{\pi}^{0} \frac{e^{im(-R+iy)}i\, dy}{e^{-R+iy} + e^{-(-R+iy)}}$$

$$= \int_{-R}^{R} \frac{e^{imx}\, dx}{e^x + e^{-z}} + \int_0^{\pi} \frac{e^{imR}e^{-my}i\, dy}{e^R e^{iy} + e^{-R}e^{-iy}} - e^{-m\pi} \int_R^{-R} \frac{e^{imx}\, dx}{e^x + e^{-x}}$$
$$+ \int_{\pi}^{0} \frac{e^{-imR}e^{-my}i\, dy}{e^{-R}e^{iy} + e^R e^{-iy}}$$

The second and fourth of these integrals approach zero as R approaches infinity, since their integrands approach zero as R approaches infinity, and the paths of integration are independent of R. Hence, letting $R \to \infty$, we have, from (5),

$$\int_{-\infty}^{\infty} \frac{e^{imx}\, dx}{e^x + e^{-x}} + e^{-m\pi} \int_{-\infty}^{\infty} \frac{e^{imx}\, dx}{e^x + e^{-x}} = \pi e^{-m\pi/2}$$

or

$$(1 + e^{-m\pi}) \int_{-\infty}^{\infty} \frac{e^{imx}\, dx}{e^x + e^{-x}} = \pi e^{-m\pi/2}$$

Equating the real parts of this equation, we have the desired result

$$\int_{-\infty}^{\infty} \frac{\cos mx \, dx}{e^x + e^{-x}} = \frac{\pi e^{-m\pi/2}}{1 + e^{-m\pi}} = \frac{\pi}{e^{m\pi/2} + e^{-m\pi/2}}$$

One further theorem from the theory of residues which is of considerable practical importance is the following.

Theorem 4. If $f(z)$ is analytic within and on a closed curve C, except at a finite number of poles, and if $f(z)$ has neither poles nor zeros on C, then

$$\frac{1}{2\pi i} \int_C \frac{f'(z)}{f(z)} \, dz = N - P$$

where N is the number of zeros of $f(z)$ within C, and P is the number of poles of $f(z)$ within C, each counted the appropriate number of times.

To prove this, suppose first that at a point $z = a_k$ within C, $f(z)$ has a zero of order n_k. Then $f(z)$ can be written

$$f(z) = (z - a_k)^{n_k} \phi(z)$$

where $\phi(z)$ is nonvanishing and analytic in a sufficiently small region around $z = a_k$. From this,

$$f'(z) = (z - a_k)^{n_k} \phi'(z) + n_k (z - a_k)^{n_k-1} \phi(z)$$

and thus

$$\frac{f'(z)}{f(z)} = \frac{(z - a_k)^{n_k} \phi'(z) + n_k (z - a_k)^{n_k-1} \phi(z)}{(z - a_k)^{n_k} \phi(z)}$$
$$= \frac{\phi'(z)}{\phi(z)} + \frac{n_k}{z - a_k}$$

Since $\phi(z)$, and hence $\phi'(z)$, is analytic at $z = a_k$, and since $\phi(z)$ does not vanish at $z = a_k$, the fraction $\phi'(z)/\phi(z)$ is analytic at $z = a_k$. Hence $f'(z)/f(z)$ has a simple pole with residue n_k at every point, a_k, where $f(z)$ has a zero of order n_k.

Suppose next that $f(z)$ has a pole of order p_k at the point $z = b_k$. Then we can write

$$f(z) = \frac{c_{p_k}}{(z - b_k)^{p_k}} + \frac{c_{p_k-1}}{(z - b_k)^{p_k-1}} + \cdots + \frac{c_1}{(z - b_k)}$$
$$+ \text{ terms analytic at } z = b_k$$

Hence, putting these fractions over a common denominator, we have around $z = b_k$,

$$f(z) = \frac{1}{(z - b_k)^{p_k}} \Psi(z) = (z - b_k)^{-p_k} \Psi(z)$$

where

$$\Psi(z) \equiv c_{p_k} + c_{p_k-1}(z - b_k) + c_{p_k-2}(z - b_k)^2 + \cdots$$

is obviously analytic and nonvanishing at $z = b_k$. Therefore around b_k,

$$f'(z) = (z - b_k)^{-p_k}\Psi'(z) - p_k(z - b_k)^{-p_k-1}\Psi(z)$$

and thus

$$\frac{f'(z)}{f(z)} = \frac{(z - b_k)^{-p_k}\Psi'(z) - p_k(z - b_k)^{-p_k-1}\Psi(z)}{(z - b_k)^{-p_k}\Psi(z)}$$

$$= \frac{\Psi'(z)}{\Psi(z)} - \frac{p_k}{z - b_k}$$

The first fraction here is clearly analytic; hence $f'(z)/f(z)$ has a simple pole with residue $-p_k$ at every point $z = b_k$ where $f(z)$ has a pole of order p_k.

Applying the residue theorem to $f'(z)/f(z)$ over the region bounded by C, we thus have

$$\int_C \frac{f'(z)}{f(z)} \, dz = 2\pi i \sum \text{residues}$$

$$= 2\pi i \left(\sum n_k - \sum p_k \right)$$

$$= 2\pi i (N - P)$$

since $\sum n_k$ is the total multiplicity of all the zeros of $f(z)$ within C and $\sum p_k$ is the total multiplicity of all the poles of $f(z)$ within C. Dividing by $2\pi i$, we obtain the assertion of the theorem.

An important alternative form of the last theorem can be derived by noting that

$$\frac{1}{2\pi i} \int_C \frac{f'(z)}{f(z)} \, dz = \frac{1}{2\pi i} \int_C d[\log f(z)]$$

Hence, performing the integration,

$$N - P = \frac{1}{2\pi i} \{\text{variation of } \log f(z) \text{ in going completely around } C\}$$

Now

$$\log f(z) = \log |f(z)| + i \arg f(z)$$

Clearly, $\log |f(z)|$ is the same at the beginning and at the end of any closed curve, and therefore

$$N - P = \frac{1}{2\pi i} \{\text{variation of } i \arg f(z) \text{ around } C\}$$

$$= \frac{\text{variation of } \arg f(z) \text{ around } C}{2\pi}$$

In particular, if $f(z)$ is analytic everywhere within C (so that $P = 0$), we have the important result:

Corollary 1. If $f(z)$ is analytic within and on a closed curve C, then the number of zeros of $f(z)$ within C is equal to $1/2\pi$ times the net variation in the argument of $f(z)$ as z traverses the curve C in the counterclockwise sense. In geometric terms, this means that if the locus of $f(z)$ is plotted for z ranging over the given contour C, then the number of times this locus encircles the origin is the number of zeros of $f(z)$ within C. This is known as the **principle of the argument,** and in its geometric form is the basis of the well-known Nyquist stability criterion which is encountered in the study of servomechanisms and amplifier circuits, for instance.

EXERCISES

Evaluate the following definite integrals by the method of residues:

1. $\displaystyle\int_0^{2\pi} \frac{d\theta}{1 - 2p \sin\theta + p^2}$ $\quad (0 < p < 1)$ $\qquad\qquad Ans.\ \dfrac{2\pi}{1 - p^2}$

2. $\displaystyle\int_0^{2\pi} \frac{\sin^2\theta\, d\theta}{a + b\cos\theta}$ $\quad (a > b > 0)$ $\qquad Ans.\ \dfrac{2\pi}{b^2}(a - \sqrt{a^2 - b^2})$

3. $\displaystyle\int_0^{2\pi} \frac{d\theta}{(a + b\cos\theta)^2}$ $\quad (a > b > 0)$ $\qquad Ans.\ \dfrac{2\pi a}{(a^2 - b^2)^{\frac{3}{2}}}$

4. $\displaystyle\int_0^{2\pi} \frac{d\theta}{\cos\theta + 2\sin\theta + 4}$ $\qquad$ 5. $\displaystyle\int_0^{2\pi} \frac{d\theta}{\sin\theta + 2\cos\theta + 4}$

6. $\displaystyle\int_0^{2\pi} \frac{\cos 2\theta\, d\theta}{5 + 4\sin\theta}$

7. $\displaystyle\int_0^{2\pi} \frac{\cos^2 3\theta\, d\theta}{1 - 2p\cos 2\theta + p^2}$ $\quad (0 < p < 1)$ $\qquad Ans.\ \dfrac{\pi(1 - p + p^2)}{1 - p}$

8. $\displaystyle\int_{-\infty}^{\infty} \frac{dx}{x^4 + a^4}$ $\qquad\qquad\qquad\qquad\qquad\qquad Ans.\ \dfrac{\pi}{\sqrt{2}\, a^3}$

9. $\displaystyle\int_{-\infty}^{\infty} \frac{dx}{(1 + x^2)^3}$ $\qquad\qquad\qquad\qquad\qquad\qquad Ans.\ \dfrac{3\pi}{8}$

10. $\displaystyle\int_{-\infty}^{\infty} \frac{x^2\, dx}{1 + x^6}$ $\qquad\qquad\qquad\qquad\qquad\qquad Ans.\ \dfrac{\pi}{3}$

11. $\displaystyle\int_0^{\infty} \frac{dx}{(a^2 + x^2)^2}$ $\qquad$ 12. $\displaystyle\int_0^{\infty} \frac{dx}{1 + x^6}$

13. $\displaystyle\int_{-\infty}^{\infty} \frac{x^2\, dx}{(1 + x^4)^2}$ $\qquad$ 14. $\displaystyle\int_0^{\infty} \frac{dx}{(1 + x^2)(4 + x^2)(9 + x^2)}$

15. $\displaystyle\int_0^{\infty} \frac{\cos mx\, dx}{1 + x^4}$ $\qquad Ans.\ \dfrac{\pi\, e^{-(m/\sqrt{2})}}{2\sqrt{2}}\left(\cos\dfrac{m}{\sqrt{2}} + \sin\dfrac{m}{\sqrt{2}}\right)$

16. $\displaystyle\int_0^{\infty} \frac{\cos mx\, dx}{(a^2 + x^2)^2}$ $\quad (a, m > 0)$ $\qquad Ans.\ \dfrac{\pi(1 + am)e^{-am}}{4a^3}$

17. $\displaystyle\int_{-\infty}^{\infty} \frac{x\sin x\, dx}{1 + x^2}$ $\qquad\qquad\qquad\qquad\qquad Ans.\ \dfrac{\pi}{e}$

18. $\displaystyle\int_{-\infty}^{\infty} \frac{\cos mx\, dx}{(x - a)^2 + b^2}$ $\quad (m, b > 0)$ $\qquad Ans.\ \dfrac{\pi\cos ma\, e^{-mb}}{b}$

19. $\displaystyle\int_{-\infty}^{\infty} \frac{\sin mx\, dx}{(x - a)^2 + b^2}$ $\quad (m, b > 0)$

20. $\int_{-\infty}^{\infty} \dfrac{\cos mx \, dx}{(1 + x^2)(4 + x^2)}$ **21.** $\int_0^{\infty} \dfrac{x \sin 2x \, dx}{x^4 + 5x^2 + 4}$

22. $\int_0^{\infty} \dfrac{x^{a-1} \, dx}{x^2 + 13x + 36}$ *Ans.* $\dfrac{\pi}{5 \sin a\pi} \, (4^{a-1} - 9^{a-1})$

23. $\int_0^{\infty} \dfrac{x^{a-1} \, dx}{(x + 1)(x + 2)(x + 3)}$. Verify that the same answer is obtained whether a is allowed to approach 2 before the integral is evaluated, or afterwards.

24. $\int_0^{\infty} \dfrac{x^{\frac{1}{2}} \, dx}{1 + x^3}$ **25.** $\int_0^{\infty} \dfrac{\sqrt{x} \, dx}{x^2 + 6x + 10}$

26. Show that $\int_0^{\infty} \dfrac{\sin x}{x} \, dx = \dfrac{\pi}{2}$ (Hint: Integrate $\dfrac{e^{iz}}{z}$ around the contour shown in Fig. 12.5, and let $r \to 0$ and $R \to \infty$.)

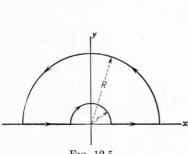   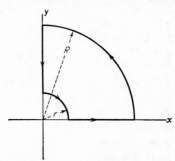

FIG. 12.5.   FIG. 12.6.

27. If $f(z)$ has a number of first-order poles on the real axis, but otherwise satisfies all the conditions of Theorem 2, show that the principal value of

$$\int_{-\infty}^{\infty} e^{imx} f(x) dx$$

is equal to $2\pi i$ times the sum of the residues of $e^{imz} f(z)$ at its poles in the upper half plane, plus $i\pi$ times the sum of the residues of $e^{imz} f(z)$ at its poles on the real axis. (Hint: Use a contour like that of Exercise 26, suitably indented around each of the poles of $f(z)$ which lies on the real axis.)

28. Find the principal value of

$$\int_{-\infty}^{\infty} \frac{\cos ax}{x - b} \, dx \quad \text{and} \quad \int_{-\infty}^{\infty} \frac{\sin ax}{x - b} \, dx$$

29. Show that

$$\int_0^{\infty} \frac{\cos x}{\sqrt{x}} \, dx = \int_0^{\infty} \frac{\sin x}{\sqrt{x}} \, dx = \sqrt{\frac{\pi}{2}}$$

Hint: Integrate $e^{iz}/\sqrt{z}$ around the contour shown in Fig. 12.6, and recall that

$$\int_0^{\infty} e^{-x^2} \, dx = \frac{\sqrt{\pi}}{2}$$

30. Show that

$$\Gamma(n)\Gamma(1 - n) = \frac{\pi}{\sin n\pi} \qquad 0 < n < 1$$

(Hint: Consider the integral $\int_0^\infty \frac{y^{n-1}}{1 + y} dy$, and evaluate it first by the method of residues and then by making the substitution $y = x/(1 - x)$ and expressing it in terms of gamma functions.)

12.3 The Complex Inversion Integral. We are now in a position to appreciate more fully the significance of the complex inversion integral of Laplace transform theory. In Sec. 5.8, we defined the Laplace transform of a function, $f(t)$, to be

$$(1) \qquad \mathcal{L}\{f(t)\} = \int_0^\infty f(t)e^{-st} dt$$

and we showed that conversely

$$(2) \qquad f(t) = \frac{1}{2\pi i} \int_{a-i\infty}^{a+i\infty} \mathcal{L}\{f(t)\}e^{st} ds$$

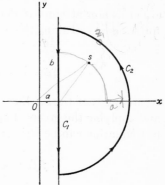

FIG. 12.7.

s being a complex variable. It is interesting now to reconsider the derivation of (2) in the light of complex variable theory and to investigate how this formula can be applied to the determination of a function when its transform is known.

In the complex plane let $\phi(z)$ be a function of z, analytic on the line $x = a$ and in the entire half plane R to the right of this line. Moreover, let $|\phi(z)|$ approach zero uniformly as z becomes infinite through this half plane. Then if s is any point in the half plane R, we can choose a semicircular contour C, as shown in Fig. 12.7, and apply Cauchy's integral —p.338 formula, getting

$$(3) \qquad \phi(s) = \frac{1}{2\pi i} \int_C \frac{\phi(z)dz}{z - s} = \frac{1}{2\pi i} \int_{a+ib}^{a-ib} \frac{\phi(z)dz}{z - s} + \frac{1}{2\pi i} \int_{C_2} \frac{\phi(z)dz}{z - s}$$

Now for values of z on the path of integration, C_2, and for b sufficiently large,

$$|z - s| \geq b - |s - a| > b - |s|$$

Hence

$$\left| \int_{C_2} \frac{\phi(z)dz}{z - s} \right| \leq \int_{C_2} \frac{|\phi(z)||dz|}{|z - s|}$$

$$\leq \frac{M}{b - |s|} \int_{C_2} |dz|$$

$$= \frac{\pi b M}{b - |s|}$$

where M is the maximum value of $|\phi(z)|$ on C_2. As $b \to \infty$, the fraction

$$\frac{b}{b - |s|}$$

approaches 1, and at the same time M approaches zero. Hence

$$\lim_{b \to \infty} \int_{C_2} \frac{\phi(z)dz}{z - s} = 0$$

and (3) reduces to

$$\phi(s) = \lim_{b \to \infty} \frac{1}{2\pi i} \int_{a+ib}^{a-ib} \frac{\phi(z)dz}{z - s} = \frac{1}{2\pi i} \int_{a-i\infty}^{a+i\infty} \frac{\phi(z)dz}{s - z}$$

Let us now attempt to determine the function of t whose Laplace transform is $\phi(s)$. Taking the inverse of $\phi(s)$ as defined by the last expression, we have

$$\mathcal{L}^{-1}\{\phi(s)\} = f(t) = \mathcal{L}^{-1}\left\{\frac{1}{2\pi i} \int_{a-i\infty}^{a+i\infty} \frac{\phi(z)dz}{s - z}\right\}$$

Assuming that the operations of integrating along the vertical line $x = a$ and applying the inverse Laplace transformation can be interchanged, the last equation can be written

$$f(t) = \frac{1}{2\pi i} \int_{a-i\infty}^{a+i\infty} \mathcal{L}^{-1}\left\{\frac{\phi(z)}{s - z}\right\} dz$$

or, since the operator $\mathcal{L}^{-1}$ refers only to the variable s,

$$f(t) = \frac{1}{2\pi i} \int_{a-i\infty}^{a+i\infty} \phi(z)\mathcal{L}^{-1}\left\{\frac{1}{s - z}\right\} dz$$

Since the specific result

$$\mathcal{L}^{-1}\left\{\frac{1}{s - z}\right\} = e^{zt}$$

is known to us through independent reasoning, we have finally

$$f(t) = \frac{1}{2\pi i} \int_{a-i\infty}^{a+i\infty} \phi(z)e^{tz} dz$$

which, except that the variable of integration is z instead of s, is exactly Eq. (2). From this approach it is clear that the inversion integral is a line integral in the complex plane, taken along a vertical line *to the right of all the singularities of the transform,* $\phi(s)$ or along any other path into which this can legitimately be deformed.

Example 1

What is

$$\mathcal{L}^{-1}\left\{\frac{s}{s^2 + k^2}\right\}$$

Using the inversion integral, we have

$$f(t) = \frac{1}{2\pi i} \int_{a-i\infty}^{a+i\infty} \frac{se^{st}\,ds}{s^2 + k^2}$$

where, since the poles of the transform are at $s = \pm ik$, on the imaginary axis, a can be taken to be any positive number we please.   To evaluate this integral, we apply

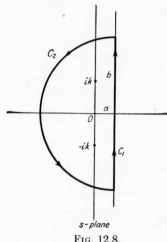

s-plane

FIG. 12.8.

the theory of residues to the integral of $se^{st}/(s^2 + k^2)$ around the semicircular contour shown in Fig. 12.8, getting

$$(4) \quad f(t) = \frac{1}{2\pi i} \int_{a-ib}^{a+ib} \frac{se^{st}\,ds}{s^2 + k^2} + \frac{1}{2\pi i} \int_{C_2} \frac{se^{st}\,ds}{s^2 + k^2}$$

$$= 2\pi i \sum \text{residues of } \frac{se^{st}}{2\pi i(s^2 + k^2)} \text{ at } s = \pm ik$$

$$= \sum \text{residues of } \frac{se^{st}}{s^2 + k^2} \text{ at } s = \pm ik$$

At $s = ik$, the residue is

$$(5) \qquad \lim_{s \to ik} \left[(s - ik) \frac{se^{st}}{(s - ik)(s + ik)} \right] = \frac{ike^{ikt}}{2ik} = \frac{e^{ikt}}{2}$$

At $s = -ik$, the residue is

$$(6) \qquad \lim_{s \to -ik} \left[(s + ik) \frac{se^{st}}{(s + ik)(s - ik)} \right] = \frac{-ike^{-ikt}}{-2ik} = \frac{e^{-ikt}}{2}$$

Now along C_2

$$s = a + be^{i\theta}, \qquad b - a \leqq |s| < b + a \qquad ds = ibe^{i\theta}\,d\theta$$

and

$$|s^2 + k^2| \geqq |s^2| - k^2 = |s|^2 - k^2 \geqq (b - a)^2 - k^2$$

(handwritten at top:) $s = a + b e^{i\theta}$ $ds = i \, b e^{i\theta} d\theta$
$< a + b$ $< i b d\theta \quad < b d\theta$

Hence

$$\left| \int_{C_2} \frac{s e^{st} ds}{s^2 + k^2} \right| \leq \int_{C_2} \frac{|s||e^{st}||ds|}{|s^2 + k^2|}$$

(handwritten: $e^{i\theta}$)

$$< \frac{b + a}{(b - a)^2 - k^2} \int_{\pi/2}^{3\pi/2} |e^{[a + b(\cos\theta + i\sin\theta)]t}|b \, d\theta$$

$$= \frac{b(b + a)e^{at}}{(b - a)^2 - k^2} \int_{\pi/2}^{3\pi/2} e^{bt \cos\theta} \, d\theta$$

In the last integral let

$$\theta = \frac{\pi}{2} + \phi$$

Then

$$\left| \int_{C_2} \frac{s e^{st} ds}{s^2 + k^2} \right| < \frac{b(b + a)e^{at}}{(b - a)^2 - k^2} \int_0^{\pi} e^{-bt \sin\phi} \, d\phi$$

$$= \frac{2b(b + a)e^{at}}{(b - a)^2 - k^2} \int_0^{\pi/2} e^{-bt \sin\phi} \, d\phi$$

$$< \frac{2b(b + a)e^{at}}{(b - a)^2 - k^2} \int_0^{\pi/2} e^{-bt(2\phi/\pi)} \, d\phi$$

since it is evident from the graph of the sine curve that

$$\sin\phi \geq \frac{2\phi}{\pi} \geq 0 \qquad \text{for } 0 \leq \phi \leq \frac{\pi}{2}$$

The integration can now be performed explicitly, giving

$$\left| \int_{C_2} \frac{s e^{st} ds}{s^2 + k^2} \right| < \frac{2b(b + a)e^{at}}{(b - a)^2 - k^2} \left[\frac{e^{-2bt\phi/\pi}}{-2bt/\pi} \right]_0^{\pi/2}$$

$$= \frac{2b(b + a)e^{at}}{(b - a)^2 - k^2} \left(-\frac{\pi}{2bt} \right) (e^{-bt} - 1)$$

Since the last expression approaches zero as b approaches infinity, it is clear that (4) reduces to

$$f(t) = \frac{1}{2\pi i} \int_{a - i\infty}^{a + i\infty} \frac{s e^{st} ds}{s^2 + k^2} = \frac{e^{ikt} + e^{-ikt}}{2} = \cos kt$$

This example has been merely a new approach to a result with which we were already familiar. However, in more difficult applications the use of the inversion integral and contour integration is often either the only or at least the best way of finding a function when its transform is known.

EXERCISES

Using the complex inversion integral, find y if

1. $\mathcal{L}(y) = \dfrac{1}{(s + 1)(s + 2)}$

2. $\mathcal{L}(y) = \dfrac{s}{s^2 + 4s + 5}$

3. $\mathcal{L}(y) = \dfrac{1}{(s + 2)^2}$

4. $\mathcal{L}(y) = \dfrac{1}{s^2 + 1}$

5. $\mathcal{L}(y) = \dfrac{1}{s(s^2 + 1)}$

6. $\mathcal{L}(y) = \dfrac{s}{s^3 + 1}$

7. $\mathcal{L}(y) = \dfrac{s}{(s^2 + 1)^2}$

8. $\mathcal{L}(y) = \dfrac{1}{(s^2 + 1)(s^2 + 2)}$

9. $\mathcal{L}(y) = \dfrac{s + 1}{(s + 2)^2(s + 3)}$

10. $\mathcal{L}(y) = \dfrac{s}{(s - 1)(s^2 + 4s + 8)}$

CHAPTER 13

CONFORMAL MAPPING

13.1 The Geometrical Representation of Functions of z. Up to this point we have made no attempt to provide a geometrical representation of a function of a complex variable. To do so now requires a decided departure from the conventional methods of cartesian plotting, which associate a curve with a real function, $y = f(x)$, and a surface with a real function, $z = f(x,y)$. In the complex domain, a functional relation $w = f(z)$, that is,

$$u + iv = f(x + iy)$$

involves *four* real variables, namely, the two independent variables x and y, and the two dependent variables u and v. Hence a space of *four* dimensions is required if we are to plot $w = f(z)$ in the cartesian fashion. To avoid the difficulties inherent in such a device, we choose instead to proceed as follows.

Let there be given two planes, one the z-plane, in which the point $x + iy$ is to be plotted, and the other the w-plane, in which the point $u + iv$ is to be plotted. A function $w = f(z)$ is now represented, not by a locus of points in a space of four dimensions, but by a correspondence between the points of these two cartesian planes. Whenever a point is given in the z-plane, the function $w = f(z)$ determines one or more values of $u + iv$, and hence one or more points in the w-plane. As z ranges over any configuration in the z-plane, the corresponding point, $u + iv$, describes some configuration in the w-plane. The function $w = f(z)$ thus defines a **mapping** or a **transformation** of the z-plane into the w-plane, and in turn is represented geometrically by this mapping.

Example 1

Discuss the way in which the z-plane is mapped on the w-plane by the function $w = z^2$.

In this case we have

$$u + iv = (x + iy)^2 = (x^2 - y^2) + 2ixy$$

and thus

(1) $$u = x^2 - y^2, \qquad v = 2xy$$

383

These are the equations of the transformation between the two planes. From them, numerous properties of the correspondence can easily be inferred.

For instance, lines parallel to the y-axis, *i.e.*, lines with equations $x = c_1$, map into curves in the w-plane whose parametric equations are

$$u = c_1^2 - y^2, \qquad v = 2c_1 y$$

Eliminating the parameter y, we find the equation

$$u = c_1^2 - \frac{v^2}{4c_1^2}$$

This defines a family of parabolas having the origin of the w-plane as focus, the line $v = 0$ as axis, and all opening to the left.

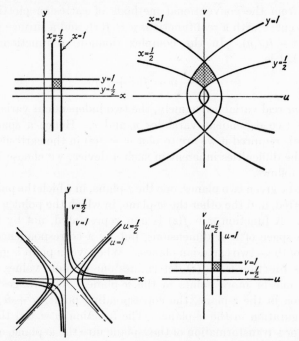

Fig. 13.1.   Plot illustrating the mapping of certain lines by the function $w = z^2$.

Similarly, lines parallel to the x-axis, *i.e.*, lines with equations $y = c_2$, map into curves in the w-plane whose parametric equations are

$$u = x^2 - c_2^2, \qquad v = 2c_2 x$$

Eliminating x, we obtain

$$u = \frac{v^2}{4c_2^2} - c_2^2$$

which is the equation of a family of parabolas having the origin as focus, the line $v = 0$ as axis, but this time all opening to the right.

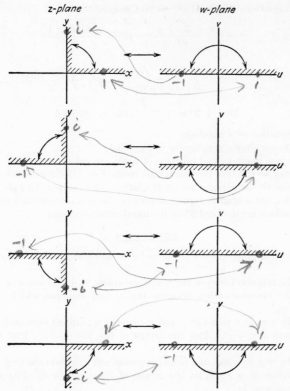

z-plane   w-plane

Fig. 13.2. Plot illustrating the two-valued character of the mapping defined by $z = w^{\frac{1}{2}}$.

Mapping from the w-plane back onto the z-plane is even more immediate. The lines $u = k_1$ correspond to the rectangular hyperbolas

$$x^2 - y^2 = k_1$$

The lines $v = k_2$ correspond to the rectangular hyperbolas

$$xy = \tfrac{1}{2}k_2$$

The images of other curves or regions can, with varying degrees of difficulty, be found in the same fashion. For instance, to find the curve into which the line

$$y = 2x + 1$$

is transformed, we must eliminate x and y between this equation and the equations of the transformation. To do this, we first substitute for y in Eqs. (1), getting

$$u = x^2 - (2x + 1)^2 = -3x^2 - 4x - 1$$
$$v = 2x(2x + 1) = 4x^2 + 2x$$

Solving these equations for x and x^2, we find at once

$$x = \frac{4u + 3v + 4}{-10}, \qquad x^2 = \frac{u + 2v + 1}{5}$$

Hence

$$\frac{u + 2v + 1}{5} = \left(\frac{4u + 3v + 4}{-10}\right)^2$$

or

$$16u^2 + 24uv + 9v^2 + 12u - 16v = 4$$

which is the equation of a parabola.

These results are shown graphically in Fig. 13.1.

Although w is a single-valued function of z, the converse is not true. In fact when w is given, z may be either of the two square roots of w. Because of this, the mapping from the z-plane to the w-plane covers the latter twice, as Fig. 13.2 shows. This of course is nothing but a graphic representation of the now familiar fact that the angles of complex numbers are doubled when the numbers are squared.

EXERCISES

1. Discuss the mapping between the z- and w-planes which is defined by the function $w = (\bar{z})^2$.

2. What is the relation between the transformations $w = f(z)$ and $w = f(\bar{z})$?

3. Discuss the transformation between the z- and w-planes which is defined by $w = x - iy$.

4. Discuss the way in which the z- and w-planes are mapped onto each other by the transformation $w = z^3$. Plot the image of the line $v = 1$. Plot the image of the line $x + y = 1$.

5. Discuss the way in which the z- and w-planes are mapped onto each other by the transformation $w = z^4$. Plot the image of the line $v = 1$. Plot the image of the line $x + y = 1$.

6. Discuss the mapping between the z- and w-planes which is effected by the transformation $w = 1/z$. In particular find the image of the square whose vertices are $z = 1 + i, 2 + i, 2 + 2i,$ and $1 + 2i$.

7. Discuss the transformation defined by $w = (x^2 - y^2) + ixy$. In what significant way does it differ from the transformation defined by $w = z^2 = (x^2 - y^2) + 2ixy$?

8. Discuss the transformation defined by $w = e^z$. What is the image of the square whose vertices are $w = 1 + i, 2 + i, 2 + 2i,$ and $1 + 2i$? What is the image of the line $y = x$?

9. Discuss the transformation defined by the function $w^2 = z^3$. Plot the image of the line $y = x$. Plot the image of the line $y = x + 1$.

10. Find the equations of the transformation defined by the function $w = (z - i)/z$, and show that every circle through the origin in the z-plane is transformed into a straight line in the w-plane.

13.2 Conformal Mapping. In Sec. 13.1, we saw that every function of a complex variable maps the xy-plane into the uv-plane. We now propose to investigate in more general terms the character of this transformation when the mapping function $w = u(x,y) + iv(x,y)$ is analytic.

At the outset it is important to know when the transformation equations can be solved for x and y as single-valued functions of u and v, that is, when the transformation has a single-valued inverse.   The condition for this is simply that the **Jacobian** of the transformation,

$$J\left(\frac{u,v}{x,y}\right) \equiv \begin{vmatrix} \dfrac{\partial u}{\partial x} & \dfrac{\partial u}{\partial y} \\ \dfrac{\partial v}{\partial x} & \dfrac{\partial v}{\partial y} \end{vmatrix}$$

should be different from zero.*

Since $w = f(z)$ is assumed to be analytic, u and v must satisfy the Cauchy-Riemann equations.   Hence, substituting,

$$J\left(\frac{u,v}{x,y}\right) \equiv \begin{vmatrix} \dfrac{\partial u}{\partial x} & -\dfrac{\partial v}{\partial x} \\ \dfrac{\partial v}{\partial x} & \dfrac{\partial u}{\partial x} \end{vmatrix}$$

$$= \left(\frac{\partial u}{\partial x}\right)^2 + \left(\frac{\partial v}{\partial x}\right)^2 = \left|\frac{\partial u}{\partial x} + i\frac{\partial v}{\partial x}\right|^2 = |f'(z)|^2$$

Therefore, *a single-valued inverse will exist wherever the derivative of the mapping function is different from zero.*   Exceptional points, where

$$f'(z) = 0$$

are known as **critical points** of the transformation.

Now consider a point z and its image $w = f(z)$, where $f(z)$ is analytic, and let

$$\Delta z = |\Delta z| e^{i\theta}$$

and

$$\Delta w = |\Delta w| e^{i\phi}$$

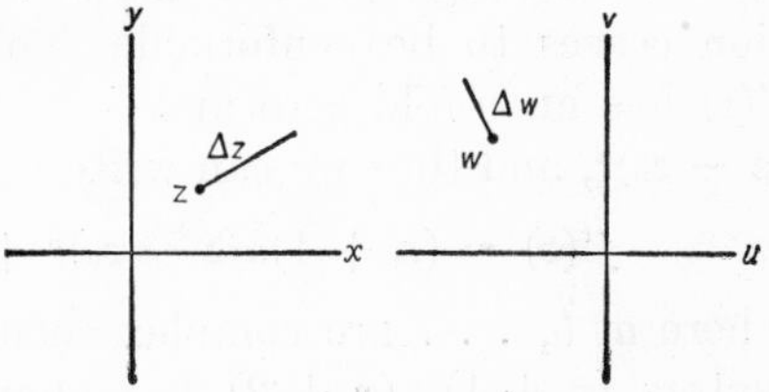

FIG. 13.3.

be corresponding increments of these quantities (Fig. 13.3).   Then

$$f'(z) = \lim_{\Delta z \to 0}\left(\frac{\Delta w}{\Delta z}\right) = \lim_{\Delta z \to 0}\left(\frac{|\Delta w| e^{i\phi}}{|\Delta z| e^{i\theta}}\right) = \lim_{\Delta z \to 0}\left(\frac{|\Delta w|}{|\Delta z|} e^{i(\phi-\theta)}\right)$$

From this it is apparent that

$$\lim_{\Delta z \to 0}\left(\frac{|\Delta w|}{|\Delta z|}\right) = |f'(z)| \quad \text{and} \quad \lim_{\Delta z \to 0}(\phi - \theta) = \arg f'(z)$$

or, to an arbitrary degree of approximation,

$$(1) \qquad\qquad |\Delta w| = |f'(z)||\Delta z|$$
$$(2) \qquad\qquad \arg \Delta w = \arg \Delta z + \arg f'(z)$$

* See, for instance, R. S. Burington and C. C. Torrance, "Higher Mathematics," pp. 125–129, McGraw-Hill Book Company, Inc., New York, 1939.

Now $f'(z)$, and hence both $|f'(z)|$ and $\arg f'(z)$, are independent of the manner in which $\Delta z \to 0$ since $f(z)$ is assumed to be analytic; in other words, they depend solely on z and not on the orientation of the increment Δz.   Hence from (1) we conclude that *infinitesimal lengths, regardless of their direction, are magnified by a factor which depends only upon the point at which they are drawn.*   Since infinitesimal lengths are magnified by the factor $|f'(z)|$, it follows that infinitesimal areas are magnified by the factor $|f'(z)|^2$, that is, by $J(u,v/x,y)$.

Similarly we conclude from (2) that the difference between the angles of an infinitesimal segment and its image is independent of the direction of the segment and depends only on the point at which the segment is drawn.   As an immediate consequence of this it follows that *angles are preserved in magnitude and sense*, since the sides of any angle are rotated in the same direction by the same amount.

A transformation possessing these two properties is said to be **conformal,** since an infinitesimal configuration and its image *conform* to each other, in the sense of being approximately similar.   This is not true of large figures, which may bear little or no resemblance to their images.

When $f'(z) = 0$, $\arg f'(z)$ is undefined.   The angle through which infinitesimal segments are rotated is thus undefined, and the transformation ceases to be conformal.   To investigate this case, suppose that $f'(z)$ has an n-fold zero at $z = z_0$.   Then $f'(z)$ must contain the factor $(z - z_0)^n$, and thus we can write

$$f'(z) = (n + 1)a(z - z_0)^n + (n + 2)b(z - z_0)^{n+1} + \cdots$$

where a, b, $\ldots$ are complex coefficients of no concern to us, and the factors $(n + 1)$, $(n + 2)$, $\ldots$ have been inserted for convenience in integrating:

$$f(z) = f(z_0) + a(z - z_0)^{n+1} + b(z - z_0)^{n+2} + \cdots$$

If we set

$$z - z_0 = \Delta z \qquad \text{and} \qquad f(z) - f(z_0) = \Delta w$$

the last expression can be written

$$\frac{\Delta w}{a(\Delta z)^{n+1}} = 1 + \frac{b}{a}\Delta z + \cdots$$

As $\Delta z \to 0$, the right member approaches 1.   Therefore

$$\lim_{\Delta z \to 0} (\arg \Delta w) - \lim_{\Delta z \to 0} [\arg a(\Delta z)^{n+1}] = \arg 1 = 0$$

or, to an arbitrary degree of approximation,

$$\arg \Delta w = \arg a + (n + 1) \arg \Delta z$$

Now let Δz_1 and Δz_2 be two infinitesimal segments which make an angle θ with each other, and let Δw_1 and Δw_2 be their images. From the last expression we have

$$\arg \Delta w_1 = \arg a + (n + 1) \arg \Delta z_1$$
$$\arg \Delta w_2 = \arg a + (n + 1) \arg \Delta z_2$$

Hence, subtracting,

$$\arg \Delta w_2 - \arg \Delta w_1 = (n + 1)(\arg \Delta z_2 - \arg \Delta z_1) = (n + 1)\theta$$

Thus *at a critical point of a transformation where $f'(z)$ has an n-fold zero, angles are not preserved but are magnified $n + 1$ times.*

Example 1 of the last section furnishes an excellent example of this behavior. Although the mapping function, $f(z) = z^2$, is everywhere analytic, the derivative, $f'(z) = 2z$, has a simple zero at $z = 0$. Therefore, as we found, angles with vertex at the origin are not preserved but instead are doubled.

The prime reason for the great importance of conformal transformations in applications is that *solutions of Laplace's equation remain solutions when subjected to a conformal transformation.* In other words, if $\phi(x,y)$ satisfies the equation

$$\frac{\partial^2 \phi}{\partial x^2} + \frac{\partial^2 \phi}{\partial y^2} = 0$$

then when $\phi(x,y)$ is transformed into a function of u and v by a conformal transformation, it will satisfy the equation

$$\frac{\partial^2 \phi}{\partial u^2} + \frac{\partial^2 \phi}{\partial v^2} = 0$$

To prove this, let $w = u(x,y) + iv(x,y)$ define a conformal transformation, by means of which $\phi(x,y)$ is transformed into a function of u and v. Then

$$\frac{\partial \phi}{\partial x} = \frac{\partial \phi}{\partial u}\frac{\partial u}{\partial x} + \frac{\partial \phi}{\partial v}\frac{\partial v}{\partial x} \qquad \text{and} \qquad \frac{\partial \phi}{\partial y} = \frac{\partial \phi}{\partial u}\frac{\partial u}{\partial y} + \frac{\partial \phi}{\partial v}\frac{\partial v}{\partial y}$$

A second differentiation of each of these yields the results

$$\frac{\partial^2 \phi}{\partial x^2} = \frac{\partial \phi}{\partial u}\frac{\partial^2 u}{\partial x^2} + \left[\frac{\partial^2 \phi}{\partial u^2}\frac{\partial u}{\partial x} + \frac{\partial^2 \phi}{\partial v \partial u}\frac{\partial v}{\partial x}\right]\frac{\partial u}{\partial x} + \frac{\partial \phi}{\partial v}\frac{\partial^2 v}{\partial x^2}$$
$$+ \left[\frac{\partial^2 \phi}{\partial u \partial v}\frac{\partial u}{\partial x} + \frac{\partial^2 \phi}{\partial v^2}\frac{\partial v}{\partial x}\right]\frac{\partial v}{\partial x}$$

$$\frac{\partial^2 \phi}{\partial y^2} = \frac{\partial \phi}{\partial u}\frac{\partial^2 u}{\partial y^2} + \left[\frac{\partial^2 \phi}{\partial u^2}\frac{\partial u}{\partial y} + \frac{\partial^2 \phi}{\partial v \partial u}\frac{\partial v}{\partial y}\right]\frac{\partial u}{\partial y} + \frac{\partial \phi}{\partial v}\frac{\partial^2 v}{\partial y^2}$$
$$+ \left[\frac{\partial^2 \phi}{\partial u \partial v}\frac{\partial u}{\partial y} + \frac{\partial^2 \phi}{\partial v^2}\frac{\partial v}{\partial y}\right]\frac{\partial v}{\partial y}$$

If these are added, we obtain

$$\frac{\partial^2 \phi}{\partial x^2} + \frac{\partial^2 \phi}{\partial y^2} = \frac{\partial \phi}{\partial u}\left[\frac{\partial^2 u}{\partial x^2} + \frac{\partial^2 u}{\partial y^2}\right] + \frac{\partial^2 \phi}{\partial u^2}\left[\left(\frac{\partial u}{\partial x}\right)^2 + \left(\frac{\partial u}{\partial y}\right)^2\right]$$

$$+ 2\frac{\partial^2 \phi}{\partial u\,\partial v}\left[\frac{\partial u}{\partial x}\frac{\partial v}{\partial x} + \frac{\partial u}{\partial y}\frac{\partial v}{\partial y}\right] + \frac{\partial \phi}{\partial v}\left[\frac{\partial^2 v}{\partial x^2} + \frac{\partial^2 v}{\partial y^2}\right]$$

$$+ \frac{\partial^2 \phi}{\partial v^2}\left[\left(\frac{\partial v}{\partial x}\right)^2 + \left(\frac{\partial v}{\partial y}\right)^2\right]$$

Since $f(z)$ is analytic, u and v themselves satisfy Laplace's equation. Hence the first and fourth groups of terms vanish identically. Moreover, u and v also satisfy the Cauchy-Riemann equations; hence the coefficient of the cross partial, $\dfrac{\partial^2 \phi}{\partial u\,\partial v}$, also vanishes identically. Using the Cauchy-Riemann equations again, what remains can be written

$$\frac{\partial^2 \phi}{\partial x^2} + \frac{\partial^2 \phi}{\partial y^2} = \frac{\partial^2 \phi}{\partial u^2}\left[\left(\frac{\partial u}{\partial x}\right)^2 + \left(-\frac{\partial v}{\partial x}\right)^2\right] + \frac{\partial^2 \phi}{\partial v^2}\left[\left(\frac{\partial v}{\partial x}\right)^2 + \left(\frac{\partial u}{\partial x}\right)^2\right]$$

$$= \left[\left(\frac{\partial u}{\partial x}\right)^2 + \left(\frac{\partial v}{\partial x}\right)^2\right]\left[\frac{\partial^2 \phi}{\partial u^2} + \frac{\partial^2 \phi}{\partial v^2}\right]$$

$$= |f'(z)|^2\left[\frac{\partial^2 \phi}{\partial u^2} + \frac{\partial^2 \phi}{\partial v^2}\right]$$

At any point where the transformation is conformal, that is, where $f'(z) \neq 0$, the vanishing of $\dfrac{\partial^2 \phi}{\partial x^2} + \dfrac{\partial^2 \phi}{\partial y^2}$ thus implies the vanishing of $\dfrac{\partial^2 \phi}{\partial u^2} + \dfrac{\partial^2 \phi}{\partial v^2}$.

Suppose now that it is required to solve Laplace's equation, subject to certain boundary conditions, within a region R. Unless R is of a very simple shape, a direct attack upon the problem will usually be exceedingly difficult. However, it may be possible to find a conformal transformation which will convert R into some simpler region R', such as a circle or a half plane. If this is the case, Laplace's equation can be solved in R', subject to the transformed boundary conditions, and the resulting solution when carried back to R by the inverse transformation will be the required solution of the original problem.

EXERCISES

1. What is the length of the curve into which the upper half of the circle $|z| = a$ is transformed by the function $w = 1/z$? What is the length of the arc into which this function transforms the segment of $y = 1 - x$ which lies in the first quadrant?

2. What is the area of the region into which the square with vertices $z = 0, 1, 1 + i,$ i is transformed by the function $w = z^2$? by $w = z^3$?

3 What are the critical points of the transformation $w = 3z - z^3$? What is the locus of points at which the magnification is 1? What is the locus of points at which infinitesimal segments are rotated through 45°? through 90°?

4. Are there any points at which infinitesimal segments are left unchanged in magnitude and direction by the transformation $w = 3z^2 - 2z^3$?

5. If $u = 2x^2 + y^2$ and $v = y^2/x$, show that the curves $u = $ constant and $v = $ constant cut orthogonally at all intersections but that the transformation defined by $f(z) = u + iv$ is not conformal. Give a specific illustration of the latter fact.

13.3 The Bilinear Transformation. The simplest and yet one of the most important classes of conformal transformations consists of the Möbius,* or **bilinear,** or **linear fractional transformations,** defined by the family of functions

$$(1) \qquad w = \frac{az + b}{cz + d} \qquad ad - bc \neq 0$$

The restriction $ad - bc \neq 0$ is necessary to ensure that the transformation is conformal, for

$$\frac{dw}{dz} = \frac{ad - bc}{(cz + d)^2}$$

and thus if $ad - bc = 0$, every point of the z-plane is a critical point. Moreover, if $ad = bc$, then $a/c = b/d$, which shows that the numerator and denominator of w are proportional for all values of z. In other words, w is a constant independent of z, and thus the entire z-plane is mapped into the same point in the w-plane!

It is convenient to investigate the general bilinear transformation by considering first the three special cases

$a.\ w = z + \lambda$

$b.\ w = \mu z$

$c.\ w = \dfrac{1}{z}$

where λ and μ are any complex constants.

In case a, w is found by adding a constant vector λ to each z. Hence the transformation is just a translation in the direction defined by arg λ through a distance equal to $|\lambda|$. In particular we note for later use that this rigid motion necessarily transforms circles into circles.

In case b, w is found by rotating each z through a fixed angle equal to arg μ, and then multiplying its length by the factor $|\mu|$. In this case, too, circles are transformed into circles.

To prove this, let us first write the equation of the general circle

$$a(x^2 + y^2) + bx + cy + d = 0 \qquad a,\ b,\ c,\ d \text{ real}$$

* Named for the German geometer A. F. Möbius (1790–1868).

in terms of z and $\bar{z}$ by means of the relations

$$x = \frac{z + \bar{z}}{2}, \qquad y = \frac{z - \bar{z}}{2i}, \qquad x^2 + y^2 = z\bar{z}$$

The result is

$$az\bar{z} + \frac{b - ic}{2} z + \frac{b + ic}{2} \bar{z} + d = 0$$

or, renaming the coefficients,

$$(2) \qquad (A + \bar{A})z\bar{z} + Bz + \bar{B}\bar{z} + (D + \bar{D}) = 0$$

where now A, B, C, D can be arbitrary complex numbers. If the substitution

$$z = \frac{w}{\mu}$$

is performed on (2), the result is

$$(A + \bar{A}) \frac{w}{\mu} \frac{\bar{w}}{\bar{\mu}} + B \frac{w}{\mu} + \bar{B} \frac{\bar{w}}{\bar{\mu}} + (D + \bar{D}) = 0$$

or

$$(3) \qquad (A + \bar{A})w\bar{w} + (B\bar{\mu})w + (\bar{B}\mu)\bar{w} + (D + \bar{D})\mu\bar{\mu} = 0$$

Since the coefficients of the first and last terms in (3) are purely real, and since the coefficients of w and $\bar{w}$ are conjugates, this equation has the same structure as (2) and hence represents a circle also. If $a = 0$, so that $A + \bar{A} = 0$, both the given circle and its image reduce to straight lines.

In case c we can write

$$w = \frac{1}{z} = \frac{\bar{z}}{z\bar{z}}$$

which shows that w is of length $\frac{1}{|z|}$ and has the direction of $\bar{z}$. To describe the geometrical process by which a point with these characteristics can be obtained from a given z, we must first define the process of **inversion**.

Let C be a circle with center O and radius r, and let P be any point in the plane of C. Then the **inverse of** P with respect to C is the point P' on the ray OP, for which

$$(4) \qquad OP \cdot OP' = r^2$$

From the symmetry of the relation it is clear that P is also the inverse of P'.

Geometrically, a point and its inverse are related as follows. From any point P outside a circle C with center O, let the two tangents to C be drawn, and let the points of contact of these tangents be joined (Fig. 13.4). The intersection of this chord with the line OP is the inverse P' of P.

Conversely, let P' be any point in the interior of C. At P' erect a perpendicular to OP' and at the point where this meets C let the tangent to C be drawn. The intersection of this tangent and the line OP' is the inverse P of P'. The consistency of these constructions with the definitive property (4) is evident, since

$$\Delta OP'T_1 \sim \Delta OT_1P$$

and thus

$$\frac{OP'}{OT_1} = \frac{OT_1}{OP}$$

or

$$OP \cdot OP' = (OT_1)^2 = r^2$$

It is evident now that the construction of w from z in case c requires that the inverse of z in the unit circle be found and then reflected in the

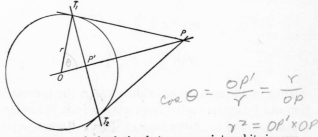

$$\cos\theta = \frac{OP'}{r} = \frac{r}{OP}$$

$$r^2 = OP' \times OP$$

Fig. 13.4.   Plot showing the geometrical relation between a point and its inverse.

real axis; for the first of these steps gives a complex number whose length is $\frac{1}{|z|}$, and the second achieves the direction of $\bar{z}$, as required.

To show that circles are also transformed into circles in case c, let the substitution $z = 1/w$ be made in the self-conjugate form of the equation of a circle (2). This gives

$$(A + \bar{A})\frac{1}{w}\frac{1}{\bar{w}} + \frac{B}{w} + \frac{\bar{B}}{\bar{w}} + (D + \bar{D}) = 0$$

or

$$(D + \bar{D})w\bar{w} + \bar{B}w + B\bar{w} + (A + \bar{A}) = 0$$

which is also the equation of a circle. If $(A + \bar{A}) = 0$, the original circle reduces to a straight line whose image is a circle passing through the origin, since its equation contains no constant term. Conversely, any circle passing through the origin is transformed into a straight line.

The three special transformations which we have just considered can be used to synthesize the general bilinear transformation. To see this, suppose first that $c \neq 0$. Then the general transformation is equivalent to the following chain of special transformations.

$$w_1 = z + \frac{d}{c}$$

$$w_2 = cw_1 = cz + d$$

$$w_3 = \frac{1}{w_2} = \frac{1}{cz + d}$$

$$w_4 = \left(\frac{bc - ad}{c}\right) w_3 = \frac{bc - ad}{c(cz + d)}$$

$$w = \frac{a}{c} + w_4 = \frac{a}{c} + \frac{bc - ad}{c(cz + d)} = \frac{az + b}{cz + d}$$

On the other hand, if $c = 0$ it is clear from the restriction $ad - bc \neq 0$ that neither a nor d can be zero. Hence we can write

$$w_1 = z + \frac{b}{a}$$

$$w = \frac{a}{d} w_1 = \frac{a}{d}\left(z + \frac{b}{a}\right) = \frac{az + b}{d}$$

Thus in all cases we have shown that the general bilinear transformation can be compounded from a succession of simple transformations of types a, b, and c. Since each of these is known to transform circles into circles, including straight lines as limiting cases, it is now clear that *the general bilinear transformation maps circles into circles.*

The general bilinear transformation

$$w = \frac{az + b}{cz + d}$$

depends on three essential constants, namely, the ratios of any three of the constants a, b, c, d to the fourth. Hence it is evident that three conditions are necessary to determine a bilinear transformation. In particular, the requirement that three distinct values of z, say z_1, z_2, z_3, have specified images w_1, w_2, w_3, leads to a unique transformation.

Although the transformation which sends three given points into three specified image points can be found by imposing these conditions on the general equation and solving for the constants, it is generally simpler to make use of the fact that if w_1, w_2, w_3, w_4 are, respectively, the images of z_1, z_2, z_3, z_4, then

$$\frac{(w_1 - w_2)(w_3 - w_4)}{(w_1 - w_4)(w_3 - w_2)} = \frac{(z_1 - z_2)(z_3 - z_4)}{(z_1 - z_4)(z_3 - z_2)}$$

To establish this relation, we observe that

$$w_i - w_j = \frac{az_i + b}{cz_i + d} - \frac{az_j + b}{cz_j + d} = \frac{(ad - bc)(z_i - z_j)}{(cz_i + d)(cz_j + d)}$$

Hence

$$\frac{(w_1 - w_2)(w_3 - w_4)}{(w_1 - w_4)(w_3 - w_2)} = \frac{\left[\dfrac{(ad - bc)(z_1 - z_2)}{(cz_1 + d)(cz_2 + d)}\right]\left[\dfrac{(ad - bc)(z_3 - z_4)}{(cz_3 + d)(cz_4 + d)}\right]}{\left[\dfrac{(ad - bc)(z_1 - z_4)}{(cz_1 + d)(cz_4 + d)}\right]\left[\dfrac{(ad - bc)(z_3 - z_2)}{(cz_3 + d)(cz_2 + d)}\right]}$$

$$= \frac{(z_1 - z_2)(z_3 - z_4)}{(z_1 - z_4)(z_3 - z_2)}$$

The last fraction is called the **cross ratio** or **anharmonic ratio** of the four numbers z_1, z_2, z_3, z_4, and the result we have just established states that *the cross ratio of four points is invariant under a bilinear transformation.*

Suppose now that it is required to find the transformation which sends z_1, z_2, z_3 into w_1, w_2, w_3, respectively. If w is the image of a general point z under this transformation, then according to the last result, the cross ratio of w_1, w_2, w_3, and w must equal the cross ratio of z_1, z_2, z_3, and z. That is

$$\frac{(w_1 - w_2)(w_3 - w)}{(w_1 - w)(w_3 - w_2)} = \frac{(z_1 - z_2)(z_3 - z)}{(z_1 - z)(z_3 - z_2)}$$

This equation is clearly bilinear in w and z, and is satisfied by the three pairs of values (z_1, w_1), (z_2, w_2) and (z_3, w_3). Moreover, everything in it is known except the variables w and z, themselves; hence it is only necessary to solve for w in terms of z to obtain the desired transformation in standard form.

Example 1

What is the bilinear transformation which sends the points $z = -1, 0, 1$ into the points $w = 0, i, 3i$, respectively?

Setting up the proper cross ratios we have

$$\frac{(0 - i)(3i - w)}{(0 - w)(3i - i)} = \frac{(-1 - 0)(1 - z)}{(-1 - z)(1 - 0)}$$

or

$$\frac{3i - w}{2w} = \frac{1 - z}{1 + z}$$

Solving for w, we obtain without difficulty

$$w = -3i \frac{z + 1}{z - 3}$$

Example 2

What is the most general bilinear transformation which maps the upper half of the z-plane onto the interior of the unit circle in the w-plane (Fig. 13.5)?

Let the required transformation be

$$w = \frac{az + b}{cz + d}$$

Since the boundaries of corresponding regions must correspond under any transformation, the unit circle in the w-plane must be the image of the real axis in the z-plane. Therefore for all real values of z we must have

$$|w| = \left| \frac{az + b}{cz + d} \right| = \frac{|a|}{|c|} \frac{\left| z + \dfrac{b}{a} \right|}{\left| z + \dfrac{d}{c} \right|} = 1$$

In particular, from the limiting case, $|z| \to \infty$, we find

$$\frac{|a|}{|c|} = 1$$

and thus for real values of z

$$\left| z + \frac{b}{a} \right| = \left| z + \frac{d}{c} \right|$$

This equation expresses the fact that the complex numbers b/a and d/c are equally far

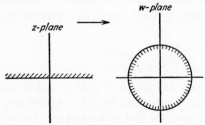

FIG. 13.5.

from all points on the real axis, which is possible if and only if b/a and d/c are conjugates, say $-\lambda$ and $-\bar{\lambda}$.

Thus we can write

$$\begin{aligned}
w &= \frac{az + b}{cz + d} \\
&= \frac{a}{c} \left[\frac{z + (b/a)}{z + (d/c)} \right] \\
&= \frac{a}{c} \left(\frac{z - \lambda}{z - \bar{\lambda}} \right) \\
&= e^{i\theta} \left(\frac{z - \lambda}{z - \bar{\lambda}} \right)
\end{aligned}$$

the last step following since a/c is a complex number of absolute value 1.

So far we have only enforced the condition that the boundaries of the two regions correspond. It is now necessary to make sure that the regions themselves correspond as required and that the upper half of the z-plane has not been mapped into the *outside* of the circle $|w| = 1$. This is most easily verified by checking some convenient point, say $z = \lambda$. This maps into $w = 0$, which is inside the circle $|w| = 1$, and thus if λ is restricted to be a point in the *upper* half of the z-plane, the solution is complete.

As a special case of some interest, let $e^{i\theta} = -1$, and let λ be a pure imaginary, say ik, where $k > 0$. Then

$$w = -\frac{z - ik}{z + ik}$$

Now

$$\mathcal{I}(w) = \frac{w - \bar{w}}{2i} = -\frac{1}{2i}\left(\frac{z - ik}{z + ik} - \frac{\bar{z} + ik}{\bar{z} - ik}\right)$$

or, reducing to a common denominator and simplifying,

$$\mathcal{I}(w) = \frac{k(z + \bar{z})}{(z + ik)(\bar{z} - ik)}$$

The denominator of the last fraction is the product of the expression $z + ik$ and its conjugate, $\bar{z} - ik$, and hence is a positive real quantity. The factor k is positive by hypothesis, and thus the imaginary part of w will be positive if and only if $z + \bar{z}$ is positive. Since $z + \bar{z}$ equals twice the real part of z, this shows that the transformation

$$w = -\frac{z - ik}{z + ik}$$

not only maps the upper half of the z-plane onto the unit circle, $|w| \leq 1$, but does it in such a way that the first quadrant of the z-plane (where $\Re(z) > 0$) corresponds to the upper half of the circle (where $\mathcal{I}(w) > 0$), and the second quadrant of the z-plane corresponds to the lower half of the circle.

Example 3

Find a transformation which will map an infinite sector of angle $\pi/4$ onto the interior of the unit circle.

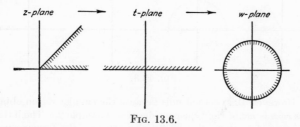

FIG. 13.6.

Since the boundary of the sector consists of portions of two straight lines, yet its image is to be a single circle, it is apparent that the mapping cannot be accomplished by a bilinear transformation alone. However, a simple combination of a power function and a linear fractional function will define a suitable transformation. Specifically, the transformation

$$t = z^4$$

will open out the sector in the z-plane into the upper half of the auxiliary t-plane (Fig. 13.6). Following this, the upper half of the t-plane can be mapped onto the unit circle in the w-plane by any transformation of the family we obtained in the last example, say

$$w = \frac{t - i}{t + i}$$

Combining these two, we have for the required transformation,

$$w = \frac{z^4 - i}{z^4 + i}$$

Example 4

Find a transformation which will map a 60° sector of the unit circle in the z-plane into the upper half of the w-plane.

At first glance it would seem that this problem can be solved simply by opening the given sector into a full circle by the transformation

$$t = z^6$$

and then mapping the circle from the t-plane into the upper half of the w-plane by means of the inverse of one of the transformations of the family we obtained in

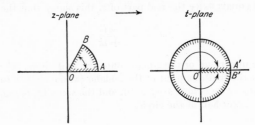

FIG. 13.7.

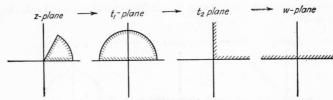

FIG. 13.8.

Example 2. However, this method fails because the circular region obtained in the t-plane in this case is *not* of the type considered in Example 2. The latter consisted of a simple circular boundary plus its interior, whereas the former consists of the interior of a circle "cut" along a radius, *i.e.*, with one radius actually a part of the boundary (Fig. 13.7).

To avoid this difficulty, let us first map the sector onto a semicircle, by the transformation

$$t_1 = z^3$$

Then let us map the semicircle from the t_1-plane onto the first quadrant of the t_2-plane by means of the transformation

$$t_2 = -i\left(\frac{t_1 - 1}{t_1 + 1}\right)$$

which is the inverse of the transformation (with $k = 1$) which we obtained as a special case at the conclusion of Example 2. Finally, let us open out the first quadrant of the t_2-plane into the upper half of the w-plane by the transformation

$$w = t_2^2$$

Combining these three transformations, we find

$$w = -\left(\frac{z^3 - 1}{z^3 + 1}\right)^2$$

as the required solution.

Example 5

A thin sheet of metal coincides with the first quadrant of the z-plane. The upper and lower faces of the sheet are perfectly insulated against the flow of heat. Find the steady-state temperature at any point of the sheet if the boundary temperatures are as shown in Fig. 13.9a.

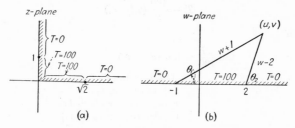

FIG. 13.9.

Under the assumptions of the problem, the flow of heat in the sheet is two-dimensional, and we must accordingly solve Laplace's equation (*i.e.*, the two-dimensional steady-state heat equation derived in Sec. 7.2)

$$\frac{\partial^2 T}{\partial x^2} + \frac{\partial^2 T}{\partial y^2} = 0$$

subject to the given conditions along the boundaries of the first quadrant. To do this, it is convenient to map the first quadrant of the z-plane onto the upper half of the w-plane by the transformation

$$w = z^2 = (x^2 - y^2) + 2ixy$$

This reduces the problem to that of finding a solution of Laplace's equation in the upper half plane which assumes along the real axis the boundary conditions shown in Fig. 13.9b.

Now either the real or the imaginary part of any analytic function is automatically a solution of Laplace's equation. In particular, the imaginary part of the function

$$f(w) = \frac{100}{\pi} \log\left(\frac{w - 2}{w + 1}\right)$$

will be a solution which will also satisfy the boundary conditions. For the imaginary part of this function is

$$\frac{100}{\pi}[\arg(w - 2) - \arg(w + 1)] = \frac{100}{\pi}(\theta_2 - \theta_1)$$

and for points on the real axis to the right of $u = 2$, both θ_1 and θ_2 are zero, so that

$$T = \frac{100}{\pi} (\theta_2 - \theta_1) = \frac{100}{\pi} (0 - 0) = 0$$

Moreover, between $u = -1$ and $u = 2$, $\theta_1 = 0$ and $\theta_2 = \pi$; hence in this range,

$$T = \frac{100}{\pi} (\pi - 0) = 100$$

Finally, to the left of $u = -1$ both θ_1 and θ_2 are equal to π, giving

$$T = \frac{100}{\pi} (\pi - \pi) = 0$$

Now

$$T = \frac{100}{\pi} (\theta_2 - \theta_1)$$

can be written

$$
\begin{aligned}
\tan \frac{\pi T}{100} &= \tan (\theta_2 - \theta_1) \\
&= \frac{\tan \theta_2 - \tan \theta_1}{1 + \tan \theta_1 \tan \theta_2} \\
&= \frac{v/(u - 2) - v/(u + 1)}{1 + [v^2/(u - 2)(u + 1)]} \\
&= \frac{3v}{u^2 + v^2 - u - 2}
\end{aligned}
$$

Returning to the z-plane by the transformation

$$
\begin{aligned}
u &= x^2 - y^2 \\
v &= 2xy
\end{aligned}
$$

we find as the solution to the original problem,

$$T = \frac{100}{\pi} \tan^{-1} \left[\frac{6xy}{(x^2 + y^2)^2 - x^2 + y^2 - 2} \right]$$

EXERCISES

1. What is the cross ratio of the four 4th roots of -1?
2. What is the cross ratio of the four complex 6th roots of 1?   *Ans.* $-\frac{1}{3}$
3. Show that there are two points which are left invariant by the general bilinear transformation. What is the condition that these two points should coincide?
4. Find the invariant points of the transformation $w = -\dfrac{2z + 4i}{iz + 1}$, and prove that these two points, together with any point z and its image w, form a set of four points having a constant cross ratio. What is this cross ratio?   *Ans.* $-\frac{3}{2}$
5. What is the Möbius transformation which sends the points $z = 0$, -1, ∞ into the points $w = -1$, $-2 - i$, i, respectively? What is the image of the circle $|z| = 1$ under this transformation?

         Ans.   The required transformation is $w = \dfrac{iz - 2}{z + 2}$

6. Find the Möbius transformation which sends the points $z = 0$, $-i$, $2i$ into the points $w = 5i$, ∞, $-\dfrac{i}{3}$, respectively What are the invariant points of this transformation?

$$Ans. \quad \text{The required transformation is } w = \frac{-3z + 5i}{-iz + 1}$$

7. What is the most general bilinear transformation which maps the upper half of the z-plane onto the lower half of the w-plane?

8. Prove that $w = z/(1 - z)$ maps the upper half of the z-plane into the upper half of the w-plane. What is the image of the unit circle $|z| = 1$ under this transformation?

9. Find a transformation which will map an infinite sector of angle $\pi/3$ onto the interior of the unit circle.

10. Show that along the circle $|cz + d| = \sqrt{ad - bc}$ the transformation $w = \dfrac{az + b}{cz + d}$ does not alter the lengths of infinitesimal segments. What happens to segments inside this circle? outside this circle?

11. Find a transformation which will map a 45° sector of the unit circle in the z-plane onto the upper half of the w-plane.

12. Find a transformation which will map the upper half of the unit circle onto the entire unit circle.

13. Find the steady-state temperature distribution in the unit circle if the upper half of the boundary of the circle is kept at the temperature 100° and the lower half of the boundary is kept at the temperature 0°.

14. Find the steady-state temperature distribution in a piece of metal coinciding with the first quadrant of the z-plane if $T = 100$ along the positive x-axis, and $T = 0$ along the positive y-axis.

15. Show that $w = z + (1/z)$ maps the portion of the upper half of the z-plane exterior to the circle $|z| = 1$ onto the entire upper half of the w-plane. Use this result to find the steady-state temperature distribution in the upper half of the z-plane exterior to the unit circle, if $T = 100$ along the linear portion of the boundary and $T = 0$ along the circular portion of the boundary.

13.4 The Schwarz-Christoffel Transformation.

In general, the conformal transformation of one given region into another is exceedingly difficult. The existence of such a representation is assured by the famous theorem of Riemann: *Any two simply connected regions can be mapped conformally on each other.* However, the determination of the specific function which accomplishes a required mapping is usually out of the question. In fact, in addition to the simple regions which we found could be mapped by means of the elementary functions, the only class of regions for which conformal transformations of practical interest exist are those bounded by polygons having a finite number of vertices (one or more of which may lie at infinity). These can always be mapped onto a half plane, and hence onto any region into which a half plane can be transformed, by means of a transformation which we shall now discuss.

Consider then the problem of mapping a polygonal boundary in the

w-plane onto the real axis in the z-plane.   To do this, we must arrange to translate each vertex of the polygon to a point on the z-axis, and at the same time convert the corresponding angle of the polygon into a straight angle.

To see how this may be done, we recall the mapping properties of the function

$$z - z_0 = (w - w_0)^{\pi/\alpha}$$

Clearly this takes the sector between $\theta = 0$ and $\theta = \alpha$, at w_0, and opens it out into a half plane, z_0 being the image of w_0, the vertex of the sector.

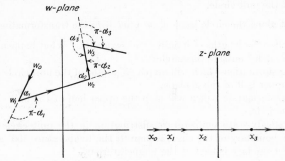

Fig. 13.10.

Writing this function as

$$w - w_0 = (z - z_0)^{\alpha/\pi}$$

we have

$$\frac{dw}{dz} = \frac{\alpha}{\pi} (z - z_0)^{\left(\frac{\alpha}{\pi} - 1\right)}$$

Hence it appears that a mapping function for which

$$(1) \qquad \frac{dw}{dz} = K(z - x_1)^{(\alpha_1/\pi) - 1}(z - x_2)^{(\alpha_2/\pi) - 1} \cdots (z - x_n)^{(\alpha_n/\pi) - 1}$$

may simultaneously carry each vertex of the given polygon into a point on the x-axis and transform each angle of the polygon into a straight angle.

To verify that this is the case, we have, from (1),

$$(2) \quad \arg dw = \arg K + \left(\frac{\alpha_1}{\pi} - 1\right) \arg (z - x_1) + \left(\frac{\alpha_2}{\pi} - 1\right) \arg (z - x_2)$$

$$+ \cdots + \left(\frac{\alpha_n}{\pi} - 1\right) \arg (z - x_n) + \arg dz$$

Now suppose that we start at a point w_0 on the side of the polygon leading to the vertex w_1 and trace the path of w as z moves along the x-axis from the corresponding point x_0. Until z reaches x_1 every term on the right of (2) remains constant. For arg K is fixed, since K is a complex constant; and clearly arg dz is zero. Moreover, arg $(z - x_1)$, arg $(z - x_2)$, . . . are all equal to π, since each is the argument of a negative real number. Therefore the values of w which correspond to these values of z all lie on a straight line, since all the increments dw have the same direction. However, as z passes through x_1, the difference $(z - x_1)$ changes abruptly from negative to positive, and thus arg $(z - x_1)$ decreases abruptly from π to 0. Hence arg dw changes by the amount

$$\left(\frac{\alpha_1}{\pi} - 1\right)(-\pi) = \pi - \alpha_1$$

But from Fig. 13.10, it is evident that this is the precise amount through which it is necessary to turn in order that w should begin to move in the direction of the next side of the polygon.

As z moves from x_1 to x_2, the same situation exists. Arg dw remains constant, and thus w moves in a straight line until z reaches x_2. Here arg $(z - x_2)$ changes suddenly from π to 0, and as a consequence arg dw increases by the amount $(\pi - \alpha_2)$, which is the exact amount of rotation required to give the direction of the next side of the polygon.

Thus as z traverses the x-axis it is clear that w moves over the boundary of a polygon whose angles are exactly those of the given figure. Moreover, it is evident that the region which is mapped onto the half plane is the region which contains the angles α_1, α_2, α_3, ... The required transformation will be obtained if we can ensure that the lengths of the sides of the polygon, as well as its angles, have the correct values.

Now the mapping function, w, obtained by integrating (1) is

$$(3) \quad w = K \int [(z - x_1)^{\frac{\alpha_1}{\pi} - 1}(z - x_2)^{\frac{\alpha_2}{\pi} - 1} \cdots (z - x_n)^{\frac{\alpha_n}{\pi} - 1}]dz + C$$

and this can be thought of as the result of the two transformations

$$(4) \quad t = \int [(z - x_1)^{\frac{\alpha_1}{\pi} - 1}(z - x_2)^{\frac{\alpha_2}{\pi} - 1} \cdots (z - x_n)^{\frac{\alpha_n}{\pi} - 1}]dz$$

$$(5) \quad w = Kt + C$$

The first of these maps the x-axis into some polygon which the second then translates, rotates, and either stretches or shrinks, as the case may be. If, then, the polygon determined by (4) is similar to the given polygon, the constants in (5) can always be determined so as to make the two polygons coincide.

Now in order that two polygons should be similar, not only must corresponding angles be equal but corresponding sides must be proportional, as well. For triangles, this is automatically the case. For quadrilaterals, one further condition is required, namely, that two pairs of corresponding sides should have the same ratio. For pentagons, two such conditions are required, and in general for a polygon of n sides, $n - 3$ conditions, over and above the equality of corresponding angles, are necessary for similarity. Hence in mapping a polygon of n sides, three of the values $x_1, x_2, \ldots, x_n$ can be assigned arbitrarily, following which the remaining $n - 3$ are determined by the conditions of similarity. In many important problems, a vertex of the polygon, usually an infinite one, will correspond to $z = \infty$. In this case dw/dz contains one less term than usual, and hence one less parameter. Therefore only two of the $n - 1$ images $x_1, x_2 \ldots, x_n$ can be specified arbitrarily. In either case the resulting transformation is known as the Schwarz-Christoffel* transformation. Obviously, since w is analytic everywhere except possibly at the points $x_1, x_2, \ldots, x_n$, the transformation is conformal.

Example 1

Find the transformation which maps the semi-infinite strip shown in Fig. 13.11a onto the half plane, as indicated.

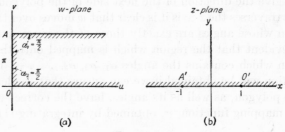

FIG. 13.11.

The required transformation is defined by

$$\frac{dw}{dz} = K(z + 1)^{\frac{\pi/2}{\pi} - 1} (z - 1)^{\frac{\pi/2}{\pi} - 1}$$
$$= K(z + 1)^{-\frac{1}{2}}(z - 1)^{-\frac{1}{2}}$$

or

$$w = K \int \frac{dz}{\sqrt{z^2 - 1}}$$
$$= K \cosh^{-1} z + C$$

Since $w = 0$ corresponds to $z = 1$, we have

$$0 = K \cosh^{-1} 1 + C \qquad \text{or} \qquad C = 0$$

* Named for the German mathematicians H. A. Schwarz (1843–1921) and E. B. Christoffel (1829–1900) who discovered it independently about 1865.

Also $w = i\pi$ corresponds to $z = -1$, and thus

$$i\pi = K \cosh^{-1}(-1) = K(i\pi) \quad \text{or} \quad K = 1$$

Therefore

$$w = \cosh^{-1} z$$

or

$$z = \cosh w$$

Broken down into real and imaginary parts, this becomes the transformation

$$x + iy = \cosh u \cos v + i \sinh u \sin v \qquad (P.316)$$

or

$$x = \cosh u \cos v$$
$$y = \sinh u \sin v$$

Eliminating u and v, in turn, we have also

$$\frac{x^2}{\cosh^2 u} + \frac{y^2}{\sinh^2 u} = 1$$
$$\frac{x^2}{\cos^2 v} - \frac{y^2}{\sin^2 v} = 1$$

which, if necessary, can be solved for u and v in terms of x and y.

Example 2

Find the temperature at any point in the region shown in Fig. 13.12a.

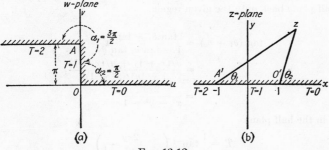

FIG. 13.12.

The first step here is to map the given region onto a half plane, in which Laplace's equation can be more conveniently solved. Hence assigning images to A and O as shown, we write

$$\frac{dw}{dz} = K(z + 1)^{\frac{1}{2}}(z - 1)^{-\frac{1}{2}} = K\sqrt{\frac{z+1}{z-1}}$$

or (as differentiation will verify immediately)

$$w = K(\sqrt{z^2 - 1} + \cosh^{-1} z) + C$$

Now when $w = 0$, $z = 1$. Hence $C = 0$. Also when $w = i\pi$, $z = -1$, and thus

$$i\pi = K \cosh^{-1}(-1) = K(i\pi) \quad \text{or} \quad K = 1$$

Therefore the required mapping is accomplished by the function

(6)
$$w = \sqrt{z^2 - 1} + \cosh^{-1} z$$

To solve Laplace's equation in the half plane, we observe that the imaginary part of the analytic function

$$f(z) = \frac{1}{\pi} \log [(z + 1)(z - 1)]$$

namely

$$\frac{1}{\pi} [\arg (z + 1) + \arg (z - 1)] \equiv \frac{\theta_1 + \theta_2}{\pi}$$

is necessarily a harmonic function. Moreover, on the real axis it satisfies the required boundary conditions. For to the right of $x = 1$ its value is

$$\frac{0 + 0}{\pi} = 0$$

between $x = -1$ and $x = 1$ its value is

$$\frac{0 + \pi}{\pi} = 1$$

and to the left of -1 its value is

$$\frac{\pi + \pi}{\pi} = 2$$

Hence the solution of the original problem can be obtained by mapping this solution for the half plane back onto the given region.

Now

$$\begin{aligned}
\tan (\theta_1 + \theta_2) &= \frac{\tan \theta_1 + \tan \theta_2}{1 - \tan \theta_1 \tan \theta_2} \\
&= \frac{y/(x + 1) + y/(x - 1)}{1 - [y^2/(x^2 - 1)]} \\
&= \frac{2xy}{x^2 - y^2 - 1}
\end{aligned}$$

and thus in the half plane

(7)
$$T = \frac{1}{\pi} \tan^{-1} \left(\frac{2xy}{x^2 - y^2 - 1} \right)$$

The mapping function (6) cannot conveniently be broken down into real and imaginary parts and solved for x and y in terms of u and v. Hence an explicit expression for T in terms of u and v cannot be obtained. However, it is only a matter of arithmetic to plot the isothermal curves in the given region. For from (7), corresponding values of x and y, that is, values of z, can be tabulated for any given value of T. These values when substituted into (6) determine values of w whose locus is the isotherm defined by the value of T under consideration.

EXERCISES

1. Find the transformation which will map the interior of the infinite strip

$$0 \leq \mathscr{I}(w) \leq \pi$$

onto the upper half of the z-plane.　(Hint: Consider the strip as the limiting form of the quadrilateral shown in Fig. 13.13, as w_1 and w_3 approach infinity, and let w_1, w_2, and w_3 correspond, respectively, to $z = 0$, 1, and ∞, with the image of w_4 to be determined.)　　　　　　　　　　　　*Ans.*　$w = \log z$

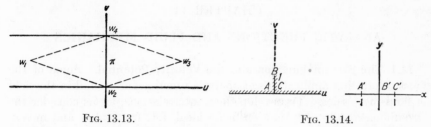

FIG. 13.13.　　　　　　　　　　　　　　FIG. 13.14.

2. Find the transformation which will map the region shown in Fig. 13.14 onto the upper half of the z-plane, as indicated.　　　　　　*Ans.*　$w = \sqrt{z^2 - 1}$

3. Use the results of Exercise 2 to find the steady-state temperature distribution in the upper half of the w-plane if the u-axis is kept at the temperature $T = 0$ and the segment of the v-axis between 0 and 1 is kept at the temperature 100.

4. Find the transformation which will map the region shown in Fig. 13.15 onto the upper half of the z-plane, as indicated.

$$Ans.\quad w = 2\sqrt{z + 1} + \log\left(\frac{\sqrt{z + 1} - 1}{\sqrt{z + 1} + 1}\right)$$

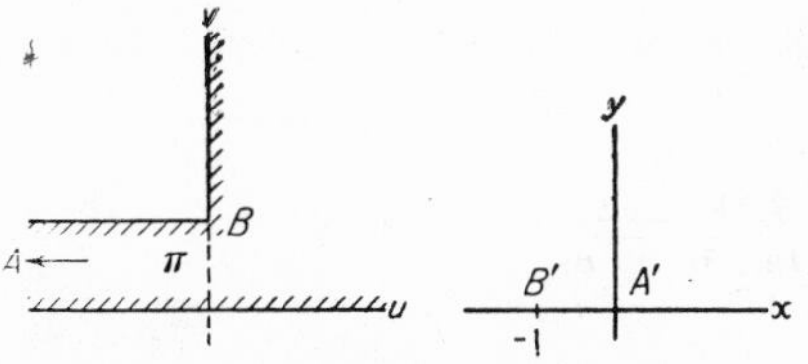

FIG. 13.15. 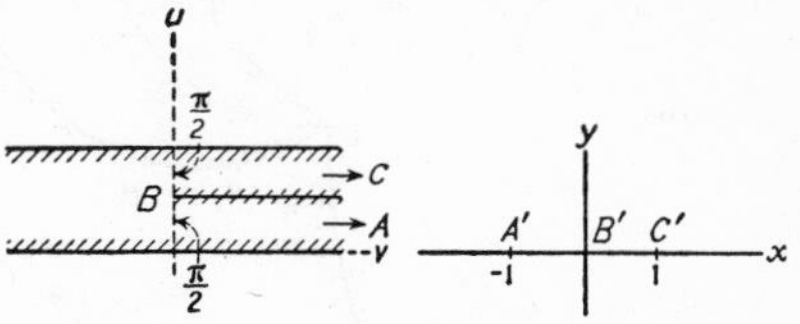　　　　　　　　　　　　　　FIG. 13.16.

5. Find the transformation which will map the region shown in Fig. 13.16 onto the upper half of the z-plane, as indicated.

CHAPTER 14

ANALYTIC FUNCTIONS AND FLUID MECHANICS

14.1 The Stream Function and the Velocity Potential. Some of the most interesting applications of analytic functions are found in the field of fluid mechanics. To develop these interrelations, let us consider the two-dimensional steady motion of an ideal, *i.e.*, frictionless and incompressible, fluid. Let any convenient axes be drawn in the plane of the motion, and let Γ be any streamline, *i.e.*, the path followed by any particular particle of the fluid.

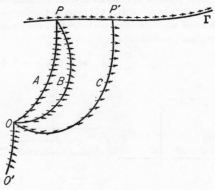

Fig. 14.1.

If the velocity of the fluid is known at every point, the rate at which fluid crosses an arc, such as OAP, may, by a proper choice of units, be taken equal to the line integral of the component of the velocity normal or transverse to the curve. Moreover, if there are no sources or sinks in the region, *i.e.*, if there are no points at which fluid is spontaneously created or destroyed, the amount of fluid which crosses OAP per unit time will be exactly equal to the amount crossing any other curve joining O and P, such as OBP. In fact, the rate at which fluid crosses OAP is exactly the same as the rate at which it crosses any other curve, OCP', if P' is on the same streamline as P. For the nature of a streamline is that the velocity of the fluid is tangent to it at all points, and hence no fluid can ever cross an arc, PP', of a streamline. Therefore, since fluid cannot accumulate between OAP and OCP', because of its incompressible

408

character, or cross the arc PP', whatever crosses OAP must just equal the amount crossing OCP' in the same time.

Thus each streamline has associated with it a definite value of what we shall call the **stream function,** ψ, namely, the common value of the rate of flow across any curve drawn from the origin to a point of that streamline, the flow being considered positive if the fluid moves across the curve in the clockwise direction as viewed from O.   A change of origin from O to O' will in general change the value of the stream function for each streamline.   However, the change consists merely in adding to each value of the stream function a constant equal to the rate of flow across the arc OO'.

If the stream function is known, the character of the entire motion is known, because from the stream function the components of the fluid velocity at any point can be found at once.   To see this, let QR be an infinitesimal arc ds of any curve in the plane of the fluid, and let V_x and V_y be the component velocities of the fluid at a point of ds (Fig. 14.2).

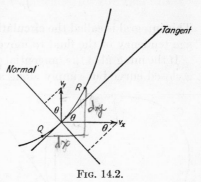

FIG. 14.2.

The rate of flow across QR, that is, $d\psi$, can be found either from the normal component of the actual velocity, V, or from the normal components of V_x and V_y.   Choosing the latter point of view, we have

$$d\psi = [V_x \sin \theta - V_y \cos \theta]ds$$

or, noting that $\cos \theta \, ds = dx$ and $\sin \theta \, ds = dy$,

$$(1) \qquad d\psi = -V_y \, dx + V_x \, dy$$

Identifying this with the usual expression for the total differential of a function $\psi(x,y)$, we have

$$d\psi \equiv \frac{\partial \psi}{\partial x} \, dx + \frac{\partial \psi}{\partial y} \, dy = -V_y \, dx + V_x \, dy$$

Thus, since dx and dy are independent quantities, we have finally

$$V_x = \frac{\partial \psi}{\partial y}$$

$$(2)$$

$$V_y = -\frac{\partial \psi}{\partial x}$$

Now let C be any closed curve in the plane of the fluid, and consider the line integral of the tangential component of the fluid velocity around C (Fig. 14.3). Again fixing our attention on the x- and y-components of the velocity instead of on the total velocity, this line integral can be written

$$\int_C (V_x \cos \theta + V_y \sin \theta)ds$$

or

$$\int_C V_x \, dx + V_y \, dy$$

This integral is called the **circulation,** K, and in a sense measures the average tendency of the fluid to move or *circulate* around the curve C.

If the integral of the tangential component of V is calculated not around a closed curve but simply along an arc joining a fixed reference point P_0 to a general point P, and if this line integral is independent of the path, we obtain a function of the coordinates of P which is called the **velocity potential,** ϕ, of the flow. Recalling similar discussions, it is clear that the line integral will be independent of the path and the potential will exist, provided that the corresponding line integral around every closed curve drawn in the fluid is zero. Motion for which this is the case is said to be **irrotational,** and what we have just observed is that *a velocity potential will exist wherever the fluid motion is irrotational.* This result is analogous to our earlier conclusion that the stream function will exist only in regions free of sources and sinks.

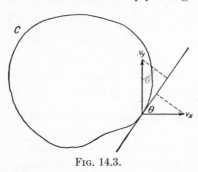

FIG. 14.3.

Considering the question analytically, and applying Green's lemma to the integral for the circulation, we have

$$K = \int_C V_x \, dx + V_y \, dy = \int \int_R \left[\frac{\partial V_y}{\partial x} - \frac{\partial V_x}{\partial y} \right] dA$$

Hence the condition that the circulation around every closed curve should vanish is that

$$\frac{\partial V_y}{\partial x} - \frac{\partial V_x}{\partial y} = 0$$

It is customary to write

$$\frac{\partial V_y}{\partial x} - \frac{\partial V_x}{\partial y} = 2\omega$$

and to call 2ω the **vorticity** of the motion.

Applying the formula

$$dK = \left[\frac{\partial V_y}{\partial x} - \frac{\partial V_x}{\partial y}\right] dA$$

to a circle of infinitesimal radius, ϵ, we have

$$dK = (2\omega)(\pi\epsilon^2)$$
$$= (2\pi\epsilon)(\omega\epsilon)$$

Since the first factor is a length, the second must be a velocity. Hence ω appears as the angular velocity of the fluid at a general point.

The velocity components, V_x and V_y, can also be found from the velocity potential. For since

(3) $$\phi = \int V_x\,dx + V_y\,dy$$

it follows from Theorem 4, Sec. 10.2, that

$$V_x = \frac{\partial\phi}{\partial x}$$

(4)

$$V_y = \frac{\partial\phi}{\partial y}$$

Equations (4) appear somewhat more "natural" than do the corresponding relations (2), since they express each velocity component as a derivative with respect to the corresponding variable, and not as a derivative with respect to the opposite variable.

The possibility of applying complex variable theory to fluid mechanics is now apparent. For, from (2) and (4), we have

$$V_x = \frac{\partial\phi}{\partial x} = \frac{\partial\psi}{\partial y}$$
$$V_y = \frac{\partial\phi}{\partial y} = -\frac{\partial\psi}{\partial x}$$

Hence ϕ and ψ satisfy the Cauchy-Riemann equations (and therefore Laplace's equation) and thus

$$\phi(x,y) + i\psi(x,y)$$

is always an analytic function. Extending an earlier definition, this function is usually called the **complex potential**. Conversely, starting with any analytic function we may interpret its real and imaginary components as a velocity potential and a stream function (or vice versa) and obtain thereby a description of some particular flow pattern. As we shall see in the next section, certain simple functions of z, thus considered, lead to results of fundamental importance in aerodynamics.

14.2 Special Flow Patterns. As a first example of the use of analytic functions in investigating flow patterns, consider the function

$$f(z) = A \log z \qquad A > 0$$

Then we can write

$$\phi + i\psi = A[\log r + i\theta]$$

and thus

(1) $$\phi = A \log r$$
(2) $$\psi = A\theta$$

From (2) it is evident that the streamlines, *i.e.*, the curves on which ψ is a constant, are the radial lines extending outward from the origin. The equipotential lines, or curves of constant ϕ, are clearly the circles with center at the origin.

The rate of flow across any curve encircling the origin is a constant, namely,

$$\psi_c = \int_C d\psi = \int_0^{2\pi} A \, d\theta = 2\pi A$$

Thus, fluid is emanating from the origin at a rate equal to $2\pi A$.

The circulation around any closed curve is

$$
\begin{aligned}
K &= \int_C d\phi \\
&= A \int_C d(\log r) \\
&= 0
\end{aligned}
$$

since $\log r$ is the same at the beginning and at the end of any closed path.

For obvious reasons this type of flow is called a **point source,** or just a **source,** and its standard form is taken to be

(3) $$f(z) = \frac{A}{2\pi} \log z$$

The positive constant A is called the **strength** of the source.

If $A < 0$, the results of the preceding discussion are still valid in all respects except that now the fluid is flowing *toward* the origin instead of away from it. In this case the configuration is called a **sink.**

If A is imaginary, say $-(iK/2\pi)$, we have

(4) $$f(z) = -\frac{iK}{2\pi} \log z$$

or

$$\phi + i\psi = -\frac{iK}{2\pi} (\log r + i\theta)$$

and thus

(5)
$$\phi = \frac{K\theta}{2\pi}$$

(6)
$$\psi = -\frac{K \log r}{2\pi}$$

In this case the streamlines, ψ = constant, are the circles with center at the origin, and the equipotentials are the radial lines through the origin.

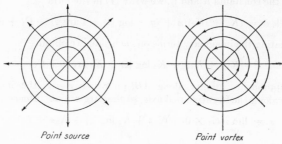

Point source   Point vortex

Fig. 14.4.

The circulation around any curve enclosing the origin is now

$$\int_C d\phi = \frac{K}{2\pi} \int_0^{2\pi} d\theta = K$$

This configuration is called a **point vortex**.

Example 1

Find the streamlines for a liquid flowing out of an infinitely long straight channel into an infinite plane region (Fig. 14.5a).

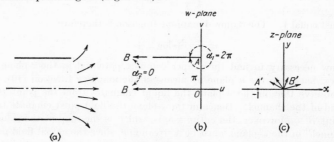

(a)   (b)   (c)

Fig. 14.5.

From the evident symmetry of the entire configuration about the center line of the channel we need only consider one-half of the flow. For convenience, we take the half breadth of the channel to be π. In the hope that our problem will be easier to solve in a half plane, we now proceed to set up the Schwarz-Christoffel transformation which maps the "polygon" consisting of the upper boundary and center line of the channel in the w-plane into the real axis in the z-plane. The point A we map into the point $z = -1$; the infinite end of the channel, B, where the flow is assumed to be uniform, we map into the point $z = 0$. At A we have the angle $\alpha_1 = 2\pi$, and at B we have the angle $\alpha_2 = 0$. Hence the required transformation is defined by

$$\frac{dw}{dz} = K(z + 1)z^{-1} = K\left(1 + \frac{1}{z}\right)$$

and

$$(7) \qquad w = K(z + \log z) + C$$

To determine the constants K and C, we write (7) in the form

$$u + iv = (K_1 + iK_2)(x + iy + \log |z| + i \arg z) + C_1 + iC_2$$

from which, equating the imaginary terms on each side, we obtain

$$(8) \qquad v = K_1 y + K_2 x + K_2 \log |z| + K_1 \arg z + C_2$$

Now when w approaches infinity along AB, on which $v = \pi$, the image point z approaches zero along the negative real axis, so that $\arg z = \pi$. Hence

$$\pi = \lim_{z \to 0^-} (K_1 \times 0 + K_2 x + K_2 \log |z| + K_1 \pi + C_2)$$

Obviously K_2 must be zero to keep $\log |z|$ from making the right member infinite; hence

$$(9) \qquad \pi = K_1 \pi + C_2$$

Also, as w approaches infinity along OB, on which $v = 0$, the image point z approaches zero along the positive real axis. In this case $\arg z = 0$ and thus from (8)

$$0 = \lim_{z \to 0^+} (K_1 \arg z + C_2) = C_2$$

Thus $C_2 = 0$, and so from (9), $K_1 = 1$.

Finally, the point $w = i\pi$ must map into $z = -1$. Hence from (7)

$$i\pi = -1 + \log (-1) + C_1$$
$$= -1 + i\pi + C_1$$

and C_1 must equal 1. The required mapping function is therefore

$$(10) \qquad w = z + \log z + 1$$

It is now necessary to find the proper complex potential in the z-plane and to transform it back into the w-plane by means of the mapping function (10). To do this, we observe that in the w-plane the liquid emanates from the point B at the infinite end of the channel. Hence in the z-plane the fluid must emanate from the image point B'. Moreover, the entire x-axis, which is the map of the sides of the "half channel" in the w-plane, must be a streamline, since the actual fluid motion is always tangent to the channel walls. The flow pattern corresponding to these requirements is simply a point source at B'. Taking the strength of the source to be 2π, for convenience, we then have in the z-plane the complex potential

$$f(z) = \phi + i\psi = \log z \qquad \text{or} \qquad z = e^{\phi + i\psi}$$

Hence, using (10), the complex potential in the w-plane is defined implicitly by

$$(11) \qquad w = e^{\phi + i\psi} + (\phi + i\psi) + 1$$

Breaking (11) into its real and imaginary parts, we have further

$$u = e^{\phi} \cos \psi + \phi + 1$$
$$v = e^{\phi} \sin \psi + \psi$$

For a fixed value of ψ these are the parametric equations of the corresponding stream-line. Similarly, by fixing ϕ and treating ψ as a parameter, we obtain the equipotential curves. A few curves of each family are shown in Fig. 14.6.

It is interesting to observe that this problem is identical with the electrical problem of finding the potential around two paral-lel plates charged to different potentials. From this point of view the streamlines in Fig. 14.6 are the equipotentials and the lines of constant velocity potential are the lines of force.

Two other very simple complex potentials of great importance are

$$(12) \qquad f(z) = Uz$$
$$(13) \qquad f(z) = -iVz$$

Since the first of these can be written

$$\phi + i\psi = Ux + iUy$$

or

$$\phi = Ux \qquad \text{and} \qquad \psi = Uy$$

it clearly represents uniform fluid motion with velocity U along the x-axis. Similarly for (13),

$$\phi = Vy \qquad \text{and} \qquad \psi = -Vx$$

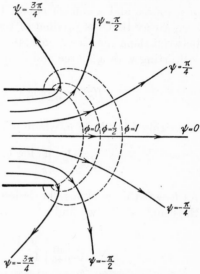

Fig. 14.6.   Plot showing the streamlines for flow from a uniform channel.

which represents a uniform flow along the y-axis with velocity V.

EXERCISES

1. Determine the complex potential, the velocity potential, and the stream function for a point source in a uniform stream.   Assuming both the strength of the source and the velocity of the stream to be unity, plot the streamlines $\psi = 0$, $\psi = \pm 0.05$, $\psi = \pm 0.10$.

2. Find the complex potential, the velocity potential, and the stream function for a point vortex in a uniform stream.   Plot the streamline $\psi = 0$.

3. Find the complex potential, the velocity potential, and the stream function for a source and a sink of equal strength situated in a uniform stream (a) if the direction of the stream is parallel to the line joining the source and the sink and (b) if the direction of the stream is perpendicular to the line joining the source and the sink. In each case determine the streamline corresponding to $\psi = 0$.

4. Find the equation of the family of streamlines for potential flow in the interior of an angle of 60°.

5. Find the transformation which will map a uniform flow parallel to the x-axis into

the flow around the outside of a 90° angle, and plot several of the streamlines for the latter flow.

6. Determine the complex potential, the velocity potential, and the stream function for two equal sources situated at the points $z = \pm b$. Explain how this configuration also describes the flow from a single source situated at a distance b from a straight barrier of infinite extent.

14.3 The Flow Past a Cylinder. Another pattern of considerable interest is the **doublet,** which is defined to be the limiting configuration of a source and a sink of equal strength which approach each other in such a way that the product of their common strength and the distance between them remains a constant.

Starting with a source and a sink at b and $-b$, respectively, we have

$$f(z) = \frac{A}{2\pi} \log (z - b) - \frac{A}{2\pi} \log (z + b)$$

or writing $(A)(2b) = \mu$, where μ is a constant,

$$f(z) = \frac{\mu}{4\pi} \frac{\log (z - b) - \log (z + b)}{b}$$

As $b \to 0$ this assumes the indeterminate form $0/0$. Evaluating it in the usual fashion we find

$$f(z) = \lim_{b \to 0} \left[\frac{\mu}{4\pi} \frac{\log (z - b) - \log (z + b)}{b} \right]$$

$$= \frac{\mu}{4\pi} \lim_{b \to 0} \left(\frac{-1}{z - b} - \frac{1}{z + b} \right)$$

(1) $$= -\frac{\mu}{2\pi z}$$

If a uniform flow in the direction of the negative x-axis (the axis of the doublet) is superimposed upon this, we have a new pattern whose complex potential is

$$-Uz - \frac{\mu}{2\pi z}$$

Hence

$$\phi + i\psi = -U(x + iy) - \frac{\mu}{2\pi} \left(\frac{x - iy}{x^2 + y^2} \right)$$

and thus

$$\psi = -Uy + \frac{\mu y}{2\pi(x^2 + y^2)}$$

If we change to polar coordinates, the equation of the family of stream-lines assumes the simpler form

$$\psi = -Ur \sin\theta + \frac{\mu \sin\theta}{2\pi r}$$

(2)
$$= -U \sin\theta \left(r - \frac{a^2}{r}\right)$$

where $a^2 = \mu/2\pi U$.

In this form it is apparent that the streamline $\psi = 0$ is composite, consisting of the x-axis (from the factor $\sin\theta = 0$), and the circle $r = a$.

Considering this circle as a rigid object in the fluid, we have in effect solved the problem of finding the streamlines past a smooth circle or circular cylinder placed in a uniform stream.

It is now a matter of considerable importance to determine the resultant force experienced by the circle due to the motion of the fluid past it. Since we are now working in polar coordinates, a necessary preliminary must be to obtain expres-

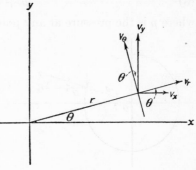

FIG. 14.7.

sions for the component velocities of the fluid in the direction of increasing r and of increasing θ.

Now

$$V_x = \frac{\partial\psi}{\partial y} \quad \text{and} \quad V_y = -\frac{\partial\psi}{\partial x}$$

Also, since $x = r \cos\theta$ and $y = r \sin\theta$, we have

$$\frac{\partial x}{\partial r} = \cos\theta, \qquad \frac{\partial y}{\partial r} = \sin\theta, \qquad \frac{\partial x}{\partial\theta} = -r \sin\theta, \qquad \frac{\partial y}{\partial\theta} = r \cos\theta$$

Hence, from Fig. 14.7, we can write

$$
\begin{aligned}
V_r &= V_x \cos\theta + V_y \sin\theta \\
&= \frac{1}{r}\left[\frac{\partial\psi}{\partial y}(r\cos\theta) + \frac{\partial\psi}{\partial x}(-r\sin\theta)\right] \\
&= \frac{1}{r}\left[\frac{\partial\psi}{\partial y}\frac{\partial y}{\partial\theta} + \frac{\partial\psi}{\partial x}\frac{\partial x}{\partial\theta}\right] \\
&= \frac{1}{r}\frac{\partial\psi}{\partial\theta}
\end{aligned}
$$

$$
\begin{aligned}
V_\theta &= -V_x \sin\theta + V_y \cos\theta \\
&= -\frac{\partial\psi}{\partial y}(\sin\theta) - \frac{\partial\psi}{\partial x}(\cos\theta) \\
&= -\left[\frac{\partial\psi}{\partial y}\frac{\partial y}{\partial r} + \frac{\partial\psi}{\partial x}\frac{\partial x}{\partial r}\right] \\
&= -\frac{\partial\psi}{\partial r}
\end{aligned}
$$

Applying these results to the stream function (2), we find

$$V_r = \frac{1}{r}\left[-U \cos \theta \left(r - \frac{a^2}{r}\right)\right] \qquad = -U \cos \theta \left[1 - \frac{a^2}{r^2}\right]$$

$$V_\theta = -\left[-U \sin \theta \left(1 + \frac{a^2}{r^2}\right)\right] \qquad = U \sin \theta \left[1 + \frac{a^2}{r^2}\right]$$

On the circle $r = a$, these give

$$V_r = 0, \qquad V_\theta = 2U \sin \theta$$

Now according to **Bernoulli's equation**,

(3) $$p + \tfrac{1}{2}\rho V^2 = H$$

where p is the pressure at any point in the fluid, ρ is the density, V is the total velocity, and H is a constant. Hence the pressure at any point on the circle $r = a$ is

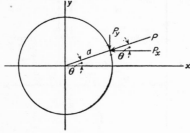

FIG. 14.8.

$$p = H - \tfrac{1}{2}\rho(V_r^2 + V_\theta^2)$$
$$= H - 2\rho U^2 \sin^2 \theta$$

Since the fluid is assumed to be frictionless, this pressure acts perpendicular to the surface of the cylinder. Hence, resolving it into its horizontal and vertical components, we have (Fig. 14.8)

$$p_x = -p \cos \theta = -H \cos \theta + 2\rho U^2 \cos \theta \sin^2 \theta$$
$$p_y = -p \sin \theta = -H \sin \theta + 2\rho U^2 \sin^3 \theta$$

On an infinitesimal arc of the circle, $a\, d\theta$, the forces due to these pressures are, respectively,

$$dF_x = ap_x\, d\theta \qquad \text{and} \qquad dF_y = ap_y\, d\theta$$

Hence, integrating around the entire circle, we find for the components of the total force on the circle

$$F_x = -aH \int_0^{2\pi} \cos \theta\, d\theta + 2\rho U^2 a \int_0^{2\pi} \cos \theta \sin^2 \theta\, d\theta$$

$$= -aH \sin \theta \Big|_0^{2\pi} + 2\rho U^2 a \frac{\sin^3 \theta}{3} \Big|_0^{2\pi}$$

$$= 0$$

$$F_y = -aH \int_0^{2\pi} \sin \theta\, d\theta + 2\rho U^2 a \int_0^{2\pi} \sin^3 \theta\, d\theta$$

$$= aH \cos \theta \Big|_0^{2\pi} + 2\rho U^2 a \left[\frac{\cos^3 \theta}{3} - \cos \theta\right]_0^{2\pi}$$

$$= 0$$

These results could, of course, have been predicted from the symmetry of the pressure distribution.

In as much as actual tests on circular objects in a uniform stream reveal a resultant force at right angles to the stream, the theoretical picture which we have thus far created is definitely inadequate. In an attempt to bring theory into better correspondence with fact, let us superpose a point vortex on the last flow pattern. By introducing a circulation of fluid around the circle, this will produce a higher resultant velocity on one side than on the other and hence, according to Bernoulli's equation, a difference in pressure will result which will lead to a net force on the circle.

Adding the complex potential for a point vortex,

$$\frac{-Ki \log z}{2\pi}$$

to the complex potential for the last flow, we have

$$f(z) = -Uz - \frac{\mu}{2\pi z} - \frac{Ki \log z}{2\pi}$$

$$= -U(x + iy) - \frac{\mu(x - iy)}{2\pi(x^2 + y^2)} - \frac{Ki(\log r + i\theta)}{2\pi}$$

and thus

$$\psi = -Uy + \frac{\mu y}{2\pi(x^2 + y^2)} - \frac{K \log r}{2\pi}$$

$$= -U \sin \theta \left[r - \frac{a^2}{r} \right] - \frac{K \log r}{2\pi}$$

From this it is easy to verify the important fact that the circle $r = a$ is still a streamline, i.e., is still associated with a constant value of ψ. If this were not the case, the continuation would, of course, be impossible.

Now on the circle $r = a$, the radial component of velocity

$$V_r = \frac{1}{r} \frac{\partial \psi}{\partial \theta} \bigg|_{r=a}$$

is still zero, while the tangential component is

(4) $$V_\theta = - \frac{\partial \psi}{\partial r} \bigg|_{r=a} = 2U \sin \theta + \frac{K}{2\pi a}$$

Hence, by Bernoulli's equation the pressure normal to the circle at any point is

$$p = H - \frac{1}{2} \rho V^2$$

$$= H - \frac{1}{2} \rho \left[2U \sin \theta + \frac{K}{2\pi a} \right]^2$$

Integrating the x- and y-components of the forces due to this pressure distribution, we find

$$F_x = \int_0^{2\pi} - ap \cos \theta \, d\theta$$

$$= -a \int_0^{2\pi} \cos \theta \left\{ H - 2\rho U^2 \sin^2 \theta - \frac{\rho UK}{\pi a} \sin \theta - \frac{\rho K^2}{8\pi^2 a^2} \right\} d\theta$$

$$= \left\{ -aH \sin \theta + \frac{2a\rho U^2 \sin^3 \theta}{3} + \frac{\rho UK}{2\pi} \sin^2 \theta + \frac{\rho K^2 \sin \theta}{8\pi^2 a} \right\} \Big|_0^{2\pi}$$

$$= 0$$

$$F_y = \int_0^{2\pi} - ap \sin \theta \, d\theta$$

$$= -a \int_0^{2\pi} \sin \theta \left\{ H - 2\rho U^2 \sin^2 \theta - \frac{\rho UK}{\pi a} \sin \theta - \frac{\rho K^2}{8\pi^2 a^2} \right\} d\theta$$

$$= \left\{ aH \cos \theta + 2a\rho U^2 \left(\frac{\cos^3 \theta}{3} - \cos \theta \right) \right.$$

$$\left. + \frac{\rho UK}{\pi} \left(\frac{\theta}{2} - \frac{\sin 2\theta}{4} \right) - \frac{\rho K^2 \cos \theta}{8\pi^2 a} \right\} \Big|_0^{2\pi}$$

$$= \rho UK$$

Thus when circulation, K, is present, a circle experiences a force ρUK at right angles to a stream of velocity U. This important result is known as the **Kutta-Joukowski** law.

It is interesting to investigate the nature of the stream lines for different values of the circulation K. From Eq. (4) giving the tangential velocity on the circle, $r = a$, namely,

$$V_\theta = 2U \sin \theta + \frac{K}{2\pi a}$$

it is clear that this component will vanish when and only when

$$\sin \theta = - \frac{K}{4\pi a U}$$

that is, when

$$\theta = - \sin^{-1} \frac{K}{4\pi a U}$$

If $\frac{K}{4\pi a U} < 1$, there are thus two points on the circle at which $V_\theta = 0$. Since V_r is identically zero on the circumference of the circle, it follows that at these two points the resultant velocity is also zero. These points are called **stagnation points**. If $K/4\pi a U = 1$, the two stagnation points

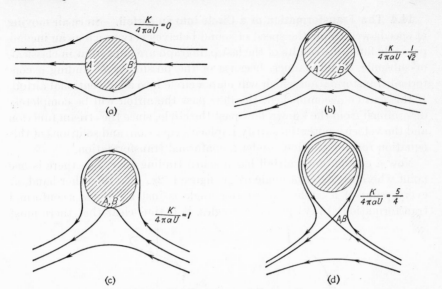

Fig. 14.9.   Plot showing various positions of the stagnation points in the flow past a cylinder.

coalesce into one, and if $\dfrac{K}{4\pi aU} > 1$ they do not exist.   Figure 14.9 shows each of these possibilities.

EXERCISES

1. Find the complex potential, the velocity potential, and the stream function for a doublet in a uniform stream whose direction is perpendicular to the axis of the doublet.   Plot several of the streamlines.   Is there a circular streamline?
2. Work Exercise 1 if the direction of the stream makes an angle α with the axis of the doublet.
3. Transform the noncirculatory flow past a circle of unit radius by means of the transformation

$$w = i\left(z + \frac{1}{z}\right)$$

and discuss the nature of the transformed flow.
4. Transform the noncirculatory flow past a circle of unit radius by means of the transformation

$$w = z - \frac{1}{z}$$

and discuss the nature of the transformed flow.

   Ans.   The transformed flow pattern represents the flow past a thin plate of width 4 placed perpendicular to a uniform stream.
5. Make plots showing the variation of the normal pressure with θ for a circle in a uniform stream if $K/4\pi aU = 0, 1/\sqrt{2}, 1, 2$.

14.4 The Transformation of a Circle into an Airfoil. Since air moving at speeds well below the speed of sound behaves very much as an incompressible fluid, the results of the last paragraph are important in classical, or subsonic, aerodynamics, because of the possibility of finding a conformal transformation which will map a circle into a conventional airfoil. If this can be accomplished, the flow past the airfoil will be completely determined from the known flow past the circle, since the stream function and the velocity potential satisfy Laplace's equation, and solutions of this equation remain solutions under a conformal transformation.

Now a conventional airfoil has a sharp trailing edge, *i.e.*, there is one point where the exterior angle of the figure is 2π. On the other hand, at every point of a circle the exterior angle is just π. Since a conformal transformation always preserves angles, it is thus clear that there must

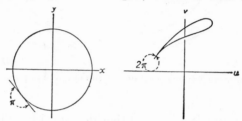

Fig. 14.10.

be one and only one point on the circumference of the circle at which the transformation is not conformal but has a critical point where angles are doubled. In other words, there must be one point on the circle where the derivative of the mapping function has a simple zero. Clearly there can be no other critical point outside the circle, for if such were the case the flow past the circle would not be correctly transformed into the flow past the airfoil. Additional critical points inside the circle, however, are harmless, and even necessary, as we shall soon see.

Now suppose that

$$f(z) = \phi + i\psi$$

is the complex potential for the flow past the circle. Then

$$\frac{df}{dz} = \frac{\partial \phi}{\partial x} + i\frac{\partial \psi}{\partial x} = V_x - iV_y$$

and thus at any point the resultant velocity in the z-plane is

$$V_z = \sqrt{V_x^2 + V_y^2} = \left|\frac{df}{dz}\right|$$

Moreover, under the appropriate conformal transformation, $f(z)$ becomes (as a function of $w = u + iv$) the complex potential in the w-, or airfoil, plane. The general properties of the complex potential of course hold just as well in the w-plane as in the z-plane. Hence in the plane of the airfoil we have

$$\frac{df}{dw} = V_u - iV_v \quad \text{and} \quad V_w = \sqrt{V_u^2 + V_v^2} = \left| \frac{df}{dw} \right|$$

Now

$$\frac{df}{dw} = \frac{df}{dz}\frac{dz}{dw} = \frac{df/dz}{dw/dz}$$

where the derivative dw/dz is of course to be found from the mapping relation between the z- and w-planes. Hence, taking absolute values,

$$\left| \frac{df}{dw} \right| = \frac{\left| \dfrac{df}{dz} \right|}{\left| \dfrac{dw}{dz} \right|}$$

which shows that the resultant velocities in the two planes are connected by the relation

$$V_w = \frac{V_z}{\left| \dfrac{dw}{dz} \right|}$$

This implies that at any point where the derivative of the mapping function vanishes, a finite velocity in the z-plane is magnified into an infinite velocity in the w-plane. But we have already seen that in order to obtain an airfoil with a sharp trailing edge, it is necessary that the derivative of the mapping function have a first-order zero at the point which transforms into the trailing edge. Hence it appears that the fluid in the plane of the airfoil moves with infinite velocity at the trailing edge. To avoid this physical impossibility, Joukowski proposed that the circulation constant K be assigned a value which would locate one of the two stagnation points on the circle at the point which is to map into the trailing edge of the airfoil. Since the velocity at a stagnation point is zero, this effectively eliminates the infinite velocity at the trailing edge. This assumption is customarily referred to as the **Joukowski hypothesis.**

To map a circle into an airfoil, we use a transformation of the form

$$w = z + a_0 + \frac{a_1}{z} + \frac{a_2}{z^2} + \cdots$$

where higher powers of z are necessarily absent so that dw/dz will remain finite as $z \to \infty$, and the regions at infinity in the two planes will be conformally mapped. We shall assume that w contains only a finite number of terms, so that

$$\frac{dw}{dz} = 1 - \frac{a_1}{z^2} - \frac{2a_2}{z^3} - \cdots - \frac{na_n}{z^{n+1}}$$

$$= \frac{z^{n+1} - a_1 z^{n-1} - 2a_2 z^{n-2} - \cdots - na_n}{z^{n+1}}$$

The critical points of the transformation are then the $n + 1$ roots of the equation

(1) $$z^{n+1} - a_1 z^{n-1} - 2a_2 z^{n-2} - \cdots - na_n = 0$$

obtained by equating to zero the numerator of dw/dz.

Now from algebra we recall that the sum of the roots of a polynomial equation

$$x^{n+1} + b_0 x^n + b_1 x^{n-1} + \cdots + b_n = 0$$

is equal to the negative of the second coefficient, b_0. Applying this result to Eq. (1), in which the coefficient of z^n is zero, we see that the sum of the roots is zero:

$$z_1 + z_2 + \cdots + z_{n+1} = 0$$

But the sum of m complex numbers is simply m times the complex number which is the coordinate of the center of gravity of the set of points represented by the numbers. Hence the critical points of the required transformation must have their center of gravity at the origin.

With this in mind, the transformation of a circle into an airfoil can be described as follows. Choose any $n + 1$ points, $z_1, z_2, \ldots z_{n+1}$, in the z-plane as the critical points of the transformation, and set up a coordinate system with the origin at the center of gravity of these points. Draw the circle which is to be mapped into the airfoil so that it passes through one of these points and encloses all the rest. Map this circle by means of the transformation defined by

$$\frac{dw}{dz} = \frac{(z - z_1)(z - z_2) \cdots (z - z_{n+1})}{z^{n+1}}$$

In the special case when $n = 1$ and there are just two critical points, z_1 and z_2, it is necessary that they be symmetrically located with respect to the origin. Choosing the real axis to be the line passing through them, the transformation becomes

$$\frac{dw}{dz} = \frac{(z - c)(z + c)}{z^2} = 1 - \frac{c^2}{z^2}$$

$$w = z + \frac{c^2}{z}$$

This is known as the **Joukowski transformation**.

The airfoil which is the image of a circle under a Joukowski transformation can be very easily constructed point by point. For the image of any z can be found by first inverting z in the circle $|z| = c$, then reflecting in the real axis, and finally adding z itself to the result of the first two steps. Figure 14.11 shows the details of this construction.

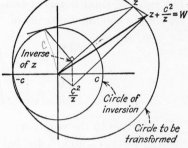

EXERCISES

Construct the curve into which each of the following circles is mapped by the transformation $w = z + 1/z$.

1. $(x - 1)^2 + (y - 1)^2 = 5$
2. $x^2 + (y - 1)^2 = 2$
3. $(x - 1)^2 + (y - 1)^2 = 6$

Fig. 14.11.   Plot showing the geometrical method of carrying out the Joukowski transformation.

4. In Exercise 1, if the undisturbed flow past the circle is in the direction of the negative x-axis, what is the value of K required by the Joukowski hypothesis?
5. Find the transformation whose singular points are $z = 2, -2, -i$. Explain how the image of a circle under this transformation can be constructed point by point.

14.5 The Force on an Airfoil.

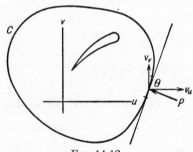

Fig. 14.12.

To obtain a formula for the lift on an airfoil, let us consider the motion of the fluid contained between the airfoil and any simple closed curve C encircling the airfoil. If F_u and F_v are the components of the force which acts on the airfoil, then the fluid within C experiences equal and opposite forces, $-F_u$ and $-F_v$. In addition, this fluid is acted upon by the pressure normal to the boundary, C. By Newton's law, these forces must equal the rate of increase of momentum of the fluid passing out of the region bounded by C.

Now the rate at which fluid leaves the interior of C through an infinitesimal arc ds is (Fig. 14.12)

$$\rho(V_u \sin \theta - V_v \cos \theta)ds = \rho(V_u \, dv - V_v \, du)$$

By virtue of its horizontal velocity this fluid carries out momentum in the u direction at the rate

(1) $$\rho V_u(V_u \, dv - V_v \, du) = \rho(V_u^2 \, dv - V_u V_v \, du)$$

By virtue of its vertical velocity it carries out momentum in the v direction at the rate

$$(2) \qquad \rho V_v(V_u\,dv - V_v\,du) = \rho(V_uV_v\,dv - V_v^2\,du)$$

The rates of total outward transfer of momentum, dM_u/dt and dM_v/dt, are simply the line integrals of (1) and (2) around C:

$$\frac{dM_u}{dt} = -\rho \int_C (V_uV_v\,du - V_u^2\,dv)$$

$$\frac{dM_v}{dt} = -\rho \int_C (V_v^2\,du - V_uV_v\,dv)$$

In addition to the reactions, $-F_u$ and $-F_v$, the fluid within C is acted upon by forces P_u and P_v due to the fluid pressure p normal to C. Resolving the force acting on an infinitesimal arc of C into its components, and integrating around C, we obtain

$$P_u = - \int_C p \sin \theta \, ds = - \int_C p \, dv$$

$$P_v = \int_C p \cos \theta \, ds = \int_C p \, du$$

Now applying Newton's law and equating the forces to the corresponding rates of change of momentum, we have

$$(3) \qquad -F_u - \int_C p\,dv = -\rho \int_C (V_uV_v\,du - V_u^2\,dv)$$

$$(4) \qquad -F_v + \int_C p\,du = -\rho \int_C (V_v^2\,du - V_uV_v\,dv)$$

In these we must now substitute for the pressure, using Bernoulli's equation,

$$p = H - \tfrac{1}{2}\rho(V_u^2 + V_v^2)$$

Then subtracting Eq. (3) from i times Eq. (4), we find

$$F_u - iF_v = - \int_C \left[H - \frac{\rho}{2}(V_u^2 + V_v^2) \right](i\,du + dv)$$

$$- i\rho \int_C (V_v^2\,du - V_uV_v\,dv) + \rho \int_C (V_uV_v\,du - V_u^2\,dv)$$

$$= -iH \int_C (du - i\,dv) + \frac{\rho}{2} \int_C (V_u^2 + V_v^2 - 2V_v^2 - 2iV_uV_v)i\,du$$

$$+ \frac{\rho}{2} \int_C (V_u^2 + V_v^2 + 2iV_uV_v - 2V_u^2)dv$$

or, collecting terms and noting that the first integral is **zero**,

$$
\begin{aligned}
F_u - iF_v &= \frac{\rho}{2} \int_C (V_u^2 - V_v^2 - 2iV_uV_v)i\, du - (V_u^2 - V_v^2 - 2iV_uV_v)dv \\
&= \frac{\rho i}{2} \int_C (V_u - iV_v)^2(du + i\, dv)
\end{aligned}
$$

$$(5) \qquad = \frac{\rho i}{2} \int_C \left(\frac{df}{dw}\right)^2 dw$$

since

$$V_u - iV_v = \frac{\partial \phi}{\partial u} - i\left(-\frac{\partial \psi}{\partial u}\right) = \frac{\partial \phi}{\partial u} + i\frac{\partial \psi}{\partial u}$$

which is one of the standard forms of the derivative with respect to w of the complex potential

$$f(w) = \phi(u,v) + i\psi(u,v)$$

for the flow past the airfoil.

The value of the integral in (5) can be computed by the theory of residues. To do this, we write

$$
\begin{aligned}
F = F_u - iF_v &= \frac{\rho i}{2} \int_C \left(\frac{df}{dz}\frac{dz}{dw}\right)^2 dw
\end{aligned}
$$

$$(6) \qquad\qquad = \frac{\rho i}{2} \int_C \left(\frac{df}{dz}\right)^2 \frac{dz}{dw}\, dz$$

which eliminates the necessity of transforming the complex potential from the plane of the circle into the plane of the airfoil, and permits us instead to use the simpler expressions

$$f(z) = -Uz - \frac{\mu}{2\pi z} - \frac{iK \log z}{2\pi}$$

and

$$f'(z) = -U + \frac{\mu}{2\pi z^2} - \frac{iK}{2\pi z}$$

Now $(df/dz)^2$ has a pole of order 4 at $z = 0$, and dz/dw has $n + 1$ simple poles, since dw/dz has $n + 1$ simple zeros. Moreover, from the construction of the transformation, it is clear that these $n + 2$ singularities lie on or within the circle which is being mapped, and are therefore necessarily within the path of integration, C. This makes the application of the method of residues a formidable undertaking, and thus we resort to a slightly different approach and expand the integrand in powers of $1/z$.

To do this, we first write

$$\frac{dz}{dw} = \frac{1}{\dfrac{dw}{dz}} = \frac{1}{1 - \dfrac{a_1}{z^2} - \dfrac{2a_2}{z^3} - \cdots} = b_0 + \frac{b_1}{z} + \frac{b_2}{z^2} + \cdots$$

By cross multiplying and equating coefficients, we find

$$b_0 = 1, \qquad b_1 = 0, \; \ldots$$

Hence, substituting into (6),

$$F = F_u - iF_v = \frac{\rho i}{2} \int_C \left[-U + \frac{\mu}{2\pi z^2} - \frac{iK}{2\pi z} \right]^2 \left[1 + \frac{b_2}{z^2} + \cdots \right] dz$$

where the values of the coefficients $b_2, \; \ldots$ are irrelevant.

Expanding the integrand, we find

$$F_u - iF_v$$
$$= \frac{\rho i}{2} \int_C \left[U^2 + \frac{KiU}{\pi z} - \left(\frac{K^2}{4\pi^2} + \frac{\mu U}{\pi} \right) \frac{1}{z^2} - \cdots \right] \left[1 + \frac{b_2}{z^2} + \cdots \right] dz$$
$$= \frac{\rho i}{2} \int_C \left[U^2 + \frac{iKU}{\pi z} + \left(b_2 U^2 - \frac{K^2}{4\pi^2} - \frac{\mu U}{\pi} \right) \frac{1}{z^2} - \cdots \right] dz$$

This expression is valid outside any circle enclosing all the singularities of the integrand. In particular, it is a valid representation of the integrand on C. Hence without recourse to the theory of residues, as such, but merely by recalling that

$$\int_C \frac{dz}{z^n} = \begin{cases} 2\pi i, & n = 1 \\ 0, & n \neq 1 \end{cases}$$

we obtain

$$F_u - iF_v = \left(\frac{\rho i}{2} \right) \left(\frac{iKU}{\pi} \right) (2\pi i) = -\rho U i K$$

Therefore $F_u = 0$ and $F_v = \rho U K$, which shows that the airfoil, like the circle, is acted upon by a resultant force normal to the air stream, whose magnitude is given by the Kutta-Joukowski law.

The extension of these ideas to the resolution of the resultant force, $\rho U K$, into lift and drag components and to the calculation of the moment acting on an airfoil must be left to more inclusive texts on aerodynamics.

CHAPTER 15

VECTOR ANALYSIS

15.1 The Algebra of Vectors. In our study of complex variables we found the notion of a **vector,** *i.e.,* a quantity possessing both magnitude and direction, of considerable use in describing the geometric representation of complex numbers. Developed in a somewhat different direction, the study of vector quantities leads into what is known as vector analysis, a subject of considerable utility in discussing physical quantities such as velocity, acceleration, and force which have both direction and magnitude.

In addition to vector quantities such as these, almost any physical discussion will also involve quantities like mass, length, time, work, and electric charge which possess only magnitude and are known as **scalars.** To distinguish vectors from scalars, we shall consistently write the former in boldface type thus, **V.** This is a rather common notation, although a number of authors indicate that a symbol stands for a vector quantity by putting a stroke over the symbol thus, $\bar{V}$.

Two vectors whose magnitudes, or lengths, are equal and whose directions are the same are said to be **equal** regardless of the point in space from which they may be drawn. If two vectors have the same length but are oppositely directed, either is said to be the **negative** of the other. The magnitude, or length, of a vector we shall indicate by ordinary absolute value signs. Thus the scalar quantity

$$|V|$$

represents the length of the vector **V.** A vector is **zero** if and only if its length is zero.

The **sum** of two vectors is defined by the parallelogram law exactly as the sum of two complex numbers is defined. By the **difference** of two vectors, **A − B,** we mean the sum of the first and the negative of the second, **A + (−B)** (Fig. 15.1). By the **product of a scalar and a vector,** *a***V,** we mean a vector whose direction is either the same as or exactly opposite to that of **V,** according as *a* is positive or negative, and whose length is |*a*| times the length of **V.**

In addition to the product of a scalar and a vector, two other types of product are defined in vector analysis. The first is the **scalar** or **dot** or **inner product,** indicated by placing a dot between the two factors. By definition, this is a *scalar* equal to the product of the lengths of the two

429

factors and the cosine of the angle between them.   That is,

$$(1) \qquad \mathbf{A} \cdot \mathbf{B} = |\mathbf{A}||\mathbf{B}| \cos \theta$$

Since $|\mathbf{A}| \cos \theta$ is the length of the projection of the vector $\mathbf{A}$ in the direction of $\mathbf{B}$, and since $|\mathbf{B}| \cos \theta$ is the projection of $\mathbf{B}$ in the direction of $\mathbf{A}$, it follows that *the dot product of two vectors is equal to the length of either of*

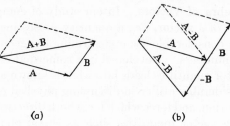

(a)   (b)

FIG. 15.1.

them, multiplied by the projection of the other upon it (Fig. 15.2).   Two particular cases of this are worthy of note: If one of the vectors, say $\mathbf{A}$, is of unit length, then $\mathbf{A} \cdot \mathbf{B}$ becomes simply

$$|\mathbf{B}| \cos \theta$$

which is just the projection of $\mathbf{B}$ in the direction of the unit vector, $\mathbf{A}$. On the other hand, if $\mathbf{A} = \mathbf{B}$, then $\cos \theta = \cos 0 = 1$, and we have

$$(2) \qquad \mathbf{A} \cdot \mathbf{A} = |\mathbf{A}|^2$$

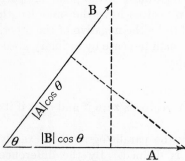

FIG. 15.2.

From the definitive relation (1), it is clear that *dot multiplication is commutative*, that is,

$$(3) \qquad \mathbf{A} \cdot \mathbf{B} = \mathbf{B} \cdot \mathbf{A}$$

However, if the dot product of two vectors is zero, it does not follow that one or the other of the factors is zero, for there is a third possibility, namely, $\cos \theta = 0$.   Thus *if $\mathbf{A} \cdot \mathbf{B} = 0$, then either at least one of the vectors $\mathbf{A}$, $\mathbf{B}$ is zero or $\mathbf{A}$ and $\mathbf{B}$ are perpendicular.*

The third type of product with which we shall deal is the **vector** or **cross** product, indicated by placing a cross between the factors.   If $\mathbf{A}$ and $\mathbf{B}$ are the factors, then by definition $\mathbf{A} \times \mathbf{B}$ is a vector, $\mathbf{V}$, whose length is the product of the lengths of $\mathbf{A}$ and $\mathbf{B}$ and the sine of the angle between them, and whose direction is perpendicular to the plane of $\mathbf{A}$ and $\mathbf{B}$ and so sensed that a right-handed screw turned from $\mathbf{A}$ toward $\mathbf{B}$

through the smaller of the angles between these vectors would advance in the direction of **V**. Since $|\mathbf{B}|\sin\theta$ is the length of the projection of **B** in a direction perpendicular to **A,** or in other words is the altitude of the parallelogram having **A** and **B** as adjacent sides, it follows that the magnitude of $\mathbf{A}\times\mathbf{B}$ is equal to the area of this parallelogram.

From the fact that $\sin(-\theta)=-\sin\theta$, it is clear that when the factors in a cross product are interchanged, so that the sign of θ is reversed,

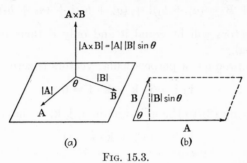

FIG. 15.3.

the sign of the cross product itself is changed.   Hence *cross multiplication is not commutative*, and we have in fact

(4) $$\mathbf{A}\times\mathbf{B}=-\mathbf{B}\times\mathbf{A}$$

We must therefore be careful to preserve the proper order of factors in any expression involving vector multiplication.

If $\mathbf{A}\times\mathbf{B}=0$, we cannot conclude that either **A** or **B** is zero, for this product will also vanish if $\sin\theta=0$. Hence *if* $\mathbf{A}\times\mathbf{B}=0$ *either at least one of the vectors,* **A, B,** *is zero or* **A** *and* **B** *are parallel.*

It is often convenient to be able to refer vector expressions to a cartesian frame of reference.   To provide for this, we define **i, j,** and **k** to be vectors of unit length directed,

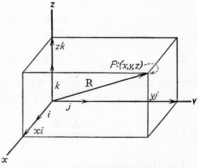

FIG. 15.4.

respectively, along the positive x, y, and z axes of a right-handed coordinate system.   Then $x\mathbf{i}, y\mathbf{j},$ and $z\mathbf{k}$ represent vectors of length x, y, and z, whose directions are those of the respective axes; and from the definition of vector addition it is evident that the vector joining the origin to a general point P (Fig. 15.4) can be written

(5) $$\mathbf{R}=x\mathbf{i}+y\mathbf{j}+z\mathbf{k}$$

In more general terms, any vector whose components along the axes are, respectively, a_1, a_2, and a_3 can be written

$$(6) \qquad \mathbf{A} = a_1\mathbf{i} + a_2\mathbf{j} + a_3\mathbf{k}$$

If further,

$$\mathbf{B} = b_1\mathbf{i} + b_2\mathbf{j} + b_3\mathbf{k}$$

then

$$\mathbf{A} + \mathbf{B} = (a_1 + b_1)\mathbf{i} + (a_2 + b_2)\mathbf{j} + (a_3 + b_3)\mathbf{k}$$

Clearly, two vectors will be equal if and only if their respective components are equal.

Since the dot product of perpendicular vectors is zero, it follows that

$$(7) \qquad \mathbf{i} \cdot \mathbf{j} = \mathbf{j} \cdot \mathbf{k} = \mathbf{k} \cdot \mathbf{i} = 0$$

Moreover, applying (2) to the unit vectors $\mathbf{i}, \mathbf{j}, \mathbf{k}$, we have

$$(8) \qquad \mathbf{i} \cdot \mathbf{i} = \mathbf{j} \cdot \mathbf{j} = \mathbf{k} \cdot \mathbf{k} = 1$$

Hence if we write

$$\mathbf{A} \cdot \mathbf{B} = (a_1\mathbf{i} + a_2\mathbf{j} + a_3\mathbf{k}) \cdot (b_1\mathbf{i} + b_2\mathbf{j} + b_3\mathbf{k})$$

and expand and simplify, we obtain the important result

$$(9) \qquad \mathbf{A} \cdot \mathbf{B} = a_1b_1 + a_2b_2 + a_3b_3$$

In particular, taking $\mathbf{B} = \mathbf{A}$, we have

$$\mathbf{A} \cdot \mathbf{A} = |\mathbf{A}|^2 = a_1^2 + a_2^2 + a_3^2$$

or

$$(10) \qquad |\mathbf{A}| = \sqrt{a_1^2 + a_2^2 + a_3^2}$$

On the other hand, if we write $\mathbf{A} \cdot \mathbf{B} = |\mathbf{A}||\mathbf{B}| \cos \theta$ and then solve for $\cos \theta$, using (9) and (10), we obtain the useful formula

$$(11) \qquad \cos \theta = \frac{\mathbf{A} \cdot \mathbf{B}}{|\mathbf{A}||\mathbf{B}|} = \frac{a_1b_1 + a_2b_2 + a_3b_3}{\sqrt{a_1^2 + a_2^2 + a_3^2} \sqrt{b_1^2 + b_2^2 + b_3^2}}$$

For the cross products of the unit vectors, we find at once

$$(12) \qquad \begin{aligned} \mathbf{i} \times \mathbf{i} &= \mathbf{j} \times \mathbf{j} = \mathbf{k} \times \mathbf{k} = 0 \\ \mathbf{i} \times \mathbf{j} &= -\mathbf{j} \times \mathbf{i} = \mathbf{k} \\ \mathbf{j} \times \mathbf{k} &= -\mathbf{k} \times \mathbf{j} = \mathbf{i} \\ \mathbf{k} \times \mathbf{i} &= -\mathbf{i} \times \mathbf{k} = \mathbf{j} \end{aligned}$$

Hence if we expand

$$\mathbf{A} \times \mathbf{B} = (a_1\mathbf{i} + a_2\mathbf{j} + a_3\mathbf{k}) \times (b_1\mathbf{i} + b_2\mathbf{j} + b_3\mathbf{k})$$

we obtain

(13) $\mathbf{A} \times \mathbf{B} = (a_2 b_3 - a_3 b_2)\mathbf{i} + (a_3 b_1 - a_1 b_3)\mathbf{j} + (a_1 b_2 - a_2 b_1)\mathbf{k}$

which is precisely the expanded form of the determinant

(14) $$\mathbf{A} \times \mathbf{B} = \begin{vmatrix} \mathbf{i} & \mathbf{j} & \mathbf{k} \\ a_1 & a_2 & a_3 \\ b_1 & b_2 & b_3 \end{vmatrix}$$

The noncommutative character of vector multiplication thus corresponds to the fact that interchanging two rows of a determinant changes the sign of the determinant.

Example 1

Using vector methods, obtain the formula for the cosine of the difference of two angles.

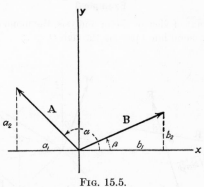

FIG. 15.5.

To do this, let us consider two vectors in the xy-plane

$$\mathbf{A} = a_1 \mathbf{i} + a_2 \mathbf{j}$$
$$\mathbf{B} = b_1 \mathbf{i} + b_2 \mathbf{j}$$

making angles α and β with the positive x-axis. Then, by Eq. (11), we have

$$\cos(\alpha - \beta) = \frac{a_1 b_1 + a_2 b_2}{\sqrt{a_1^2 + a_2^2} \sqrt{b_1^2 + b_2^2}}$$

Now regardless of the quadrant in which α and β may lie,

$$\frac{a_1}{\sqrt{a_1^2 + a_2^2}} = \cos \alpha, \quad \frac{a_2}{\sqrt{a_1^2 + a_2^2}} = \sin \alpha, \quad \frac{b_1}{\sqrt{b_1^2 + b_2^2}} = \cos \beta, \quad \frac{b_2}{\sqrt{b_1^2 + b_2^2}} = \sin \beta$$

Hence, substituting,

$$\cos(\alpha - \beta) = \cos \alpha \cos \beta + \sin \alpha \sin \beta$$

Example 2

If (x,y,z) and (x',y',z') are two right-handed cartesian coordinate systems having a common origin, obtain by vector methods the transformation equations connecting the two systems of coordinates.

To do this, let **i**, **j**, **k** and **i′**, **j′**, **k′** be unit vectors in the direction of the respective axes, and let P be a general point in space having coordinates x, y, z and x', y', z' in the respective systems. Now the coordinates x', y', z' are simply the components of the vector OP along the x', y', z'-axes. Hence if we write

$$\mathbf{R} = OP = x\mathbf{i} + y\mathbf{j} + z\mathbf{k}$$

and observe that the dot products of this vector with **i′**, **j′**, and **k′** are its components in these directions, we find the required formulas to be

$$x' = \mathbf{R} \cdot \mathbf{i'} = (x\mathbf{i} + y\mathbf{j} + z\mathbf{k}) \cdot \mathbf{i'} = x(\mathbf{i} \cdot \mathbf{i'}) + y(\mathbf{j} \cdot \mathbf{i'}) + z(\mathbf{k} \cdot \mathbf{i'})$$
$$y' = \mathbf{R} \cdot \mathbf{j'} = (x\mathbf{i} + y\mathbf{j} + z\mathbf{k}) \cdot \mathbf{j'} = x(\mathbf{i} \cdot \mathbf{j'}) + y(\mathbf{j} \cdot \mathbf{j'}) + z(\mathbf{k} \cdot \mathbf{j'})$$
$$z' = \mathbf{R} \cdot \mathbf{k'} = (x\mathbf{i} + y\mathbf{j} + z\mathbf{k}) \cdot \mathbf{k'} = x(\mathbf{i} \cdot \mathbf{k'}) + y(\mathbf{j} \cdot \mathbf{k'}) + z(\mathbf{k} \cdot \mathbf{k'})$$

The products $(\mathbf{i} \cdot \mathbf{i'})$, $(\mathbf{j} \cdot \mathbf{i'})$, . . . , $(\mathbf{k} \cdot \mathbf{k'})$ are of course just the cosines of the angles between the various axes of the two systems, and are known from the data of the problem.

Example 3

Discuss from the point of view of vector analysis, the moment of a force **F** about a point O and about a general line l passing through O.

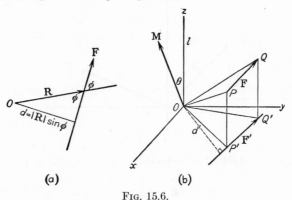

(a)   (b)

FIG. 15.6.

In mechanics the **moment M of a force F about a point** O is defined to be the magnitude of the force times the perpendicular distance d from the given point to the line of action of the force. Now if **R** is the vector drawn from O to any point on the line of **F** (Fig. 15.6a), we have $d = |\mathbf{R}| \sin \phi$. Hence

$$M = |\mathbf{F}|d = |\mathbf{R}||\mathbf{F}| \sin \phi = |\mathbf{R} \times \mathbf{F}|$$

and so, as far as magnitude is concerned, the cross product **R × F** gives correctly the moment of **F** about O. Moreover, the vector **M = R × F** is normal to the plane of **R** and **F** and so directed that **R**, **F**, and **M** form a right-handed system. Hence, since the tendency of **F** is to produce rotation about an axis through O having exactly the direction of **M**, this direction is an inherent characteristic of the moment, and thus it is natural to define

(15) $$\mathbf{M} = \mathbf{R} \times \mathbf{F}$$

as the **vector moment** of the force **F** about the point O.

Now let l be any line through O. Then as defined in mechanics, **the moment of the force F about the line** l is the product of the magnitude of the projection of **F** on a plane perpendicular to l times the perpendicular distance from l to the line of action of this component. In Fig. 15.6b, l is taken as the z-axis. The vector PQ represents the force **F**, and $P'Q'$ represents its projection on some plane perpendicular to l, which we take as the xy-plane. The vector **M** is the vector representing the moment of **F** about O, and is therefore perpendicular to the plane OPQ. The angle between **M** and l we call θ.

Now the magnitude of the moment of **F** about l, namely,

$$|\mathbf{M}_l| = |\mathbf{F}'|d'$$

is numerically just twice the area of $\Delta OP'Q'$, and similarly the moment of **F** about O is twice the area of ΔOPQ. Moreover, from the fact that $P'Q'$ is the projection of PQ, it follows that $\Delta OP'Q'$ is the projection of ΔOPQ, the angle between the planes of the triangles being the same as the angle θ between the respective normals, l and **M**. Hence

$$\text{Area } \Delta OP'Q' = (\text{area } \Delta OPQ) \cos \theta$$

from which, multiplying through by 2, we get

$$|\mathbf{M}_l| = |\mathbf{M}| \cos \theta$$

But $|\mathbf{M}| \cos \theta$ is just the component of **M** in the direction of l. Therefore, *the moment of a force* **F** *about any line* l *through a point* O *is equal to the projection on* l *of the vector moment of* **F** *about* O.

When we consider products involving three rather than two vectors, we encounter the following possibilities.

$$(\mathbf{A} \cdot \mathbf{B})\mathbf{C}$$
$$\mathbf{A} \cdot (\mathbf{B} \times \mathbf{C})$$
$$\mathbf{A} \times (\mathbf{B} \times \mathbf{C})$$

The first case can be dismissed with a word. For $\mathbf{A} \cdot \mathbf{B}$ is just a scalar and thus $(\mathbf{A} \cdot \mathbf{B})\mathbf{C}$ is simply a vector whose direction is the same as that of **C** and whose length is $\mathbf{A} \cdot \mathbf{B}$ times the length of **C**.

For the second product, $\mathbf{A} \cdot (\mathbf{B} \times \mathbf{C})$, which is known as a **scalar triple product,** we observe first that the parentheses enclosing the vector product $\mathbf{B} \times \mathbf{C}$ are superfluous. There is in fact only one alternative interpretation, namely $(\mathbf{A} \cdot \mathbf{B}) \times \mathbf{C}$ and this is meaningless, since both factors in a cross product must be vectors, whereas $\mathbf{A} \cdot \mathbf{B}$ is a scalar. Thus no meaning but the intended one can be attached to $\mathbf{A} \cdot \mathbf{B} \times \mathbf{C}$, and thus it is customary to omit the parentheses.

Geometrically, *the scalar triple product* $\mathbf{A} \cdot \mathbf{B} \times \mathbf{C}$ *represents the volume of the parallelepiped having the vectors* **A**, **B**, *and* **C** *as concurrent edges.* For if we regard the parallelogram on **B** and **C** as the base of this figure, then $\mathbf{B} \times \mathbf{C}$ is a vector whose direction is perpendicular to the base and whose magnitude is equal to the area of the base. Moreover, the altitude of the parallelepiped is the projection of $\mathbf{A}$ on $\mathbf{B} \times \mathbf{C}$. Hence $\mathbf{A} \cdot \mathbf{B} \times \mathbf{C}$, whose value is just the magnitude of $\mathbf{B} \times \mathbf{C}$ multiplied by the projection of $\mathbf{A}$ on $\mathbf{B} \times \mathbf{C}$, is equal to the volume of the parallelepiped. If θ is less than $\pi/2$, that is, if $\mathbf{A}$ and $\mathbf{B} \times \mathbf{C}$ lie on the same side of the plane of $\mathbf{B}$ and $\mathbf{C}$, then $\cos \theta$ is positive and so too is the scalar triple product. In

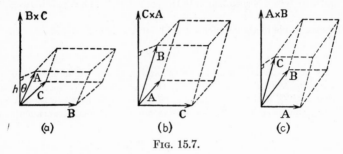

Fig. 15.7.

particular, changing the order of the factors $\mathbf{B}$ and $\mathbf{C}$ gives the product $\mathbf{C} \times \mathbf{B}$ whose direction is opposite to that of $\mathbf{B} \times \mathbf{C}$; hence

$$(16) \qquad \mathbf{A} \cdot \mathbf{B} \times \mathbf{C} = -\mathbf{A} \cdot \mathbf{C} \times \mathbf{B}$$

Since the volume of a parallelepiped is independent of the face which is chosen as its base, it follows by applying the preceding argument to Fig. 15.7b and c that

$$\mathbf{B} \cdot \mathbf{C} \times \mathbf{A} \qquad \text{and} \qquad \mathbf{C} \cdot \mathbf{A} \times \mathbf{B}$$

also give the volume of the same parallelepiped. From this fact, together with (16), we therefore can write

$$(17) \quad \mathbf{A} \cdot \mathbf{B} \times \mathbf{C} = \mathbf{B} \cdot \mathbf{C} \times \mathbf{A} = \mathbf{C} \cdot \mathbf{A} \times \mathbf{B}$$
$$= -\mathbf{A} \cdot \mathbf{C} \times \mathbf{B} = -\mathbf{B} \cdot \mathbf{A} \times \mathbf{C} = -\mathbf{C} \cdot \mathbf{B} \times \mathbf{A}$$

which shows that *any cyclic permutation of the factors in a scalar triple product leaves the product unchanged, whereas a permutation which destroys the original cyclic arrangement changes the sign of the product.*

Furthermore, since the order of factors in a dot product is immaterial, we find by considering the first and third members of (17)

$$\mathbf{A} \cdot \mathbf{B} \times \mathbf{C} = \mathbf{C} \cdot \mathbf{A} \times \mathbf{B}$$
$$= \mathbf{A} \times \mathbf{B} \cdot \mathbf{C}$$

Hence the dot and cross can be interchanged in any scalar triple product without altering its value. For this reason it is customary to omit these symbols and write a scalar triple product simply as

$$[\mathbf{ABC}]$$

If the vectors **A, B, C** all lie in the same plane or are all parallel to the same plane, they necessarily form a parallelepiped of zero volume, and conversely.   Hence

$$\mathbf{A} \cdot \mathbf{B} \times \mathbf{C} = 0$$

is a necessary and sufficient condition that three vectors, **A, B,** and **C,** be parallel to one and the same plane.   In particular, if two factors of a scalar triple product have the same direction, the product is zero.   Analytically, if we write

$$\mathbf{A} = a_1\mathbf{i} + a_2\mathbf{j} + a_3\mathbf{k}$$
$$\mathbf{B} = b_1\mathbf{i} + b_2\mathbf{j} + b_3\mathbf{k}$$
$$\mathbf{C} = c_1\mathbf{i} + c_2\mathbf{j} + c_3\mathbf{k}$$

we have

$$\mathbf{A} \cdot \mathbf{B} \times \mathbf{C}$$
$$= (a_1\mathbf{i} + a_2\mathbf{j} + a_3\mathbf{k}) \cdot \{(b_2c_3 - b_3c_2)\mathbf{i} + (b_3c_1 - b_1c_3)\mathbf{j} + (b_1c_2 - b_2c_1)\mathbf{k}\}$$
$$= a_1(b_2c_3 - b_3c_2) + a_2(b_3c_1 - b_1c_3) + a_3(b_1c_2 - b_2c_1)$$

which is just the expanded form of the determinant

$$(18) \qquad\qquad [\mathbf{ABC}] = \begin{vmatrix} a_1 & a_2 & a_3 \\ b_1 & b_2 & b_3 \\ c_1 & c_2 & c_3 \end{vmatrix}$$

Relations (17) are thus equivalent to the familiar fact that interchanging any two rows in a determinant changes the sign of the determinant.

To express the **vector triple product** **A** × (**B** × **C**) in a simple form, we first observe that it is a vector which is perpendicular to **A** and to **B** × **C**.   But **B** × **C** is itself perpendicular to the plane of **B** and **C,** and thus any vector, such as **A** × (**B** × **C**), which is perpendicular to **B** × **C** must lie in the plane of **B** and **C** (Fig. 15.8).   Hence the vector **A** × (**B** × **C**) must be expressible as the vector sum of its components in the directions of **B** and **C**:

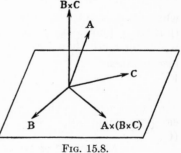

Fig. 15.8.

$$\mathbf{A} \times (\mathbf{B} \times \mathbf{C}) = \lambda\mathbf{B} + \mu\mathbf{C}$$

To find λ and μ, we first use the fact that **A** × (**B** × **C**) is also perpendicular to **A,** and thus its dot product with **A** must be zero:

$$0 = \mathbf{A} \cdot \{\mathbf{A} \times (\mathbf{B} \times \mathbf{C})\} = \mathbf{A} \cdot \{\lambda\mathbf{B} + \mu\mathbf{C}\} = \lambda(\mathbf{A} \cdot \mathbf{B}) + \mu(\mathbf{A} \cdot \mathbf{C})$$

Hence

$$\frac{\lambda}{\mu} = -\frac{(\mathbf{A} \cdot \mathbf{C})}{(\mathbf{A} \cdot \mathbf{B})}$$

from which

$$\lambda = \nu(\mathbf{A} \cdot \mathbf{C}), \qquad \mu = -\nu(\mathbf{A} \cdot \mathbf{B})$$

and

$$\mathbf{A} \times (\mathbf{B} \times \mathbf{C}) = \nu\{(\mathbf{A} \cdot \mathbf{C})\mathbf{B} - (\mathbf{A} \cdot \mathbf{B})\mathbf{C}\}$$

where ν is a factor of proportionality, independent of $\mathbf{A}$, $\mathbf{B}$, and $\mathbf{C}$, which remains to be determined.

The simplest way to determine ν is to check some specific product, say $\mathbf{i} \times (\mathbf{i} \times \mathbf{j})$. For this,

$$\mathbf{i} \times (\mathbf{i} \times \mathbf{j}) = \nu\{(\mathbf{i} \cdot \mathbf{j})\mathbf{i} - (\mathbf{i} \cdot \mathbf{i})\mathbf{j}\}$$
$$\mathbf{i} \times \mathbf{k} = \nu\{0\mathbf{i} - 1\mathbf{j}\}$$
$$-\mathbf{j} = -\nu\mathbf{j}$$

which requires that $\nu = 1$. Therefore

(19)
$$\boxed{\mathbf{A} \times (\mathbf{B} \times \mathbf{C}) = (\mathbf{A} \cdot \mathbf{C})\mathbf{B} - (\mathbf{A} \cdot \mathbf{B})\mathbf{C}}$$

By a straightforward application of this formula we find that

$$(\mathbf{A} \times \mathbf{B}) \times \mathbf{C} = -\mathbf{C} \times (\mathbf{A} \times \mathbf{B}) = -(\mathbf{C} \cdot \mathbf{B})\mathbf{A} + (\mathbf{C} \cdot \mathbf{A})\mathbf{B}$$

which is not equal to $\mathbf{A} \times (\mathbf{B} \times \mathbf{C})$. Hence the position of the parentheses in a vector triple product is significant.

With a knowledge of scalar and vector triple products, products involving more than three vectors can be expanded without difficulty. For instance,

$$(\mathbf{A} \times \mathbf{B}) \cdot (\mathbf{C} \times \mathbf{D})$$

can be regarded as the scalar triple product of the vectors $\mathbf{A}$, $\mathbf{B}$, and $(\mathbf{C} \times \mathbf{D})$. This allows us to write

$$\mathbf{A} \times \mathbf{B} \cdot (\mathbf{C} \times \mathbf{D}) = \mathbf{A} \cdot \{\mathbf{B} \times (\mathbf{C} \times \mathbf{D})\}$$
$$= \mathbf{A} \cdot \{(\mathbf{B} \cdot \mathbf{D})\mathbf{C} - (\mathbf{B} \cdot \mathbf{C})\mathbf{D}\}$$
$$= (\mathbf{A} \cdot \mathbf{C})(\mathbf{B} \cdot \mathbf{D}) - (\mathbf{A} \cdot \mathbf{D})(\mathbf{B} \cdot \mathbf{C})$$

Similarly, $(\mathbf{A} \times \mathbf{B}) \times (\mathbf{C} \times \mathbf{D})$ can be thought of as the vector triple product of $(\mathbf{A} \times \mathbf{B})$, $\mathbf{C}$, and $\mathbf{D}$ or of $\mathbf{A}$, $\mathbf{B}$, and $(\mathbf{C} \times \mathbf{D})$. Taking the first point of view and applying (19), we find

$$(\mathbf{A} \times \mathbf{B}) \times (\mathbf{C} \times \mathbf{D}) = [(\mathbf{A} \times \mathbf{B}) \cdot \mathbf{D}]\mathbf{C} - [(\mathbf{A} \times \mathbf{B}) \cdot \mathbf{C}]\mathbf{D}$$
$$= [ABD]\mathbf{C} - [ABC]\mathbf{D}$$

which is a vector in the plane of **C** and **D**.   From the second point of view,

$$(A \times B) \times (C \times D) = -(C \times D) \times (A \times B)$$
$$= -\{[(C \times D) \cdot B]A - [(C \times D) \cdot A]B\}$$
$$= -[CDB]A + [CDA]B$$

which is a vector in the plane of **A** and **B**.   The two results together show that $(A \times B) \times (C \times D)$ is directed along the line of intersection of the plane of **A** and **B** and the plane of **C** and **D**.

EXERCISES

In each of the following problems the symbols **A, B, C**, and **D** refer to the vectors

$$A = 2i - 2j + k \qquad C = 12i - 4j - 3k$$
$$B = i + 8j - 4k \qquad D = i + j + k$$

1. What is $A + B$? $A - D$? $2B - 3C + D$?
2. What is the length of each of the vectors **A, B, C, D**?
3. What is $A \cdot B$? $A \cdot C$? $C \cdot D$?
4. What is $B \times C$? $B \times D$? $A \times D$?
5. What is the projection of **B** on **D**?   What is the projection of **D** on **B**?
6. What is the angle between **A** and **B**?   What is the angle between **C** and **D**?
7. What is [ABC]? [BCD]?
8. What is the volume of the parallelepiped having $A + C$, $A - C$, and **D** as concurrent edges?   What is the volume of the parallellepiped having $A + 2C$, $A + 3C$, and **C** as concurrent edges?
9. What is $A \times (B \times C)$? $(A \times B) \times C$? $B \times (A \times C)$?
10. What is $(A \times B) \cdot (C \times D)$?
11. What is $(A \times C) \times (B \times D)$? $(A \times C) \times (A \times D)$?
12. Express the unit vectors **i, j**, and **k** as linear combinations of **A, B**, and **C**.
13. Determine a, b, and c so that $i + 2j + 3k = aA + bB + cC$.
14. What force acting in the direction of **D** will be required to produce a component of 20 lb in the direction of **B**?
15. What is the moment about a line through the origin having the direction of **A**, due to a 20-lb force acting at the point $-3, 1, 4$ in the direction of **C**?
16. P, Q, and R are three points in a plane π.   If **P, Q**, and **R** are the vectors from the origin to these points, prove that the vector

$$(P \times Q) + (Q \times R) + (R \times P)$$

is perpendicular to π.
17. Prove that $(P \times Q) \cdot (Q \times R) \times (R \times P) = [PQR]^2$
18. Prove that $\{P \times (Q \times R)\} + \{Q \times (R \times P)\} + \{R \times (P \times Q)\} = 0$
19. Prove that

$$\{(P \times Q) \cdot (R \times S)\} + \{(Q \times R) \cdot (P \times S)\} + \{(R \times P) \cdot (Q \times S)\} = 0$$

20. If **A** is a constant vector, show that the locus of the end points of the vectors **R** which satisfy the equation $(R - A) \cdot A = 0$ is a plane perpendicular to **A** at its end point.   What is the locus of the end points of the vectors which satisfy the equation $(R - A) \cdot R = 0$?

15.2 Vector Functions of One Variable. If t is a scalar variable, and if to each value of t in some range there corresponds a value of a vector $\mathbf{V}$, we say that $\mathbf{V}$ is a vector function of t and we write

$$\mathbf{V} = \mathbf{F}(t)$$

By the derivative of a vector function, $\mathbf{F}(t)$, we mean, as usual,

$$\frac{d\mathbf{F}}{dt} = \lim_{\Delta t \to 0} \frac{\Delta \mathbf{F}}{\Delta t} = \lim_{\Delta t \to 0} \frac{\mathbf{F}(t + \Delta t) - \mathbf{F}(t)}{\Delta t}$$

From this definition it follows at once that sums and products of vectors can be differentiated by formulas just like those of ordinary calculus, provided that the proper order of factors is maintained wherever the order is significant. Specifically we have

(1)
$$\frac{d(\mathbf{A} \pm \mathbf{B})}{dt} = \frac{d\mathbf{A}}{dt} \pm \frac{d\mathbf{B}}{dt}$$

(2)
$$\frac{d(a\mathbf{A})}{dt} = \frac{da}{dt}\mathbf{A} + a\frac{d\mathbf{A}}{dt}$$

(3)
$$\frac{d(\mathbf{A} \cdot \mathbf{B})}{dt} = \frac{d\mathbf{A}}{dt} \cdot \mathbf{B} + \mathbf{A} \cdot \frac{d\mathbf{B}}{dt}$$

(4)
$$\frac{d(\mathbf{A} \times \mathbf{B})}{dt} = \frac{d\mathbf{A}}{dt} \times \mathbf{B} + \mathbf{A} \times \frac{d\mathbf{B}}{dt}$$

(5)
$$\frac{d[\mathbf{ABC}]}{dt} = \left[\frac{d\mathbf{A}}{dt}\mathbf{BC} \right] + \left[\mathbf{A}\frac{d\mathbf{B}}{dt}\mathbf{C} \right] + \left[\mathbf{AB}\frac{d\mathbf{C}}{dt} \right]$$

(6)
$$\frac{d\{\mathbf{A} \times (\mathbf{B} \times \mathbf{C})\}}{dt} = \frac{d\mathbf{A}}{dt} \times (\mathbf{B} \times \mathbf{C}) + \mathbf{A} \times \left(\frac{d\mathbf{B}}{dt} \times \mathbf{C} \right)$$
$$+ \mathbf{A} \times \left(\mathbf{B} \times \frac{d\mathbf{C}}{dt} \right)$$

The simplest example of a vector function of one variable is the set of vectors drawn from the origin to the points of some curve C on which the scalar variable t is a parameter. Conversely, if the values of a vector function, $\mathbf{F}(t)$, be drawn from a common origin, their end points will define a curve, C.

This point of view leads to an important geometric interpretation of the derivative, $d\mathbf{F}/dt$. For as Fig. 15.9 shows, $\Delta \mathbf{F}$ has the direction of an infinitesimal chord of C. Therefore as $\Delta t \to 0$, the direction of $\Delta \mathbf{F}$ approaches the direction of the tangent to C. Since Δt is just a scalar, the direction of $d\mathbf{F}/dt$ is the limiting direction of $\Delta \mathbf{F}$, that is, $d\mathbf{F}/dt$ *is a vector tangent to the curve, C, which is the locus of the ends of the vectors,* $\mathbf{F}(t)$. In particular, if the scalar variable t is taken to be the arc length s of C measured from some reference point on C, we have

$$\lim_{\Delta s \to 0} \left| \frac{\Delta \mathbf{F}}{\Delta s} \right| = \lim_{\Delta s \to 0} \frac{\text{infinitesimal chord}}{\text{infinitesimal arc}} = 1$$

Hence $d\mathbf{F}/ds$ *is a unit vector tangent to the curve* C *defined by the* vector function $\mathbf{F}(t)$.

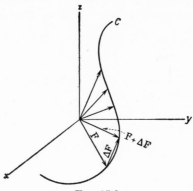

FIG. 15.9.

Example 1

What is the angle between the tangents to the curve defined by $\mathbf{F}(t) = t\mathbf{i} + t^2\mathbf{j} + t^4\mathbf{k}$ at the points where $t = 1$ and $t = 2$?

Since the tangent at a general point of this curve is given by

$$\frac{d\mathbf{F}}{dt} = \mathbf{i} + 2t\mathbf{j} + 4t^3\mathbf{k}$$

the tangents at $t = 1$ and $t = 2$ are, respectively,

$$\mathbf{T}_1 = \mathbf{i} + 2\mathbf{j} + 4\mathbf{k}$$
$$\mathbf{T}_2 = \mathbf{i} + 4\mathbf{j} + 32\mathbf{k}$$

Hence

$$\cos \theta = \frac{\mathbf{T}_1 \cdot \mathbf{T}_2}{|\mathbf{T}_1||\mathbf{T}_2|} = \frac{1 \cdot 1 + 2 \cdot 4 + 4 \cdot 32}{\sqrt{1 + 4 + 16}\sqrt{1 + 16 + 1{,}024}}$$

$$= \frac{137}{\sqrt{21}\sqrt{1{,}041}}$$

$$= 0.9266$$

and

$$\theta = \cos^{-1} 0.9266 = 22°5'$$

In the important case in which the independent variable is the time and $\mathbf{F}(t)$ represents the vectors drawn from a fixed point to the instantaneous positions of a moving particle, we can write

$$\frac{d\mathbf{F}}{dt} = \lim_{\Delta t \to 0} \left(\frac{\Delta \mathbf{F}}{\Delta s} \frac{\Delta s}{\Delta t} \right) = \frac{d\mathbf{F}}{ds} \frac{ds}{dt}$$

Since ds/dt is the speed v of the moving particle, and since $d\mathbf{F}/ds$ is a unit vector tangent to the path of the particle, the quantity $d\mathbf{F}/dt$ agrees both in magnitude and in direction with the velocity of the particle, and thus can properly be called the **vector velocity v.**

If we define the **vector acceleration** to be the time derivative of the vector velocity, and denote by $\mathbf{T}$ a unit vector tangent to C at a general point, we can write

$$\mathbf{a} = \frac{d\mathbf{v}}{dt} = \frac{d(v\mathbf{T})}{dt} = \frac{dv}{dt}\mathbf{T} + v\frac{d\mathbf{T}}{dt}$$

$$= \frac{dv}{dt}\mathbf{T} + v\frac{d\mathbf{T}}{ds}\frac{ds}{dt}$$

(7)
$$= \frac{dv}{dt}\mathbf{T} + v^2\frac{d\mathbf{T}}{ds}$$

In the first term on the right in (7), the scalar quantity dv/dt is the rate of change of the tangential velocity; hence the product $(dv/dt)\mathbf{T}$ is in magnitude and direction just the **tangential acceleration.**

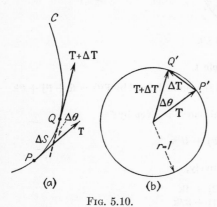

FIG. 5.10.

To interpret the second term in (7), we observe that since $\mathbf{T}$ is a unit vector it can vary only in direction. Hence if the various values of $\mathbf{T}$ are drawn from a common origin, the locus of their end points will be a curve on a sphere of unit radius. Now the length of the increment $\Delta\mathbf{T}$ (Fig. 15.10b) is approximately the length of the arc $P'Q'$ which in turn is equal to $\Delta\theta$, the angle between the tangents to C at the points P and Q, a distance Δs apart. Hence

$$\left|\frac{d\mathbf{T}}{ds}\right| = \lim_{\Delta s \to 0}\frac{|\Delta\mathbf{T}|}{\Delta s} = \lim_{\Delta s \to 0}\left(\frac{\text{angle between tangents to } C \text{ at } P \text{ and } Q}{\text{arc length along } C \text{ between } P \text{ and } Q}\right)$$
$$= \text{curvature of } C = \frac{1}{R}$$

Moreover, from Fig. 15.10b it is evident that the limiting direction of $\Delta\mathbf{T}$ is perpendicular to $\mathbf{T}$, that is, to C itself, in the plane which $\mathbf{T}$ and $\mathbf{T} + \Delta\mathbf{T}$ determine in the limit. If C is a plane curve, this is of course just the plane in which C lies. If C is a twisted curve, this plane, which is known as the **osculating plane,** will vary from point to point along C. Hence to summarize, $d\mathbf{T}/ds$ *is a vector which is perpendicular to C in the osculating plane, and whose magnitude is equal to the curvature K of C.*

If, finally, we let $\mathbf{N}$ denote a unit vector normal to C in the osculating plane and define the **radius of curvature** of C to be

$$\rho = \frac{1}{K}$$

we can write Eq. (7) in the form

$$(8) \qquad \mathbf{a} = \frac{dv}{dt}\,\mathbf{T} + \frac{v^2}{\rho}\,\mathbf{N}$$

which shows that *the vector acceleration of a moving particle is the sum of a component of magnitude* $\dfrac{v^2}{\rho}$ *normal to the path in the osculating plane and a component of magnitude* dv/dt *along the tangent to the path.*

To illustrate further the usefulness of vector analysis in the study of dynamics, let us consider the behavior of a system of mass particles $\{m_i\}$ moving with respective velocities $\{\mathbf{v}_i\}$ under the influence of forces $\{\mathbf{F}_i\}$. As a preliminary, we need to recall Newton's law

$$(9) \qquad m_i \frac{d\mathbf{v}_i}{dt} = \mathbf{F}_i$$

and the following definitions.

The vector

$$\mathbf{M}_i = m_i\mathbf{v}_i$$

is called the **momentum** of the particle m_i.

If $\mathbf{R}_i$ is the vector from a fixed point O to the mass particle m_i, then the vector

$$\mathbf{H}_i = \mathbf{R}_i \times m_i\mathbf{v}_i = \mathbf{R}_i \times \mathbf{M}_i$$

is called the **moment of momentum** or **angular momentum** of m_i about O.

The terminus of the vector

$$\mathbf{R}_g = \frac{\displaystyle\sum_{i=1}^{n} \mathbf{R}_i m_i}{\displaystyle\sum_{i=1}^{n} m_i}$$

is called the **center of gravity** of the system of particles $\{m_i\}$.

If we let $m = \displaystyle\sum_{i=1}^{n} m_i$ denote the mass of all the particles together, we can write the relation defining the center of gravity in the form

$$m\mathbf{R}_g = \sum_{i=1}^{n} m_i\mathbf{R}_i$$

Hence, differentiating with respect to time,

$$m \frac{d\mathbf{R}_g}{dt} = \sum_{i=1}^{n} m_i \frac{d\mathbf{R}_i}{dt}$$

or, letting $\mathbf{v}_g$ denote the velocity of the center of gravity,

$$m\mathbf{v}_g = \sum_{i=1}^{n} m_i\mathbf{v}_i$$

Differentiating again with respect to time, we find

$$m \frac{d\mathbf{v}_g}{dt} = \sum_{i=1}^{n} m_i \frac{d\mathbf{v}_i}{dt}$$

But by Newton's law, $m_i(d\mathbf{v}_i/dt) = \mathbf{F}_i$, and thus the last equation can be written

$$(10) \qquad m \frac{d\mathbf{v}_g}{dt} = \sum_{i=1}^{n} \mathbf{F}_i \equiv \mathbf{F}$$

The sum, $\sum_{i=1}^{n} \mathbf{F}_i \equiv \mathbf{F}$, is the vector sum of all the forces acting on each of the particles, and it therefore includes, in addition to the external forces, the internal forces which the particles exert on each other. However, the internal forces necessarily occur in equal and opposite pairs, and thus cancel completely, leaving $\sum_{i=1}^{n} \mathbf{F}_i$ just the sum of all the external forces which act on the system. Hence Eq. (10) shows that *the center of gravity of a system of mass particles moves like a particle having the total mass of the system and acted upon by the resultant of all the external forces which act upon the system.*

Now consider the definitive relation $\mathbf{H}_i = \mathbf{R}_i \times m_i\mathbf{v}_i$, and differentiate with respect to time:

$$\frac{d\mathbf{H}_i}{dt} = \frac{d\mathbf{R}_i}{dt} \times m_i\mathbf{v}_i + \mathbf{R}_i \times m_i \frac{d\mathbf{v}_i}{dt}$$

Since $d\mathbf{R}_i/dt = \mathbf{v}_i$, the first term on the right vanishes because it involves the cross product of vectors having the same direction. Hence, applying Newton's law to the remaining term, we find

$$(11) \qquad \frac{d\mathbf{H}_i}{dt} = \mathbf{R}_i \times \mathbf{F}_i$$

or, summing over all particles and denoting the total angular momentum by **H**,

$$(12) \qquad \frac{d\mathbf{H}}{dt} = \sum_{i=1}^{n} \mathbf{R}_i \times \mathbf{F}_i$$

But $\mathbf{R}_i \times \mathbf{F}_i$ is just the vector moment of the force $\mathbf{F}_i$ about the point from which $\mathbf{R}_i$ is drawn, and thus the sum $\sum_{i=1}^{n} \mathbf{R}_i \times \mathbf{F}_i$ is just the resultant moment of the various forces, say $\mathfrak{M}$. Since all internal forces occur in pairs which are equal and opposite and act in the same line, the moments due to them cancel completely, leaving $\mathfrak{M}$ just the resultant moment of all the external forces. Hence we have shown that *for a system of mass particles, the time rate of change of angular momentum about any point is equal to the moment of the resultant of the external forces about that point.*

If we have a system of particles acted upon by various forces, it is usually convenient to find the moment of the applied forces about an arbitrary point by first finding their moment about the center of gravity of the system. To accomplish this transfer, we note that the vector from the center of

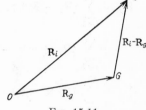

FIG. 15.11.

gravity to the particle m_i is $\mathbf{R}_i - \mathbf{R}_g$ (Fig. 15.11) and hence the moment about the center of gravity of the force acting on m_i is

$$(\mathbf{R}_i - \mathbf{R}_g) \times \mathbf{F}_i$$

Summing for all particles, and letting $\mathfrak{M}_g$ denote the total moment about the center of gravity, we find

$$\mathfrak{M}_g = \sum_{i=1}^{n} (\mathbf{R}_i - \mathbf{R}_g) \times \mathbf{F}_i$$

$$= \sum_{i=1}^{n} \mathbf{R}_i \times \mathbf{F}_i - \sum_{i=1}^{n} \mathbf{R}_g \times \mathbf{F}_i$$

$$= \sum_{i=1}^{n} \mathbf{R}_i \times \mathbf{F}_i - \mathbf{R}_g \times \sum_{i=1}^{n} \mathbf{F}_i$$

$$= \mathfrak{M} - \mathbf{R}_g \times \mathbf{F}$$

or

$$(13) \qquad \mathfrak{M} = \mathfrak{M}_g + \mathbf{R}_g \times \mathbf{F}$$

Hence, *the moment about an arbitrary point O of a set of forces acting on a system of particles is equal to the moment of these forces about the center of gravity of the system, plus the moment about O of the resultant of these forces acting at the center of gravity.*

A similar result holds for the transfer of angular momentum. For the velocity of m_i relative to the center of gravity is

$$\frac{d(\mathbf{R}_i - \mathbf{R}_g)}{dt} = \mathbf{v}_i - \mathbf{v}_g$$

and thus the angular momentum of m_i about the center of gravity is

$$(\mathbf{R}_i - \mathbf{R}_g) \times m_i(\mathbf{v}_i - \mathbf{v}_g)$$

Summing over all particles and letting $\mathbf{H}_g$ denote the total angular momentum about the center of gravity, we find

$$
\begin{aligned}
\mathbf{H}_g &= \sum_{i=1}^{n} (\mathbf{R}_i - \mathbf{R}_g) \times m_i(\mathbf{v}_i - \mathbf{v}_g) \\
&= \sum_{i=1}^{n} \{\mathbf{R}_i \times m_i\mathbf{v}_i - \mathbf{R}_i \times m_i\mathbf{v}_g - \mathbf{R}_g \times m_i\mathbf{v}_i + \mathbf{R}_g \times m_i\mathbf{v}_g\} \\
(14) \quad &= \sum_{i=1}^{n} (\mathbf{R}_i \times m_i\mathbf{v}_i) - \left(\sum_{i=1}^{n} m_i\mathbf{R}_i\right) \times \mathbf{v}_g - \mathbf{R}_g \times \sum_{i=1}^{n} (m_i\mathbf{v}_i) \\
&\qquad\qquad\qquad\qquad\qquad\qquad + (\mathbf{R}_g \times \mathbf{v}_g) \sum_{i=1}^{n} m_i
\end{aligned}
$$

The first term on the right is by definition equal to $\mathbf{H}$. Also, from the definition of $\mathbf{R}_g$, we have

$$\sum_{i=1}^{n} m_i\mathbf{R}_i = m\mathbf{R}_g$$

and thus by differentiating we obtain

$$\sum_{i=1}^{n} m_i\mathbf{v}_i = m\mathbf{v}_g$$

Substituting these results into the second and third terms in (14), we find

$$\mathbf{H}_g = \mathbf{H} - m\mathbf{R}_g \times \mathbf{v}_g - \mathbf{R}_g \times m\mathbf{v}_g + \mathbf{R}_g \times \mathbf{v}_g m$$

or

$$(15) \qquad\qquad\qquad \mathbf{H} = \mathbf{H}_g + \mathbf{R}_g \times m\mathbf{v}_g$$

That is, *the angular momentum of a system of particles about any point O* *is equal to the angular momentum of the particles about the center of gravity of the system, plus the angular momentum about O of a particle equal to the total mass of the system and moving with the center of gravity.*

Finally, we may obtain a result for the angular momentum analogous to (10) by differentiating (15):

$$\frac{d\mathbf{H}}{dt} = \frac{d\mathbf{H}_g}{dt} + \frac{d(\mathbf{R}_g \times m\mathbf{v}_g)}{dt}$$

$$= \frac{d\mathbf{H}_g}{dt} + \frac{d\mathbf{R}_g}{dt} \times m\mathbf{v}_g + \mathbf{R}_g \times \frac{d(m\mathbf{v}_g)}{dt}$$

Now $d\mathbf{H}/dt = \mathfrak{M}$ by (12), and $d(m\mathbf{v}_g)/dt = \mathbf{F}$ by (10). Moreover, $d\mathbf{R}_g/dt = \mathbf{v}_g$,

and thus

$$\frac{d\mathbf{R}_g}{dt} \times m\mathbf{v}_g = \mathbf{v}_g \times m\mathbf{v}_g = 0$$

Hence the expression for $d\mathbf{H}/dt$ reduces to

$$\mathfrak{M} = \frac{d\mathbf{H}_g}{dt} + \mathbf{R}_g \times \mathbf{F}$$

But, by (13),

$$\mathfrak{M} = \mathfrak{M}_g + \mathbf{R}_g \times \mathbf{F}$$

and thus, finally,

(16) $$\frac{d\mathbf{H}_g}{dt} = \mathfrak{M}_g$$

which shows that *the time rate of change of angular momentum about the moving center of gravity is equal to the moment of all the external forces about the center of gravity.*

EXERCISES

1. If $\mathbf{R} = \mathbf{A} \cos kt + \mathbf{B} \sin kt$, show that $\mathbf{R} \times \mathbf{V} = $ constant.

2. What is the derivative of $\mathbf{F} \cdot \dfrac{d\mathbf{F}}{dt} \times \dfrac{d^2\mathbf{F}}{dt^2}$? of $\mathbf{F} \times \left(\dfrac{d\mathbf{F}}{dt} \times \dfrac{d^2\mathbf{F}}{dt^2}\right)$?

3. What is the angle between the tangents to the curve

$$x = t, \qquad y = t^2, \qquad z = t^3$$

at $t = 1$ and $t = -1$?

4. If $\mathbf{R} = t^2\mathbf{i} - t^3\mathbf{j} + t^5\mathbf{k}$ is the vector from the origin to a moving particle, find the resultant velocity of the particle at $t = 1$. What is the component of this velocity in the direction of the vector $8\mathbf{i} - \mathbf{j} + 4\mathbf{k}$?

5. If a particle starts to move from the point $(0,1,2)$ with component velocities $v_x = 1 + 2t, v_y = t^3, v_z = 2t - t^2$, find the vector from the origin to the instantaneous position of the particle.

6. If $\mathbf{R}_1, \mathbf{R}_2, \ldots, \mathbf{R}_n$ are the vectors from an arbitrary origin to the mass particles $m_1, m_2, \ldots, m_n$, and if $\mathbf{C}$ is the vector from the origin to the center of gravity of

the system of particles, show that for any vector $\mathbf{R}$

$$\sum_{i=1}^{n} m_i(\mathbf{R} - \mathbf{R}_i)^2 = m(\mathbf{R} - \mathbf{C})^2 + \sum_{i=1}^{n} m_i(\mathbf{C} - \mathbf{R}_i)^2$$

where m is the total mass of all the particles.

7. Solve the differential equation

$$\frac{d^2\mathbf{R}}{dt^2} = \mathbf{A}$$

where $\mathbf{A}$ is a constant vector. Write the result in scalar form, and discuss its significance in the case $\mathbf{A} = -g\mathbf{k}$, where g is the acceleration of gravity.

8. What is the equation of the osculating plane to the space curve

$$x = t^4, \qquad y = t^2, \qquad z = t^3$$

at the point $P_1:(x_1,y_1,z_1)$ whose parameter is $t = t_1$. (Hint: Let $P:(x,y,z)$ be a general point in the osculating plane, and impose the condition that the vector joining P to P_1 be coplanar with the vectors $\mathbf{T}$ and $d\mathbf{T}/dt$, at P_1.)

9. If a particle moves under the influence of a force which is always directed toward a fixed point, show that $(d^2\mathbf{R}/dt^2) \times \mathbf{R} = 0$, where the origin of $\mathbf{R}$ is the center of force.

10. If a particle moves along a plane curve in such a way that $(d^2\mathbf{R}/dt^2) \times \mathbf{R} = 0$, show that the radius vector $\mathbf{R}$ sweeps over equal areas in equal times. This is a generalization of one of the laws of planetary motion discovered by Kepler. (Hint: Consider the time derivative of $d\mathbf{R}/dt \times \mathbf{R}$.)

15.3 The Operator ∇. Let $\phi(x,y,z)$ be a scalar function of position defined throughout some region of space, and let $\mathbf{R} = x\mathbf{i} + y\mathbf{j} + z\mathbf{k}$ be the vector drawn from the origin O to a general point P. If we move

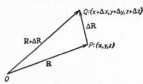

FIG. 15.12.

from P to a neighboring point $Q:(x + \Delta x, y + \Delta y, z + \Delta z)$ (Fig. 15.12), the function $\phi(x,y,z)$ will change by approximately the small amount

$$\Delta\phi = \frac{\partial\phi}{\partial x}\Delta x + \frac{\partial\phi}{\partial y}\Delta y + \frac{\partial\phi}{\partial z}\Delta z$$

If we divide this change $\Delta\phi$ by the distance $\Delta s = |\Delta\mathbf{R}|$ we obtain a measure of the rate at which ϕ changes when we move from P to Q. For instance, if $\phi(x,y,z)$ is the temperature at a general point in space then $\Delta\phi/\Delta s$ is the average rate of change of temperature in degrees per unit length in the direction in which Δs is measured. The limiting value of the ratio $\Delta\phi/\Delta s$ as Q approaches P along the segment PQ is called the **derivative of ϕ in the direction** PQ or just the **directional derivative** of ϕ:

$$(1) \qquad \frac{d\phi}{ds} = \frac{\partial\phi}{\partial x}\frac{dx}{ds} + \frac{\partial\phi}{\partial y}\frac{dy}{ds} + \frac{\partial\phi}{\partial z}\frac{dz}{ds}$$

The form of Eq. (1) suggests that $d\phi/ds$ can be thought of as the dot product of two vectors, and in fact we can write

$$\frac{d\phi}{ds} = \left\{\frac{\partial\phi}{\partial x}\,\mathbf{i} + \frac{\partial\phi}{\partial y}\,\mathbf{j} + \frac{\partial\phi}{\partial z}\,\mathbf{k}\right\} \cdot \left\{\frac{dx}{ds}\,\mathbf{i} + \frac{dy}{ds}\,\mathbf{j} + \frac{dz}{ds}\,\mathbf{k}\right\}$$

$$= \left\{\frac{\partial\phi}{\partial x}\,\mathbf{i} + \frac{\partial\phi}{\partial y}\,\mathbf{j} + \frac{\partial\phi}{\partial z}\,\mathbf{k}\right\} \cdot \frac{\mathbf{i}\,dx + \mathbf{j}\,dy + \mathbf{k}\,dz}{ds}$$

or, since $\mathbf{i}\,dx + \mathbf{j}\,dy + \mathbf{k}\,dz = d\mathbf{R}$,

(2) $$\frac{d\phi}{ds} = \left\{\frac{\partial\phi}{\partial x}\,\mathbf{i} + \frac{\partial\phi}{\partial y}\,\mathbf{j} + \frac{\partial\phi}{\partial z}\,\mathbf{k}\right\} \cdot \frac{d\mathbf{R}}{ds}$$

The vector function

$$\mathbf{i}\,\frac{\partial\phi}{\partial x} + \mathbf{j}\,\frac{\partial\phi}{\partial y} + \mathbf{k}\,\frac{\partial\phi}{\partial z}$$

which we have here stumbled upon is known as the **gradient of** ϕ, or simply **grad** ϕ. Its significance can easily be determined by writing Eq. (2) in the form

(2.1) $$\frac{d\phi}{ds} = \operatorname{grad} \phi \cdot \frac{d\mathbf{R}}{ds}$$

Since Δs is by definition just the length of $\Delta\mathbf{R}$, it follows that $d\mathbf{R}/ds$ is a unit vector. Hence the dot product, $\operatorname{grad} \phi \cdot (d\mathbf{R}/ds)$, is just the projec-

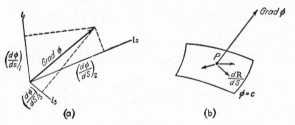

FIG. 15.13.

tion of $\operatorname{grad} \phi$ in the direction of $d\mathbf{R}/ds$. Thus according to Eq. (2.1), $\operatorname{grad} \phi$ *has the property that its projection in any direction is equal to the derivative of ϕ in that direction* (Fig. 15.13a). Since the maximum projection of a vector is the vector itself, $\operatorname{grad} \phi$ must therefore extend in the direction of the greatest rate of change of ϕ, and must have that rate of change for its length.

If we set $\phi(x,y,z) = c$, we obtain, as c takes on different values, a family of surfaces known as the **level surfaces** of ϕ; and on the assumption that ϕ is a single-valued function, one and only one level surface passes through any given point. If we now consider the level surface of ϕ which passes through P and fix our attention on neighboring points Q which lie on this same surface, we have

$$\frac{\Delta\phi}{\Delta s} = 0$$

since ϕ has the same value at all points of a level surface.   Hence by (2.1),

$$\text{grad } \phi \cdot \frac{d\mathbf{R}}{ds} = 0$$

for any vector $d\mathbf{R}/ds$, which has the limiting direction of a secant PQ of the level surface.   Such vectors are clearly all tangent to $\phi = c$ at P; hence, from the vanishing of the dot product, grad $\phi \cdot d\mathbf{R}/ds$, it follows that grad ϕ is perpendicular to every tangent to the level surface at P. In other words, *the gradient of ϕ at any point P is perpendicular to the level surface of ϕ which passes through that point* (Fig. 15.13b).   Grad ϕ evidently depends only upon the intrinsic properties of ϕ, and is quite independent of any coordinate system.   It follows therefore that in the expression

$$\mathbf{i}\frac{\partial\phi}{\partial x} + \mathbf{j}\frac{\partial\phi}{\partial y} + \mathbf{k}\frac{\partial\phi}{\partial z}$$

$\mathbf{i}$, $\mathbf{j}$, and $\mathbf{k}$ may be replaced by any other set of mutually perpendicular unit vectors, provided that $\frac{\partial\phi}{\partial x}$, $\frac{\partial\phi}{\partial y}$, $\frac{\partial\phi}{\partial z}$ are replaced by the directional derivatives of ϕ along the new axes.

The gradient of a function ϕ is frequently written in operational form as

$$\text{grad } \phi = \left(\mathbf{i}\frac{\partial}{\partial x} + \mathbf{j}\frac{\partial}{\partial y} + \mathbf{k}\frac{\partial}{\partial z}\right)\phi$$

The operational "vector" which is thus defined is usually denoted by the symbol ∇ (read "del"):

(3) $$\nabla \equiv \mathbf{i}\frac{\partial}{\partial x} + \mathbf{j}\frac{\partial}{\partial y} + \mathbf{k}\frac{\partial}{\partial z}$$

In this notation our earlier results can be written

(4) $$\text{grad } \phi = \nabla\phi$$
(5) $$d\phi = \nabla\phi \cdot d\mathbf{R}$$
(6) $$\frac{d\phi}{ds} = \nabla\phi \cdot \frac{d\mathbf{R}}{ds}$$

Also, if ϕ is a function of u, and u is a function of x, y, and z, then

$$\nabla\phi = \mathbf{i}\frac{\partial\phi}{\partial x} + \mathbf{j}\frac{\partial\phi}{\partial y} + \mathbf{k}\frac{\partial\phi}{\partial z}$$

$$= \mathbf{i}\frac{d\phi}{du}\frac{\partial u}{\partial x} + \mathbf{j}\frac{d\phi}{du}\frac{\partial u}{\partial y} + \mathbf{k}\frac{d\phi}{du}\frac{\partial u}{\partial z}$$

$$= \frac{d\phi}{du}\left(\mathbf{i}\frac{\partial u}{\partial x} + \mathbf{j}\frac{\partial u}{\partial y} + \mathbf{k}\frac{\partial u}{\partial z}\right)$$

$$(7) \qquad\qquad = \frac{d\phi}{du}\,\nabla u$$

Example 1

What is the directional derivative of the function $\phi(x,y,z) = xy^2 + yz^3$ at the point $(2,-1,1)$ in the direction of the vector $\mathbf{i} + 2\mathbf{j} + 2\mathbf{k}$?

Our first step must be to find the gradient of ϕ at the point $(2,-1,1)$. This is

$$\nabla\phi = \mathbf{i}\frac{\partial(xy^2 + yz^3)}{\partial x} + \mathbf{j}\frac{\partial(xy^2 + yz^3)}{\partial y} + \mathbf{k}\frac{\partial(xy^2 + yz^3)}{\partial z}$$

$$= y^2\mathbf{i} + (2xy + z^3)\mathbf{j} + 3yz^2\mathbf{k}\,\Big|_{2,-1,1}$$

$$= \mathbf{i} - 3\mathbf{j} - 3\mathbf{k}$$

The projection of this in the direction of the given vector will be the required directional derivative. Since this projection can be found at once as the dot product of $\nabla\phi$ and a unit vector in the given direction, we next reduce $\mathbf{i} + 2\mathbf{j} + 2\mathbf{k}$ to a unit vector by dividing it by its magnitude, getting

$$\frac{\mathbf{i} + 2\mathbf{j} + 2\mathbf{k}}{\sqrt{1 + 4 + 4}} = \frac{1}{3}\mathbf{i} + \frac{2}{3}\mathbf{j} + \frac{2}{3}\mathbf{k}$$

The answer to our problem is therefore

$$\nabla\phi \cdot \left(\frac{1}{3}\mathbf{i} + \frac{2}{3}\mathbf{j} + \frac{2}{3}\mathbf{k}\right) = (\mathbf{i} - 3\mathbf{j} - 3\mathbf{k}) \cdot \left(\frac{1}{3}\mathbf{i} + \frac{2}{3}\mathbf{j} + \frac{2}{3}\mathbf{k}\right) = -\frac{11}{3}$$

The negative sign of course indicates that ϕ decreases in the given direction.

Example 2

What is the unit normal to the surface $xy^3z^2 = 4$ at the point $(-1,-1,2)$?

Let us regard the given surface as a particular level surface of the function $\phi = xy^3z^2$. Then the gradient of this function at the point $(-1,-1,2)$ will be perpendicular to the level surface through $-1,-1,2$, which is the given surface. When the gradient has been found, the unit normal can be obtained at once by dividing the gradient by its magnitude:

$$\nabla\phi = y^3z^2\mathbf{i} + 3xy^2z^2\mathbf{j} + 2xy^3z\mathbf{k}\,\Big|_{-1,-1,2}$$

$$= -4\mathbf{i} - 12\mathbf{j} + 4\mathbf{k}$$

$$|\nabla\phi| = \sqrt{16 + 144 + 16} = 4\sqrt{11}$$

Hence the required unit normal is

$$\frac{\nabla \phi}{|\nabla \phi|} = \frac{-4\mathbf{i} - 12\mathbf{j} + 4\mathbf{k}}{4 \sqrt{11}} = \frac{-\mathbf{i}}{\sqrt{11}} - \frac{3\mathbf{j}}{\sqrt{11}} + \frac{\mathbf{k}}{\sqrt{11}}$$

Depending on which side of the surface we wish the normal to extend, it may be necessary to reverse the direction of this result by multiplying it by -1.

The vector character of the operator ∇ suggests that we also consider dot and cross products in which it appears as one factor. If

$$\mathbf{F} = F_1\mathbf{i} + F_2\mathbf{j} + F_3\mathbf{k}$$

is a vector whose components are functions of x, y, and z, this leads to the combinations

$$\nabla \cdot \mathbf{F} = \left(\mathbf{i}\frac{\partial}{\partial x} + \mathbf{j}\frac{\partial}{\partial y} + \mathbf{k}\frac{\partial}{\partial z} \right) \cdot (F_1\mathbf{i} + F_2\mathbf{j} + F_3\mathbf{k})$$

(8)
$$= \frac{\partial F_1}{\partial x} + \frac{\partial F_2}{\partial y} + \frac{\partial F_3}{\partial z}$$

which is known as the **divergence** of the vector $\mathbf{F}$, and

$$\nabla \times \mathbf{F} = \left(\mathbf{i}\frac{\partial}{\partial x} + \mathbf{j}\frac{\partial}{\partial y} + \mathbf{k}\frac{\partial}{\partial z} \right) \times (F_1\mathbf{i} + F_2\mathbf{j} + F_3\mathbf{k})$$

$$= \mathbf{i}\left(\frac{\partial F_3}{\partial y} - \frac{\partial F_2}{\partial z} \right) + \mathbf{j}\left(\frac{\partial F_1}{\partial x} - \frac{\partial F_3}{\partial z} \right) + \mathbf{k}\left(\frac{\partial F_2}{\partial x} - \frac{\partial F_1}{\partial y} \right)$$

(9)
$$= \begin{vmatrix} \mathbf{i} & \mathbf{j} & \mathbf{k} \\ \dfrac{\partial}{\partial x} & \dfrac{\partial}{\partial y} & \dfrac{\partial}{\partial z} \\ F_1 & F_2 & F_3 \end{vmatrix}$$

which is known as the **curl** of $\mathbf{F}$.

Both the divergence and the curl admit of physical interpretations which justify their names. For instance, to illustrate the significance of the divergence consider a region of space filled with a moving fluid and let

$$\mathbf{v} = v_1\mathbf{i} + v_2\mathbf{j} + v_3\mathbf{k}$$

be a vector function representing at each point the velocity with which the particle of fluid instantaneously at that point is moving. If we fix our attention on an infinitesimal volume in the region occupied by the fluid there will be flow through each of its faces, and as a result, the amount of fluid within the element may vary with time. To measure this variation, let us compute the loss of fluid from the element in the time Δt.

Now the amount of fluid which passes through one face of the element ΔV in time Δt is approximately equal to the component of the velocity normal to the face times the area of the face times Δt. Hence computing the loss of fluid through each face in turn, we have approximately

Right face: $\left(v_2 + \dfrac{\partial v_2}{\partial y} \Delta y\right) \Delta x\, \Delta z\, \Delta t$

Left face: $-v_2\, \Delta x\, \Delta z\, \Delta t$

Front face: $\left(v_1 + \dfrac{\partial v_1}{\partial x} \Delta x\right) \Delta y\, \Delta z\, \Delta t$

Rear face: $-v_1\, \Delta y\, \Delta z\, \Delta t$

Top face: $\left(v_3 + \dfrac{\partial v_3}{\partial z} \Delta z\right) \Delta x\, \Delta y\, \Delta t$

Bottom face: $-v_3\, \Delta x\, \Delta y\, \Delta t$

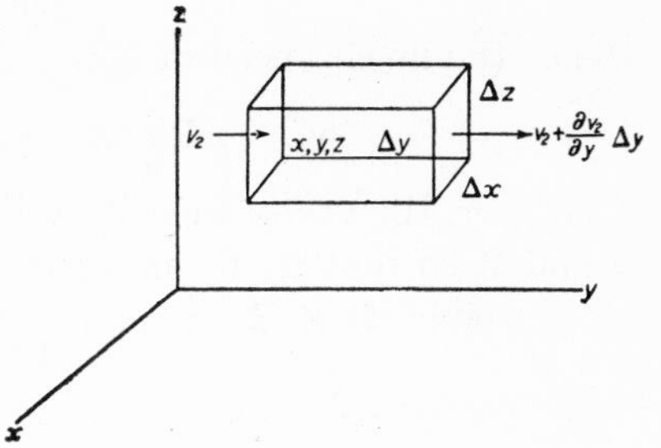

FIG. 15.14.

If we add these and convert the resulting estimate of the absolute loss of fluid from ΔV in time Δt into the loss per unit volume per unit time by dividing by $\Delta x\, \Delta y\, \Delta z\, \Delta t$, we obtain

$$\text{Rate of loss per unit volume} = \frac{\partial v_1}{\partial x} + \frac{\partial v_2}{\partial y} + \frac{\partial v_3}{\partial z}$$

which is precisely the divergence of the vector **v**. Thus, fluid mechanics affords one possible interpretation of the divergence as the rate of loss of fluid per unit volume. If the fluid is incompressible, there can be neither gain nor loss in a general volume element. Hence

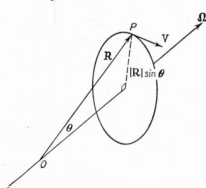

FIG. 15.15.

$$\nabla \cdot \mathbf{v} \equiv \frac{\partial v_1}{\partial x} + \frac{\partial v_2}{\partial y} + \frac{\partial v_3}{\partial z} = 0$$

which is known as the **equation of continuity** for incompressible fluids. On the other hand, if ΔV encloses a source of fluid then there is a net loss of fluid through the surface of ΔV equal to the amount *diverging* from the source. Similar results of course hold for such things as electric and magnetic flux, which exhibit many of the characteristics of incompressible fluids.

As a possible interpretation of the curl, let us consider a body rotating with uniform angular speed ω about an axis l. Further, let us define the vector angular velocity $\mathbf{\Omega}$ to be a vector of length ω, extending along l in the direction in which a right-handed screw would advance if subject to the same rotation as the body. Finally, let $\mathbf{R}$ be the vector drawn from any point O on the axis l to an arbitrary point in the body P.

From Fig. 15.15 it is evident that the radius at which P rotates is

$$|\mathbf{R}|\,\sin\,\theta.$$

Hence the linear speed of P is

$$|\mathbf{v}| = \omega|\mathbf{R}|\,\sin\,\theta = |\mathbf{\Omega}||\mathbf{R}|\,\sin\,\theta = |\mathbf{\Omega}\times\mathbf{R}|$$

Moreover, the vector velocity $\mathbf{v}$ is directed perpendicular to the plane of $\mathbf{\Omega}$ and $\mathbf{R}$ so that $\mathbf{\Omega}$, $\mathbf{R}$, and $\mathbf{v}$ form a right-handed system. Hence the cross product $\mathbf{\Omega}\times\mathbf{R}$ gives not only the magnitude of $\mathbf{v}$ but the direction as well.

Now if we take the point O as the origin of coordinates, we can write

$$\mathbf{R} = x\mathbf{i} + y\mathbf{j} + z\mathbf{k} \qquad \text{and} \qquad \mathbf{\Omega} = \Omega_1\mathbf{i} + \Omega_2\mathbf{j} + \Omega_3\mathbf{k}$$

Hence the equation

$$(10) \qquad\qquad\qquad \mathbf{v} = \mathbf{\Omega}\times\mathbf{R}$$

can be written at length in the form

$$\mathbf{v} = (\Omega_2 z - \Omega_3 y)\mathbf{i} + (\Omega_3 x - \Omega_1 z)\mathbf{j} + (\Omega_1 y - \Omega_2 x)\mathbf{k}$$

If we take the curl of $\mathbf{v}$, we have therefore

$$\nabla\times\mathbf{v} = \begin{vmatrix} \mathbf{i} & \mathbf{j} & \mathbf{k} \\ \dfrac{\partial}{\partial x} & \dfrac{\partial}{\partial y} & \dfrac{\partial}{\partial z} \\ (\Omega_2 z - \Omega_3 y) & (\Omega_3 x - \Omega_1 z) & (\Omega_1 y - \Omega_2 x) \end{vmatrix}$$

Expanding this, remembering that $\mathbf{\Omega}$ is a constant vector, we find

$$\nabla\times\mathbf{v} = 2\Omega_1\mathbf{i} + 2\Omega_2\mathbf{j} + 2\Omega_3\mathbf{k} = 2\mathbf{\Omega}$$

or

$$\mathbf{\Omega} = \tfrac{1}{2}\nabla\times\mathbf{v}$$

The angular velocity of a uniformly rotating body is thus one-half the curl of the linear velocity of any point of the body. The aptness of the name *curl* in this connection is apparent.

The results of applying the operator ∇ to various combinations of scalar and vector functions can be found by the following formulas.

$$(11) \qquad \nabla\cdot(\phi\mathbf{v}) = \phi\nabla\cdot\mathbf{v} + \mathbf{v}\cdot\nabla\phi$$

$$(12) \qquad \nabla\times(\phi\mathbf{v}) = \phi\nabla\times\mathbf{v} + (\nabla\phi)\times\mathbf{v}$$

$$(13) \qquad \nabla\cdot(\mathbf{u}\times\mathbf{v}) = \mathbf{v}\cdot\nabla\times\mathbf{u} - \mathbf{u}\cdot\nabla\times\mathbf{v}$$

$$(14) \qquad \nabla\times(\mathbf{u}\times\mathbf{v}) = \mathbf{v}\cdot\nabla\mathbf{u} - \mathbf{u}\cdot\nabla\mathbf{v} + \mathbf{u}\nabla\cdot\mathbf{v} - \mathbf{v}\nabla\cdot\mathbf{u}$$

$$(15) \qquad \nabla(\mathbf{u}\cdot\mathbf{v}) = \mathbf{u}\cdot\nabla\mathbf{v} + \mathbf{v}\cdot\nabla\mathbf{u} + \mathbf{u}\times(\nabla\times\mathbf{v}) + \mathbf{v}\times(\nabla\times\mathbf{u})$$

(16) $\nabla \times \nabla \phi = 0$

(17) $\nabla \cdot \nabla \times \phi = 0$

(18) $\nabla \times (\nabla \times \mathbf{v}) = \nabla(\nabla \cdot \mathbf{v}) - \nabla \cdot \nabla \mathbf{v} = \nabla(\nabla \cdot \mathbf{v}) - \nabla^2 \mathbf{v}$

These identities can all be verified by direct expansion. However, it is easier to establish them by treating ∇ as a vector in the appropriate vector formulas and then subsequently giving ∇ its operational meaning. In doing this, it is convenient to regard first one and then the other of the factors upon which ∇ acts, as being a constant, and then to add these partial results. As a notation to aid us in this it will be helpful to attach to ∇ a subscript indicating the one factor upon which it is temporarily assumed to operate, whenever it is followed by more than one variable factor.

To prove (11), we first suppose that ϕ is a constant. Then

$$\nabla_v \cdot (\phi \mathbf{v}) = \phi \nabla \cdot \mathbf{v}$$

On the other hand, regarding $\mathbf{v}$ as a constant, we have

$$\nabla_\phi \cdot (\phi \mathbf{v}) = \nabla_\phi \phi \cdot \mathbf{v} = \mathbf{v} \cdot \nabla \phi$$

Hence, when both ϕ and $\mathbf{v}$ are regarded as variables we have, on adding the two partial results,

$$\nabla_v \cdot (\phi \mathbf{v}) + \nabla_\phi \cdot (\phi \mathbf{v}) \equiv \nabla \cdot (\phi \mathbf{v}) = \phi \nabla \cdot \mathbf{v} + \mathbf{v} \cdot \nabla \phi$$

The proof of (12) follows in exactly the same way.

To prove (13), we have, from the properties of a scalar triple product,

$$\nabla_u \cdot (\mathbf{u} \times \mathbf{v}) = \mathbf{v} \cdot \nabla \times \mathbf{u} \quad \text{and} \quad \nabla_v \cdot (\mathbf{u} \times \mathbf{v}) = -\mathbf{u} \cdot \nabla \times \mathbf{v}$$

Hence, adding these two partial results, we find

$$\nabla \cdot (\mathbf{u} \times \mathbf{v}) = \mathbf{v} \cdot \nabla \times \mathbf{u} - \mathbf{u} \cdot (\nabla \times \mathbf{v})$$

To prove (14), we have

$$\nabla_u \times (\mathbf{u} \times \mathbf{v}) = (\nabla_u \cdot \mathbf{v})\mathbf{u} - (\nabla_u \cdot \mathbf{u})\mathbf{v}$$
$$= (\mathbf{v} \cdot \nabla)\mathbf{u} - \mathbf{v}\nabla \cdot \mathbf{u}$$

and

$$\nabla_v \times (\mathbf{u} \times \mathbf{v}) = (\nabla_v \cdot \mathbf{v})\mathbf{u} - (\nabla_v \cdot \mathbf{u})\mathbf{v}$$
$$= \mathbf{u}\nabla \cdot \mathbf{v} - (\mathbf{u} \cdot \nabla)\mathbf{v}$$

Hence, adding,

$$\nabla \times (\mathbf{u} \times \mathbf{v}) = \mathbf{v} \cdot \nabla \mathbf{u} - \mathbf{u} \cdot \nabla \mathbf{v} + \mathbf{u}\nabla \cdot \mathbf{v} - \mathbf{v}\nabla \cdot \mathbf{u}$$

To prove (15), we note that

$$\mathbf{u} \times (\nabla \times \mathbf{v}) = \mathbf{u} \times (\nabla_v \times \mathbf{v}) = (\mathbf{u} \cdot \mathbf{v})\nabla_v - (\mathbf{u} \cdot \nabla)\mathbf{v} = \nabla_v(\mathbf{u} \cdot \mathbf{v}) - \mathbf{u} \cdot \nabla \mathbf{v}$$

and

$$\mathbf{v} \times (\nabla \times \mathbf{u}) = \mathbf{v} \times (\nabla_u \times \mathbf{u}) = (\mathbf{v} \cdot \mathbf{u})\nabla_u - (\mathbf{v} \cdot \nabla)\mathbf{u} = \nabla_u(\mathbf{u} \cdot \mathbf{v}) - \mathbf{v} \cdot \nabla\mathbf{u}$$

Hence, transposing and adding, we find

$$\nabla_u(\mathbf{u} \cdot \mathbf{v}) + \nabla_v(\mathbf{u} \cdot \mathbf{v}) \equiv \nabla(\mathbf{u} \cdot \mathbf{v})$$
$$= \mathbf{u} \times (\nabla \times \mathbf{v}) + \mathbf{v} \times (\nabla \times \mathbf{u}) + \mathbf{u} \cdot \nabla\mathbf{v} + \mathbf{v} \cdot \nabla\mathbf{u}$$

To establish (16), we merely apply the definition of the curl, getting

$$\nabla \times \nabla\phi = \nabla \times \left(\mathbf{i}\frac{\partial\phi}{\partial x} + \mathbf{j}\frac{\partial\phi}{\partial y} + \mathbf{k}\frac{\partial\phi}{\partial z} \right)$$
$$= \begin{vmatrix} \mathbf{i} & \mathbf{j} & \mathbf{k} \\ \dfrac{\partial}{\partial x} & \dfrac{\partial}{\partial y} & \dfrac{\partial}{\partial z} \\ \dfrac{\partial\phi}{\partial x} & \dfrac{\partial\phi}{\partial y} & \dfrac{\partial\phi}{\partial z} \end{vmatrix}$$

which is obviously identically zero. Thus we have shown that *the curl of a gradient is zero.* Similarly (17) can be established by regarding it as a scalar triple product and writing it in the usual determinant form,

$$\nabla \cdot \nabla \times \mathbf{v} = \begin{vmatrix} \dfrac{\partial}{\partial x} & \dfrac{\partial}{\partial y} & \dfrac{\partial}{\partial z} \\ \dfrac{\partial}{\partial x} & \dfrac{\partial}{\partial y} & \dfrac{\partial}{\partial z} \\ v_1 & v_2 & v_3 \end{vmatrix}$$

This evidently vanishes identically, as asserted. Hence we can say that *the divergence of a curl is identically zero.*

To establish the last formula, we merely apply the usual rule for expanding a vector triple product,

$$\nabla \times (\nabla \times \mathbf{v}) = (\nabla \cdot \mathbf{v})\nabla - (\nabla \cdot \nabla)\mathbf{v} = \nabla(\nabla \cdot \mathbf{v}) - \nabla^2\mathbf{v}$$

where the conventional symbol ∇^2 has been substituted for the second-order operator,

$$\nabla \cdot \nabla = \left(\mathbf{i}\frac{\partial}{\partial x} + \mathbf{j}\frac{\partial}{\partial y} + \mathbf{k}\frac{\partial}{\partial z} \right) \cdot \left(\mathbf{i}\frac{\partial}{\partial x} + \mathbf{j}\frac{\partial}{\partial y} + \mathbf{k}\frac{\partial}{\partial z} \right)$$
$$= \frac{\partial^2}{\partial x^2} + \frac{\partial^2}{\partial y^2} + \frac{\partial^2}{\partial z^2}$$

EXERCISES

1. Prove that $\nabla \cdot \mathbf{R} = 3$.
2. Prove that $\nabla \times \mathbf{R} = 0$.
3. Prove that $\mathbf{A} \cdot \nabla\mathbf{R} = \mathbf{A}$.
4. Prove that $\nabla(\mathbf{A} \cdot \mathbf{R}) = \mathbf{A}$.

5. Prove that $(\mathbf{A} \times \nabla) \times \mathbf{R} = -2\mathbf{A}$.   What is $(\mathbf{A} \times \nabla) \cdot \mathbf{R}$?

6. Prove that $\nabla r^n = n r^{n-2} \mathbf{R}$.

7. For what values of n is $\nabla^2 r^n = 0$?

8. Prove that $\nabla \cdot \left[\dfrac{\mathbf{A} \times \mathbf{R}}{r} \right] = 0$.

9. Prove that $\nabla \times \left[\dfrac{\mathbf{A} \times \mathbf{R}}{r} \right] = \dfrac{\mathbf{A}}{r} + \dfrac{\mathbf{A} \cdot \mathbf{R}}{r^3} \mathbf{R}$.

10. Prove that $\nabla \phi_1 \times \nabla \phi_2 = \nabla \times (\phi_1 \nabla \phi_2)$.

11. Prove that the curl of any vector whose direction is constant is perpendicular to that direction.

12. Determine n so that $\nabla \cdot (r^n \mathbf{R})$ will vanish identically.

13. Prove that the curl of $f(r)\mathbf{R}$ is identically zero.

14. If $\mathbf{V}_1$ and $\mathbf{V}_2$ are the vectors which join the fixed points $P_1 : (x_1, y_1, z_1)$ and $P_2 : (x_2, y_2, z_2)$ to the variable point $P : (x, y, z)$, prove that gradient of $\mathbf{V}_1 \cdot \mathbf{V}_2$ is $\mathbf{V}_1 + \mathbf{V}_2$.   What is $\nabla \cdot (\mathbf{V}_1 \times \mathbf{V}_2)$?   What is $\nabla \times (\mathbf{V}_1 \times \mathbf{V}_2)$?

15. Compute the divergence and curl of the vector $xyz\mathbf{i} + 3x^2 y\mathbf{j} + (xz^2 - y^2 z)\mathbf{k}$.

16. What is the directional derivative of the function $2xy + z^2$ in the direction of the vector $\mathbf{i} + 2\mathbf{j} + 2\mathbf{k}$ at the point $(1, -1, 3)$?

17. What is the unit normal to the surface $z = x^2 + y^2$ at the point $(1, -2, 5)$?

18. What is the angle between the normals to the surface $xy = z^2$ at the points $(1, 4, -2)$ and $(-3, -3, 3)$?

19. If $u = x + y + z$, $v = x + y$, and $w = -2xz - 2yz - z^2$, show that

$$[\nabla u \, \nabla v \, \nabla w] = 0.$$

20. If three functions u, v, and w are connected by a relation, $f(u, v, w) = 0$, prove that $[\nabla u \, \nabla v \, \nabla w] = 0$.   [Hint: Consider the dot product of ∇f and $(\nabla u \times \nabla v)$.]

15.4 Integral Theorems.   Many of the most important results in vector analysis involve line and surface integrals.   The former we discussed in detail in Chap. 10; hence our preliminary work here is only a matter of translating that earlier work into the language of vectors and indicating its natural generalization to surface integrals.

To do this, let $\mathbf{F}(x, y, z)$ be a vector function defined throughout some region of space, and let C be any curve in this region.   Then if $\mathbf{T}$ denotes a unit vector tangent to C at a general point, the dot product $\mathbf{F} \cdot \mathbf{T}$ is the tangential component of $\mathbf{F}$ along C, and

(1) $$\int_C \mathbf{F} \cdot \mathbf{T} \, ds$$

is then the line integral of the tangential component of $\mathbf{F}$.   Now we have already seen that if $\mathbf{R}$ is the vector drawn from the origin to a general point of C, then $\dfrac{d\mathbf{R}}{ds}$ is a unit vector tangent to C.   Hence (1) may also be written

(2) $$\int_C \mathbf{F} \cdot d\mathbf{R}$$

Although (2) is the line integral which we shall encounter most frequently, other types may of course arise. For instance, we might consider

$$\int_C \mathbf{F} \times d\mathbf{R}$$

or

$$\int_C \phi \, d\mathbf{R}$$

where ϕ is a scalar point function. In each of these integrals the element of integration is a vector quantity, and thus the integrated result is also a vector. However, the actual integration can be made to depend upon ordinary scalar line integrals, for we have $d\mathbf{R} = \mathbf{i} \, dx + \mathbf{j} \, dy + \mathbf{k} \, dz$ and thus

$$\int_C \mathbf{F} \times d\mathbf{R} = \int_C \begin{vmatrix} \mathbf{i} & \mathbf{j} & \mathbf{k} \\ F_1 & F_2 & F_3 \\ dx & dy & dz \end{vmatrix}$$

$$= \mathbf{i} \int_C (F_2 \, dz - F_3 \, dy) + \mathbf{j} \int_C (F_3 \, dx - F_1 \, dz)$$

$$+ \mathbf{k} \int_C (F_1 \, dy - F_2 \, dx)$$

and

$$\int_C \phi \, d\mathbf{R} = \int_C \phi(\mathbf{i} \, dx + \mathbf{j} \, dy + \mathbf{k} \, dz)$$

$$= \mathbf{i} \int_C \phi \, dx + \mathbf{j} \int_C \phi \, dy + \mathbf{k} \int_C \phi \, dz$$

In general, the integral

$$\int_A^B \mathbf{F} \cdot d\mathbf{R}$$

will depend upon the path of integration from A to B. However, *if* **F** *is the gradient of some scalar point function* ϕ, *the integral of the tangential component of* **F** *is independent of the path.* For as we showed in Sec. 15.3,

$$\nabla\phi \cdot d\mathbf{R} = d\phi$$

and thus if

$$\mathbf{F} = \nabla\phi$$

then

$$\int_A^B \mathbf{F} \cdot d\mathbf{R} = \int_A^B \nabla\phi \cdot d\mathbf{R} = \int_A^B d\phi = \phi \Big|_A^B$$

which clearly depends only on the coordinates of the end points A and B, and not upon the path which joins them.

The converse is also true, and *if the line integral of the tangential component of* **F** *between any two points is independent of the path, then* **F** *is the gradient of some scalar point function* ϕ. To prove this, let P_0 be an arbitrary fixed point and P be a general point, and define

(3)
$$\phi(x,y,z) = \int_{P_0}^{P} \mathbf{F} \cdot d\mathbf{R} = \int_{P_0}^{P} \mathbf{F} \cdot \mathbf{T}\, ds$$

Since the integral, by hypothesis, is independent of the path, the function ϕ depends on the end points alone, and is therefore a function of position only. Now along any particular curve C from P_0 to P, ϕ is a function of the arc length s, and its derivative from (3) is the continuous function

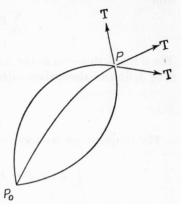

(4)
$$\frac{d\phi}{ds} = \mathbf{F} \cdot \mathbf{T}$$

Moreover, curves can obviously be drawn from P_0 to P on which the unit tangent $\mathbf{T}$ will have any prescribed direction at P (Fig. 15.16). Thus in every direction at a general point P, the function ϕ has a

FIG. 15.16.

continuous directional derivative, and thus must possess a gradient $\nabla\phi$ such that

(5)
$$\frac{d\phi}{ds} = \nabla\phi \cdot \mathbf{T}$$

Comparing (4) and (5), we obtain

$$\mathbf{F} \cdot \mathbf{T} = \nabla\phi \cdot \mathbf{T}$$

Since this holds for every unit vector $\mathbf{T}$, it follows that

$$\mathbf{F} = \nabla\phi$$

as asserted.

The surface integrals with which we shall deal will usually be integrals of the normal component of a vector function $\mathbf{F}$ over some surface S. Their definition parallels, with obvious modifications, the definition of a line integral.

FIG. 15.17.

Let the given surface S be subdivided into infinitesimal elements of area ΔS_i, and let $P_i:(x_i,y_i,z_i)$ be an arbitrary point in ΔS_i. Let one side of S be considered positive, and at each point P_i let a unit normal $\mathbf{N}_i$ be drawn to S on the positive side (Fig. 15.17). If S is a closed surface, we shall invariably choose the outside to be positive. Then if the given function $\mathbf{F}$ be evaluated at P_i, the dot product

$$\mathbf{F}(x_i,y_i,z_i) \cdot \mathbf{N}_i$$

will be the component of $\mathbf{F}$ normal to S at the point P_i. Now form the sum

$$\sum_i \mathbf{F}(x_i,y_i,z_i) \cdot \mathbf{N}_i \, \Delta S_i$$

The limit of this sum as the maximum chord of each ΔS_i approaches zero is by definition the surface integral, over S, of the normal component of $\mathbf{F}$:

$$(6) \qquad \int_S \mathbf{F} \cdot \mathbf{N} \, dS$$

The frequent use we have made of Green's lemma,

$$\int_C P \, dx + Q \, dy = \int \int_A \left(\frac{\partial Q}{\partial x} - \frac{\partial P}{\partial y}\right) dA$$

illustrates how convenient it sometimes is to be able to change from a line integral to an integral over an area, *i.e.*, to a surface integral. As an exploratory step in an attempt to extend this valuable device from plane areas and their boundary curves to areas bounded by closed curves on more general surfaces, let us restate Green's lemma in vector form. To do this, we define a vector function

$$\mathbf{F} = P\mathbf{i} + Q\mathbf{j}$$

Then, observing that in the xy-plane

$$\mathbf{R} = x\mathbf{i} + y\mathbf{j} \qquad \text{and} \qquad d\mathbf{R} = \mathbf{i} \, dx + \mathbf{j} \, dy$$

we have

$$P \, dx + Q \, dy = \mathbf{F} \cdot d\mathbf{R}$$

Also we note that

$$\frac{\partial Q}{\partial x} - \frac{\partial P}{\partial y}$$

can be expressed as

$$\mathbf{k} \cdot \nabla \times \mathbf{F}$$

since the latter, regarded as an ordinary scalar triple product, can be written

$$\begin{vmatrix} 0 & 0 & 1 \\ \dfrac{\partial}{\partial x} & \dfrac{\partial}{\partial y} & \dfrac{\partial}{\partial z} \\ P & Q & 0 \end{vmatrix} = \frac{\partial Q}{\partial x} - \frac{\partial P}{\partial y}$$

With these substitutions, Green's lemma appears as

$$\int_C \mathbf{F} \cdot d\mathbf{R} = \int \int_A \mathbf{k} \cdot \nabla \times \mathbf{F} \, dA$$

The essential property of $\mathbf{k}$ in the last integral is that it is a unit vector perpendicular to each surface element of the area, A, over which the integration is performed. Recognizing this, we are thus led to suspect that Green's lemma can be generalized to curved surfaces by writing

$$(7) \quad \int_C \mathbf{F} \cdot d\mathbf{R} = \int \int_S \mathbf{N} \cdot \nabla \times \mathbf{F} \, dS$$

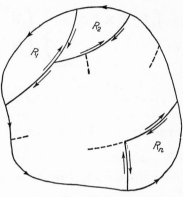

where the line integral is taken around C in the positive direction, that is, so that an observer moving in the direction of integration would always have the positive side of the area, S, on his left. This exceedingly important result, which we shall soon prove to be correct, is known as **Stokes' theorem.**[*] In words, it asserts that *the integral of the normal component of the curl of a vector, $\mathbf{F}$, over any portion of a surface, S, is equal to the line integral of the tangential component of $\mathbf{F}$ around the curve bounding S.*

FIG. 15.18.

In proving Stokes' theorem, we shall assume that the surface S has been decomposed (if necessary) into regions whose projections on each of the coordinate planes are the interiors of simple closed curves, over each of which the projected portion of S is a single-valued function of the coordinates in that plane. In general, any surface S can be dissected in this fashion, and thus if we can prove the theorem for a subregion such as we have described, its truth for any "nonpathological" surface will follow. For if the theorem is true for $R_1, R_2, \ldots, R_n$ (Fig. 15.18) then

$$\int_{C_1} \mathbf{F} \cdot d\mathbf{R} = \int \int_{R_1} \mathbf{N} \cdot \nabla \times \mathbf{F} \, dS$$

$$\int_{C_2} \mathbf{F} \cdot d\mathbf{R} = \int \int_{R_2} \mathbf{N} \cdot \nabla \times \mathbf{F} \, dS$$

$$\cdots \cdots \cdots \cdots \cdots \cdots$$

$$\int_{C_n} \mathbf{F} \cdot d\mathbf{R} = \int \int_{R_n} \mathbf{N} \cdot \nabla \times \mathbf{F} \, dS$$

where C_i is the complete boundary of the subregion R_i. When these expressions are added, the surface integrals on the right combine to give

---

[*] G. G. Stokes (1819–1903) was a great English mathematical physicist.

precisely the surface integral of the theorem. At the same time, the line integrals combine to give the line integral around the actual boundary of S, plus the line integral over all the auxiliary interior boundary arcs taken twice in opposite directions. The latter cancel identically, leaving just the line integral around C itself, and the theorem follows.

Now if we write

$$\mathbf{F} = u\mathbf{i} + v\mathbf{j} + w\mathbf{k}$$

we have

$$\int\int_S \mathbf{N} \cdot \nabla \times \mathbf{F}\, dS = \int\int_S \mathbf{N} \cdot \nabla \times (u\mathbf{i} + v\mathbf{j} + w\mathbf{k})dS$$

$$= \int\int_S \mathbf{N} \cdot \nabla \times \mathbf{i}u\, dS + \int\int_S \mathbf{N} \cdot \nabla \times \mathbf{j}v\, dS$$

$$+ \int\int_S \mathbf{N} \cdot \nabla \times \mathbf{k}w\, dS$$

To evaluate the first of these three integrals, let dS be the surface element on S which has the element $dx\, dy$ for its projection on the xy-plane (Fig. 15.19). Then

(8)
$$\mathbf{N} \cdot \mathbf{k}\, dS = dx\, dy$$

since $\mathbf{N} \cdot \mathbf{k}$ is equal to the cosine of the angle through which dS is projected onto the element $dx\, dy$.

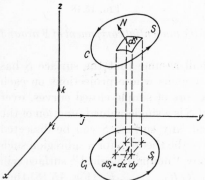

FIG. 15.19.

Now on the surface S, z is a function of x and y, say

$$z = f(x,y)$$

and so as far as the values involved in the integration are concerned,

$$u(x,y,z) = u[x,y,f(x,y)] \equiv \phi(x,y)$$

Hence

(9)
$$\frac{\partial \phi}{\partial y} = \frac{\partial u}{\partial y} + \frac{\partial u}{\partial z}\frac{\partial f}{\partial y}$$

Also the vector $\mathbf{R}$ from the origin to a general point on the surface is a function of x and y only, for on S

$$\mathbf{R} = x\mathbf{i} + y\mathbf{j} + z\mathbf{k} = x\mathbf{i} + y\mathbf{j} + f(x,y)\mathbf{k}$$

Hence

(10)
$$\frac{\partial \mathbf{R}}{\partial y} = \mathbf{j} + \frac{\partial f}{\partial y}\mathbf{k}$$

Since in computing $\partial \mathbf{R}/\partial y$, x is held fixed, this derivative is a vector tangent to the curve cut from S by the plane $x = $ constant, and hence is tangent to the surface S itself.   Being tangent to S, $\partial \mathbf{R}/\partial y$ is therefore perpendicular to the normal to S, and thus

$$\mathbf{N} \cdot \frac{\partial \mathbf{R}}{\partial y} = 0$$

or, substituting for $\dfrac{\partial \mathbf{R}}{\partial y}$ from (10),

$$\mathbf{N} \cdot \left(\mathbf{j} + \frac{\partial f}{\partial y} \mathbf{k} \right) = \mathbf{N} \cdot \mathbf{j} + \mathbf{N} \cdot \mathbf{k} \frac{\partial f}{\partial y} = 0$$

which shows that

(11) $$\mathbf{N} \cdot \mathbf{j} = - \mathbf{N} \cdot \mathbf{k} \frac{\partial f}{\partial y}$$

Now

$$\mathbf{N} \cdot \nabla \times \mathbf{i} u = \mathbf{N} \cdot \begin{vmatrix} \mathbf{i} & \mathbf{j} & \mathbf{k} \\ \dfrac{\partial}{\partial x} & \dfrac{\partial}{\partial y} & \dfrac{\partial}{\partial z} \\ u & 0 & 0 \end{vmatrix}$$

$$= \mathbf{N} \cdot \mathbf{j} \frac{\partial u}{\partial z} - \mathbf{N} \cdot \mathbf{k} \frac{\partial u}{\partial y}$$

Hence, substituting for $\mathbf{N} \cdot \mathbf{j}$ from (11),

$$\mathbf{N} \cdot \nabla \times \mathbf{i} u = - \mathbf{N} \cdot \mathbf{k} \frac{\partial u}{\partial z} \frac{\partial f}{\partial y} - \mathbf{N} \cdot \mathbf{k} \frac{\partial u}{\partial y} = - \mathbf{N} \cdot \mathbf{k} \left(\frac{\partial u}{\partial y} + \frac{\partial u}{\partial z} \frac{\partial f}{\partial y} \right)$$

or, using (9) and then (8),

$$(\mathbf{N} \cdot \nabla \times \mathbf{i} u) dS = \left(- \mathbf{N} \cdot \mathbf{k} \frac{\partial \phi}{\partial y} \right) dS$$

$$= - \frac{\partial \phi}{\partial y} \, dx \, dy$$

Since the variation of the element dS over S corresponds to the variation of the element $dx \, dy$ over the projection, S_1, of S, it follows that

(12) $$\iint_S \mathbf{N} \cdot \nabla \times \mathbf{i} u \, dS = - \iint_{S_1} \frac{\partial \phi}{\partial y} \, dx \, dy$$

Moreover, since the integral on the right in (12) is taken over a plane region, Green's lemma can obviously be applied to it (with $P \equiv \phi$ and $Q \equiv 0$), giving

(13) $$- \iint_{S_1} \frac{\partial \phi}{\partial y} \, dx \, dy = \int_{C_1} \phi \, dx$$

where C_1 is the boundary of S_1.

Now the value of $u(x,y,z)$ at any point P on C, namely, $u[x,y,f(x,y)]$ is exactly the value of $\phi(x,y) \equiv u[x,y,f(x,y)]$ at the point on C_1 which is the projection of P. Moreover, the increment dx between two points on C is exactly the x-increment between the projections of these points on C_1. Hence

$$\int_{C_1} \phi(x,y)dx = \int_{C} u(x,y,z)dx$$

and thus, substituting this into (13) and then using (12), we have

(14) $$\iint_S \mathbf{N} \cdot \nabla \times \mathbf{i}u \, dS = \int_C u(x,y,z)dx$$

In an exactly similar fashion we can show that

(15) $$\iint_S \mathbf{N} \cdot \nabla \times \mathbf{j}v \, dS = \int_C v \, dy$$

(16) $$\iint_S \mathbf{N} \cdot \nabla \times \mathbf{k}w \, dS = \int_C w \, dz$$

Hence, adding (14), (15), and (16), we obtain

$$\iint_S \mathbf{N} \cdot (\nabla \times \mathbf{i}u + \nabla \times \mathbf{j}v + \nabla \times \mathbf{k}w)dS = \int_C (u \, dx + v \, dy + w \, dz)$$

or

$$\iint_S \mathbf{N} \cdot \nabla \times \mathbf{F} \, dS = \int_C \mathbf{F} \cdot d\mathbf{R}$$

Having thus proved Stokes' theorem for surfaces which have single-valued projections on the coordinate planes, we conclude on the basis of our preliminary remarks that it also is true for a general surface.

On page 458 we found that a necessary and sufficient condition that the line integral

$$\int_C \mathbf{F} \cdot d\mathbf{R}$$

be independent of the path is that $\mathbf{F}$ be the gradient of some scalar function ϕ. By means of Stokes' theorem we can modify this criterion and obtain the following: *A necessary and sufficient condition that*

$$\int_C \mathbf{F} \cdot d\mathbf{R}$$

be independent of the path is that the curl of $\mathbf{F}$ vanish identically.

The necessity of this condition is apparent, for if

$$\int_C \mathbf{F} \cdot d\mathbf{R}$$

is independent of the path, then $\mathbf{F} = \nabla \phi$ and, as we proved in Sec. 15.3, the curl of any gradient is necessarily zero. On the other hand, if

$\nabla \times \mathbf{F} = 0$, then, by Stokes' theorem,

$$\int_C \mathbf{F} \cdot d\mathbf{R} = \iint_S \mathbf{N} \cdot \nabla \times \mathbf{F} \, dS = 0$$

where C is any closed curve in the region in which $\nabla \times \mathbf{F} = 0$. But the vanishing of a line integral around every closed curve in a region implies that the line integral is independent of the path, in that region, as we stated in Sec. 10.2. Hence $\nabla \times \mathbf{F} = 0$ is also a sufficient condition that

$$\int_C \mathbf{F} \cdot d\mathbf{R}$$

be independent of the path.

Now if $\mathbf{F} = P\mathbf{i} + Q\mathbf{j} + R\mathbf{k}$ and $\mathbf{R} = x\mathbf{i} + y\mathbf{j} + z\mathbf{k}$ then

$$\int_C \mathbf{F} \cdot d\mathbf{R} = \int_C P \, dx + Q \, dy + R \, dz$$

Hence if $P \, dx + Q \, dy + R \, dz$ is an exact differential, say $d\phi$, then

$$\int_C \mathbf{F} \cdot d\mathbf{R}$$

is clearly a function of its end points only. On the other hand, if

$$\int_C \mathbf{F} \cdot d\mathbf{R}$$

is independent of the path, we know that $\mathbf{F} = \nabla\phi$, and therefore

$$\mathbf{F} \cdot d\mathbf{R} = \nabla\phi \cdot d\mathbf{R} = d\phi$$

Hence $P \, dx + Q \, dy + R \, dz$ is an exact differential. Thus the statements that

$$\int_C \mathbf{F} \cdot d\mathbf{R}$$

is independent of the path and that $P \, dx + Q \, dy + R \, dz$ is an exact differential are completely equivalent, and thus we can say $P \, dx + Q \, dy + R \, dz$ is an exact differential if and only if $\nabla \times \mathbf{F} = 0$, where

$$\mathbf{F} = P\mathbf{i} + Q\mathbf{j} + R\mathbf{k}$$

The condition that

$$\int_C P \, dx + Q \, dy$$

be independent of the path, namely,

$$\frac{\partial Q}{\partial x} - \frac{\partial P}{\partial y} = 0$$

which we used so often in our discussion of analytic functions, is just a special case of this vector result, for if

$$\mathbf{F} = P\mathbf{i} + Q\mathbf{j}$$

then

$$\nabla \times \mathbf{F} = \begin{vmatrix} \mathbf{i} & \mathbf{j} & \mathbf{k} \\ \dfrac{\partial}{\partial x} & \dfrac{\partial}{\partial y} & \dfrac{\partial}{\partial z} \\ P & Q & 0 \end{vmatrix} = \mathbf{k}\left(\dfrac{\partial Q}{\partial x} - \dfrac{\partial P}{\partial y}\right)$$

which is zero if and only if $\dfrac{\partial Q}{\partial x} - \dfrac{\partial P}{\partial y} = 0$.

Example 1

Prove that

$$\int_C \phi \, d\mathbf{R} = \int\!\!\int_S \mathbf{N} \times \nabla\phi \, dS$$

where ϕ is a scalar point function and C is the closed curve bounding the surface S.

To establish this, let us apply Stokes' theorem to the vector function

$$\phi\mathbf{C}$$

where $\mathbf{C}$ is an arbitrary constant vector.   Then

$$\int_C \phi\,\mathbf{C} \cdot d\mathbf{R} = \int\!\!\int_S \mathbf{N} \cdot \nabla \times (\phi\mathbf{C})dS$$

Since ϕ is a scalar, it can be moved across the symbols of dot and cross multiplication, and thus the last equation can be written

$$\int_C \mathbf{C} \cdot \phi\, d\mathbf{R} = \int\!\!\int_S \mathbf{N} \cdot \nabla\phi \times \mathbf{C}\, dS$$

If we make a cyclic permutation of the elements in the scalar triple product on the right, which is possible in this case since $\mathbf{C}$ is a constant, we have

$$\int_C \mathbf{C} \cdot \phi\, d\mathbf{R} = \int\!\!\int_S \mathbf{C} \cdot \mathbf{N} \times \nabla\phi\, dS$$

Finally, removing the constant vector $\mathbf{C}$ from each integral, we have

$$\mathbf{C} \cdot \int_C \phi\, d\mathbf{R} = \mathbf{C} \cdot \int\!\!\int_S \mathbf{N} \times \nabla\phi\, dS$$

This relation implies that the vectors

$$\int_C \phi\, d\mathbf{R} \qquad \text{and} \qquad \int\!\!\int_S \mathbf{N} \times \nabla\phi\, dS$$

have equal projections in the direction of any arbitrary vector $\mathbf{C}$.   Since this is possible if and only if the vectors are equal, it follows that

$$\int_C \phi\, d\mathbf{R} = \int\!\!\int_S \mathbf{N} \times \nabla\phi\, dS$$

as asserted.

As a companion to Stokes' theorem we have the so-called **divergence theorem**:

$$\iint_S \mathbf{N} \cdot \mathbf{F}\, dS = \iiint_V \nabla \cdot \mathbf{F}\, dV$$

which relates the integral of the normal component of a vector $\mathbf{F}$ over a closed surface S to the integral of the divergence of $\mathbf{F}$ throughout the volume bounded by S. To prove this, we shall suppose that the closed surface S has the property that no line parallel to one of the coordinate axes cuts it in more than two points. If this is not the case, we can always subdivide the volume enclosed by S into regions whose boundary surfaces do have this property. Then if the theorem be established for each of the regions and the results added, the integrals over all the auxiliary interfaces will occur twice with opposite signs and will cancel, leaving just the integral of the theorem.

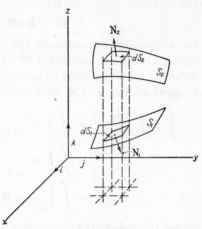

FIG. 15.20.

If we let $\mathbf{F} = u\mathbf{i} + v\mathbf{j} + w\mathbf{k}$, the divergence theorem can be written at length in the form

$$\iint_S \mathbf{N} \cdot (u\mathbf{i} + v\mathbf{j} + w\mathbf{k}) dS = \iiint_V \left(\frac{\partial u}{\partial x} + \frac{\partial v}{\partial y} + \frac{\partial w}{\partial z} \right) dV$$

or

(17) $$\iint_S \mathbf{N} \cdot \mathbf{i} u\, dS + \iint_S \mathbf{N} \cdot \mathbf{j} v\, dS + \iint_S \mathbf{N} \cdot \mathbf{k} w\, dS$$

$$= \iiint_V \frac{\partial u}{\partial x}\, dV + \iiint_V \frac{\partial v}{\partial y}\, dV + \iiint_V \frac{\partial w}{\partial z}\, dV$$

We shall establish the theorem by proving that respective integrals on each side of (17) are equal.

To do this, let us first consider

$$\iiint_V \frac{\partial w}{\partial z}\, dV$$

If we take $dV = dx\, dy\, dz$ and perform the z integration first, we have

$$\iint \int_{z \text{ on } S_1}^{z \text{ on } S_2} \frac{\partial w}{\partial z}\, dz\, dx\, dy$$

where S_1 and S_2 are, respectively, the lower and upper halves of the closed surface S. Carrying out the z-integration, we have

$$\int \int w \Big|_{z \text{ on } S_1}^{z \text{ on } S_2} dx\, dy = \int \int \left(w \Big|_{\text{on } S_2} - w \Big|_{\text{on } S_1} \right) dx\, dy$$

Now the element $dx\, dy$ is the common projection of dS_1 and dS_2 on the xy-plane; hence we have

$$dx\, dy = \mathbf{k} \cdot \mathbf{N}_2\, dS_2 = -\mathbf{k} \cdot \mathbf{N}_1\, dS_1$$

the minus sign appearing in the last term because the *outer* normal, $\mathbf{N}_1$, makes an angle of more that $90°$ with the direction of $\mathbf{k}$. Therefore, substituting for $dx\, dy$, that is, transferring the integration from the common projection of S_1 and S_2 back onto S_1 and S_2 themselves, we find

$$\int \int \int_V \frac{\partial w}{\partial z}\, dV = \int \int w \Big|_{\text{on } S_2} dx\, dy - \int \int w \Big|_{\text{on } S_1} dx\, dy$$

$$= \int \int w \Big|_{\text{on } S_2} \mathbf{k} \cdot \mathbf{N}_2\, dS_2 + \int \int w \Big|_{\text{on } S_1} \mathbf{k} \cdot \mathbf{N}_1\, dS_1$$

$$= \int \int_{S_2} w\mathbf{k} \cdot \mathbf{N}\, dS + \int \int_{S_1} w\mathbf{k} \cdot \mathbf{N}\, dS$$

where the subscripts have been dropped from the integrands, as superfluous, since the ranges of integration are now explicitly indicated. Finally, since S_1 and S_2 together make up the entire closed surface S, we may combine the last two integrals, getting

$$\int \int \int_V \frac{\partial w}{\partial z}\, dV = \int \int_S w\mathbf{k} \cdot \mathbf{N}\, dS$$

In a similar manner we can show that

$$\int \int \int_V \frac{\partial u}{\partial x}\, dV = \int \int_S u\mathbf{i} \cdot \mathbf{N}\, dS$$

$$\int \int \int_V \frac{\partial v}{\partial y}\, dV = \int \int_S v\mathbf{j} \cdot \mathbf{N}\, dS$$

Adding the last three equations we obtain the expanded form of the divergence theorem (17), which completes the proof.

Example 2

Verify the divergence theorem for the function

$$\mathbf{F} = a(x + y)\mathbf{i} + a(y - x)\mathbf{j} + z^2\mathbf{k}$$

over the hemisphere bounded by the xy-plane and the upper half of the sphere

$$x^2 + y^2 + z^2 = a^2$$

Working first with the volume integral, we calculate

$$\nabla \cdot \mathbf{F} = \frac{\partial[a(x+y)]}{\partial x} + \frac{\partial[a(y-x)]}{\partial y} + \frac{\partial z^2}{\partial z} = 2(a+z)$$

Since $\nabla \cdot \mathbf{F}$ depends only on z, we can choose the volume element to be a horizontal disk for which $dV = \pi x^2 \, dz$ (Fig. 15.21a), and obtain the result by a single integration:

$$\iiint_V \nabla \cdot \mathbf{F} \, dV = \int_0^a 2(a+z)\pi x^2 \, dz$$

$$= 2\pi \int_0^a (a+z)(a^2 - z^2)dz$$

$$= 2\pi \left[a^3 z + \frac{a^2 z^2}{2} - \frac{a z^3}{3} - \frac{z^4}{4} \right]_0^a$$

$$= \frac{11\pi a^4}{6}$$

The surface integral of the theorem must be computed in two parts corresponding to the hemispherical component and the plane component of the boundary of V.

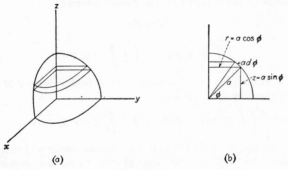

FIG. 15.21.

On the curved surface, the unit normal, which is just a unit vector in the radial direction, is

$$\mathbf{N} = \frac{x\mathbf{i} + y\mathbf{j} + z\mathbf{k}}{a}$$

Hence

$$\mathbf{N} \cdot \mathbf{F} = \left[\frac{x\mathbf{i} + y\mathbf{j} + z\mathbf{k}}{a} \right] \cdot [a(x+y)\mathbf{i} + a(y-x)\mathbf{j} + z^2\mathbf{k}]$$

$$= \frac{ax^2 + ay^2 + z^3}{a}$$

$$= \frac{a^3 - az^2 + z^3}{a}$$

since $x^2 + y^2 = a^2 - z^2$ on the hemisphere. This, also, depends only on z, and thus the surface element can be taken as a horizontal band around the hemisphere, for which, using ϕ as the variable of integration (Fig. 15.21b),

$$dS = (2\pi r)(ad\phi) = 2\pi a^2 \cos \phi \, d\phi$$

Then

$$\iint_{\text{(hemisphere)}} \mathbf{N} \cdot \mathbf{F} \, dS = \int_0^{\pi/2} 2\pi a^2 \cos \phi \left[\frac{a^3 - a^3 \sin^2 \phi + a^3 \sin^3 \phi}{a} \right] d\phi$$

$$= 2\pi a^4 \left[\sin \phi - \frac{\sin^3 \phi}{3} + \frac{\sin^4 \phi}{4} \right]_0^{\pi/2}$$

$$= \frac{11}{6} \pi a^4$$

On the base of the hemisphere the unit normal in the outward direction is $-\mathbf{k}$. Hence

$$\mathbf{N} \cdot \mathbf{F} = -\mathbf{k} \cdot [a(x + y)\mathbf{i} + a(y - x)\mathbf{j} + z^2 \mathbf{k}] = -z^2$$

However, z is identically zero over the base of the figure, and thus

$$\iint_{\text{(base)}} \mathbf{N} \cdot \mathbf{F} \, dS = \iint_{\text{(base)}} (-z^2) dS = 0$$

The total surface integral is therefore

$$\tfrac{11}{6}\pi a^4 + 0 = \tfrac{11}{6}\pi a^4$$

which is the value we found earlier for the volume integral.

Example 3

Prove that

$$\iint_S \mathbf{N} \times \mathbf{F} \, dS = \iiint_V \nabla \times \mathbf{F} \, dV$$

To show this, let us apply the divergence theorem to the vector $\mathbf{F} \times \mathbf{C}$, where $\mathbf{C}$ is an arbitrary constant vector. Then

$$\iint_S (\mathbf{F} \times \mathbf{C}) \cdot \mathbf{N} \, dS = \iiint_V \nabla \cdot (\mathbf{F} \times \mathbf{C}) dV$$

Now taking advantage of the fact that $\mathbf{C}$ is a constant vector and that a cyclic permutation of the elements of a scalar triple product leaves the product unchanged, we can write

$$\iint_S \mathbf{C} \cdot \mathbf{N} \times \mathbf{F} \, dS = \iiint_V \mathbf{C} \cdot \nabla \times \mathbf{F} \, dV$$

or, taking the constant vector $\mathbf{C}$ across each integral sign,

$$\mathbf{C} \cdot \iint_C \mathbf{N} \times \mathbf{F} \, dS = \mathbf{C} \cdot \iiint_V \nabla \times \mathbf{F} \, dV$$

Since this is an identity for all vectors $\mathbf{C}$, it follows that

$$\iint_S \mathbf{N} \times \mathbf{F} \, dS = \iiint_V \nabla \times \mathbf{F} \, dV$$

as asserted.

Various important theorems stem from the divergence theorem. For instance if u and v are two scalar point functions, and if we set

$$\mathbf{F} = u \, \nabla v$$

then

$$\mathbf{N} \cdot \mathbf{F} = \mathbf{N} \cdot (u \, \nabla v) = u\mathbf{N} \cdot \nabla v$$

and, by Eq. (11), Sec. 15.3, with $\phi = u$ and $\mathbf{v} = \nabla v$,

$$\begin{aligned} \nabla \cdot \mathbf{F} &= \nabla \cdot (u \, \nabla v) \\ &= u \, \nabla \cdot \nabla v + \nabla v \cdot \nabla u \\ &= \nabla u \cdot \nabla v + u \, \nabla^2 v \end{aligned}$$

Hence, applying the divergence theorem to the vector $\mathbf{F} = u \, \nabla v$, we have

$$(18) \qquad \iiint_V (\nabla u \cdot \nabla v + u \, \nabla^2 v) dV = \iint_S \mathbf{N} \cdot u \, \nabla v \, dS$$

This is known as the **first form of Green's theorem.**

If we interchange the roles of u and v in (18), we obtain

$$(19) \qquad \iiint_V (\nabla u \cdot \nabla v + v \, \nabla^2 u) dV = \iint_S \mathbf{N} \cdot v \, \nabla u \, dS$$

On subtracting (19) from (18), we find

$$(20) \qquad \iiint_V (u \, \nabla^2 v - v \, \nabla^2 u) dV = \iint_S \mathbf{N} \cdot (u \, \nabla v - v \, \nabla u) dS$$

This is known as the **second or symmetric form of Green's theorem.**

Let us now apply the divergence theorem to the function

$$\mathbf{F} = -\nabla \left(\frac{1}{r} \right)$$

where $r = |\mathbf{R}| = |x\mathbf{i} + y\mathbf{j} + z\mathbf{k}| = \sqrt{x^2 + y^2 + z^2}$.
By direct calculation we find

$$\begin{aligned} \nabla r &= \mathbf{i} \frac{\partial r}{\partial x} + \mathbf{j} \frac{\partial r}{\partial y} + \mathbf{k} \frac{\partial r}{\partial z} \\ &= \frac{x\mathbf{i} + y\mathbf{j} + z\mathbf{k}}{\sqrt{x^2 + y^2 + z^2}} \\ &= \frac{\mathbf{R}}{r} \end{aligned}$$

Hence by Eq. (7), Sec. 15.3,

$$\begin{aligned} \mathbf{F} &= -\nabla \left(\frac{1}{r} \right) = - \frac{d(1/r)}{dr} \nabla r \\ &= \frac{1}{r^2} \frac{\mathbf{R}}{r} \\ &= \frac{\mathbf{R}}{r^3} \end{aligned}$$

Substituting this into the divergence theorem, we therefore have

$$(21) \qquad \iint_S \left(\frac{\mathbf{N} \cdot \mathbf{R}}{r^3} \right) dS = \iiint_V \left(\nabla \cdot \frac{\mathbf{R}}{r^3} \right) dV$$

Now by Eq. (11), Sec. 15.3,

$$\nabla \cdot \left(\frac{\mathbf{R}}{r^3}\right) = \frac{1}{r^3}\,\nabla \cdot \mathbf{R} + \mathbf{R} \cdot \nabla\left(\frac{1}{r^3}\right)$$

$$= \frac{3}{r^3} + \mathbf{R} \cdot \frac{d(1/r^3)}{dr}\,\nabla r$$

$$= \frac{3}{r^3} + \mathbf{R} \cdot \left(\frac{-3}{r^4}\right)\left(\frac{\mathbf{R}}{r}\right)$$

$$= \frac{3}{r^3} - 3\,\frac{\mathbf{R} \cdot \mathbf{R}}{r^5}$$

$$= 0$$

Hence we conclude from (21) that

$$(22) \qquad \int\int_S \left(\frac{\mathbf{N} \cdot \mathbf{R}}{r^3}\,dS\right) = 0$$

provided, of course, that $r \neq 0$, that is, provided that the origin from which $\mathbf{R}$ is drawn is not within the volume V enclosed by the surface S.

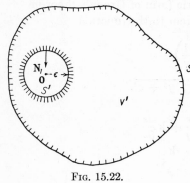

Since the divergence theorem requires that the function to which it is applied have continuous first partial derivatives throughout the volume of integration, it cannot be applied directly to $\mathbf{R}/r^3$ if the origin of $\mathbf{R}$ is within S. In this case we therefore modify the region of integration by describing an infinitesimal sphere S' about O (Fig. 15.22). In the region V' between S and S' the function $\mathbf{R}/r^3$

Fig. 15.22.

satisfies the conditions of the divergence theorem, and thus we can write

$$\int\int_{S+S'} \left(\mathbf{N} \cdot \frac{\mathbf{R}}{r^3}\right) dS = \int\int\int_{V'} \left(\nabla \cdot \frac{\mathbf{R}}{r^3}\right) dV = 0$$

or

$$(23) \qquad \int\int_S \left(\mathbf{N} \cdot \frac{\mathbf{R}}{r^3}\right) dS + \int\int_{S'} \left(\mathbf{N} \cdot \frac{\mathbf{R}}{r^3}\right) dS = 0$$

Now on S' the length of the radius vector $\mathbf{R}$ is $r = \epsilon$. Moreover, on S' the direction of the outer normal to V' is exactly opposite to the direction of $\mathbf{R}$, and thus

$$\mathbf{N} \cdot \mathbf{R} = -\frac{\mathbf{R}}{\epsilon} \cdot \mathbf{R} = -\frac{\epsilon^2}{\epsilon} = -\epsilon$$

Therefore Eq. (23) becomes

$$\iint_S \left(\mathbf{N} \cdot \frac{\mathbf{R}}{r^3}\right) dS + \iint_{S'} \left(\frac{-\epsilon}{\epsilon^3}\right) dS = 0$$

or

$$\iint_S \left(\mathbf{N} \cdot \frac{\mathbf{R}}{r^3}\right) dS = \frac{1}{\epsilon^2} \iint_{S'} dS = \frac{4\pi\epsilon^2}{\epsilon^2} = 4\pi$$

This result, coupled with (22), gives us **Gauss' theorem :***

(24)
$$\iint_S \left(\mathbf{N} \cdot \frac{\mathbf{R}}{r^3}\right) dS = \begin{cases} 0, & O \text{ outside } S \\ 4\pi, & O \text{ inside } S \end{cases}$$

Since $\mathbf{R}/r$ is a unit vector in the direction of $\mathbf{R}$, say $\mathbf{R}_1$, we can also write Gauss' theorem in the form

(24.1)
$$\iint_S \left(\mathbf{N} \cdot \frac{\mathbf{R}_1}{r^2}\right) dS = \begin{cases} 0, & O \text{ outside } S \\ 4\pi, & O \text{ inside } S \end{cases}$$

EXERCISES

1. Write Stokes' theorem in cartesian form.
2. Write the divergence theorem in cartesian form.
3. Write both forms of Green's theorem in cartesian coordinates.
4. Write Gauss' theorem in cartesian coordinates.
5. What is $\iint_S \mathbf{N} \cdot \nabla \times \mathbf{F} \, dS$ if S is a closed surface?
6. What is $\int_C \mathbf{T} \cdot d\mathbf{R}$, where $\mathbf{T}$ is a unit tangent to the curve C?
7. Verify Stokes' theorem for $\mathbf{F} = xy\mathbf{i} + yz\mathbf{j} + x^2\mathbf{k}$ over the surface of the unit cube if the face in the xy-plane is missing.
8. Evaluate $\iint_S \mathbf{N} \cdot \nabla \times \mathbf{F} \, dS$ over the upper half of the sphere $x^2 + y^2 + z^2 = 1$

    if $\mathbf{F} = \frac{x^2 + y^2}{y}\mathbf{i} + \frac{y}{x^2 + y^2}\mathbf{j} + xy^2\mathbf{k}$. (Hint: Use Stokes' theorem to transform the given integral into a line integral.)
9. What is the surface integral of the normal component of the curl of

    $$\mathbf{F} = (x + y)\mathbf{i} + (y - x)\mathbf{j} + z^3\mathbf{k}$$

    over the upper half of the unit sphere?
10. Verify the divergence theorem for the function

    $$\mathbf{F} = x^2\mathbf{i} + z\mathbf{j} + yz\mathbf{k}$$

    over the unit cube.
11. Verify the divergence theorem for the function

    $$\mathbf{F} = y\mathbf{i} + x\mathbf{j} + z^2\mathbf{k}$$

    over the cylindrical region bounded by $x^2 + y^2 = a^2$, $z = 0$, $z = h$.

* Named for Karl Friedrich Gauss (1777–1855), considered by most authorities to be the greatest mathematician who ever lived.

12. Verify the divergence theorem for the function

$$\mathbf{F} = 2xz\mathbf{i} + yz\mathbf{j} + z^2\mathbf{k}$$

over the upper half of the sphere $x^2 + y^2 + z^2 = a^2$.

Ans. The common value of the integrals is $\dfrac{5\pi a^4}{4}$

13. Find the integral of the normal component of $\mathbf{F} = x\mathbf{i} + y\mathbf{j} + z^2\mathbf{k}$ over the entire surface of the right circular cone whose base is the circle $x^2 + y^2 = a^2$, and whose vertex is $(0,0,h)$.

14. Show that $\displaystyle\int_C \mathbf{A} \times \mathbf{R} \cdot d\mathbf{R} = 2 \int\int_S \mathbf{N} \cdot \mathbf{A}\, dS$, where $\mathbf{A}$ is a constant vector.

15. Prove that $\displaystyle\int_C d\mathbf{R} \times \mathbf{F} = \int\int_S (\mathbf{N} \times \nabla) \times \mathbf{F}\, dS$. (Hint: Apply Stokes' theorem to $\mathbf{F} \times \mathbf{C}$, where $\mathbf{C}$ is an arbitrary constant vector.)

16. Prove that $\displaystyle\int\int_S \phi \mathbf{N}\, dS = \int\int\int_V \nabla\phi\, dV$.

17. If a vector function $\mathbf{F}$ is perpendicular to a given surface S at each point of S, prove that the curl of $\mathbf{F}$ either vanishes identically or is everywhere tangent to S. (Hint: Apply Stokes' theorem to $\mathbf{F}$ over the portion of S bounded by an arbitrary closed curve on S.)

18. If a vector function $\mathbf{F}$ is perpendicular at all points to the closed surface bounding a region V, prove that $\displaystyle\int\int\int_V \nabla \times \mathbf{F}\, dV = 0$. (Hint: Use the result of Example 3, Sec. 15.4.)

19. Prove that $\displaystyle\int\int_S \mathbf{N} \times (\mathbf{C} \times \mathbf{R}) dS = 2\mathbf{C}V$, where V is the volume bounded by S. (Hint: Use the result of Example 3, Sec. 15.4.)

20. Show that $\displaystyle\int\int\int_V \left[\dfrac{\partial^2 u}{\partial x^2} + \dfrac{\partial^2 u}{\partial y^2} + \dfrac{\partial^2 u}{\partial z^2} \right] dV = \int\int_S \dfrac{du}{dn}\, dS$, where $\dfrac{du}{dn}$ is the directional derivative of u in the direction of the outer normal to S.

15.5 Further Applications.

The integral theorems of the last section are often useful in deriving partial differential equations. As an illustration, let us obtain by vector methods the partial differential equation of heat flow, which we derived in Chap. **7** by quite a different argument.

Our analysis here is based upon the same experimental laws which we used in our earlier derivation. To recall them briefly:

The rate at which heat flows through an infinitesimal area ΔS is proportional to the area, and to the temperature gradient normal to the area, and takes place in the direction of decrease of temperature.

The rate at which heat leaves an infinitesimal volume ΔV is proportional to the mass enclosed by the volume and to the rate of decrease of temperature within the volume.

If we let

Q = quantity of heat   (calories)
u = temperature   (degrees centigrade)

t = time   (seconds)

ρ = density   (grams per cubic centimeter)

k = thermal conductivity   (calories per second per square centimeter per degree per centimeter)

c = specific heat   (calories per gram)

u = gradient of the temperature   (degrees per centimeter)

$\mathbf{N}$ = unit normal to S

these laws can be written, respectively,

$$\frac{\partial Q}{\partial t} = -k(\mathbf{N} \cdot \nabla u)\Delta S$$

$$\frac{\partial Q}{\partial t} = -c\,\frac{\partial u}{\partial t}\,(\rho\,\Delta V)$$

For noninfinitesimal elements of area and volume, we find from these, by integration

$$\frac{\partial Q}{\partial t} = -\iint_S \mathbf{N} \cdot (k\,\nabla u)dS$$

$$\frac{\partial Q}{\partial t} = -\iiint_V c\rho\,\frac{\partial u}{\partial t}\,dV$$

If we now let S be the closed surface bounding an arbitrary volume in the region in which the heat flow takes place and equate the amount of heat leaving V, as computed from the flow through S, to the amount of heat leaving V, as computed from the temperature changes within V, we find

$$-\iint_S \mathbf{N} \cdot (k\,\nabla u)dS = -\iiint_V c\rho\,\frac{\partial u}{\partial t}\,dV$$

If we use the divergence theorem to transform the integral on the left from a surface to a volume integral, we obtain

$$\iiint_V \nabla \cdot (k\,\nabla u)dV = \iiint_V c\rho\,\frac{\partial u}{\partial t}\,dV$$

or

$$\iiint_V \left[\nabla \cdot (k\,\nabla u) - c\rho\,\frac{\partial u}{\partial t}\right] dV = 0$$

Since the last integral is zero for *every* volume V within the conducting body, it follows that the integrand must vanish identically, that is,

$$\nabla \cdot (k\,\nabla u) - c\rho\,\frac{\partial u}{\partial t} = 0$$

If the thermal conductivity k is a constant, we can move it across the operator in the left member and obtain the usual form of the heat equation for uniform bodies:

$$\nabla^2 u = \frac{c\rho}{k} \frac{\partial u}{\partial t} = a^2 \frac{\partial u}{\partial t}$$

As an example of the use of Green's theorem, let us now investigate the question of whether or not a solution of the heat equation satisfying prescribed boundary conditions over a given region is necessarily unique. In our discussion of boundary value problems in Chap. 7, we assumed that this was the case, and indeed it is hard to conceive of it being otherwise in a physical problem. Whatever our convictions in the matter may be, it is nonetheless interesting to examine the question analytically, as we are now in a position to do.

Let us suppose, then, that we are to solve the equation

$$a^2 \frac{\partial u}{\partial t} = \nabla^2 u$$

throughout a region V bounded by the closed surface S, subject to the boundary condition

$$u = f(x,y,z,t) \qquad \text{on } S$$

and the initial condition

$$u(x,y,z,0) = g(x,y,z) \qquad \text{throughout } V$$

Further, let us suppose that we have two solutions of the problem, u_1 and u_2, each of which, with its derivatives through the second, is continuous in V.

If we define a new function

$$w(x,y,z,t) = u_2(x,y,z,t) - u_1(x,y,z,t)$$

it is clear from the linearity of the heat equation that w also satisfies this equation. Moreover, w obviously assumes boundary and initial conditions which are identically zero. Finally, w is continuous and differentiable, since it is the difference of two such functions.

Now consider the volume integral

$$(1) \qquad J(t) = \tfrac{1}{2} \int \int \int_V w^2(x,y,z,t)\, dV$$

Clearly $J(t)$ is a continuous function which is always equal to or greater than zero, since its integrand is everywhere nonnegative. Also since $w = 0$ when $t = 0$, it follows that

$$J(0) = 0$$

Now

$$J'(t) = \frac{1}{2} \int \int \int_V 2w \frac{\partial w}{\partial t} \, dV$$

and thus, since w satisfies the heat equation, we have

(2) $$J'(t) = \frac{1}{a^2} \int \int \int_V w \, \nabla^2 w \, dV$$

To this let us apply the first form of Green's theorem [Eq. (18), Sec. 15.4] with both u and v in the formula taken to be the function w of the present problem. Then

(3) $$\int \int \int_V (w \, \nabla^2 w + \nabla w \cdot \nabla w) dV = \int \int_S \mathbf{N} \cdot w \, \nabla w \, dS$$

Since the function w vanishes identically on S, the integral on the right of (3) is zero, and we have

$$\int \int \int_V w \, \nabla^2 w \, dV = - \int \int \int_V \nabla w \cdot \nabla w \, dV$$

Hence, substituting into (2),

$$J'(t) = -\frac{1}{a^2} \int \int \int_V \nabla w \cdot \nabla w \, dV$$

$$= -\frac{1}{a^2} \int \int \int_V \left[\left(\frac{\partial w}{\partial x}\right)^2 + \left(\frac{\partial w}{\partial y}\right)^2 + \left(\frac{\partial w}{\partial z}\right)^2 \right] dV$$

which shows that

$$J'(t) \leqq 0$$

Now by the law of the mean

$$\frac{J(t) - J(0)}{t} = J'(t_1) \qquad 0 < t_1 < t$$

or

$$J(t) = J(0) + tJ'(t_1) \qquad 0 < t_1 < t$$

But we have already verified that $J(0) = 0$. Hence

$$J(t) = tJ'(t_1)$$

which shows that

(4) $$J(t) \leqq 0$$

since we have just proved that $J'(t)$ is negative for all positive values of t. However, as we observed earlier, the definition of $J(t)$ shows that

(5) $$J(t) \geqq 0$$

The only way in which the inequalities (4) and (5) can be simultaneously fulfilled is for $J(t)$ to be identically zero. But this is possible if and only if the integrand of $J(t)$ vanishes identically. Hence

$$w(x,y,z,t) = u_2(x,y,z,t) - u_1(x,y,z,t) = 0$$

or

$$u_2(x,y,z,t) = u_1(x,y,z,t)$$

which proves that solutions of the heat equation satisfying sufficient continuity conditions are unique.

As a final application, we shall develop the concept of the potential, and obtain the partial differential equation satisfied by the gravitational potential. To do this, let us suppose that we have a **field of force** of some kind, or in other words, let us consider a region of space at every point of which a force vector **F** is defined. The field might, for instance, be **gravitational,** with **F** the force exerted on a unit mass anywhere in the field by the attraction of various fixed bodies. On the other hand, we might have an **electrostatic field** with **F** the force experienced by a unit charge attracted or repelled according to Coulomb's law by various fixed charges; or we might have a **magnetic field,** with **F** the force acting on a unit magnetic pole situated at a general point of the field. In any case, we call the force experienced by a unit test body of the appropriate nature the **field intensity.**

Now when a unit body is moved around an arbitrary closed path in the field, the amount of work that must be done is the line integral of the tangential component of the force **F**, that is,

$$W = \int_C \mathbf{F} \cdot d\mathbf{R}$$

If there is no dissipation of energy due to friction or similar effects then, according to the law of conservation of energy, the last integral must be zero, and as a consequence we conclude that the work done in moving a unit body from one point to another, namely,

$$\int_A^B \mathbf{F} \cdot d\mathbf{R}$$

is independent of the path. Fields of force for which this is true are said to be **conservative.**

If in a conservative field we define

$$\phi(x,y,z) = \int_{P_0}^P \mathbf{F} \cdot d\mathbf{R}$$

where P_0 is a fixed point and P is a general point, the function ϕ, being independent of the path between P_0 and P, is a function of position only, which we call the **potential.** Clearly the potential is determined only to within an additive constant associated with the arbitrary lower limit P_0.

Now if we write

$$\phi(x,y,z) = \int_{P_0}^{P} \mathbf{F} \cdot \frac{d\mathbf{R}}{ds} \, ds$$

we see, by differentiating the integral with respect to s, that the directional derivative of ϕ is

$$\frac{d\phi}{ds} = \mathbf{F} \cdot \frac{d\mathbf{R}}{ds}$$

However, we have seen that in general the directional derivative of a scalar point function is given by

$$\frac{d\phi}{ds} = \nabla\phi \cdot \frac{d\mathbf{R}}{ds}$$

Hence, identifying the two expressions for $d\phi/ds$, which of course hold for all directions at P, we conclude that

(6) $\mathbf{F} = \nabla\phi$

which shows that *in a conservative field the intensity,* $\mathbf{F}$, *is equal to the gradient of the potential.* This result makes the determination of the appropriate po-

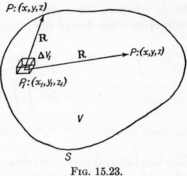

Fig. 15.23.

tential function of prime importance in most field problems.*

If we are concerned with a gravitational field, or with any other field associated with the inverse-square law, it is evident that the potential at a point $P:(x,y,z)$ due to the matter in an element of volume

$$\Delta V_1 = \Delta x_1 \, \Delta y_1 \, \Delta z_1$$

enclosing the point $P_1:(x_1,y_1,z_1)$ is

$$\Delta\phi = \frac{\Delta m}{r} = \frac{\rho(x_1,y_1,z_1)\Delta V_1}{r}$$

where $\rho(x_1,y_1,z_1)$ is the density of the attracting material, and

$$r = \sqrt{(x - x_1)^2 + (y - y_1)^2 + (z - z_1)^2}$$

* It is instructive to compare this discussion with the work in Chap. 14 on the velocity potential. The latter, which arose from a velocity field rather than a force field, had the property that its derivative in any direction gave the component of the fluid velocity in that direction, and thus a knowledge of the velocity potential was tantamount to a knowledge of the entire behavior of the fluid.

is the length of the vector joining (x_1,y_1,z_1) to (x,y,z) (Fig 15.23). For

$$\nabla(\Delta\phi) = \nabla\left(\frac{\Delta m}{r}\right)$$

$$= \Delta m \, \nabla\left(\frac{1}{r}\right)$$

$$= -\Delta m \, \frac{\mathbf{R}_1}{r^2}$$

which is a force of magnitude $\Delta m/r^2$ directed from P toward P_1, that is, precisely the force Δm is known to exert on a unit mass at P, according to Newton's law of universal gravitation.

Now let P be restricted to lie on the surface S which encloses V, and let us compute the surface integral ΔI of the normal component of the attractive force due to the infinitesimal amount of matter in ΔV_1:

$$\Delta I = \int\int_S \mathbf{N} \cdot \nabla\left(\frac{\Delta m}{r}\right) dS$$

$$= \Delta m \int\int_S \mathbf{N} \cdot \nabla\left(\frac{1}{r}\right) dS$$

$$= -\rho(x_1,y_1,z_1)\Delta V_1 \int\int_S \left(\frac{\mathbf{N}\cdot\mathbf{R}_1}{r^2}\right) dS$$

The last integral may be evaluated at once by Gauss' theorem. Specifically, since the origin of $\mathbf{R}_1$, namely, the point (x_1,y_1,z_1) lies within S we have

$$\int\int_S \left(\frac{\mathbf{N}\cdot\mathbf{R}_1}{r^2}\right) dS = 4\pi$$

and thus

$$\Delta I = -4\pi\rho(x_1,y_1,z_1)\Delta V_1$$

If we next take into account all the material within V, by letting ΔV_1 range over the entire volume V, we obtain

$$I = -4\pi \int\int\int_V \rho(x_1,y_1,z_1)dV_1 = -4\pi \int\int\int_V \rho(x,y,z)dV$$

At the same time, from the very definition of I as the surface integral of the normal component of the field intensity, we have the alternative expression

$$I = \int\int_S \mathbf{N} \cdot \nabla\phi \, dS$$

Hence, equating,

$$\int\int_S \mathbf{N} \cdot \nabla\phi \, dS = -4\pi \int\int\int_V \rho(x,y,z)dV$$

If we now apply the divergence theorem to the integral on the left, we have

$$\int\int\int_V \nabla \cdot (\nabla\phi)dV = -4\pi \int\int\int_V \rho(x,y,z)dV$$

or

$$\int\int\int_V [\nabla^2\phi + 4\pi\rho(x,y,z)]dV = 0$$

Since this holds for every volume V, it follows that the integrand must vanish identically, and thus

$$\nabla^2\phi = -4\pi\rho(x,y,z)$$

This is **Poisson's equation,*** and we have thus shown *in regions occupied by matter, the gravitational potential satisfies Poisson's equation.* In empty space, $\rho(x,y,z) = 0$ and thus *the gravitational potential in empty space satisfies Laplace's equation.* Precisely the same results hold for the electrostatic and magnetic potentials.

EXERCISES

1. What is the potential function for a field of force in which the attraction on a particle varies inversely as the distance from the origin? directly as the square of the distance from the origin?
2. Find the potential function associated with the force field due to uniform rotation about the z-axis.
3. Show that the gravitational attraction due to a homogeneous circular disk at a point on the axis of the disk is

$$\frac{2M}{a^2}\left[1 - \frac{d}{\sqrt{d^2 + a^2}}\right]$$

where M is the mass of the disk, a is the radius of the disk, and d is the distance from the center of the disk to the point where the attraction is computed.

4. If M is the mass of a uniform sphere of radius a, and if P is a point whose distance from the center of the sphere is r, show that the attraction at P due to the sphere is

$$\mathbf{F} = \begin{cases} -\dfrac{M\mathbf{R}}{a^3}, & r \leqq a \\[2mm] -\dfrac{M\mathbf{R}}{r^3}, & r \geqq a \end{cases}$$

What is the potential at P due to the sphere?

5. Prove that a solution of the heat equation possessing continuous second derivatives, which takes on prescribed initial values throughout a region V and whose normal derivative takes on prescribed values on the boundary of V, is unique.

* Siméon Denis Poisson (1781–1840) was a great French mathematician and mathematical physicist.

CHAPTER 16

NUMERICAL ANALYSIS

16.1 The Numerical Solution of Equations. In many engineering problems one of the decisive steps is the determination of the numerical value of one or more of the roots of some equation. A great many methods have been devised for doing this, some applicable only to polynomial equations, others adapted to equations of all types, transcendental as well as algebraic. In this section we shall discuss two procedures for the numerical solution of single equations. The first is the **method of interpolation or false position,** which is the simplest and one of the best methods of solving equations of all types. The other is **Graeffe's root-squaring process,** which can be applied only to polynomial equations, but which possesses the desirable feature of giving all roots, complex as well as real.

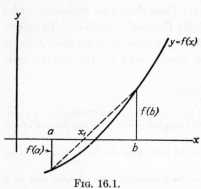

FIG. 16.1.

The method of interpolation is in essence a straightforward combination of curve plotting and proportional part interpolation. If $f(x) = 0$ is the equation to be solved, we begin by tabulating $f(x)$ for various simple values of x until we find two values, $x = a$ and $x = b$, say, at which $f(x)$ is of opposite sign. Then having verified that $f(x)$ is continuous between a and b, it is evident that a root of $f(x) = 0$ must lie in the interval (a,b). Graphically, we have the situation shown in Fig. 16.1.

To estimate the location of the root between a and b, we imagine the arc of $y = f(x)$ over the interval (a,b) to be replaced by its chord, and then by ordinary interpolation we determine where this chord crosses the x-axis.

x	$f(x)$
a	$f(a)$
x_1	0
b	$f(b)$

$$\frac{x_1 - a}{b - a} = \frac{0 - f(a)}{f(b) - f(a)}$$

$$x_1 = a - \frac{f(a)}{f(b) - f(a)} (b - a)$$

482

We now evaluate $f(x)$ for $x = x_1$, and then, depending upon whether the result is positive or negative, we also evaluate $f(x)$ a little to one side or the other of x_1, until two functional values of opposite sign tell us that again we have "bracketed" the root. Interpolation between these values, just as before, gives us a still more accurate approximation to the root, and so on, until the desired accuracy is obtained.

Example 1

Find all the positive roots of the equation $\cosh x \cos x = -1$.

To reduce the labor of performing the initial isolation of the roots, it is convenient here, as in many cases, to write the equation in the form of an equality between two functions of x

$$\cos x = \frac{-1}{\cosh x}$$

and to consider the equivalent problem of finding where the two curves

$$y = \cos x \qquad \text{and} \qquad y = \frac{-1}{\cosh x}$$

intersect. Clearly at each of these intersections $\cos x$ will equal $-1/\cosh x$, since each is equal to the common value of y. Hence the abscissa of each intersection will be a root of the original equation.

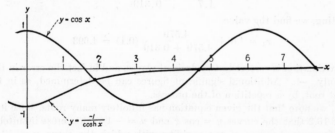

Fig. 16.2.

Now $y = \cos x$ and $y = -1/\cosh x$ can be sketched without difficulty, giving the curves shown in Fig. 16.2. By inspection it is evident that the abscissa of the first intersection is about 1.9, or in other words, the smallest positive root of the given equation is approximately 1.9. Hence we evaluate $f(x) = \cosh x \cos x + 1$ in the neighborhood of $x = 1.9$, getting

x	$f(x)$
1.8	0.294
1.9	−0.105

Interpolating to find the value of x which corresponds to $f(x) = 0$, we obtain

$$x_1 = 1.8 + \frac{0.294}{0.294 + 0.105}\,(0.1) = 1.874$$

Evaluating $f(x)$ in the neighborhood of $x = 1.874$, we find

x	$f(x)$
1.874	0.00482
1.875	0.00043
1.876	−0.00371

Evidently the value of the root correct to three decimal places is 1.875. Interpolating between 1.875 and 1.876 to find the next significant figure, we have

$$x_1 = 1.8751$$

From Fig. 16.2 it appears that the second root of the given equation is only slightly less than $x = 3\pi/2 = 4.71$. Hence we tabulate $f(x)$ in the neighborhood of $x = 4.7$, getting

x	$f(x)$
4.6	−4.579
4.7	0.319

Interpolating, we find the value

$$x_2 = 4.6 + \frac{4.579}{4.579 + 0.319} (0.1) = 4.693$$

This approximation is correct to two decimal places, and in fact the error in the third place is only −1. Additional significant figures can be determined, as in the case of the first root, by a repetition of the process.

Finally, we note that the given equation has infinitely many roots, since it is clear from Fig. 16.2 that the curves $y = \cos x$ and $y = -1/\cosh x$ cross infinitely many times. Moreover, because of the rapidity with which the curve $y = -1/\cosh x$ approaches the x-axis, these intersections, after the first one or two, occur almost exactly at the points where $y = \cos x$ crosses the x-axis. Hence to a high degree of approximation the third, fourth, . . . , nth, . . . roots of $\cosh x \cos x = -1$ are

$$x_3 = \frac{5\pi}{2}, \qquad x_4 = \frac{7\pi}{2}, \qquad \cdots, \qquad x_n = \frac{2n - 1}{2} \pi, \cdots$$

The method of interpolation can of course be applied to polynomial equations, but it is often more convenient, especially if complex roots are also desired, to use Graeffe's root-squaring process. To present the theory of this method, let us assume first that the roots of the given equation,

$$(1) \qquad x^n + a_1 x^{n-1} + a_2 x^{n-2} + a_3 x^{n-3} + \cdots + a_{n-1} x + a_n = 0$$

say $-r_1, -r_2, -r_3, \ldots, -r_n$, are all real and distinct, and have been arranged in decreasing order of absolute value from $-r_1$ to $-r_n$.

Now let us rewrite Eq. (1), with all even powers of x on one side and all odd powers of x on the other,

$$(x^n + a_2 x^{n-2} + a_4 x^{n-4} + \cdots) = -(a_1 x^{n-1} + a_3 x^{n-3} + a_5 x^{n-5} + \cdots)$$

and then square both sides:

$$
\begin{aligned}
& x^{2n} + a_2^2 x^{2n-4} + a_4^2 x^{2n-8} + \cdots && a_1^2 x^{2n-2} + a_3^2 x^{2n-6} + a_5^2 x^{2n-10} + \cdots \\
& \quad + 2a_2 x^{2n-2} + 2a_4 x^{2n-4} + \cdots && \quad + 2a_1 a_3 x^{2n-4} + 2a_1 a_5 x^{2n-6} + \cdots \\
& \qquad + 2a_2 a_4 x^{2n-6} + \cdots && \qquad + 2a_3 a_5 x^{2n-8} + \cdots \\
& \quad \cdots \cdots && = && \quad \cdots \cdots
\end{aligned}
$$

Collecting terms again on the left, we obtain

$$(2) \quad x^{2n} - (a_1^2 - 2a_2)x^{2n-2} + (a_2^2 - 2a_1 a_3 + 2a_4)x^{2n-4}$$
$$- (a_3^2 - 2a_2 a_4 + 2a_1 a_5 - 2a_6)x^{2n-6} + \cdots = 0$$

Since Eq. (2) was obtained from (1) by squaring, it is evident that it will vanish for any value of x for which Eq. (1) vanishes. In other words, any root of the original equation (1) is also a root of the derived equation (2). Now in (2) let $y = -x^2$. Then

$$
\begin{aligned}
x^{2n} &= (x^2)^n = (-y)^n = (-1)^n y^n \\
x^{2n-2} &= (x^2)^{n-1} = (-y)^{n-1} = -(-1)^n y^{n-1} \\
x^{2n-4} &= (x^2)^{n-2} = (-y)^{n-2} = (-1)^n y^{n-2} \\
& \quad \cdots \cdots \cdots \cdots \cdots \cdots \cdots \cdots
\end{aligned}
$$

and Eq. (2) becomes, after dividing out $(-1)^n$,

$$(3) \quad y^n + (a_1^2 - 2a_2)y^{n-1} + (a_2^2 - 2a_1 a_3 + 2a_4)y^{n-2}$$
$$+ (a_3^2 - 2a_2 a_4 + 2a_1 a_5 - 2a_6)y^{n-3} + \cdots = 0$$

By virtue of the substitution $y = -x^2$, it is evident that the roots of (3) are $-(-r_1)^2, -(-r_2)^2, \ldots, -(-r_n)^2$ or

$$-r_1^2, -r_2^2, \ldots, -r_n^2$$

We have thus constructed a new equation whose roots are numerically equal to the squares of the roots of the original equation. Obviously by repeating this process, equations can be obtained whose roots are numerically equal to the 4th, 8th, 16th, 32nd, . . . powers of the roots of Eq. (1).

The effect of this root-squaring process is to give equations whose roots are more and more widely separated. For instance, if two roots of the given equation are in the ratio 5:4, then their 128th powers are in the ratio

$$5^{128}:4^{128} \quad \text{or} \quad 2.54 \times 10^{12}:1$$

This is a highly desirable situation, for as we shall soon see, equations whose roots are widely separated can readily be solved with considerable accuracy.

The squaring process which leads to equations whose roots are high powers of the roots of a given equation may be carried out systematically in tabular form as follows. Write down the successive coefficients in the original equation, taking care to write zero for the coefficient of any missing term. Then under each coefficient write its square and twice all products of coefficients symmetrically located on each side of it, the signs of these products being alternately negative and positive as coefficients farther and farther from the one in question are multiplied. The

1	a_1	a_2	a_3	$\cdots$	a_{n-2}	a_{n-1}	a_n
1	a_1^2 $-2a_2$	a_2^2 $-2a_1a_3$ $+2a_4$	a_3^2 $-2a_2a_4$ $+2a_1a_5$ $-2a_6$	$\cdots$ $\cdots$ $\cdots$ $\cdots$	a_{n-2}^2 $-2a_{n-3}a_{n-1}$ $+2a_{n-4}a_n$	a_{n-1}^2 $-2a_{n-2}a_n$	a_n^2

sum of the terms placed below any coefficient in this array is the coefficient of the corresponding term in the new equation.

Now suppose that by a number of repetitions of this process an equation

$$(4) \qquad z^n + \alpha_1 z^{n-1} + \alpha_2 z^{n-2} + \cdots + \alpha_{n-1} z + \alpha_n = 0$$

has been obtained whose roots are numerically the mth powers of those of the given equation, or specifically $-r_1^m, -r_2^m, \ldots, -r_n^m$. From the usual relations between the roots and the coefficients of a polynomial equation, it follows then that

$$\alpha_1 = -(\text{sum of the roots}) = r_1^m + r_2^m + \cdots + r_n^m$$
$$\alpha_2 = (\text{sum of the roots taken two at a time})$$
$$= r_1^m r_2^m + r_1^m r_3^m + \cdots + r_2^m r_3^m + \cdots$$
$$(5) \quad \alpha_3 = -(\text{sum of the roots taken three at a time})$$
$$= r_1^m r_2^m r_3^m + r_1^m r_2^m r_4^m + \cdots$$
$$\cdots \cdots \cdots \cdots \cdots \cdots \cdots \cdots \cdots \cdots \cdots \cdots \cdots$$
$$\alpha_n = (-1)^n (\text{product of all the roots}) = r_1^m r_2^m r_3^m \cdots r_n^m$$

Under the hypothesis that $|r_1| > |r_2| > |r_3| \cdots$ and that m is large, say 128 or 256, it follows that r_1^m is enormously larger than r_2^m, which in turn is enormously larger than r_3^m, and so on. Hence to a high degree of approximation

$$\alpha_1 = r_1^m$$
$$\alpha_2 = r_1^m r_2^m$$
$$\alpha_3 = r_1^m r_2^m r_3^m$$
$$\cdots \cdots \cdots \cdots$$
$$\alpha_{n-1} = r_1^m r_2^m r_3^m \cdots r_{n-1}^m$$
$$\alpha_n = r_1^m r_2^m r_3^m \cdots r_{n-1}^m r_n^m$$

since in each case, the first term is very much larger than any or all of the succeeding terms.

Thus $|r_1|$ can be found simply by extracting the mth root of the second coefficient in the final equation (4). Similarly, since the ratio of the third coefficient to the second is

$$\frac{r_1^m r_2^m}{r_1^m} = r_2^m$$

$|r_2|$ can be found by extracting the mth root of this ratio. In the same way $|r_3|$ is the mth root of the ratio of the fourth coefficient to the third, and so on. The signs of the roots cannot be determined by this procedure, but can easily be inferred from a rough sketch of the original function, supplemented by Descartes's rule of signs. Example 2 will make the details clear.

Just how many root-squaring operations must be performed in a given case, *i.e.*, just how large m should be, cannot be told in advance. An adequate working rule is to continue until each new coefficient (with certain exceptions in the cases of coincident or complex roots) is essentially the square of the preceding one, *i.e.*, until the product terms in the calculation of the new coefficients make no appreciable contribution.

The case of equal roots can be handled without difficulty by returning to Eq. (4) and supposing two of the r's to be equal, say $r_3 = r_4$. Then when all but the dominant terms in each coefficient are rejected, we find from (5) that

$$\alpha_1 = r_1^m$$
$$\alpha_2 = r_1^m r_2^m$$
$$\alpha_3 = r_1^m r_2^m r_3^m + r_1^m r_2^m r_4^m = 2r_1^m r_2^m r_3^m$$
$$\alpha_4 = r_1^m r_2^m r_3^m r_4^m = r_1^m r_2^m r_3^{2m}$$
$$\cdots \cdots \cdots \cdots \cdots \cdots \cdots \cdots \cdots \cdots \cdots \cdots \cdots$$
$$\alpha_{n-1} = r_1^m r_2^m r_3^m r_4^m r_5^m \cdots r_{n-1}^m = r_1^m r_2^m r_3^{2m} r_5^m \cdots r_{n-}^m$$
$$\alpha_n = r_1^m r_2^m r_3^m r_4^m r_5^m \cdots r_{n-1}^m r_n^m = r_1^m r_2^m r_3^{2m} r_5^m \cdots r_{n-1}^m r_n^m$$

Hence to a high degree of approximation, the final equation is

$$z^n + r_1^m z^{n-1} + r_1^m r_2^m z^{n-2} + 2r_1^m r_2^m r_3^m z^{n-3} + r_1^m r_2^m r_3^{2m} z^{n-4} + \cdots = 0$$

Evidently for each pair of equal roots there will be one term (the fourth in this case) which, as the root-squaring process is repeated, does not approach the square of its previous value, but instead approaches one-half this value. In other words, when two equal roots are present, there is always one coefficient for which in the root-squaring procedure the product of adjacent terms never becomes negligible, but always makes a contribution approaching one-half the square of the coefficient itself:

. . .	. . .	$r_1^m r_2^m$	$2r_1^m r_2^m r_3^m$	$r_1^m r_2^m r_3^{2m}$	. . .	. . .
			$4r_1^{2m} r_2^{2m} r_3^{2m}$ $-2(r_1^m r_2^m)(r_1^m r_2^m r_3^{2m})$ . . .			
			$2r_1^{2m} r_2^{2m} r_3^{2m}$			

When one or more coefficients behave in this manner as successive equations are constructed the presence of repeated roots is *always* indicated, and the process can be terminated as soon as all but the exceptional coefficient or coefficients are uninfluenced by the product terms.

The determination of the roots in this case, once it is recognized, is simple enough. All roots except the repeated one can be found just as before by extracting the mth root of the ratios of successive pairs of non-exceptional coefficients. The repeated root can be found by extracting the $(2m)$th root of the ratio of the coefficients immediately following and immediately preceding the exceptional coefficient. Here again, the signs of the roots must be determined by subsequent inspection.

Example 2

Solve the equation $x^3 + 8x^2 + 21x + 18 = 0$.

The construction of the successive equations presents no difficulty and is adequately set forth in the table on page 489. Evidently by the time $m = 64$ all coefficients except the second, whose exceptional behavior indicates a double root, are uninfluenced by the product terms. Hence the process can be terminated.

In this case the numerical value of the double root can be found by extracting the 128th root of the quotient of the third coefficient divided by the first:

$$\log_{10} |r_1| = \frac{\log_{10} (1.1789 \times 10^{61}) - \log_{10} (1)}{128} = 0.47712$$

$$|r_1| = 3.000$$

Of course this is also the absolute value of the second root r_2.

To find the numerical value of the third root, we proceed as usual and extract the 64th root of the quotient of the fourth coefficient divided by the third:

$$\log_{10} |r_3| = \frac{\log_{10} (2.1750 \times 10^{80}) - \log_{10} (1.1789 \times 10^{61})}{64} = 0.30103$$

$$|r_3| = 2.000$$

From the fact that each of the coefficients in the original equation is positive, it follows that all the roots are negative. Hence the roots are -2, -3, -3, as could have been determined by inspection in this simple case.

	1	8	21	18
	1	64 -42	441 -288	324
$(m = 2)$	1	22	153	324
	1	484 -306	23,409 $-14,256$	104,976
$(m = 4)$	1	178	9,153	104,976
	1	3.1684×10^4 -1.8306×10^4	8.3777×10^7 -3.7371×10^7	1.1020×10^{10}
$(m = 8)$	1	1.3378×10^4	4.6406×10^7	1.1020×10^{10}
	1	1.7897×10^8 -0.9281×10^8	2.1535×10^{15} -0.2949×10^{15}	1.2144×10^{20}
$(m = 16)$	1	0.8616×10^8	1.8586×10^{15}	1.2144×10^{20}
	1	0.7424×10^{16} -0.3717×10^{16}	3.4544×10^{30} -0.0209×10^{30}	1.4748×10^{40}
$(m = 32)$	1	0.3707×10^{16}	3.4335×10^{30}	1.4748×10^{40}
	1	0.1374×10^{32} -0.0687×10^{32}	1.1789×10^{61} -0.0000×10^{61}	2.1750×10^{80}
$(m = 64)$	1	0.0687×10^{32}	1.1789×10^{61}	2.1750×10^{80}

When the given equation contains a pair of complex roots, necessarily conjugates of each other, the analysis is a little different. To investigate this case, suppose specifically that the equation to be solved is of the fourth order with roots $-r_1$, $-r_2e^{i\theta}$, $-r_2e^{-i\theta}$, $-r_3$, whose absolute values are such that $|r_1| > |r_2| > |r_3|$. The equation can then be written

$$(x + r_1)(x + r_2e^{i\theta})(x + r_2e^{-i\theta})(x + r_3) = 0$$

After m root-squaring operations have been performed, the derived equation has roots $-r_1^m$, $-r_2^m e^{im\theta}$, $-r_2^m e^{-im\theta}$, $-r_3^m$. It can therefore be written

$$(z + r_1^m)(z + r_2^m e^{im\theta})(z + r_2^m e^{-im\theta})(z + r_3^m) = 0$$

or

(6) $\quad z^4 + (r_1^m + r_2^m e^{im\theta} + r_2^m e^{-im\theta} + r_3^m)z^3$
$\quad\quad + (r_1^m r_2^m e^{im\theta} + r_1^m r_2^m e^{-im\theta} + r_1^m r_3^m + r_2^m e^{im\theta} r_2^m e^{-im\theta} + r_2^m e^{im\theta} r_3^m$
$\quad\quad\quad\quad\quad\quad\quad\quad\quad\quad\quad\quad\quad\quad\quad\quad + r_2^m e^{-im\theta} r_3^m)z^2$
$\quad\quad + (r_1^m r_2^m e^{im\theta} r_2^m e^{-im\theta} + r_1^m r_2^m e^{im\theta} r_3^m + r_1^m r_2^m e^{-im\theta} r_3^m + r_2^m e^{im\theta} r_2^m e^{-im\theta} r_3^m)z$
$\quad\quad + (r_1^m r_2^m e^{im\theta} r_2^m e^{-im\theta} r_3^m) = 0$

where the coefficients have been expressed at length as the appropriate symmetric functions of the roots.

If only terms of greatest absolute value are retained in each coefficient, Eq. (6) becomes

(7) $\quad z^4 + r_1^m z^3 + (r_1^m r_2^m e^{im\theta} + r_1^m r_2^m e^{-im\theta})z^2 + r_1^m r_2^{2m} z + r_1^m r_2^{2m} r_3^m = 0$

Now let us factor $r_1^m r_2^m$ from the third term, and substitute $2\cos m\theta$ for $e^{im\theta} + e^{-im\theta}$. Then (7) becomes

(8) $\quad\quad\quad z^4 + r_1^m z^3 + 2r_1^m r_2^m \cos m\theta\, z^2 + r_1^m r_2^{2m} z + r_1^m r_2^{2m} r_3^m = 0$

Evidently in this case there is an exceptional coefficient, namely, the third, which, instead of becoming and remaining positive as the root squaring is repeated, continually fluctuates in sign, because of the presence of the cosine factor. This is the characteristic which identifies the presence of complex roots, as many coefficients behaving in this fashion as there are pairs of complex roots.

Once this case is recognized it is a simple matter to obtain all the real roots by extracting the mth root of the ratios of successive nonexceptional coefficients, just as before. Moreover, the modulus of the complex roots can be found by taking the $(2m)$th root of the quotient of the coefficient which immediately follows the exceptional one divided by the coefficient which immediately precedes the exceptional one.

To complete the determination of the complex roots, for which at the present stage only the absolute value is known, let these roots now be written $u \pm iv$. In the original equation, the coefficient of x^{n-1} is the negative of the sum of the roots, hence

$$a_1 = -[-r_1 + (u + iv) + (u - iv) - r_3 - \cdots]$$

and thus

$$u = \frac{-a_1 - [-r_1 - r_3 - \cdots]}{2}$$

$$= \frac{1}{2}[- \text{ coefficient of } x^{n-1} - \text{ sum of all real roots}]$$

As soon as u is determined, v can be found from the familiar relation

$$r_i^2 = u^2 + v^2$$

As we have already remarked, the presence of more than one pair of complex roots is indicated by the presence of more than one coefficient which continually fluctuates in sign as the root squaring continues. In this case all real roots can be found, just as before, from adjacent pairs of nonexceptional coefficients by extracting the mth root of their quotients. The absolute values of the various complex roots can also be found, as before, by taking the $(2m)$th root of the ratios of coefficients immediately after and immediately before each exceptional one, the exceptional coefficients being necessarily nonadjacent if the pairs of complex roots are of different absolute value. The only modification required in this case is in the determination of the real parts of the various complex roots.

To illustrate this modification, let the given equation contain two pair of complex roots,

$$u_1 \pm iv_1 \qquad \text{and} \qquad u_2 \pm iv_2$$

of absolute values r_1 and r_2, together, with additional real roots $-r_3$, $-r_4 \ldots$. As before, the coefficient of x^{n-1} is the negative of the sum of the roots; hence

$$a_1 = -[(u_1 + iv_1) + (u_1 - iv_1) + (u_2 + iv_2) + (u_2 - iv_2) - r_3$$
$$- r_4 - \cdots]$$
$$= -2u_1 - 2u_2 + r_3 + r_4 + \cdots$$

or

$$u_1 + u_2 = \frac{-a_1 - (-r_3 - r_4 - \cdots)}{2}$$

$$(9) \qquad\qquad = \frac{1}{2}[- \text{ coefficient of } x^{n-1} - \text{ sum of all real roots}]$$

This is one equation in the unknown real components u_1 and u_2.

To obtain a second equation in u_1 and u_2, we make use of the fact that the coefficient of x in the original equation is equal to

$$(-1)^{n-1} (\text{sum of the roots taken } n - 1 \text{ at a time})$$

Hence

$$a_{n-1} = (-1)^{n-1}[(u_1 - iv_1)(u_2 + iv_2)(u_2 - iv_2)(-r_3)(-r_4) \cdots$$
$$+ (u_1 + iv_1)(u_2 + iv_2)(u_2 - iv_2)(-r_3)(-r_4) \cdots$$
$$+ (u_1 + iv_1)(u_1 - iv_1)(u_2 - iv_2)(-r_3)(-r_4) \cdots$$
$$+ (u_1 + iv_1)(u_1 - iv_1)(u_2 + iv_2)(-r_3)(-r_4) \cdots$$
$$+ (u_1 + iv_1)(u_1 - iv_1)(u_2 + iv_2)(u_2 - iv_2) \text{ (sum of all products}$$
$$\text{of the } n - 4 \text{ real roots taken } n - 5 \text{ at a time)]}$$

$$= (-1)^{n-1}[(u_1 - iv_1)r_2^2 \text{ (product of the } n - 4 \text{ real roots)}$$
$$+ (u_1 + iv_1)r_2^2 \text{ (product of the } n - 4 \text{ real roots)}$$
$$+ (u_2 - iv_2)r_1^2 \text{ (product of the } n - 4 \text{ real roots)}$$
$$+ (u_2 + iv_2)r_1^2 \text{ (product of the } n - 4 \text{ real roots)}$$
$$+ r_1^2 r_2^2 \text{ (sum of all products of the } n - 4 \text{ real roots taken } n - 5$$
$$\text{at a time)]}$$

$$= (-1)^{n-1}[(2u_1 r_2^2 + 2u_2 r_1^2) \text{ (product of the } n - 4 \text{ real roots)}$$
$$+ r_1^2 r_2^2 \text{ (sum of all products of the } n - 4 \text{ real roots taken } n - 5$$
$$\text{at a time)]}$$

Hence finally

$$u_1 r_2^2 + u_2 r_1^2 = \frac{(-1)^{n-1}a_{n-1} - r_1^2 r_2^2 \text{ (sum of all products of the } n - 4 \text{ real roots taken } n - 5 \text{ at a time)}}{2 \text{ (product of all } n - 4 \text{ real roots)}}$$

or

$$(10) \quad u_1 r_2^2 + u_2 r_1^2 = \left[\frac{(-1)^{n-1}a_{n-1}}{2 \text{ (product of all } n - 4 \text{ real roots)}} \right.$$
$$\left. - \frac{r_1^2 r_2^2}{2} \text{ (sum of reciprocals of all } n - 4 \text{ real roots)} \right]$$

From Eqs. (9) and (10), u_1 and u_2 can be found at once. Then v_1 and v_2 can be determined from the relations

$$r_1^2 = u_1^2 + v_1^2, \qquad r_2^2 = u_2^2 + v_2^2$$

When more than two pair of complex roots are present, this procedure may be generalized by using, in addition to the relation

$$a_1 = - \text{ sum of all the roots}$$

and the x-coefficient relation, other relations arising from the coefficients of x^2, x^3, x^4 . . . However, these further equations in the real components u_1, u_2, u_3, u_4, . . . are nonlinear, and solving for u_1, u_2, u_3, u_4, . . . may be difficult or impossible.

Example 3

Find all the roots of the equation

$$f(x) \equiv x^7 + x^6 - 4x^5 - 4x^4 - 2x^3 - 5x^2 - x - 1 = 0$$

The construction of the successive equations presents no difficulty. By the time $m = 128$, all coefficients are uninfluenced by the product terms except the fifth and the seventh, which continually fluctuate in sign. We can therefore terminate the process at this stage with the assurance that there are two pair of complex roots and three distinct real roots.

m	1	1	-4	-4	-2	-5	-1	-1
$m = 2$	1	9	20	-8	-26	29	-9	1
$m = 4$		4.1000×10	4.9200×10^{2}	1.6440×10^{3}	7.6200×10^{2}	3.5700×10^{2}	2.3000×10	
$m = 8$		6.9700×10^{2}	1.0877×10^{5}	1.9821×10^{6}	-5.7061×10^{5}	9.5686×10^{4}	-1.8500×10^{2}	
$m = 16$		2.6827×10^{5}	9.0669×10^{9}	4.0530×10^{12}	-5.3760×10^{10}	8.9486×10^{9}	-1.5715×10^{5}	
$m = 32$		5.3835×10^{10}	8.0034×10^{19}	1.6428×10^{25}	-6.9647×10^{22}	8.0060×10^{19}	6.7989×10^{9}	
$m = 64$		2.7381×10^{21}	6.4036×10^{39}	2.6988×10^{50}	2.2202×10^{45}	6.4096×10^{39}	-1.1390×10^{20}	
$m = 128$		7.4844×10^{42}	4.1006×10^{79}	7.2835×10^{100}	1.4697×10^{90}	4.1083×10^{79}	$+1.5400 \times 10^{38}$	

To find the magnitudes of the three real roots, we have

$$\log_{10} |r_1| = \frac{\log_{10} (7.4844 \times 10^{42})}{128} = 0.33495$$

$$|r_1| = 2.162$$

$$\log_{10} |r_2| = \frac{\log_{10} (4.1006 \times 10^{79}) - \log_{10} (7.4844 \times 10^{42})}{128} = 0.28702$$

$$|r_2| = 1.936$$

$$\log_{10} |r_3| = \frac{\log_{10} (7.2835 \times 10^{100}) - \log_{10} (4.1006 \times 10^{79})}{128} = 0.16601$$

$$|r_3| = 1.466$$

Since there is only one change of sign between successive coefficients in the original equation, only one of the three real roots can be positive. Since $f(2) = -39$ and $f(3) = 1,517$, the positive root must lie between 2 and 3. Hence the real roots are 2.162, -1.936, -1.466.

To find the absolute values of the complex roots, we extract the 256th root of the ratios of the coefficients just after and just before the exceptional ones. Thus

$$\log_{10} r_4 = \frac{\log_{10} (4.1083 \times 10^{79}) - \log_{10} (7.2835 \times 10^{100})}{256} = -0.08300 = 9.91700 - 10$$

$$r_4 = 0.826$$

$$\log_{10} r_5 = \frac{\log_{10} (1) - \log_{10} (4.1083 \times 10^{79})}{256} = -0.31099 = 9.68901 - 10$$

$$r_5 = 0.489$$

The real parts of these roots, u_4 and u_5, must satisfy Eqs. (9) and (10), hence

$$u_4 + u_5 = \frac{-1 - [(2.162) + (-1.936) + (-1.466)]}{2}$$

or

$$u_4 + u_5 = 0.120$$

and

$$u_4(0.489)^2 + u_5(0.826)^2 = \frac{(-1)^6(-1)}{2(2.162)(-1.936)(-1.466)}$$
$$- \frac{(0.826)^2(0.489)^2}{2} \left[\frac{1}{2.162} + \frac{1}{-1.936} + \frac{1}{-1.466} \right]$$

or

$$0.239u_4 + 0.682u_5 = -0.021$$

Solving these two equations simultaneously, we find without difficulty

$$u_4 = 0.233, \qquad u_5 = -0.113$$

Hence

$$v_4 = \sqrt{r_4^2 - u_4^2} = 0.795$$
$$v_5 = \sqrt{r_5^2 - u_5^2} = 0.476$$

The complex roots of the given equation are therefore $0.233 \pm 0.795i$ and $-0.113 \pm 0.476i$.

EXERCISES

Using the method of interpolation, find all the real roots of each of the following equations:

1. $x^3 - 2x - 5 = 0$ *Ans.* 2.095
2. $\cos x + 2x + 1 = 0$ **3.** $\log_{10} x - x + 2 = 0$
4. $\tan x + \tanh x = 0$ **5.** $\tan x = 2x$

Using Graeffe's root-squaring process, find all the roots, complex as well as real, of each of the following equations:

6. $x^4 - x^3 - 10x^2 - x + 1 = 0$ *Ans.* $x_1 = 3.7321,\ x_2 = -2.6180$
$x_3 = -0.3820,\ x_4 = 0.2680$

7. $4x^4 + 16x^3 + 25x^2 + 21x + 9 = 0$ *Ans.* $x_1 = x_2 = -1.5000$
$x_3,\ x_4 = -0.5000 \pm .8660i$

8. $16x^5 - 16x^4 - 12x^3 + 12x^2 - 1 = 0$
9. $x^5 - 5x^3 + 4x = 10$
10. $x^5 - 8x^4 + 17x^3 - 10x^2 + 10 = 0$
11. Discuss the application of the root-squaring process to an equation with a triple root. Assume for simplicity that the triple root is the root of largest absolute value.
12. Instead of drawing the chord joining two points where $f(x)$ is of opposite sign and then taking the intersection of this chord with the x-axis as an approximation to

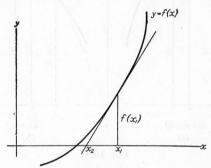

Fig. 16.3.

the root of $f(x) = 0$, as in the method of interpolation, we can, if we choose, draw the tangent to the curve $y = f(x)$ at a point near a root of $f(x) = 0$ and use the x-intercept of this tangent as an approximation to the root (Fig. 16.3). Show that this process, which is known as **Newton's method,** is essentially an iterative process based on the formula

$$x_n = x_{n-1} - \frac{f(x_{n-1})}{f'(x_{n-1})}$$

Using Newton's method find the smallest positive root of each of the following equations:

13. $x^3 + x - 1 = 0$ **14.** $x^3 - 4x^2 + 2 = 0$
15. $x = e^{-x}$ **16.** $\log_{10} x = 2x - x^2$

17. A sphere of radius 1 ft is made of material weighing 20 lb/ft³. To what depth will it sink when allowed to float in water?
18. A thin hemispherical bowl of radius 1 ft is made of material weighing 2 lb/ft². To what depth must it be filled with a liquid weighing 48 lb/ft³ in order that the center of gravity of the bowl and its contents shall be as low as possible?

19. A particle of mass m is allowed to slide from rest down the curve $y = e^x$. If motion begins at the point on the curve where $y = 10$, find the point at which the normal reaction of the particle against the curve is a maximum. (Hint: The normal reaction of the particle against the curve is made up of the centrifugal force, mv^2/r, due to its motion and the normal component of the weight, $mg \cos \theta$, where r is the radius of curvature and θ is the inclination angle of the tangent to the curve.)

20. A particle slides freely down the curve $y = x^3 - x$ from the point where $y = 1$. Where does it first leave the curve?

21. What is the minimum vertical distance between the curves

$$y = \cosh x \qquad \text{and} \qquad y = \tanh x$$

16.2 Finite Differences. Suppose that we have a function, $y = f(x)$, given in tabular form for a series of equally spaced values of x. As an

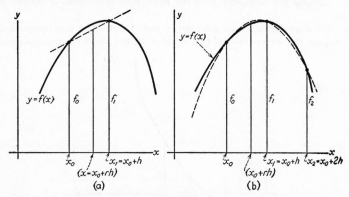

Fig. 16.4.

aid in performing necessary interpolations in such a table we may, and in fact often do, list explicitly the differences between successive values of $f(x)$. In the same way, the differences between these differences may be calculated and listed, and so on indefinitely, unless perhaps at some stage all the differences turn out to be zero. In the field of numerical mathematics, these differences play an important role, not only in interpolation but also in such processes as the construction of tables, curve fitting, the differentiation and integration of tabular functions, and the approximate solution of differential equations. In the present section, we shall develop the fundamental properties of the differences of a function, and indicate their use in carrying out the operations we have just mentioned.

Let us begin by investigating from an elementary point of view the general problem of interpolation. In its simplest form, interpolation consists in substituting the chord of a curve for the curve itself, as in Fig. 16.4a, and subsequently reading values of the function from the chord rather than from the graph of the function. Analytically, let h be the interval between successive values of x at which $f(x)$ is known, and let $x \equiv x_0 + rh$, where r is some fraction, be a point intermediate between x_0 and $x_1 \equiv x_0 + h$ at which the value of $f(x)$ is desired. Then taking the origin at x_0, we have for the equation of the chord joining the points (x_0,f_0) [now $(0,f_0)$] and (x_1,f_1) [now (h,f_1)]

$$y = f_0 + \frac{f_1 - f_0}{h}\, x$$

If we substitute $x = rh$ in this equation, we obtain the usual interpolated approximation to $f(x_0 + rh)$, namely,

$$f_0 + (f_1 - f_0)r$$

Finally, if we introduce the notation

$$(1) \qquad \Delta f_n = f_{n+1} - f_n$$

we can write

$$(2) \qquad f(x_0 + rh) = f_0 + r\,\Delta f_0$$

On the other hand, we might attempt to approximate the graph of $y = f(x)$ not by a straight line through two successive points where $f(x)$ is known, but by a parabola through three such points, as in Fig. 16.4b. In general, because of its curvature, a parabola will fit the graph of $f(x)$ more closely than will a straight line, and hence interpolation based on a parabolic approximating arc will be more accurate than ordinary linear interpolation.

To develop a formula for parabolic interpolation, we must first determine the coefficients a, b, c in the equation of the approximating arc

$$(3) \qquad y = a + bx + cx^2$$

Again taking the origin at x_0, for convenience, and substituting the coordinates of the three known points

$$(0,f_0),\ (h,f_1),\ (2h,f_2)$$

into (3), we obtain the equations

$$\begin{aligned} f_0 &= a \\ f_1 &= a + bh + ch^2 \\ f_2 &= a + 2bh + 4ch^2 \end{aligned}$$

$$f_2 - 2f_1 = -a + 2ch^2$$

$$c = \frac{f_2 - 2f_1 + f_0}{2h^2}$$

$$f_2 - 4f_1 = -3a - 2bh$$

$$b = \frac{-f_2 + 4f_1 - 3f_0}{2h}$$

Solving these simultaneously for a, b, and c, we find without difficulty

$$a = f_0$$

$$b = -\frac{f_2 - 4f_1 + 3f_0}{2h} = \frac{f_1 - f_0}{h} - \frac{f_2 - 2f_1 + f_0}{2h}$$

$$c = \frac{f_2 - 2f_1 + f_0}{2h^2}$$

Hence Eq. (3) can be written

$$y = f_0 + \left(\frac{f_1 - f_0}{h} - \frac{f_2 - 2f_1 + f_0}{2h}\right) x + \frac{f_2 - 2f_1 + f_0}{2h^2} x^2$$

$$(4) \qquad = f_0 + (f_1 - f_0)\frac{x}{h} + (f_2 - 2f_1 + f_0)\frac{x^2 - xh}{2h^2}$$

If we now evaluate (4) for $x = rh$, we obtain the approximation

$$f(x_0 + rh) = f_0 + (f_1 - f_0)r + (f_2 - 2f_1 + f_0)\frac{r(r-1)}{2}$$

Finally, we note that the third coefficient in the last expression can be written

$$f_2 - 2f_1 + f_0 = (f_2 - f_1) - (f_1 - f_0)$$
$$= \Delta f_1 - \Delta f_0$$

which shows how differences of differences enter into more advanced methods of interpolation, and also suggests a notation for such differences, namely,

$$(5) \qquad \Delta f_1 - \Delta f_0 = \Delta(\Delta f_0) = \Delta^2 f_0$$

In this notation we can write

$$(6) \qquad f(x_0 + rh) = f_0 + r \, \Delta f_0 + \frac{r(r-1)}{2} \, \Delta^2 f_0$$

The analogy between this and the familiar linear interpolation formula (2) is obvious.

By approximating $f(x)$ by polynomial functions of higher and higher order, and proceeding exactly as we did in deriving (6), more and more refined interpolation formulas can be obtained. However, the labor involved in proceeding in this fashion soon becomes prohibitive, and we now turn our attention to more efficient, operational methods of deriving such results.

To do this, let us first extend the difference notation introduced in (1) and (5), by writing

$$\Delta f_n = f_{n+1} - f_n$$
$$\Delta^2 f_n = \Delta f_{n+1} - \Delta f_n$$
$$\Delta^3 f_n = \Delta^2 f_{n+1} - \Delta^2 f_n$$
$$\cdots\cdots\cdots\cdots\cdots$$
$$\Delta^m f_n = \Delta^{m-1} f_{n+1} - \Delta^{m-1} f_n$$
$$\cdots\cdots\cdots\cdots\cdots$$

This is known as the **advancing difference notation.** Evidently the difference operator Δ has the characteristic properties of a linear operator, for

$$\Delta(f_n + g_n) = (f_{n+1} + g_{n+1}) - (f_n + g_n) = (f_{n+1} - f_n) + (g_{n+1} - g_n)$$
$$= \Delta f_n + \Delta g_n$$

and, if c is a constant,

$$\Delta(cf_n) = cf_{n+1} - cf_n = c(f_{n+1} - f_n) = c\,\Delta f_n$$

Moreover Δ obeys the usual law of exponents,

$$\Delta^k(\Delta^l f_n) = \Delta^{k+l} f_n$$

provided k and l are positive integers.

In many applications it is convenient to have the successive differences of a function prominently displayed. This we do by constructing a **difference table** in which each difference is located, in its appropriate column, midway between the elements in the preceding column of which it is the difference. For convenience in this, we write as usual

$$x_0 + nh = x_n \qquad \text{and} \qquad f(x_0 + nh) = f_n$$

x	$f(x)$	Δ	Δ^2	Δ^3	Δ^4		
x_0	f_0						
		Δf_0					
x_1	f_1		$\Delta^2 f_0$				
		Δf_1		$\Delta^3 f_0$			
x_2	f_2		$\Delta^2 f_1$		$\Delta^4 f_1$		
		Δf_2		$\Delta^3 f_1$			
x_3	f_3		$\Delta^2 f_2$				
		Δf_3					
x_4	f_4						

Example 1

Construct a difference table for the function $y = 2x^4 - 8x^2 - x + 3$ if the interval between successive values of x is $h = 0.5$.

Substituting $x = 0, 0.5, 1.0, 1.5, 2.0, \ldots$ into the given equation, we first find the corresponding values of y. Then simple subtraction serves to complete the table:

x	y	Δ	Δ^2	Δ^3	Δ^4	Δ^5
0.0	3.000					
		-2.375				
0.5	0.625		-2.250			
		-4.625		4.500		
1.0	-4.000		2.250		3.000	
		-2.375		7.500		0.000
1.5	-6.375		9.750		3.000	
		7.375		10.500		0.000
2.0	1.000		20.250		3.000	
		27.625		13.500		
2.5	28.625		33.750			
		61.375				
3.0	90.000					

Example 1 illustrates the fundamental fact that *the mth differences of a polynomial of order m are constant*, and all differences of order greater than m vanish identically. To prove this, consider

$$P(x) = A_0 x^m + A_1 x^{m-1} + \cdots + A_{m-2} x^2 + A_{m-1} x + A_m$$

Now

$$\begin{aligned}
\Delta P(x) &= P(x + h) - P(x) \\
&= A_0[(x + h)^m - x^m] \\
&\quad + A_1[(x + h)^{m-1} - x^{m-1}] \\
&\quad \cdots \cdots \cdots \cdots \cdots \\
&\quad + A_{m-2}[(x + h)^2 - x^2] \\
&\quad + A_{m-1}[(x + h) - x] \\
&\quad + A_m[1 - 1] \\
&= A_0 \left[mx^{m-1}h + \frac{m(m - 1)}{2} x^{m-2}h^2 + \cdots + mxh^{m-1} + h^m \right] \\
&\quad + A_1 \left[(m - 1)x^{m-2}h + \frac{(m - 1)(m - 2)}{2} x^{m-3}h^2 + \cdots \right. \\
&\qquad\qquad\qquad\qquad\qquad\qquad \left. + (m - 1)xh^{m-2} + h^{m-1} \right] \\
&\quad + \cdots \cdots \cdots \cdots \cdots \cdots \cdots \cdots \cdots \cdots \cdots \cdots \\
&\quad + A_{m-2}[2xh + h^2] \\
&\quad + A_{m-1}[h]
\end{aligned}$$

The last expression is obviously a polynomial of order $(m - 1)$, which shows that differencing a polynomial once reduces its order by 1. Hence differencing again will reduce its order by one more, and in general, differencing m times will leave a polynomial of order zero, that is, a constant. Clearly all further differences will be zero. This result, of course, is analogous to the fact that the mth derivative of a polynomial of order m is a constant and that all higher derivatives vanish identically.

The constancy of the mth differences of a polynomial can be used to advantage in tabulating polynomial functions. For if the constant value of the mth differences of a polynomial of order m is known, and if the leading entry in the $(m - 1)$st difference column is known, then all the $(m - 1)$st differences can be found by simple addition, using the formula

$$\Delta^{m-1} f_{n+1} = \Delta^{m-1} f_n + \Delta^m f_n$$

Then from the $(m - 1)$st differences, all the $(m - 2)$nd differences can be found by addition, from the formula

$$\Delta^{m-2} f_{n+1} = \Delta^{m-2} f_n + \Delta^{m-1} f_n$$

if the leading $(m - 2)$nd difference is known. Proceeding in this way, we can work backwards through differences of lower and lower order until we obtain the column of the functional entries themselves. Since the additions which are required in this process can be very efficiently carried out on a computing machine, this method of tabulating a function, or of extending a table, is decidedly preferable to computing the additional values one by one from the formula for the function.

Example 2

Tabulate the function $y = 9.7x^3 + 0.13x^2 + 2.437x + 0.9251$ at intervals of 0.1 beginning at $x = 0$.

If a large number of values of y are desired, it will be much easier to obtain them by working backwards from the constant third differences of y than it will be to calculate each one in turn from the given equation. Hence we compute from the given formula only enough values of y to determine the leading difference of each order:

x	y	Δ	Δ^2	Δ^3
0.0	0.9251			
		0.2547		
0.1	1.1798		0.0608	
		0.3155		0.0582
0.2	1.4953		0.1190	
		0.4345		
0.3	1.9298			

With the leading differences established, and knowing that all third differences have the same value, we can immediately fill out the second difference column, then the first difference column, and finally the column of y itself, by addition, as shown.

x	y	Δ	Δ^2	Δ^3
0.0	0.9251			
		0.2547		
0.1	1.1798		0.0608	
		0.3155		0.0582
0.2	1.4953		0.1190	
		0.4345		0.0582
0.3	1.9298		0.1772	
		0.6117		0.0582
0.4	2.5415		0.2354	
		0.8471		0.0582
0.5	3.3886		0.2936	
		1.1407		.
0.6	4.5293		.	.
.	.	.	.	
		.		
.	.			

Closely associated with the difference operator Δ is the operator E which is defined to be the operator which increases the argument of a function by one tabular interval. Thus

$$Ef(x_n) = f(x_n + h)$$

Applying E a second time, again increases the argument of f by h, that is,

$$E^2 f(x_n) = E[Ef(x_n)] = Ef(x_n + h) = f(x_n + 2h)$$

and in general we define

(7) $$E^r f(x_n) = f(x_n + rh)$$

for any real value of r. Clearly E obeys the laws

$$E(f_n + g_n) = Ef_n + Eg_n$$
$$E(cf_n) = cEf_n$$
$$E^r(E^s f_n) = E^{r+s} f_n$$

Now from the definition of Δf_n we have at once

$$\Delta f_n = f_{n+1} - f_n$$
$$= Ef_n - f_n$$

or symbolically,

$$\Delta f_n = (E - 1)f_n$$

which leads at once to the operational equivalences

$$\Delta = E - 1 \tag{8}$$
$$E = 1 + \Delta \tag{9}$$
$$E - \Delta = 1 \tag{10}$$

Example 3

Express the various differences of a function in terms of successive entries in the table of the function.

To do this, we merely replace the operator Δ in $\Delta^m f(x_n)$ by the expression $(E - 1)$, expand $(E - 1)^m$ by the binomial theorem, and apply the resulting sum, term by term, to $f(x_n)$:

$$
\begin{aligned}
\Delta^m f(x_n) &= (E - 1)^m f(x_n) \\
&= \left[E^m - mE^{m-1} + \frac{m(m - 1)}{2!} E^{m-2} - \cdots + (-1)^{m-1} mE + (-1)^m \right] f(x_n) \\
&= E^m f(x_n) - mE^{m-1}f(x_n) + \frac{m(m - 1)}{2!} E^{m-2}f(x_n) - \cdots + (-1)^m mEf(x_n) \\
&\qquad\qquad\qquad\qquad\qquad\qquad\qquad\qquad\qquad\qquad\qquad + (-1)^m f(x_n) \\
&= f(x_n + mh) - mf(x_n + \overline{m - 1}h) + \frac{m(m - 1)}{2!} f(x_n + \overline{m - 2}h) - \cdots \\
&\qquad\qquad\qquad\qquad\qquad\qquad + (-1)^{m-1} mf(x_n + h) + (-1)^m f(x_n)
\end{aligned}
$$

Specifically, taking $x_n = x_0$, we obtain

$$
\begin{aligned}
\Delta^2 f_0 &= f_2 - 2f_1 + f_0 \\
\Delta^3 f_0 &= f_3 - 3f_2 + 3f_1 - f_0 \\
\Delta^4 f_0 &= f_4 - 4f_3 + 6f_2 - 4f_1 + f_0
\end{aligned}
$$

$$\cdots \cdots \cdots \cdots \cdots \cdots$$

The first of these is of course the expression for $\Delta^2 f_0$ which we found in our preliminary discussion of interpolation.

Proceeding almost exactly as we did in Example 3, we can now give a general solution to the central problem of interpolation, that is, the determination of $f(x_0 + rh)$, r-fractional, from a table containing only the entries

$$f(x_0), \qquad f(x_0 + h), \qquad f(x_0 + 2h), \qquad f(x_0 + 3h), \qquad \cdots$$

For, using (9), we can write

$$
\begin{aligned}
f(x_0 + rh) &= E^r f_0 \\
&= (1 + \Delta)^r f_0 \\
&= \left[1 + r\Delta + \frac{r(r - 1)}{2!} \Delta^2 + \frac{r(r - 1)(r - 2)}{3!} \Delta^3 + \cdots \right] f_0 \\
&= f_0 + r\,\Delta f_0 + \frac{r(r - 1)}{2!} \Delta^2 f_0 + \frac{r(r - 1)(r - 2)}{3!} \Delta^3 f_0 + \cdots \tag{11}
\end{aligned}
$$

This highly important result is known as the **forward Gregory-Newton interpolation formula.** The first two terms constitute the formula for ordinary linear, or proportional part, interpolation. The first three terms are identical with the formula for parabolic interpolation given in Eq. (6). The higher partial sums give, respectively, the interpolation formulas that would have resulted had we approximated $f(x)$ by cubic, quartic, quintic, . . . polynomial curves.

Unless $f(x)$ itself is a polynomial, so that all its differences after some point are identically zero, Eq. (11) is an infinite series. In practical interpolation, this raises the question of the size of the error involved in using only a finite number of the terms of (11). In more advanced investigations, considerable attention is given to the error terms in interpolation formulas like (11). As far as we are concerned, however, we shall assume that the differences of $f(x)$ eventually become negligibly small and that we carry Eq. (11) far enough to include these differences.

Example 4

Compute $f(1.03)$ from the following data:

x	$f(x)$	Δ	Δ^2	Δ^3
1.00	1.000000			
		0.257625		
1.05	1.257625		0.015750	
		0.273375		0.000750
1.10	1.531000		0.016500	
		0.289875		0.000750
1.15	1.820875		0.017250	
		0.307125		0.000750
1.20	2.128000		0.018000	
		0.325125		
1.25	2.453125			

As a first step, we must construct the difference table for $f(x)$, obtaining the three columns of differences appended to the given table. Then identifying h as 0.05, x_0 as 1.00, and r as 0.6, we merely substitute into (11):

$$f(1.03) = f[1.00 + (0.6)(0.05)]$$
$$= 1.000000 + (0.6)(0.257625) + \frac{(0.6)(0.6 - 1)}{2!}(0.015750)$$
$$+ \frac{(0.6)(0.6 - 1)(0.6 - 2)}{3!}(0.000750)$$
$$= 1.152727$$

This same value could have been found in many other ways. For instance,

$$f(1.03) = f[1.05 - (0.4)(0.05)]$$
$$= 1.257625 + (-0.4)(0.273375) + \frac{(-0.4)(-0.4 - 1)}{2!}(0.016500)$$
$$+ \frac{(-0.4)(-0.4 - 1)(-0.4 - 2)}{3!}(0.000750)$$
$$= 1.152727$$

Equally well we could have written

$$f(1.03) = f[1.10 - (1.4 \times 0.05)] = f[1.15 - (2.4 \times 0.05)] = \cdots$$

obtaining $f(1.03) = 1.152727$ in each case. It is interesting to note that interpolation by proportional parts yields

$$f(1.03) = 1.000000 + (0.6 \times 0.257625) = 1.154575$$

which is significantly in error.

One drawback of the forward Gregory-Newton formula is that the differences upon which it is based lie in a line sloping diagonally downward through the table. Thus if the table is of limited extent, as is often the case with experimental data, this formula cannot be used near the lower end. In such cases, we can employ a companion formula known as the **backward Gregory-Newton formula,** derived as follows.

$$f(x_0 + rh) = E^r f_0 = \left(\frac{E}{E - \Delta}\right)^r f_0 = \left(\frac{E - \Delta}{E}\right)^{-r} f_0 = (1 - \Delta E^{-1})^{-r} f_0$$

$$= \left[1 + r(\Delta E^{-1}) + \frac{r(r + 1)}{2!} (\Delta E^{-1})^2 \right.$$

$$\left. + \frac{r(r + 1)(r + 2)}{3!} (\Delta E^{-1})^3 + \cdots \right] f_0$$

$$= f_0 + r\,\Delta E^{-1} f_0 + \frac{r(r + 1)}{2!} \Delta^2 E^{-2} f_0$$

$$+ \frac{r(r + 1)(r + 2)}{3!} \Delta^3 E^{-3} f_0 + \cdots$$

(12) $$= f_0 + r\,\Delta f_{-1} + \frac{r(r + 1)}{2!} \Delta^2 f_{-2} + \frac{r(r + 1)(r + 2)}{3!} \Delta^3 f_{-3} + \cdots$$

By various other manipulations of the operators E and Δ it is possible to obtain literally an infinite number of interpolation formulas of this general type, some of considerable practical importance. However for our purposes the two Gregory-Newton formulas will be sufficient.

Example 5

Find $f(1.8)$ from the following table:

x	$f(x)$	Δ	Δ^2	Δ^3
0.0	1.0			
		0.0		
0.5	1.0		6.0	
		6.0		6.0
1.0	7.0		12.0	
		18.0		6.0
1.5	25.0		18.0	
		36.0		
2.0	61.0			

In this case we have $h = 0.5$; hence taking x_0 to be 1.5 and r to be 0.6, we find, from the backward Gregory-Newton formula (12),

$$f(1.8) = f[1.5 + (0.6)(0.5)]$$
$$= 25 + (0.6)(18) + \frac{(0.6)(0.6 + 1)}{2!}(12) + \frac{(0.6)(0.6 + 1)(0.6 + 2)}{3!}(6)$$
$$= 44.056$$

Occasionally in analyzing emperical data it is necessary to find the equation of a polynomial curve

$$(13) \qquad y = a_0 x^m + a_1 x^{m-1} + \cdots + a_{m-1} x + a_m$$

which passes through certain prescribed points, spaced at regular intervals of x. This may be done by the methods of analytic geometry, simply by substituting the coordinates of the given points (x_0, y_0), (x_1, y_1), (x_2, y_2), $\ldots$ (x_m, y_m) into (13) and solving the resulting system of $m + 1$ linear equations for the $m + 1$ unknown coefficients, a_0, a_1, a_2, $\ldots$, a_m. However, if m is more than 2, this becomes a very laborious process, and it is much simpler to find the required equation by constructing the appropriate interpolation formula from the difference table of the function.

In fact, the Gregory-Newton formula (11)

$$y(x_0 + rh) = y_0 + r\,\Delta y_0 + \frac{r(r-1)}{2!}\,\Delta^2 y_0 + \cdots$$

extended to the column of constant differences, is a polynomial which for $r = 0, 1, 2, \ldots$ is satisfied by successive pairs of tabular values. To obtain the required polynomial in x, it is only necessary to choose r so that

$$x_0 + rh \equiv x$$

that is,

$$r = \frac{x - x_0}{h}$$

Of course, if the available portion of the table includes the entry $x_0 = 0$, the interpolation formula should be based on that point, for then the polynomial in x can be obtained from the Gregory-Newton formula simply by making the proportional change of scale

$$r = \frac{x}{h}$$

Example 6

Fit a polynomial equation of minimum order to the following data:

x	y	Δ	Δ^2	Δ^3	Δ^4
−0.2	2.60				
		0.40			
0.0	3.00		0.00		
		0.40		0.48	
0.2	3.40		0.48		0.96
		0.88		1.44	
0.4	4.28		1.92		0.96
		2.80		2.40	
0.6	7.08		4.32		0.96
		7.12		3.36	
0.8	14.20		7.68		
		14.80			
1.0	29.00				

According to the forward Gregory-Newton formula based on $x_0 = 0$, we have

$$f(x_0 + rh) = f(rh) = 3.00 + r(0.40) + \frac{r(r-1)}{2!}(0.48) + \frac{r(r-1)(r-2)}{3!}(1.44)$$
$$+ \frac{r(r-1)(r-2)(r-3)}{4!}(0.96)$$

Writing $r = \frac{x}{h} = \frac{x}{0.2} = 5x$, this becomes

$$f(x) = 3.00 + 5x(0.40) + \frac{5x(5x-1)}{2!}(0.48) + \frac{5x(5x-1)(5x-2)}{3!}(1.44)$$
$$+ \frac{5x(5x-1)(5x-2)(5x-3)}{4!}(0.96)$$

Expanding and collecting terms, we find without difficulty

$$y = f(x) = 25x^4 - x^2 + 2x + 3$$

Clearly $f(x)$ cannot be represented by a polynomial of order less than 4, since its fourth differences are the first which are constant.

If the data with which we must deal are not given at equally spaced values of x, the methods which we have so far developed cannot be applied. In such cases, instead of using the operators E and Δ, we employ **divided differences,** defined as follows. If $f(x_0)$ and $f(x_1)$ are any pair of adjacent values in a table of the function $f(x)$, then the corresponding first divided difference is

(14)　　　　　　　　$$f(x_0, x_1) = \frac{f(x_0) - f(x_1)}{x_0 - x_1}$$

If $f(x_0,x_1)$ and $f(x_1,x_2)$ are two successive first divided differences, then the corresponding second divided difference is

(15) $$f(x_0,x_1,x_2) = \frac{f(x_0,x_1) - f(x_1,x_2)}{x_0 - x_2} = \frac{\frac{f(x_0)-f(x_1)}{x_0-x_1} - \left[\frac{f(x_1)-f(x_2)}{x_1-x_2}\right]}{x_0-x_2}$$

The extension to divided differences of higher order is obvious, and we have for the mth divided differences of a function, expressions of the form

(16) $$f(x_0,x_1, \ldots, x_m) = \frac{f(x_0,x_1, \ldots, x_{m-1}) - f(x_1,x_2, \ldots, x_m)}{x_0 - x_m}$$

In every case the denominator consists of the difference between the unrepeated arguments, *i.e.*, the first and last values of x which appear in the two divided differences in the numerator. Divided differences are usually displayed in difference tables just as ordinary differences.

Example 7

Construct the divided difference table for the following data:

x	$f(x)$			
0	0			
		1		
1	1		4	
		13		1
3	27		8	
		37		1
4	64		14	
		93		
7	343			

By direct substitution into Eqs. (14), (15), and (16), we obtain the differences shown in the columns appended to the given table. For instance, the last entries in each column are, respectively,

$$93 = f(4,7) = \frac{64 - 343}{4 - 7}$$

$$14 = f(3,4,7) = \frac{37 - 93}{3 - 7}$$

$$1 = f(1,3,4,7) = \frac{8 - 14}{1 - 7}$$

By reasoning exactly as we did in establishing the corresponding results for ordinary differences, we can show the following:

Any divided difference of the sum of two functions is equal to the sum of the corresponding divided differences.

Any divided difference of a constant times a function is equal to the constant times the corresponding divided difference.

The mth divided differences of a polynomial of order m are constant. The last property is illustrated in Example 7, for the function which is tabulated is obviously $y = x^3$, and its third divided differences have the constant value 1.

Interpolation by means of divided differences in tables of unequally spaced data is accomplished by means of **Newton's divided difference formula**

$$(17) \qquad \begin{aligned} f(x) = f(x_0) &+ (x - x_0)f(x_0,x_1) \\ &+ (x - x_0)(x - x_1)f(x_0,x_1,x_2) \\ &+ (x - x_0)(x - x_1)(x - x_2)f(x_0,x_1,x_2,x_3) \\ &+ \cdots \end{aligned}$$

the formula extending until the divided differences become rigorously zero, or at least negligibly small.

The derivation of this formula will be sufficiently clear if we fix our attention upon a function whose third differences, say, are constant. In this case, if x is a general value of the argument, we have

$$(18) \qquad\qquad f(x,x_0,x_1,x_2) = f(x_0,x_1,x_2,x_3)$$

since, by hypothesis, all third differences are the same. However, by definition,

$$f(x,x_0,x_1,x_2) = \frac{f(x,x_0,x_1) - f(x_0,x_1,x_2)}{x - x_2}$$

Hence, substituting this into (18) and solving for the second divided difference, $f(x,x_0,x_1)$, we find

$$(19) \qquad f(x,x_0,x_1) = f(x_0,x_1,x_2) + (x - x_2)f(x_0,x_1,x_2,x_3)$$

But, again by definition,

$$f(x,x_0,x_1) = \frac{f(x,x_0) - f(x_0,x_1)}{x - x_1}$$

Hence, substituting into (19) and solving for $f(x,x_0)$, we find

$$(20) \quad \begin{aligned} f(x,x_0) &= f(x_0,x_1) + (x - x_1)[f(x_0,x_1,x_2) + (x - x_2)f(x_0,x_1,x_2,x_3)] \\ &= f(x_0,x_1) + (x - x_1)f(x_0,x_1,x_2) \\ &\qquad\qquad\qquad + (x - x_1)(x - x_2)f(x_0,x_1,x_2,x_3) \end{aligned}$$

Finally

$$f(x,x_0) = \frac{f(x) - f(x_0)}{x - x_0}$$

and thus, substituting into (20) and solving for $f(x)$, we obtain

$$\begin{aligned} f(x) = f(x_0) &+ (x - x_0)[f(x_0,x_1) \\ &+ (x - x_1)f(x_0,x_1,x_2) + (x - x_1)(x - x_2)f(x_0,x_1,x_2,x_3)] \\ = f(x_0) &+ (x - x_0)f(x_0,x_1) + (x - x_0)(x - x_1)f(x_0,x_1,x_2) \\ &+ (x - x_0)(x - x_1)(x - x_2)f(x_0,x_1,x_2,x_3) \end{aligned}$$

which is the formula in question.

Example 8

Find $f(2)$ from the following data:

x	$f(x)$			
-1.0	3.000			
		−5.000		
0.0	−2.000		5.500	
		3.250		−1.000
0.5	−0.375		3.500	
		6.750		−1.000
1.0	3.000		1.000	
		8.750		−1.000
2.5	16.125		−1.500	
		5.750		
3.0	19.000			

The construction of the difference table presents no problem, and using Newton's formula, with $x_0 = 0$, we can write at once

$$f(2) = -2.000 + (2 - 0)(3.250) + (2 - 0)(2 - 0.5)(3.500)$$
$$+ (2 - 0)(2 - 0.5)(2 - 1)(-1.000)$$
$$= 12.000$$

Example 9

Find the equation of the polynomial of minimum order which fits the data of Example 8.

The answer to a problem such as this is given directly by Newton's formula:

$$f(x) = -2.000 + (x - 0)(3.250) + (x - 0)(x - 0.5)(3.500)$$
$$+ (x - 0)(x - 0.5)(x - 1)(-1.000)$$
$$= -x^3 + 5x^2 + x - 2$$

A formula of considerable theoretical utility, though of limited computational value, is **Lagrange's interpolation formula***

$$(21) \quad f(x) = \frac{(x - x_1)(x - x_2) \cdots (x - x_{n-1})(x - x_n)}{(x_0 - x_1)(x_0 - x_2) \cdots (x_0 - x_{n-1})(x_0 - x_n)} f(x_0)$$
$$+ \frac{(x - x_0)(x - x_2) \cdots (x - x_{n-1})(x - x_n)}{(x_1 - x_0)(x_1 - x_2) \cdots (x_1 - x_{n-1})(x_1 - x_n)} f(x_1)$$
$$+ \cdots \cdots \cdots \cdots \cdots \cdots \cdots \cdots \cdots \cdots$$
$$+ \frac{(x - x_0)(x - x_1) \cdots (x - x_{n-2})(x - x_{n-1})}{(x_n - x_0)(x_n - x_1) \cdots (x_n - x_{n-2})(x_n - x_{n-1})} f(x_n)$$

which provides the equation of the polynomial of order n which takes on the $(n + 1)$ prescribed functional values $f(x_0)$, $f(x_1)$, . . . , $f(x_n)$, when x takes on the values x_0, x_1, . . . , x_n.

* Joseph Louis Lagrange (1736–1813) was one of the greatest of French mathematicians.

This formula can be derived without great difficulty from Newton's divided difference formula, although it is simpler merely to verify its properties. Clearly it is a polynomial of order n in x, since each term on the right is such a polynomial. Moreover, when $x = x_0$, every fraction except the first vanishes because of the factor $(x - x_0)$ which is in the numerator of every fraction after the first. At the same time, the first fraction reduces to 1, leaving just

$$f(x) = f(x_0)$$

as required when $x = x_0$. In the same way when $x = x_1$, every fraction except the second reduces to zero, and we find

$$f(x) = f(x_1)$$

Similarly we can verify without difficulty that $f(x)$ reduces to

$$f(x_2), f(x_3), \ldots, f(x_n) \qquad \text{when } x = x_2, x = x_3, \ldots, x = x_n$$

Example 10

Using Lagrange's interpolation formula, fit a polynomial to the data

x	-1	0	2	3
$f(x)$	-8	3	1	12

Substituting directly into (21), we have

$$f(x) = \frac{(x - 0)(x - 2)(x - 3)}{(-1 - 0)(-1 - 2)(-1 - 3)} (-8) + \frac{(x + 1)(x - 2)(x - 3)}{(0 + 1)(0 - 2)(0 - 3)} (3)$$
$$\frac{(x + 1)(x - 0)(x - 3)}{(2 + 1)(2 - 0)(2 - 3)} (1) + \frac{(x + 1)(x - 0)(x - 2)}{(3 + 1)(3 - 0)(3 - 2)} (12)$$
$$= 2x^3 - 6x^2 + 3x + 3$$

Any of our interpolation formulas can be used to find the derivative of a tabular function. For instance, if we consider the forward Gregory-Newton formula

$$f(x_0 + rh) = f_0 + r\,\Delta f_0 + \frac{r(r - 1)}{2!} \Delta^2 f_0 + \frac{r(r - 1)(r - 2)}{3!} \Delta^3 f_0$$
$$+ \frac{r(r - 1)(r - 2)(r - 3)}{4!} \Delta^4 f_0 + \cdots$$
$$= f_0 + r\,\Delta f_0 + \frac{r^2 - r}{2} \Delta^2 f_0 + \frac{r^3 - 3r^2 + 2r}{6} \Delta^3 f_0$$
$$+ \frac{r^4 - 6r^3 + 11r^2 - 6r}{24} \Delta^4 f_0 + \cdots$$

and differentiate with respect to r, we find

$$hf'(x_0 + rh) = \Delta f_0 + \frac{2r - 1}{2} \Delta^2 f_0 + \frac{3r^2 - 6r + 2}{6} \Delta^3 f_0$$
$$+ \frac{4r^3 - 18r^2 + 22r - 6}{24} \Delta^4 f_0 + \cdots$$

$$h^2 f''(x_0 + rh) = \Delta^2 f_0 + \frac{6r - 6}{6} \Delta^3 f_0 + \frac{12r^2 - 36r + 22}{24} \Delta^4 f_0 + \cdots$$

$$h^3 f'''(x_0 + rh) = \Delta^3 f_0 + \frac{24r - 36}{24} \Delta^4 f_0 + \cdots$$

$$h^4 f^{IV}(x_0 + rh) = \Delta^4 f_0 + \cdots$$

Specifically, if we put $r = 0$, we find for the derivatives at the tabular point x_0,

$$(22) \qquad f'(x_0) = \frac{1}{h} [\Delta f_0 - \tfrac{1}{2}\Delta^2 f_0 + \tfrac{1}{3}\Delta^3 f_0 - \tfrac{1}{4}\Delta^4 f_0 + \cdots]$$

$$(23) \qquad f''(x_0) = \frac{1}{h^2} [\Delta^2 f_0 - \Delta^3 f_0 + \tfrac{11}{12}\Delta^4 f_0 + \cdots]$$

$$(24) \qquad f'''(x_0) = \frac{1}{h^3} [\Delta^3 f_0 - \tfrac{3}{2}\Delta^4 f_0 + \cdots]$$

$$(25) \qquad f^{IV}(x_0) = \frac{1}{h^4} [\Delta^4 f_0 + \cdots]$$

The backward Gregory-Newton formula and Newton's divided difference formula can also be differentiated to furnish alternative expressions for the derivative of a tabular function. In all cases, however, unless it is clearly evident from the table of $f(x)$ that differences of some order are constant, numerical differentiation should be used only with the realization that considerable errors may be involved, the errors increasing significantly as derivatives of higher order are computed.

Example 11

Find the first and second derivatives of $\sqrt{x}$ at $x = 2.5$ from the table

x	$\sqrt{x}$	Δ	Δ^2
2.50	1.58114		
		0.01573	
2.55	1.59687		−0.00015
		0.01558	
2.60	1.61245		−0.00015
		0.01543	
2.65	1.62788		−0.00014
		0.01529	
2.70	1.64317		−0.00015
		0.01514	
2.75	1.65831		

Using Eqs. (22) and (23), with $x_0 = 2.50$ and $h = 0.05$, we find at once

$$f'(2.5) = \frac{1}{0.05} \left[0.01573 - \frac{1}{2}(-0.00015) \right] = 0.3160$$

$$f''(2.5) = \frac{1}{(0.05)^2} [-0.00015] = -0.0600$$

The correct values to four decimal places are, of course,

$$f'(2.5) = \frac{1}{2\sqrt{x}} \bigg|_{x=2.5} = 0.3162$$

and

$$f''(2.5) = \frac{-1}{4x^{\frac{3}{2}}} \bigg|_{x=2.5} = -0.0632$$

There are many formulas for numerical integration, but for most engineering applications the trapezoidal rule is quite adequate. To recall its derivation, let the required integral be

$$\int_a^b f(x)\,dx$$

and let the range of integration be divided into n equal parts, the ordinates at the points of subdivision being

$$f_0 = f(a), f_1, f_2, \ldots, f_{n-1}, f_n = f(b)$$

Now a definite integral can always be interpreted as an area, and thus any method of approximating an area is essentially a method of approximating a definite integral. If we replace the arc of $y = f(x)$ over each

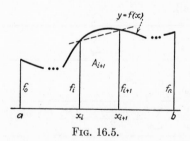

Fig. 16.5.

subinterval, $x_{i+1} - x_i$, by its chord and take the sum of the areas of the resulting trapezoids as an approximation to the true area under $y = f(x)$, we are led to the trapezoidal rule(Fig. 16.5).

In this case, making use of the fact that the area of a trapezoid is equal to the average of the parallel sides times the perpendicular distance between them, we have

$$A_1 = \left(\frac{f_0 + f_1}{2}\right) h$$

$$A_2 = \left(\frac{f_1 + f_2}{2}\right) h$$

. . . .

$$A_{n-1} = \left(\frac{f_{n-2} + f_{n-1}}{2}\right) h$$

$$A_n = \left(\frac{f_{n-1} + f_n}{2}\right) h$$

or adding

(26) $$A = h(\tfrac{1}{2}f_0 + f_1 + f_2 + \cdots + f_{n-1} + \tfrac{1}{2}f_n)$$

which is the **trapezoidal rule.**

In many important engineering applications, it is necessary to compute a **running integral** of a tabular function, *i.e.*, an integral of the form

$$\int_{x_0}^{x} f(x)\,dx$$

where x takes on successively each of the values at which $f(x)$ is tabulated. For such a calculation, the trapezoidal rule is especially well adapted, for if to the given table we adjoin a column of the averages

$$\frac{f_0 + f_1}{2}, \qquad \frac{f_1 + f_2}{2}, \qquad \cdots$$

the required integrals are precisely the sums of the entries in this column from the top down to each entry in turn, multiplied by $h \equiv \Delta x$. Moreover, each sum can be found from the preceding one by adding to it the corresponding average. The accompanying table shows the computational pattern in detail.

x	$f(x)$	Average	$\sum$		$h\sum = \int_{x_0}^{x} f(x)\,dx$
$x_0 = a$	f_0	$\cdots$	$\sum_0 = 0$		$h\sum_0 = \int_{x_0}^{x_0} f(x)\,dx$
x_1	f_1	$\dfrac{f_0 + f_1}{2}$	$\sum_1 = \sum_0 + \dfrac{f_0 + f_1}{2} = \dfrac{f_0}{2} + \dfrac{f_1}{2}$		$h\sum_1 = \int_{x_0}^{x_1} f(x)\,dx$
x_2	f_2	$\dfrac{f_1 + f_2}{2}$	$\sum_2 = \sum_1 + \dfrac{f_1 + f_2}{2} = \dfrac{f_0}{2} + f_1 + \dfrac{f_2}{2}$		$h\sum_2 = \int_{x_0}^{x_2} f(x)\,dx$
x_3	f_3	$\dfrac{f_2 + f_3}{2}$	$\sum_3 = \sum_2 + \dfrac{f_2 + f_3}{2} = \dfrac{f_0}{2} + f_1 + f_2 + \dfrac{f_3}{2}$		$h\sum_3 = \int_{x_0}^{x_3} f(x)\,dx$
$\cdots$	$\cdots$	$\cdots$	$\cdots$		$\cdots$

Example 12

Compute $\int_0^x e^x \, dx$ for $x = 0.2, 0.4, 0.6, \ldots , 1.8, 2.0$ from the following table:

x	e^x	Average	$\sum$	$h \sum = \int_0^x e^x \, dx$	True value $= e^x - 1$
0.0	1.000	.....	0.000	0.000	0.000
0.2	1.221	1.110	1.110	0.222	0.221
0.4	1.492	1.356	2.466	0.493	0.492
0.6	1.822	1.657	4.123	0.825	0.822
0.8	2.226	2.024	6.147	1.229	1.226
1.0	2.718	2.472	8.619	1.724	1.718
1.2	3.320	3.019	11.638	2.328	2.320
1.4	4.055	3.687	15.325	3.065	3.055
1.6	4.953	4.504	19.829	3.966	3.953
1.8	6.050	5.501	25.330	5.066	5.050
2.0	7.389	6.719	32.049	6.410	6.389

Following the computational scheme described above, with $h = 0.2$, we obtain the required integrals without difficulty. For purposes of comparison, the theoretical values of the integral, correct to three decimal places, are also shown. Had the interval between consecutive entries been smaller, say $h = 0.1$, the accuracy would have been significantly higher, although for $h = 0.2$ the last, and therefore the least accurate integral, is in error by only

$$\frac{6.410 - 6.389}{6.389} \times 100 = 0.3 \text{ per cent} \dagger$$

One of the most important applications of finite differences is to the numerical solution of differential equations which, because of their complexity, cannot be solved by exact methods. Of the many procedures which have been devised for doing this, we shall present only the so-called Adams method. This can be applied to simultaneous differential equations as well as to single equations of any order, and although particular

† By more advanced methods it can be shown that the dominant part of the error made by using the trapezoidal rule to approximate an integral is

$$\frac{f_n' - f_0'}{12} h^2$$

If this quantity be subtracted from the last integral, we obtain the improved value

$$6.410 - \frac{(7.389 - 1.000)(0.2)^2}{12} = 6.389$$

which, to the accuracy of the data themselves, agrees exactly with the theoretical value.

types of equations can often be solved more easily by other processes, this one is probably as useful as any single method.

The fundamental problem is to find the solution of the first-order differential equation

$$(27) \qquad \frac{dy}{dx} = f(x,y)$$

which satisfies the initial condition $y = y_0$ when $x = x_0$. We do not, of course, expect to be able to find an equation for the solution. Instead our object is merely to plot or tabulate the solution curve point by point, beginning at (x_0,y_0) and continuing at equally spaced values of x thereafter, until the solution has been extended over the required range.

To do this, we first note the obvious fact that

$$y_{n+1} - y_n = \int_{x_n}^{x_{n+1}} \left(\frac{dy}{dx}\right) dx$$

$$= \frac{1}{h} \int_{x_n}^{x_{n+1}} \left(h \frac{dy}{dx}\right) dx$$

or

$$(28) \qquad y_{n+1} = y_n + \frac{1}{h} \int_{x_n}^{x_{n+1}} p(x) dx$$

where h, as usual, is the constant interval between the successive values of x at which we intend to tabulate the solution y, and

$$p(x) \equiv h \frac{dy}{dx}$$

Now if we make a change of variable from x to r by writing

$$x = x_n + rh \qquad \text{and} \qquad dx = h\,dr$$

noting that $r = 0$ when $x = x_n$ and $r = 1$ when $x = x_{n+1}$, then Eq. (28) becomes

$$y_{n+1} = y_n + \int_0^1 p(x_n + rh)\,dr$$

To evaluate this integral, it is convenient to expand the integrand by means of the backward Gregory-Newton formula (12). Doing this, we have

$$y_{n+1} = y_n + \int_0^1 \left[p_n + r\,\Delta p_{n-1} + \frac{r^2+r}{2}\,\Delta^2 p_{n-2} + \frac{r^3 + 3r^2 + 2r}{6}\,\Delta^3 p_{n-3} \right.$$

$$\left. + \frac{r^4 + 6r^3 + 11r^2 + 6r}{24}\,\Delta^4 p_{n-4} + \cdots \right] dr$$

$$(29) \quad = y_n + p_n + \frac{1}{2}\,\Delta p_{n-1} + \frac{5}{12}\,\Delta^2 p_{n-2} + \frac{3}{8}\,\Delta^3 p_{n-3} + \frac{251}{720}\,\Delta^4 p_{n-4} \cdots$$

If we know y_n and the various p's and their differences down to and including p_n, Eq. (29) thus enables us to "reach out" one step further and compute y_{n+1}. With y_{n+1} known, we can then return to the given differential equation (27), and compute y'_{n+1}. From this, $p_{n+1} \equiv hy'_{n+1}$ can be found immediately, and another line can be added to the difference table of the p's. Then using (29) again, we can find y_{n+2}, and so on, step by step, until the solution has been extended over the desired range. All that remains is to devise a means of finding enough y's and p's, that is, y''s, to get the process under way.

It is usually convenient to begin the tabulation of y by expanding it in a Taylor's series around the point $x = x_0$:

$$(30) \quad y = y_0 + y'_0(x - x_0) + y''_0 \frac{(x - x_0)^2}{2!} + y'''_0 \frac{(x - x_0)^3}{3!} + \cdots$$

The value of y_0 is, of course, given. The value of y'_0 can be found at once by substituting x_0 and y_0 into the given differential equation (27). To find the second derivative, we need only differentiate the given equation, getting

$$(31) \qquad\qquad y'' = \frac{\partial f}{\partial x} + \frac{\partial f}{\partial y} y'$$

Since $f(x,y)$ is a given function, its partial derivatives are known, and become definite numbers when x_0 and y_0 are substituted into them. Moreover, the value of y' at (x_0,y_0) has already been found, and thus (31) furnishes the value of y''_0. Similarly, differentiating (31) and evaluating it at (x_0,y_0) will give y'''_0, and so on. In this way the first few terms of the expansion of y around the point $x = x_0$ can be constructed. In especially favorable cases (Bessel's equation would be an example) the general term of the series (30) can be found and the region of convergence established. When this happens, (30) is the required solution, and we need look no further. In general, however, successive differentiation of $f(x,y)$ becomes too complicated to continue, or if not, the resulting series converges too slowly to be of any practical value, and we must fall back on the Adams or some similar method.

With (30) available as a representation of y in the neighborhood of $x = x_0$, we can set $x = x_0 + h \equiv x_1$, and compute y_1. Similarly, setting $x = x_0 + 2h$, $x_0 + 3h$, and $x_0 + 4h$, we can find y_2, y_3, and y_4. Then substituting (x_1,y_1), (x_2,y_2), (x_3,y_3), and (x_4,y_4) into the given differential equation, we can compute y'_1, y'_2, y'_3, and y'_4 without difficulty. From these, by multiplying by h, we can find p_1, p_2, p_3, and p_4. Then having constructed the difference table of the p's, it becomes a routine matter to apply (29) and determine y_5, y_6, . . . , as outlined above.

The Adams method can easily be extended to systems of simultaneous first-order differential equations. For instance, if we have to solve

$$\frac{dy}{dx} = f(x,y,z)$$

$$\frac{dz}{dx} = g(x,y,z)$$

subject to the conditions $y = y_0$, $z = z_0$, when $x = x_0$, we first expand both y and z in terms of $(x - x_0)$, using the given differential equations to obtain the necessary first few derivatives:

$$y = y_0 + y_0'(x - x_0) + y_0'' \frac{(x - x_0)^2}{2!} + \cdots$$

$$z = z_0 + z_0'(x - x_0) + z_0'' \frac{(x - x_0)^2}{2!} + \cdots$$

From these we compute y_1, y_2, y_3, y_4, and z_1, z_2, z_3, z_4. Then substituting corresponding values, x_i, y_i, z_i into the given differential equations, we determine

$$y_1', y_2', y_3', y_4' \qquad \text{and} \qquad z_1', z_2', z_3', z_4'$$

From these we can calculate the necessary values of $p \equiv h(dy/dx)$ and of the analogous new quantity $q \equiv h(dz/dx)$. From p and q, exactly as before, we obtain the extrapolation formulas

$$(32) \quad y_{n+1} = y_n + p_n + \tfrac{1}{2}\Delta p_{n-1} + \tfrac{5}{12}\Delta^2 p_{n-2} + \tfrac{3}{8}\Delta^3 p_{n-3} + \tfrac{251}{720}\Delta^4 p_{n-4} \cdots$$

$$(33) \quad z_{n+1} = z_n + q_n + \tfrac{1}{2}\Delta q_{n-1} + \tfrac{5}{12}\Delta^2 q_{n-2} + \tfrac{3}{8}\Delta^3 q_{n-3} + \tfrac{251}{720}\Delta^4 q_{n-4} \cdots$$

These give us first the values of y_5 and z_5. Then from these, the values of p_5 and q_5 can be obtained, and a new line can be added to both the p and q difference tables. Using these new values, y_6 and z_6 can be determined, and so on, as far as necessary.

The application of the Adams method to equations of higher order is now immediate, since such an equation can always be replaced by a system of simultaneous first-order equations. For instance,

$$\frac{d^2y}{dx^2} = g\left(x,y,\frac{dy}{dx}\right)$$

is equivalent to

$$\frac{dy}{dx} = z$$

$$\frac{dz}{dx} = g(x,y,z)$$

which is just a special case, with $f(x,y,z) \equiv z$, of the general problem of two simultaneous first-order equations.

Example 13

A particle of unit mass is suspended from a spring which is slightly nonlinear, the force required to stretch the spring a distance y being $F = 25y + y^3$. If the particle is displaced a unit distance from its equilibrium position and released from rest, tabulate the first quarter cycle of its motion at intervals of time of 0.02. Determine as accurately as possible when the particle passes through its equilibrium position, and compare this with the corresponding time if the spring were strictly linear, *i.e.*, if the expression for the force in the spring did not involve the term y^3.

Neglecting friction, the differential equation which we must solve to find y is evidently

$$y'' = -25y - y^3$$

None of the exact methods which we have developed for solving differential equations is adequate to handle a nonlinear equation of this type.* Hence we must write it as a pair of simultaneous first-order equations

$$\frac{dy}{dt} = z$$

$$\frac{dz}{dt} = -25y - y^3$$

and attempt to integrate it step by step by the Adams method.

To do this, we must first find expressions for the various derivatives of y. As usual, these can easily be obtained by differentiating the given equation:

$$
\begin{aligned}
y'' &= -25y - y^3 \\
y''' &= -25y' - 3y^2y' \\
y^{IV} &= -25y'' - 3y^2y'' - 6y(y')^2 \\
y^{V} &= -25y''' - 3y^2y''' - 18yy'y'' - 6(y')^3 \\
y^{VI} &= -25y^{IV} - 3y^2y^{IV} - 24yy'y''' - 18y(y'')^2 - 36(y')^2y''
\end{aligned}
$$

. . . .

By hypothesis, $y_0 = 1$ and $y_0' = 0$. Hence substituting these values into the above expressions, we find

$$
\begin{aligned}
y_0 &= 1 \\
y_0' &= 0 \\
y_0'' &= -26 \\
y_0''' &= 0 \\
y_0^{IV} &= 728 \\
y_0^{V} &= 0 \\
y_0^{VI} &= -32{,}552
\end{aligned}
$$

. . . .

The Maclaurin expansion of y is therefore

$$y = 1 - 26\frac{t^2}{2!} + 728\frac{t^4}{4!} - 32{,}552\frac{t^6}{6!} + \cdots$$

$$= 1 - 13t^2 + \frac{91}{3}t^4 - \frac{4{,}069}{90}t^6 + \cdots$$

* In more advanced texts it is shown that equations of the form $y'' + Ay + By^3 = 0$ can always be solved exactly in terms of elliptic functions.

Substituting the values $t_1 = 0.02$, $t_2 = 0.04$, $t_3 = 0.06$, $t_4 = 0.08$ into this series, we find

$$y_1 = 0.9948, \qquad y_2 = 0.9793, \qquad y_3 = 0.9536, \qquad y_4 = 0.9180$$

To find the first few values of z, that is, of dy/dt, we must differentiate the series for y, getting

$$\frac{dy}{dt} = z = -26t + \frac{364}{3} t^3 - \frac{4,069}{15} t^5 + \cdots$$

and then evaluate it for $t = 0.02, 0.04, 0.06, 0.08$.   This gives

$$z_1 = -0.5190, \qquad z_2 = -1.0323, \qquad z_3 = -1.5340, \qquad z_4 = -2.0189$$

From these values of z we can find the corresponding values of $p \equiv h \, (dy/dt) \equiv hz$ simply by multiplying by 0.02:

$$p_1 = -0.0104, \qquad p_2 = -0.0206, \qquad p_3 = -0.0307, \qquad p_4 = -0.0404$$

To find the necessary values of $q \equiv h(dz/dt) = hy''$ we must first determine the corresponding values of y''.   These we find not by differentiating the series for y a second time, but rather by substituting into the given differential equation the values of y which we now have available.   This gives

$$y_1'' = -25.8545, \qquad y_2'' = -25.4212, \qquad y_3'' = -24.7072, \qquad y_4'' = -23.7236$$

and, multiplying by $h = 0.02$,

$$q_1 = -0.5171, \qquad q_2 = -0.5084, \qquad q_3 = -0.4941, \qquad q_4 = -0.4745$$

We can now begin the construction of the difference tables for p and q.   From these, using Eqs. (32) and (33),

$$y_{n+1} = y_n + p_n + \tfrac{1}{2}\Delta p_{n-1} + \tfrac{5}{12}\Delta^2 p_{n-2} + \tfrac{3}{8}\Delta^3 p_{n-3} + \tfrac{251}{720}\Delta^4 p_{n-4} + \cdots$$
$$z_{n+1} = z_n + q_n + \tfrac{1}{2}\Delta q_{n-1} + \tfrac{5}{12}\Delta^2 q_{n-2} + \tfrac{3}{8}\Delta^3 q_{n-3} + \tfrac{251}{720}\Delta^4 q_{n-4} + \cdots$$

we can calculate y_5 and z_5.   From z_5 we can immediately compute $p_5 = hz_5$.   To compute q_5, we first substitute y_5 into the original differential equation, getting y_5''. Then multiplication by 0.02 gives us $q_5 = hy_5''$.   With p_5 and q_5 known, a new line can be added to each difference table, permitting y_6 and z_6 to be calculated.   By repeating this process sufficiently, we obtain the data in the table on page 521.

By inspection, we see that the displacement y changes sign between $t_{15} \equiv 0.30$ and $t_{16} \equiv 0.32$.   Hence the particle passes through the equilibrium position in this interval, at an instant which can be determined by interpolation:

t	y
0.30	0.0482
0.32	−0.0628

$$t = 0.30 + \frac{0.0482}{0.0482 + 0.0628} (0.02) = 0.3087$$

If the spring were strictly linear, the differential equation would be

$$y'' + 25y = 0$$

and the required solution would be

$$y = \cos 5t$$

$\Delta^4 q$	$\Delta^3 q$	$\Delta^2 q$	Δq	b	z	t	$\Delta^3 p$	$\Delta^2 p$	Δp	p	y	t
				-0.5200	0.0000	0.00				0.0000	1.0000	0.00
			0.0029	-0.5171	-0.5190	0.02			-0.0104	-0.0104	0.9948	0.02
		0.0058	0.0087	-0.5084	-1.0323	0.04		0.0002	-0.0102	-0.0206	0.9793	0.04
	-0.0002	0.0056	0.0143	-0.4941	-1.5340	0.06	-0.0001	0.0001	-0.0101	-0.0307	0.9536	0.06
-0.0001	-0.0003	0.0053	0.0196	-0.4745	-2.0189	0.08	$+0.0003$	0.0004	-0.0097	-0.0404	0.9180	0.08
$+0.0001$	-0.0002	0.0051	0.0247	-0.4498	-2.4815	0.10	$+0.0001$	0.0005	-0.0092	-0.0496	0.8729	0.10
-0.0002	-0.0004	0.0047	0.0294	-0.4204	-2.9169	0.12	0.0000	0.0005	-0.0087	-0.0583	0.8189	0.12
-0.0002	-0.0006	0.0041	0.0335	-0.3869	-3.3208	0.14	$+0.0001$	0.0006	-0.0081	-0.0664	0.7564	0.14
-0.0003	-0.0003	0.0038	0.0373	-0.3496	-3.6895	0.16	$+0.0001$	0.0007	-0.0074	-0.0738	0.6862	0.16
-0.0002	-0.0005	0.0033	0.0406	-0.3090	-4.0189	0.18	$+0.0001$	0.0008	-0.0066	-0.0804	0.6090	0.18
-0.0002	-0.0007	0.0026	0.0432	-0.2658	-4.3065	0.20	$+0.0001$	0.0009	-0.0057	-0.0861	0.5257	0.20
-0.0004	-0.0003	0.0023	0.0455	-0.2203	-4.5499	0.22	-0.0001	0.0008	-0.0049	-0.0910	0.4372	0.22
-0.0001	-0.0004	0.0019	0.0474	-0.1729	-4.7465	0.24	$+0.0002$	0.0010	-0.0039	-0.0949	0.3441	0.24
-0.0002	-0.0006	0.0013	0.0487	-0.1242	-4.8951	0.26	-0.0001	0.0009	-0.0030	-0.0979	0.2477	0.26
$+0.0004$	-0.0002	0.0011	0.0498	-0.0744	-4.9946	0.28	$+0.0001$	0.0010	-0.0020	-0.0999	0.1487	0.28
					-5.0436	0.30	0.0000	0.0010	-0.0010	-0.1009	0.0482	0.30
											-0.0628	0.32

For motion according to this law,

$$y = 0 \quad \text{when } t = \frac{\pi}{10} = 0.3142$$

The effect of the slight nonlinearity in the spring is thus to decrease the quarter period by about $0.3142 - 0.3087 = 0.0055$, or 1.7 per cent.

EXERCISES

1. Show that the sum of the entries in any column in a difference table is equal to the difference between the first and last entries in the preceding column. (This is often a useful check on the accuracy of a table of differences.)
2. Tabulate the function $5x^2 + 2.6x - 0.73$ at intervals of 0.1 from 0 to 2.
3. Tabulate the function $x^3 - 0.65x^2 + 1.63x - 3.06$ at intervals of 0.01 from 1.0 to 1.1.
4. Compute (a) $f(0.102)$ and (b) $f(0.119)$ from the following data:

x	0.100	0.105	0.110	0.115	0.120
$f(x)$	5.111	5.421	5.751	6.101	6.471

5. Compute (a) $\sqrt{50.2}$ and (b) $\sqrt{55.9}$ from the following data:

x	$\sqrt{x}$
50	7.07107
51	7.14143
52	7.21110
53	7.28011
54	7.34847
55	7.41620
56	7.48331

6. Compute (a) $f(1.3)$ and (b) $f(1.95)$ from the following data:

x	1.1	1.2	1.5	1.7	1.8	2.0
$f(x)$	1.112	1.219	1.636	2.054	2.323	3.011

7. Compute (a) $f(3.7608)$ and (b) $f(6)$ from the following data:

x	$f(x)$
0	0.3989423
2.5069	0.3988169
5.0154	0.3984408
7.5270	0.3978138

Ans. (a) 0.3986604

8. Fit a polynomial of minimum order to the data

x	-2	-1	0	1	2
y	-1	-2	0	1	2

Ans. $y = (5x^4 - 6x^3 - 17x^2 + 42x)/24$

9. Fit a polynomial of minimum order to the data

x	-2	0	2	4
y	-3	1	5	57

Ans. $y = x^3 - 2x + 1$

10. Fit a polynomial of minimum order to the data

x	y
0.0	1.761
0.1	1.801
0.2	1.861
0.3	1.941
0.4	2.041

Ans. $y = x^2 + 0.3x + 1.761$

11. Fit a polynomial of minimum order to the data

x	y
0.2	1.125
0.4	1.187
0.6	1.215
0.8	1.392
1.0	1.721

12. Using Newton's divided difference formula, fit a polynomial of minimum order to the data

x	-1	1	4	5
y	13	15	33	67

Ans. $x^3 - 3x^2 + 17$

13. Using Newton's divided difference formula, fit a polynomial of minimum order to the data

x	1	2	4	6	9	10
y	13	18	40	78	165	202

14. Using Lagrange's interpolation formula, fit a polynomial of minimum order to the data

x	0	1	3	4
y	-4	1	29	52

15. From the following data, compute the value of y' and y'' (a) at 1.0, (b) at 1.4, and (c) at 1.15

x	y
1.0	1.000
1.1	0.911
1.2	0.848
1.3	0.817
1.4	0.824
1.5	0.875

16. From the following data, compute the first three derivatives of $\log_{10} x$ at $x = 32$. Check these against the exact values.

x	$\log_{10} x$
32.0	1.5051500
32.2	1.5078559
32.4	1.5105450
32.6	1.5132176
32.8	1.5158738
33.0	1.5185139

17. Three readings are taken at equally spaced points $x = 0, h, 2h$ near the maximum of a function $y = f(x)$. Show that the abscissa of the maximum is very nearly

$$\left(\frac{1}{2} - \frac{\Delta y_0}{\Delta^2 y_0}\right) h$$

and that the maximum ordinate is very nearly

$$y_1 - \frac{(\Delta y_1 + \Delta y_0)^2}{8 \Delta^2 y_0}$$

18. Establish the operational equivalences

$$(a) \ \ E = e^{hD}, \qquad (b) \ \ D = \frac{1}{h} \log (1 + \Delta)$$

where D is the usual differentiation operator. (Hint: Expand $f(a + h)$ in a Taylor's series around the point a, and then write the expansion in terms of the operator D.)

19. Let the **central difference operator** δ be defined by the relations

$$u_1 - u_0 = \delta u_{\frac{1}{2}}$$
$$u_2 - 2u_1 + u_0 = \delta^2 u_1$$

. . . .

Establish the operational equivalences

$$(a) \quad \delta = 2 \sinh \frac{hD}{2}, \qquad (b) \quad D = \frac{2}{h} \sinh^{-1} \frac{\delta}{2}$$

$$\left[\text{Hint: Consider the Taylor expansions of } f\left(a + \frac{h}{2}\right) \text{ and } f\left(a - \frac{h}{2}\right). \right]$$

20. Compute the integral of the following function from 0 to 1:

x	y	x	y
0.00	0.6765	0.55	1.4776
0.05	0.7312	0.60	1.5753
0.10	0.7890	0.65	1.6777
0.15	0.8503	0.70	1.7851
0.20	0.9151	0.75	1.8975
0.25	0.9834	0.80	2.0151
0.30	1.0556	0.85	2.1381
0.35	1.1316	0.90	2.2667
0.40	1.2117	0.95	2.4010
0.45	1.2960	1.00	2.5412
0.50	1.3846		

(a) Using the trapezoidal rule with $h \equiv \Delta x = 0.1$
(b) Using the trapezoidal rule with $h \equiv \Delta x = 0.05$

21. Compute $\int_0^1 e^{-x^2}\, dx$.

(a) Using the trapezoidal rule with $h \equiv \Delta x = 0.1$
(b) Using the trapezoidal rule with $h \equiv \Delta x = 0.05$

22. Compute $\int_0^{\pi/4} \sqrt{1 - \frac{1}{4}\sin^2 \phi}\, d\phi$

23. Tabulate $\int_0^x f(x)dx$, for x ranging from 0 to 1, where $f(x)$ is the function given in Exercise 20 (a) at intervals of 0.10 and (b) at intervals of 0.05.

24. Tabulate $\int_0^x \sin (x^2)dx$ for x ranging from 0 to 1 (a) at intervals of 0.1 and (b) at intervals of 0.05.

25. In Example 13, Sec. 16.2, let the initial conditions be $y_0 = 0$, $y_0' = 2$. Tabulate the first quarter cycle of the motion at intervals of time of 0.02. Determine when the maximum displacement occurs and compare the result with the linear case.

26. Tabulate the solution of the differential equation $y' + \sin y = x$ from $x = 0$ to $x = 0.1$ at intervals of 0.01 if $y = 1$ when $x = 0$.

27. Tabulate the solution of the differential equation

$$y'' + xy = e^{-x}$$

from $x = 0$ to $x = 0.5$ at intervals of 0.05 if $y_0 = 0$, $y_0' = 1$.

28. Tabulate the solution of the system

$$\frac{dy}{dx} = y^2 + xz \qquad \frac{dz}{dx} = x^2 + yz$$

from $x = 0$ to $x = 1$ at intervals of 0.1 if $y_0 = 0$, $z_0 = 0$.

29. Find the equation of the polynomial of minimum order for which y and y' take on prescribed values, (y_0, y_0') and (y_1, y_1') at $x = 0$ and $x = h$. What is the value of $y_2 \equiv y(2h)$ given by this polynomial? Indicate how this result might be used to carry out the step-by-step integration of a differential equation of the form $y' = f(x,y)$.   *Ans.* $y_2 = 5y_0 - 4y_1 + 2hy_0' + 4hy_1'$.

30. Use the formula of the last exercise to tabulate the solution of

$$y' = x - y$$

from $x = 0$ to $x = 1$ at intervals of 0.1 if $y_0 = 1$. Check against the exact solution.

31. Find the equation of the polynomial of minimum order for which y and y'' take on prescribed values (y_0, y_0'') and (y_1, y_1'') at $x = 0$ and $x = h$. What is the value of $y_2 \equiv y(2h)$ given by this polynomial? Indicate how this result might be used to carry out the step-by-step integration of a differential equation of the form $y'' = f(x,y)$.

32. Use the extrapolation formula*

$$y_{n+1} = 2y_n - y_{n-1} + h^2(y_n'' + \tfrac{1}{12}\Delta^2 y_{n-2}'')$$

to tabulate the solution of

$$y'' + 2y + 3y^3 = \cos x$$

at intervals of $\pi/36$ from $x = 0$ to the first zero of the solution, if $y_0 = 1$, $y_0' = 0$.

33. Find the value of a function at $x_0 + h$, given $f(x_0)$, $f'(x_0)$, $f(x_0 + 2h)$, and $f(x_0 + 3h)$.   *Ans.* $f_1 \equiv f(x_0 + h) = \dfrac{11f_0 + 9f_2 - 2f_3 + 6hf_0'}{18}$

34. Let $[x]^n$ denote the **factorial polynomial**

$$x(x - 1) \cdots (x - n + 1)$$

Show that

$$\Delta[x]^n = n[x]^{n-1}$$
$$\Delta^2[x]^n = n(n - 1)[x]^{n-2}$$

. . . .

35. Show that any polynomial of order n can be written as a sum of factorial polynomials

$$P_n(x) = a_0[x]^n + a_1[x]^{n-1} + a_2[x]^{n-2} + \cdots + a_{n-1}[x] + a_n$$

and show how to determine the coefficients, a_i.

36. (a) Express $P(x) \equiv x^3 - 2x^2 - 3$ in terms of factorial polynomials.

(b) Use this result to find a function whose first differences are given by $P(x)$.

Ans.   (b) $\dfrac{[x]^4}{4} + \dfrac{[x]^3}{3} - \dfrac{[x]^2}{2} - 3[x] + c$

37. Express x^5 in terms of factorial polynomials, and compute its successive differences.

* H. Levy and E. A. Baggott, "Numerical Studies in Differential Equations," vol. 1, p. 155, Watts & Co., London, 1934.

38. Let $[x]^{-n} \equiv \dfrac{1}{(x+1)(x+2) \cdots (x+n)}$

Show that

$$\Delta[x]^{-n} = -n[x]^{-n-1}$$
$$\Delta^2[x]^{-n} = (-n)(-n-1)[x]^{-n-2}$$
$$\cdots \cdots \cdots \cdots \cdots \cdots \cdots \cdots \cdots \cdots$$

39. Set up the Newton divided difference formula for the equidistant points

$$a_0 = a, \qquad a_1 = a + h, \qquad a_2 = a + 2h \cdots$$

and show that it is identical with the forward Gregory-Newton formula. Can the backward Gregory-Newton formula be derived in a similar fashion?

40. Show that

$$f(a_0, a_1) = \frac{f(a_0)}{a_0 - a_1} + \frac{f(a_1)}{a_1 - a_0}$$

$$f(a_0, a_1, a_2) = \frac{f(a_0)}{(a_0 - a_1)(a_0 - a_2)} + \frac{f(a_1)}{(a_1 - a_0)(a_1 - a_2)} + \frac{f(a_2)}{(a_2 - a_0)(a_2 - a_1)}$$

(The obvious generalization to higher differences can readily be proved by induction.)

16.3 The Method of Least Squares. The problem of curve fitting permits of two somewhat different interpretations. In the first place, we may ask for the equation of a curve of prescribed type which passes

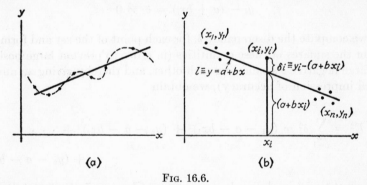

FIG. 16.6.

rigorously through each point of a given set. This was illustrated in Example 6, Sec. 16.2, where, through the use of finite differences, we found the equation of a polynomial curve of minimum order which passed through each of seven given points. On the other hand, we may weaken these requirements and ask for some simpler curve whose equation contains too few parameters to permit it to be passed exactly through each given point, but which comes "as close as possible" to each point. For instance, given a set of points as in Fig. 16.6a, a straight line coming as close as possible to each point may very well be more useful than some complicated curve passing exactly through each point. This will certainly be the case with experimental data which theoretically should fall along a straight line, but which fail to do so because of errors of observation. The necessary measure of "as close as possible" is almost universally taken to be the least-square criterion, and the process of applying this criterion is known as the **method of least squares,** which we now proceed to develop.

Let us begin by supposing that we wish to fit a straight line l whose equation is

$$(1) \qquad\qquad y = a + bx$$

to the n points

$$(x_1, y_1), (x_2, y_2), \ldots, (x_n, y_n)$$

Since two points completely determine a straight line, it will in general be impossible for the required line to pass through more than two of the given points and it may not pass through any. Hence the coordinates of the general point, (x_i, y_i), will not satisfy Eq. (1). That is, when we substitute x_i into Eq. (1) we get not y_i but rather the ordinate of l which, as we see in Fig. 16.6b, differs from y_i by δ_i. In other words

$$(2) \qquad\qquad y_i - (a + bx_i) = \delta_i \neq 0$$

If we compute the discrepancy δ_i for each point of the set and form the sum of the squares of these quantities (in order to prevent large positive and large negative δ's canceling each other, and thereby giving an unwarranted impression of accuracy), we obtain

$$(3) \quad E^2 = \sum_{i=1}^{n} \delta_i^2 = (y_1 - a - bx_1)^2 + (y_2 - a - bx_2)^2 + \cdots$$
$$+ (y_n - a - bx_n)^2$$

The quantity E^2 is obviously a measure of how well the line l fits the set of points as a whole; for E^2 will be zero if and only if each of the given points lies on l, and the larger E^2 is, the farther the points are, on the average, from l. The least-square criterion is now simply this, that *the parameters a and b should be chosen so as to make the sum of the squares of the deviations, E^2, as small as possible.*

To do this, we apply the usual conditions for minimizing a function of several variables, and equate to zero the two first partial derivatives

$$\frac{\partial E^2}{\partial a}, \qquad \frac{\partial E^2}{\partial b}$$

This gives us the two equations

$$\frac{\partial E^2}{\partial a} = 2(y_1 - a - bx_1)(-1) + 2(y_2 - a - bx_2)(-1) + \cdots$$
$$+ 2(y_n - a - bx_n)(-1) = 0$$

$$\frac{\partial E^2}{\partial b} = 2(y_1 - a - bx_1)(-x_1) + 2(y_2 - a - bx_2)(-x_2) + \cdots$$
$$+ 2(y_n - a - bx_n)(-x_n) = 0$$

or, collecting terms on the unknown coefficients a and b,

$$(4) \qquad na + b \sum_{i=1}^{n} x_i = \sum_{i=1}^{n} y_i$$

and

$$(5) \qquad a \sum_{i=1}^{n} x_i + b \sum_{i=1}^{n} x_i^2 = \sum_{i=1}^{n} x_i y_i$$

Equations (4) and (5) are two simultaneous linear equations whose solution for a and b presents no difficulty.

Example 1

By the method of least squares fit a straight line, $y = a + bx$, to the data

x	1.00	1.90	2.60	3.20	4.00
y	0.90	3.00	4.00	5.50	6.90

The coefficients $\sum_{i=1}^{n} x_i$, $\sum_{i=1}^{n} y_i$, $\sum_{i=1}^{n} x_i^2$, $\sum_{i=1}^{n} x_i y_i$, which appear in the equations determining a and b can be found most conveniently by the following tabular process

x	y	x^2	xy
1.00	0.90	1.00	0.90
1.90	3.00	3.61	5.70
2.60	4.00	6.76	10.40
3.20	5.50	10.24	17.60
4.00	6.90	16.00	27.60
$\Sigma x = 12.70$	$\Sigma y = 20.30$	$\Sigma x^2 = 37.61$	$\Sigma xy = 62.20$

Substituting these values into Eqs. (4) and (5), we get

$$5a + 12.7b = 20.30$$
$$12.7a + 37.61b = 62.20$$

Solving these simultaneously for a and b, we find

$$a = -0.989, \qquad b = 1.988$$

The required straight line is therefore

$$y = -0.989 + 1.988x$$

Viewed in more general terms, the method of least squares is simply a process for finding the best possible values for a set of m unknowns $x_1, x_2, \ldots, x_m$, connected by n linear equations

$$
\begin{aligned}
a_{11}x_1 + a_{12}x_2 + \cdots + a_{1m}x_m &= b_1 \\
a_{21}x_1 + a_{22}x_2 + \cdots + a_{2m}x_m &= b_2 \\
&\cdots\cdots\cdots\cdots\cdots\cdots \\
a_{n1}x_1 + a_{n2}x_2 + \cdots + a_{nm}x_m &= b_n
\end{aligned}
$$

where $n > m$. Since the number of equations exceeds the number of unknowns, the system does not admit of an exact solution, i.e., there is no set of values $x_1, x_2, \ldots, x_m$, for which each equation is exactly satisfied. Hence we consider the discrepancies

$$\delta_i^2 = (a_{i1}x_1 + a_{i2}x_2 + \cdots + a_{im}x_m - b_i)^2 \neq 0, \qquad i = 1, 2, \ldots n,$$

and attempt to find values for $x_1, x_2, \ldots, x_m$ which will make

$$E^2 = \sum_{i=1}^{n} \delta_i^2 = \sum_{i=1}^{n} (a_{i1}x_1 + a_{i2}x_2 + \cdots + a_{im}x_m - b_i)^2$$

as small as possible.

To minimize E^2, we must equate to zero each of its first partial derivatives

$$\frac{\partial E^2}{\partial x_1}, \frac{\partial E^2}{\partial x_2}, \ldots, \frac{\partial E^2}{\partial x_m}$$

This gives the equations

$$\frac{\partial E^2}{\partial x_1} = \sum_{i=1}^{n} 2(a_{i1}x_1 + a_{i2}x_2 + \cdots + a_{im}x_m - b_i)(a_{i1}) = 0$$

or

$$(6) \qquad x_1 \sum_{i=1}^{n} a_{i1}a_{i1} + x_2 \sum_{i=1}^{n} a_{i1}a_{i2} + \cdots + x_m \sum_{i=1}^{n} a_{i1}a_{im} = \sum_{i=1}^{n} a_{i1}b_i$$

and similarly

$$x_1 \sum_{i=1}^{n} a_{i2}a_{i1} + x_2 \sum_{i=1}^{n} a_{i2}a_{i2} + \cdots + x_m \sum_{i=1}^{n} a_{i2}a_{im} = \sum_{i=1}^{n} a_{i2}b_i$$

$$(7) \quad x_1 \sum_{i=1}^{n} a_{i3}a_{i1} + x_2 \sum_{i=1}^{n} a_{i3}a_{i2} + \cdots + x_m \sum_{i=1}^{n} a_{i3}a_{im} = \sum_{i=1}^{n} a_{i3}b_i$$

$$\cdots \cdots \cdots \cdots \cdots \cdots \cdots \cdots \cdots \cdots \cdots \cdots \cdots$$

$$x_1 \sum_{i=1}^{n} a_{im}a_{i1} + x_2 \sum_{i=1}^{n} a_{im}a_{i2} + \cdots + x_m \sum_{i=1}^{n} a_{im}a_{im} = \sum_{i=1}^{n} a_{im}b_i$$

We have thus obtained a system of m linear equations in the m unknowns $x_1, x_2, \ldots, x_m$, whose solution is now a routine matter. As a practical detail, it is worthy of note that these minimizing or **normal equations** can be written down at once, according to the following rule. *Let each of the original equations be multiplied by the coefficient of x_i in that equation, and let all the resulting equations be added. The sum is the ith normal equation.*

Example 2

By the method of least squares, fit a parabolic equation,

$$y = a + bx + cx^2$$

to the data

x	-2	-1	0	1	2	3
y	0	-2	-2	2	15	25

Substituting these pairs of values into the equation

$$y = a + bx + cx^2$$

we find that a, b, and c should satisfy the conditions

$$
\begin{aligned}
a - 2b + 4c &= 0 \\
a - b + c &= -2 \\
a &= -2 \\
a + b + c &= 2 \\
a + 2b + 4c &= 15 \\
a + 3b + 9c &= 25
\end{aligned}
$$

In general, three unknowns cannot be made to satisfy more than three conditions; hence the most we can do is to determine values of a, b, and c which will satisfy these equations as nearly as possible.

To set up the first of the three normal equations required by the method of least squares, we must multiply each of the equations of condition by the coefficient of

a in that equation and add, getting in this case simply the sum of the six equations

$$6a + 3b + 19c = 38$$

To set up the second normal equation, we multiply each equation by the coefficient of b in that equation and add, getting

$$
\begin{array}{rrrr}
-2a + & 4b - & 8c = & 0 \\
-a + & b - & c = & 2 \\
0 & 0 & 0 = & 0 \\
a + & b + & c = & 2 \\
2a + & 4b + & 8c = & 30 \\
3a + & 9b + & 27c = & 75 \\
\hline
3a + & 19b + & 27c = & 109
\end{array}
$$

In the same way, multiplying each equation by the coefficient of c in that equation and adding, we get the third normal equation

$$
\begin{array}{rrrr}
4a - & 8b + & 16c = & 0 \\
a - & b + & c = & -2 \\
0 & 0 & 0 = & 0 \\
a + & b + & c = & 2 \\
4a + & 8b + & 16c = & 60 \\
9a + & 27b + & 81c = & 225 \\
\hline
19a + & 27b + & 115c = & 285
\end{array}
$$

The solution of the three normal equations is a simple matter, and we find

$$a = -1.57, \qquad b = 3.14, \qquad c = 2.00$$

The required solution is therefore

$$y = -1.57 + 3.14x + 2.00x^2$$

The method of least squares is not limited in its application to problems in which the equations of condition are linear. Sometimes by a suitable transformation the problem can be converted into one in which the parameters do enter linearly. For instance, to fit an equation of the important type

$$y = ae^{bx}$$

we can take the natural logarithm of each side, getting

$$\log y = \log a + bx$$

Then regarding x and $\log y$ as new variables, say X and Y, and $\log a$ and b as new parameters, say A and B, the problem can be considered as requiring the determination of A and B such that the *linear* equation

$$Y = A + BX$$

gives the best possible fit to the known pairs of values of $X \ (= x)$ and

$Y \ (= \log y)$. Once A has been found, it is of course a simple matter to find the actual parameter, a, since $A = \log a$.

Similarly the fitting of a function

$$y = kx^n$$

can be reduced to a linear problem by first taking logarithms (preferably to the base 10), getting

$$\log y = \log k + n \log x$$

This equation is linear in the variables $X = \log x$ and $Y = \log y$, and in the parameters $K = \log k$ and $N = n$. Hence the determination of the parameters can be carried out as outlined above.

On the other hand it is not possible to make a rigorous linearization of general systems of nonlinear equations of condition. However, if a reasonable approximation to a solution of such a system is available, the method of least squares can be applied in the following way.

Let the equations to be satisfied (as nearly as possible) be

$$(8) \qquad f_1(x,y) = 0, \qquad f_2(x,y) = 0, \qquad \ldots, \qquad f_n(x,y) = 0$$

and suppose that (x_0,y_0) is known, by inspection or otherwise, to be an approximate solution of this system. Then we can expand each function, $f_i(x,y)$, in a generalized Taylor's series about the point (x_0,y_0), getting

$$f_i(x,y) = f_i(x_0,y_0) + \frac{\partial f_i}{\partial x}\bigg|_{x_0,y_0} (x - x_0) + \frac{\partial f_i}{\partial y}\bigg|_{x_0,y_0} (y - y_0)$$

$$+ \frac{1}{2} \left[\frac{\partial^2 f_i}{\partial x^2}\bigg|_{x_0,y_0} (x - x_0)^2 + 2 \frac{\partial^2 f_i}{\partial x\,\partial y}\bigg|_{x_0,y_0} (x - x_0)(y - y_0) \right.$$

$$\left. + \frac{\partial^2 f_i}{\partial y^2}\bigg|_{x_0,y_0} (y - y_0)^2 \right] + \cdots$$

Now if (x_0,y_0) is a reasonable approximation to the required solution, the quantities $(x - x_0)$ and $(y - y_0)$ will be small, and hence their squares and higher powers will be negligible in comparison with the quantities themselves. Omitting these terms thus reduces the set (8) to the system

$$(9) \qquad f_i(x,y) = f_i(x_0,y_0) + \frac{\partial f_i}{\partial x}\bigg|_{x_0,y_0} (x - x_0) + \frac{\partial f_i}{\partial y}\bigg|_{x_0,y_0} (y - y_0)$$

which is linear in the unknown corrections $(x - x_0)$ and $(y - y_0)$. The method of least squares can now be applied to the system (9) in a straightforward way, following which the preliminary estimate (x_0,y_0) can be appropriately corrected. The extension to systems with more than two unknowns

$$f_1(x,y,z, \ldots) = 0, \qquad f_2(x,y,z, \ldots) = 0, \qquad \ldots, \qquad f_n(x,y,z, \ldots) = 0$$

is immediate.

Example 3

Find the best estimates of the coordinates of a point P which is measured to be at a distance of 4 from the point $(5,-2)$, 5 from the point $(0,-1)$, and 3 from the line $-3x + 4y = 12$.

If x and y are the required coordinates, the conditions which they are supposed to satisfy are

$$\sqrt{(x-5)^2 + (y+2)^2} = 4$$
$$\sqrt{x^2 + (y+1)^2} = 5$$
$$-\tfrac{3}{5}x + \tfrac{4}{5}y - \tfrac{12}{5} = -3$$

The first two of these relations are based upon the familiar formula for the distance between two points; the last is based upon the use of the normal form of the equation of a line to express the distance from a ~~point~~ to a ~~line~~. *line   point.*

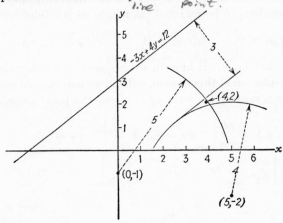

FIG. 16.7.

Now from a sketch of the conditions, such as shown in Fig. 16.7, it is clear that the point P is very near the point $(4,2)$. Hence we expand the two nonlinear conditions in a Taylor's series around the point $(4,2)$ and retain only the first powers of the departures, $(x-4)$ and $(y-2)$:

$$f_1(x,y) = \sqrt{(x-5)^2 + (y+2)^2} - 4$$
$$\doteq f_1 \Big|_{4,2} + \frac{\partial f_1}{\partial x}\Big|_{4,2}(x-4) + \frac{\partial f_1}{\partial y}\Big|_{4,2}(y-2)$$

(10)
$$= 0.1231 - 0.2425(x-4) + 0.9701(y-2) = 0$$
$$f_2(x,y) = \sqrt{x^2 + (y+1)^2} - 5$$
$$\doteq f_2 \Big|_{4,2} + \frac{\partial f_2}{\partial x}\Big|_{4,2}(x-4) + \frac{\partial f_2}{\partial y}\Big|_{4,2}(y-2)$$

(11)
$$= 0.0000 + 0.8000(x-4) + 0.6000(y-2) = 0$$

The third equation of condition is linear, and thus no approximate expansion is required. However, it must be expressed not in terms of x and y, but rather in terms of the corrections $(x - 4)$ and $(y - 2)$; hence we write it

(12)
$$f_3(x,y) = -\tfrac{3}{5}x + \tfrac{4}{5}y + \tfrac{2}{5}$$
$$= -\tfrac{3}{5}(x - 4) + \tfrac{4}{5}(y - 2) - \tfrac{1}{5} = 0\dagger$$

If we now let $u = (x - 4)$ and $v = (y - 2)$, our problem is to find the most plausible values of u and v from the three equations

$$-0.2425u + 0.9701v = -0.1231$$
$$0.8000u + 0.6000v = 0.0000$$
$$-0.6000u + 0.8000v = 0.2000$$

To obtain the first of the two normal equations, we multiply each of these equations by the coefficient of u in that equation, getting

$$1.0588u - 0.2352v = -0.0901$$

Similarly, to find the second normal equation, we multiply each of the equations of condition by the coefficient of v in that equation and add, getting

$$-0.2352u + 1.9411v = 0.0406$$

Solving the two normal equations for u and v we find

$$u = -0.083 \qquad \text{and} \qquad v = 0.011$$

Hence applying these corrections to the coordinates $(4,2)$ we obtain the improved estimates

$$(3.917,\ 2.011)$$

Example 4

By the method of least squares, fit an equation of the form

$$y = kx^n$$

to the data

x	1	2	3	4
y	2.500	8.000	19.000	50.000

and compute the value of E^2.

To find the values of k and n in the equation $y = kx^n$ we work with its logarithmic equivalent

$$\log_{10} y = \log_{10} k + n \log_{10} x$$

† We must resist the temptation to simplify (11) by dividing through by 2, and (12) by multiplying through by 5, for this would change the **weight** or relative importance of each of these equations. For the same reason we did not square the first two equations of condition before expanding them about the point $(4,2)$. Compare Exercise 4 at the end of this section.

and use the tabular process we illustrated in Example 1:

$X(= \log_{10} x)$	$Y(= \log_{10} y)$	X^2	XY
0.0000	0.3979	0.0000	0.0000
0.3010	0.9031	0.0906	0.2718
0.4771	1.2788	0.2276	0.6101
0.6021	1.6990	0.3625	1.0230
$\Sigma X = 1.3802$	$\Sigma Y = 4.2788$	$\Sigma X^2 = 0.6807$	$\Sigma XY = 1.9049$

The normal equations are therefore

$$4.0000 \log_{10} k + 1.3802n = 4.2788$$
$$1.3802 \log_{10} k + .6807n = 1.9049$$

From these we find

$$\log_{10} k = 0.3472 \quad \text{and} \quad n = 2.096$$

Hence $k = 2.224$, and the required equation is

$$y = 2.224x^{2.096}$$

To find E^2 for the function $y = 2.224x^{2.096}$, we must evaluate it for $x = 1, 2, 3, 4$, subtract these results from the corresponding values of y as originally given, square these differences, and then add them. The work is shown in the following table.

x	$y(= 2.224x^{2.096})$	y (given)	δ	δ^2
1	2.224	2.500	0.276	0.076
2	9.510	8.000	−1.510	2.280
3	22.243	19.000	−3.243	10.517
4	40.655	50.000	9.345	87.329
				$E^2 = 100.202$

Although we have no real basis for such a conviction, this value of E^2 should strike us as discouragingly large, especially in view of the fact that we have tried to choose the parameters, k and n, to make it as small as possible. To explore the matter further, let us reconsider the problem in a more elementary way and determine k and n so that the curve $y = kx^n$ will pass exactly through the points $(3,19)$ and $(4,50)$, without regard to the remaining pair of points. This requires that

$$19 = k3^n$$
$$50 = k4^n$$

Dividing the second equation by the first gives us

$$(\tfrac{4}{3})^n = \tfrac{50}{19}$$

Hence, taking logs,

$$n = \frac{\log_{10} 50 - \log_{10} 19}{\log_{10} 4 - \log_{10} 3} = 3.36$$

With n known, it is an easy matter to find k, for

$$\log_{10} k = \log_{10} 19 - 3.36 \log_{10} 3 = -0.32437 = 9.67563 - 10$$

and so $k = .474$.

Now for the function $y = 0.474x^{3.36}$, the calculation of E^2 leads to the following results:

x	$y \ (= 0.474x^{3.36})$	y (given)	δ	δ^2
1	0.474	2.500	2.026	4.105
2	4.865	8.000	3.135	9.828
3	19.000	19.000	0.000	0.000
4	50.000	50.000	0.000	0.000
				$E^2 = 13.933$ (!)

This is a remarkable improvement in the closeness of fit, which surely requires explanation.

The question will become clearer if we consider the sums of the squares of the errors associated with the respective functions when written in logarithmic form. These are

x	$\log_{10} y \ (= \log_{10} 2.224 + 2.096 \log_{10} x)$	$\log_{10} y$ (given)	δ	δ^2
1	0.3471	0.3979	0.0508	0.00258
2	0.9782	0.9031	-0.0751	0.00564
3	1.3472	1.2788	-0.0684	0.00468
4	1.6091	1.6990	0.0899	0.00808
				$E^2 = 0.02098$

and

x	$\log_{10} y \ (= \log_{10} 0.474 + 3.36 \log_{10} x)$	$\log_{10} y$ (given)	δ	δ^2
1	-0.3244	0.3979	0.7223	0.52172
2	0.6871	0.9031	0.2160	0.04666
3	1.2788	1.2788	0.0000	0.00000
4	1.6990	1.6990	0.0000	0.00000
				$E^2 = 0.56838$

The function ($y = 2.224x^{2.096}$) which we fitted logarithmically by the method of least squares fits the logarithms of the data much better than does the second function we derived. Moreover, it does this by keeping the discrepancies, δ_i, about equally small. However, a given difference, δ, in the logarithms of two numbers represents only a small difference in the numbers if the logarithms are near zero, but represents a large difference in the numbers if the logarithms themselves are large. Thus for a change of 0.10000 in the logarithms, we might have either

$$0.10000 = \text{logarithm of } 1.256$$
$$0.00000 = \text{logarithm of } \underline{1.000}$$
$$\text{Difference } 0.256$$

or

$$1.60000 = \text{logarithm of } 39.811$$
$$1.50000 = \text{logarithm of } \underline{31.623}$$
$$\text{Difference } 8.188$$

Hence the average approximation to the original data is significantly improved by keeping the errors in the larger logarithms as small as possible, even at the expense of considerably larger errors in the smaller logarithms. And clearly there is no reason to believe that the function which best fits the logarithms of the data will necessarily give the best approximation to the data themselves.

As a final approach to the problem, let us now try the general method of handling nonlinear equations of condition. Assuming again an equation of the form $y = kx^n$, and substituting the four given sets of values, we find that k and n should satisfy the conditions

$$2.5 = k$$
$$8.0 = k2^n$$
$$19.0 = k3^n$$
$$50.0 = k4^n$$

As an initial estimate of the values of k and n, let us use the values $k = 0.474$ and $n = 3.36$, which we obtained by passing the curve exactly through the points $(3,19)$ and $(4,50)$. Then expanding each of the equations of condition in a Taylor's series around $(0.474, 3.36)$, we find

$$f_1 = k - 2.500 = -2.026 + (k - 0.474) = 0$$

$$f_2 = k2^n - 8.000 \doteq (4.865 - 8.000) + 2^n \Big|_{0.474,3.36} (k - 0.474)$$
$$+ k2^n \log 2 \Big|_{0.474,3.36} (n - 3.36)$$
$$= -3.135 + 10.267(k - 0.474) + 3.372(n - 3.36) = 0$$

$$f_3 = k3^n - 19.000 \doteq (19.000 - 19.000) + 3^n \Big|_{0.474,3.36} (k - 0.474)$$
$$+ k3^n \log 3 \Big|_{0.474,3.36} (n - 3.36)$$
$$= 40.098(k - 0.474) + 20.874(n - 3.36) = 0$$

$$f_4 = k4^n - 50.000 \doteq (50.000 - 50.000) + 4^n \Big|_{0.474,3.36} (k - 0.474)$$
$$+ k4^n \log 4 \Big|_{0.474,3.36} (n - 3.36)$$
$$= 105.411(k - 0.474) + 69.314(n - 3.36) = 0$$

Letting

$$u = k - 0.474 \qquad \text{and} \qquad v = n - 3.36$$

the approximate equations of condition are

$$u \qquad\qquad = 2.026$$
$$10.267u + 3.372v = 3.135$$
$$40.098u + 20.874v = 0$$
$$105.411u + 69.314v = 0$$

The construction of the normal equations by multiplying each equation of condition by the coefficient of u and then of v in that equation, and adding, is a routine matter, and we find without difficulty

$$12,825.740u + 8,178.084v = 34.213$$
$$8,178.084u + 5,251.525v = 10.571$$

Hence

$$u = 0.197 \quad \text{and} \quad v = -0.305$$

and thus the revised estimates of k and n are

$$k = 0.474 + 0.197 = 0.671$$
$$n = 3.36 - 0.305 = 3.055$$

For the function

$$y = 0.671x^{3.055}$$

a straightforward calculation yields

$$E^2 = 22.628$$

which is still not as good as we found for the curve which passed exactly through the points (3,19) and (4,50).

However, a second application, based upon expanding the equations of condition around $k = 0.671$, $n = 3.055$, yields the improved values

$$k = 0.733, \qquad n = 3.039$$

and $E^2 = 10.052$, which is the smallest value of E^2 we have yet found. Another repetition of the process would no doubt improve this a little more.

This example makes it clear that a certain amount of judgment is involved in applying the method of least squares, and suggests that the general method of working with the nonlinear equations of condition themselves is probably preferable to a preliminary linearizing transformation.

The method of least squares has numerous theoretical as well as practical applications. In conclusion, we shall discuss one such application, bearing directly on the work of Sec. 7.5 on orthogonal functions.

We begin by assuming that we have a set of functions

$$\{\phi_i(x)\} = \phi_1(x), \phi_2(x), \ldots, \phi_n(x), \ldots$$

orthonormal (see Sec. 7.5) over the interval (a,b). In other words the ϕ's have the property that

$$\int_a^b \phi_i(x)\phi_j(x)dx = \begin{cases} 0, & i \neq j \\ 1, & i = j \end{cases}$$

Suppose now that we attempt to approximate a function $f(x)$ over the interval (a,b) by a finite linear combination of the first n of the functions $\{\phi_i(x)\}$

$$S_n = a_1\phi_1 + a_2\phi_2 + \cdots + a_n\phi_n$$

As criterion of approximation, we shall ask that the integral over (a,b) of the square of the difference between $f(x)$ and $S_n(x)$, namely,

$$(13) \quad I(a_1, a_2, \ldots, a_n) = \int_a^b [f(x) - a_1\phi_1 - a_2\phi_2 - \cdots - a_n\phi_n]^2 \, dx$$

shall be as small as possible. This of course is analogous to the earlier requirement that the sum of the squares of the vertical departures of the points of a given set from the curve being fitted to them should be a minimum. Here, however, we are fitting a curve, $S_n(x)$, not to a discrete set of points but to a continuous curve, $y = f(x)$, and thus a discrepancy, $f(x) - S_n(x)$, exists for *every* value of x on (a,b), and integration rather than summation is required. Figure 16.8 illustrates the geometry of the two situations.

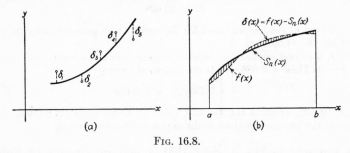

FIG. 16.8.

Applying the usual rule for differentiating an integral with respect to a parameter, we obtain as the minimizing conditions,

$$\frac{\partial I}{\partial a_i} = \int_a^b 2[f(x) - a_1\phi_1 - a_2\phi_2 - \cdots - a_n\phi_n]\phi_i \, dx = 0$$

or

$$\int_a^b f(x)\phi_i \, dx = a_1 \int_a^b \phi_1\phi_i \, dx + \cdots + a_i \int_a^b \phi_i^2 \, dx + \cdots$$
$$+ a_n \int_a^b \phi_i\phi_n \, dx = 0$$

From the orthonormal property of the ϕ's, all integrals involving the product of two different ϕ's vanish, leaving simply

$$a_i = \int_a^b f(x)\phi_i \, dx$$

which is precisely the value of the ith coefficient in the generalized Fourier series for $f(x)$ in terms of the orthonormal functions $\{\phi_i(x)\}$. Hence we have established the important fact that *of all possible linear combina-*

tions of the first n members of an orthonormal set, $\{\phi_i(x)\}$, the one which is the best least-square approximation to a given function $f(x)$ over the interval of orthogonality is the nth partial sum of the generalized Fourier expansion of $f(x)$ in terms of the ϕ's.

It is interesting to note that the partial sums of the Maclaurin or Taylor series of a given function do not possess this property. In other words, if $f(x)$ is approximated in the neighborhood of x_0 by a polynomial

$$y = a_0 + a_1(x - x_0) + \cdots + a_n(x - x_0)^n$$

the best such approximation in the least-square sense is in general not the sum of the first n terms of the Taylor expansion of $f(x)$ around x_0.

EXERCISES

1. By the usual least-square procedure, fit an equation of the form $y = a + bx$ to the data

x	1	3	6	7	9
y	1	5	6	10	12

   Ans. $y = \dfrac{2 + 113x}{102}$

2. Fit a straight line to the data of Exercise 1 by minimizing the sum of the squares of the *horizontal* distances from the points to the line. Compare your answer with the answer to Exercise 1.

3. Fit a straight line to the data of Exercise 1 by minimizing the sum of the squares of the *perpendicular* distances from the points to the line. Compare your answer with the answers to Exercises 1 and 2.

4. Find the most plausible values of x and y from the following system of equations

   $$x + y = 2$$
   $$2x - 3y = 9$$
   $$20x + 16y = 4$$

   (a) Without dividing out the factor 4 from the last equation
   (b) After dividing out the factor 4 from the last equation
   Ans. (a) $x = 1.625$, $y = -1.905$ (b) $x = 1.739$, $y = -1.811$

5. Fit a curve of the form $y = a + bx + cx^2$ to the points

x	1	2	3	4	5
y	1	8	17	25	40

6. By the method of least squares determine the best values of the rectangular coordinates of a point P, given that its measured distances from the points $(0,0)$, $(7,0)$, and $(0,6)$ are, respectively, 6.40, 4.47, and 5.38.

7. Find the best least-square approximation of the form $y = a - bx^2$ to $y = \cos x$ over the range $-\pi/2$ to $\pi/2$. Compare this with the first two terms of the Maclaurin expansion of $\cos x$.

8. By using the logarithmic method, fit a curve of the form $y = ae^{bx}$ to the data

x	0	1	2	4
y	3.0	6.5	11.8	50

What is E^2 in this case?   *Ans.* $a = 3.062$, $b = 0.696$

9. Using the general method for nonlinear equations of condition, fit a curve of the form $y = ae^{bx}$ to the data of Exercise 8, and compute E^2.

10. Fit a curve of the form $y = a + e^{bx}$ to the data

x	0	1	2	3
y	3.90	5.10	6.90	11.15

11. Fit a curve of the form $y = ae^{-bx^2}$ to the data

x	0.0	0.5	1.0	1.2
y	1.95	1.55	0.70	0.50

   (a) By the logarithmic method

   (b) By the general method for nonlinear equations of condition. Compute E^2 in each case.

12. Find the best least-square approximation of the form $y = A \sin x$ to a solution of the differential equation $y'' + x^2 y = \sin x$ over the interval $(0,\pi)$. (Hint: Substitute $y = A \sin x$ into the differential equation, and define

$$\delta(x) \equiv -A \sin x + x^2 A \sin x - \sin x.$$

Then determine A to minimize $\int_0^\pi \delta^2(x)\,dx$ by equating to zero the derivative of this integral with respect to A.)

13. What is the best least-square approximation of the form $y = 1 - ax^2$ to a solution of Bessel's equation of order 0, $xy'' + y' + xy = 0$ (a) over the interval $(0,1)$ and (b) over the interval $(0,2)$? Compare each of these with the first two terms of $J_0(x)$.

14. What is the best least-square approximation of the form $y = a - bx^2$ to a solution of the nonhomogeneous Bessel equation of order 0, $xy'' + y' + xy = 1$, over the interval $(0,1)$? What would be the best least-square approximation of the form $y = a - bx^2$ to a solution of the homogeneous Bessel equation? Explain.

15. Find the best least-square approximation of the form $y = a \sin 2t$ to a solution of the differential equation $y'' + y + y^3 = \sin 2t$ over the interval $(0,\pi/2)$.

16.4 Harmonic Analysis. In Chap. 5 we discussed at length the problem of expanding a function $y = f(x)$ in a Fourier series

$$(1) \qquad f(x) = \tfrac{1}{2}a_0 + a_1 \cos x + a_2 \cos 2x + \cdots$$
$$+ b_1 \sin x + b_2 \sin 2x + \cdots$$

and we obtained the formulas

$$(2) \qquad a_n = \frac{1}{\pi} \int_0^{2\pi} f(x) \cos nx \, dx$$

$$(3) \qquad b_n = \frac{1}{\pi} \int_0^{2\pi} f(x) \sin nx \, dx$$

for the coefficients in (1). If an explicit expression for $f(x)$ is available, and if, moreover, the products $f(x) \cos nx$ and $f(x) \sin nx$ can be integrated, then Eqs. (2) and (3) provide exact values for a_n and b_n. On the other hand, if $f(x)$ is given by a graph or a table of values, or if the integrals of $f(x) \cos nx$ and $f(x) \sin nx$ do not permit of exact evaluation, a_n and b_n can only be approximated. Numerous methods for doing this have been developed, comprising in the aggregate the field of **harmonic analysis.** Among the most convenient of these are the numerical procedures known as the 12-ordinate scheme and the 24-ordinate scheme, which we shall develop by a straightforward application of the trapezoidal rule to the integrals for a_n and b_n.

Suppose, then, that we have a periodic function $y = f(x)$ whose values are given at intervals of one-twelfth of a period. Without loss of generality we may suppose that the period of $f(x)$ is 2π, so that the interval between the given ordinates is $\Delta x = \pi/6$.

If we now apply the trapezoidal rule to Eqs. (2) and (3), we obtain

$$a_n = \frac{1}{\pi} \left[\Delta x \left(\frac{y_0 \cos nx_0}{2} + y_1 \cos nx_1 + \cdots + y_{11} \cos nx_{11} + \frac{y_{12} \cos nx_{12}}{2} \right) \right]$$

$$b_n = \frac{1}{\pi} \left[\Delta x \left(\frac{y_0 \sin nx_0}{2} + y_1 \sin nx_1 + \cdots + y_{11} \sin nx_{11} + \frac{y_{12} \sin nx_{12}}{2} \right) \right]$$

where $\Delta x = \pi/6$, $x_k = k\pi/6$, and $y_k = f(k\pi/6)$.

Now $y_0 = y_{12}$, from the periodicity of $f(x)$. Also

$$\cos nx_0 \equiv \cos 0 = 1 \qquad \text{and} \qquad \cos nx_{12} \equiv \cos 2\pi = 1$$

Hence the first and last terms in the series for a_n are identical and can be combined. Moreover,

$$\sin nx_0 \equiv \sin 0 = 0 \qquad \text{and} \qquad \sin nx_{12} \equiv \sin 2\pi = 0$$

and thus the first and last terms in the series for b_n are zero. Therefore

$$a_n = \frac{1}{6} \left(y_0 + y_1 \cos \frac{n\pi}{6} + \cdots + y_6 \cos n\pi + \cdots + y_{11} \cos \frac{11n\pi}{6} \right)$$

$$b_n = \frac{1}{6} \left(y_1 \sin \frac{n\pi}{6} + \cdots + y_6 \sin n\pi + \cdots + y_{11} \sin \frac{11n\pi}{6} \right)$$

These sums can be further simplified by noting that

$$\cos \frac{n(12 - k)\pi}{6} = \cos \frac{nk\pi}{6} \quad \text{and} \quad \sin \frac{n(12 - k)\pi}{6} = -\sin \frac{nk\pi}{6}$$

which shows that the cosine factors in the first sum are symmetrical about the term $y_6 \cos n\pi$ and that the sine factors in the second sum are negatively symmetrical about the term $y_6 \sin n\pi \, (= 0)$. Taking advantage of this, we can write

$$a_n = \frac{1}{6}\left[y_0 + (y_1 + y_{11}) \cos \frac{n\pi}{6} + \cdots + (y_5 + y_7) \cos \frac{5n\pi}{6} + y_6 \cos n\pi \right]$$

$$b_n = \frac{1}{6}\left[(y_1 - y_{11}) \sin \frac{n\pi}{6} + \cdots + (y_5 - y_7) \sin \frac{5n\pi}{6} \right]$$

The structure of these relations suggests that as a first step in reducing the calculation of a_n and b_n to a convenient tabular pattern, we form the sums and differences of the given ordinates according to the following scheme.

	y_0	y_1	y_2	y_3	y_4	y_5	y_6
(4)		y_{11}	y_{10}	y_9	y_8	y_7	
Sums:	c_0	c_1	c_2	c_3	c_4	c_5	c_6
Differences:		d_1	d_2	d_3	d_4	d_5	

In terms of the c's and d's, then, we can write

$$a_n = \frac{1}{6}\left(c_0 + c_1 \cos \frac{n\pi}{6} + \cdots + c_5 \cos \frac{5n\pi}{6} + c_6 \cos n\pi \right)$$

$$b_n = \frac{1}{6}\left(d_1 \sin \frac{n\pi}{6} + \cdots + d_5 \sin \frac{5n\pi}{6} \right)$$

Now if n is an even number, the cosine factors in a_n are symmetrical about the middle term, $c_3 \cos (n\pi/2)$, and the sine factors in b_n are negatively symmetrical about the middle term, $d_3 \sin (n\pi/2)$. On the other hand, if n is odd, the cosine terms in a_n are negatively symmetrical and the sine terms in b_n are symmetrical. Hence in every case the sums can be "folded" again, giving

$$a_n = \frac{1}{6}\left[(c_0 + c_6) + (c_1 + c_5) \cos \frac{n\pi}{6} + (c_2 + c_4) \cos \frac{n\pi}{3} \right.$$
$$\left. + c_3 \cos \frac{n\pi}{2} \right] \Bigg\} \quad n \text{ even}$$
$$b_n = \frac{1}{6}\left[(d_1 - d_5) \sin \frac{n\pi}{6} + (d_2 - d_4) \sin \frac{n\pi}{3} + d_3 \sin \frac{n\pi}{2} \right]$$

$$a_n = \frac{1}{6}\left[(c_0 - c_6) + (c_1 - c_5)\cos\frac{n\pi}{6} + (c_2 - c_4)\cos\frac{n\pi}{3} \right.$$
$$\left. + c_3\cos\frac{n\pi}{2} \right] \Bigg\} \quad n \text{ odd}$$
$$b_n = \frac{1}{6}\left[(d_1 + d_5)\sin\frac{n\pi}{6} + (d_2 + d_4)\sin\frac{n\pi}{3} + d_3\sin\frac{n\pi}{2} \right]$$

Here again the structure suggests that as a second step in organizing a computational form we calculate the sums and differences of the c's and d's as follows.

(5)

	c_0	c_1	c_2	c_3
	c_6	c_5	c_4	
Sums:	e_0	e_1	e_2	e_3
Differences:	f_0	f_1	f_2	

(6)

	d_1	d_2	d_3
	d_5	d_4	
Sums:	g_1	g_2	g_3
Differences:	h_1	h_2	

Substituting these quantities and the appropriate trigonometric functions, and carrying the computations as far as a_6 and b_6, we have

$$a_0 = \tfrac{1}{6}(e_0 + e_1 + e_2 + e_3) = \tfrac{1}{6}[(e_0 + e_3) + (e_1 + e_2)]$$
$$a_2 = \tfrac{1}{6}(e_0 + \tfrac{1}{2}e_1 - \tfrac{1}{2}e_2 - e_3) = \tfrac{1}{6}[(e_0 - e_3) + \tfrac{1}{2}(e_1 - e_2)]$$
$$a_4 = \tfrac{1}{6}(e_0 - \tfrac{1}{2}e_1 - \tfrac{1}{2}e_2 + e_3) = \tfrac{1}{6}[(e_0 + e_3) - \tfrac{1}{2}(e_1 + e_2)]$$
$$a_6 = \tfrac{1}{6}(e_0 - e_1 + e_2 - e_3) = \tfrac{1}{6}[(e_0 - e_3) - (e_1 - e_2)]$$
$$b_2 = \frac{1}{6}\left(\frac{\sqrt{3}}{2}h_1 + \frac{\sqrt{3}}{2}h_2\right) = \frac{1}{6}\left[\frac{\sqrt{3}}{2}(h_1 + h_2)\right]$$
$$b_4 = \frac{1}{6}\left(\frac{\sqrt{3}}{2}h_1 - \frac{\sqrt{3}}{2}h_2\right) = \frac{1}{6}\left[\frac{\sqrt{3}}{2}(h_1 - h_2)\right]$$
$$b_6 = 0$$
$$a_1 = \frac{1}{6}\left(f_0 + \frac{\sqrt{3}}{2}f_1 + \frac{1}{2}f_2\right) = \frac{1}{6}\left[\left(f_0 + \frac{1}{2}f_2\right) + \frac{\sqrt{3}}{2}f_1\right]$$
$$a_3 = \frac{1}{6}(f_0 - f_2)$$
$$a_5 = \frac{1}{6}\left(f_0 - \frac{\sqrt{3}}{2}f_1 + \frac{1}{2}f_2\right) = \frac{1}{6}\left[\left(f_0 + \frac{1}{2}f_2\right) - \frac{\sqrt{3}}{2}f_1\right]$$
$$b_1 = \frac{1}{6}\left(\frac{1}{2}g_1 + \frac{\sqrt{3}}{2}g_2 + g_3\right) = \frac{1}{6}\left[\left(\frac{1}{2}g_1 + g_3\right) + \frac{\sqrt{3}}{2}g_2\right]$$
$$b_3 = \frac{1}{6}(g_1 - g_3)$$
$$b_5 = \frac{1}{6}\left(\frac{1}{2}g_1 - \frac{\sqrt{3}}{2}g_2 + g_3\right) = \frac{1}{6}\left[\left(\frac{1}{2}g_1 + g_3\right) - \frac{\sqrt{3}}{2}g_2\right]$$

Now form the sums and differences of the e's

$$
\begin{array}{cc}
e_0 & e_1 \\
e_3 & e_2 \\
\text{Sums: } j_1 & j_2 \\
\text{Differences: } k_1 & k_2
\end{array}
$$

and let

$$\frac{1}{2} j_2 = j_2', \qquad \frac{1}{2} k_2 = k_2', \qquad \frac{\sqrt{3}}{2} h_1 = h_1', \qquad \frac{\sqrt{3}}{2} h_2 = h_2'$$

Then

$$
\begin{aligned}
a_0 &= \tfrac{1}{6}(j_1 + j_2) \\
a_2 &= \tfrac{1}{6}(k_1 + k_2') & b_2 &= \tfrac{1}{6}(h_1' + h_2') \\
a_4 &= \tfrac{1}{6}(j_1 - j_2') & b_4 &= \tfrac{1}{6}(h_1' - h_2') \\
a_6 &= \tfrac{1}{6}(k_1 - k_2)
\end{aligned}
$$

Further, let

$$\frac{\sqrt{3}}{2} f_1 = f_1', \qquad \frac{1}{2} f_2 = f_2', \qquad \frac{1}{2} g_1 = g_1', \qquad \frac{\sqrt{3}}{2} g_2 = g_2'$$

$$f_0 + f_2' = p, \qquad g_1' + g_3 = q$$

Then

$$
\begin{aligned}
a_1 &= \tfrac{1}{6}(p + f_1') & b_1 &= \tfrac{1}{6}(q + g_2') \\
a_3 &= \tfrac{1}{6}(f_0 - f_2) & b_3 &= \tfrac{1}{6}(g_1 - g_3) \\
a_5 &= \tfrac{1}{6}(p - f_1') & b_5 &= \tfrac{1}{6}(q - g_2')
\end{aligned}
$$

The successive condensations which lead from the given ordinates $y_0, y_1, \ldots, y_{12}$ to the final formulas for a_n and b_n can easily be arranged in tabular form. One convenient layout is the following.

y_0 to y_6: _____ _____ _____ _____ _____

y_{11} to y_7: _____ _____ _____ _____

_____

Sums: (c_0 to c_6): _____ _____ _____ _____ _____

Differences: (d_1 to d_5): _____ _____ _____ _____

c_0 to c_3: _____ _____ _____ _____

c_6 to c_4: _____ _____ _____

_____

Sums: (e_0 to e_3): _____ _____ _____ _____

Differences: (f_0 to f_2): _____ _____ _____

d_1 to d_3: _____ _____ _____

d_5 to d_4: _____ _____

_____

Sums: (g_1 to g_3): _____ _____ _____

Differences: (h_1 to h_2): _____ _____

e_0 to e_1: _____ _____
e_3 to e_2: _____ _____

Sums: $(j_1$ to $j_2)$: _____ _____
Differences: $(k_1$ to $k_2)$: _____ _____

	$j_2 =$ _____	$k_2 =$ _____			$h_1 =$ _____	$h_2 =$ _____
$\times 0.500$	$j'_2 =$ _____	$k'_2 =$ _____	$\times 0.866$		$h'_1 =$ _____	$h'_2 =$ _____

	$j_1 =$ _____	$k_1 =$ _____	$j_1 =$ _____	$k_1 =$ _____	$h'_1 =$ _____
	$j_2 =$ _____	$k'_2 =$ _____	$j'_2 =$ _____	$k_2 =$ _____	$h'_2 =$ _____

Sum: $6a_0 =$ _____ $6a_2 =$ _____ $6b_2 =$ _____
Difference: $6a_4 =$ _____ $6a_6 =$ _____ *$6b_4 =$ _____

	$f_2 =$ _____	$g_1 =$ _____			$f_1 =$ _____	$g_2 =$ _____
$\times 0.500$	$f'_2 =$ _____	$g'_1 =$ _____	$\times 0.866$		$f'_1 =$ _____	$g'_2 =$ _____

$f_0 =$ _____	$g'_1 =$ _____
$f'_2 =$ _____	$g_3 =$ _____

Sum: $p =$ _____ $q =$ _____

$p =$ _____	$f_0 =$ _____	$q =$ _____	$g_1 =$ _____
$f'_1 =$ _____	$f_2 =$ _____	$g'_2 =$ _____	$g_3 =$ _____

Sum: $6a_1 =$ _____ $6b_1 =$ _____
Difference: $6a_5 =$ _____ $6a_3 =$ _____ $6b_5 =$ _____ $6b_3 =$ _____

In exactly the same way, by assuming that $y = f(x)$ is given at intervals of one-twenty-fourth of a period rather than at intervals of one-twelfth of a period, we obtain the so-called 24-ordinate scheme of harmonic

---

* When as few as 12 ordinates are used in the numerical evaluation of the integrals which give a_n and b_n, appreciable errors may occur in the later coefficients because of the rapid variation of the sine and cosine factors upon which they depend. In particular, according to the 12-ordinate scheme, $b_6 = 0$ irrespective of the function under consideration. Similarly the expression for a_6 which we have obtained through the use of the trapezoidal rule is significantly inaccurate. In fact, an alternative derivation based on the method of least squares, and paralleling the theoretical development at the end of Sec. 16.3, leads to the formula $12a_6 = k_1 - k_2$, which shows that the use of the trapezoidal rule yields a value of a_6 which in general is twice as large as it should be. The values of the other a's and b's, however, turn out to be the same regardless of which of the two methods is used to derive them.

TABLE 16.1

$(y_0$ to $y_{12})$	0.0000	0.1667	0.3333	0.5000	0.6667	0.8333	1.0000	0.9444	0.8889	0.8333	0.7778	0.7222	0.6667
$(y_{23}$ to $y_{13})$		0.0556	0.1111	0.1667	0.2222	0.2778	0.3333	0.3889	0.4444	0.5000	0.5556	0.6111	
Sums: $(c_0\text{–}c_{12})$	0.0000	0.2223	0.4444	0.6667	0.8889	1.1111	1.3333	1.3333	1.3333	1.3333	1.3334	1.3333	0.6667
Differences: $(d_1\text{–}d_{11})$		0.1111	0.2222	0.3333	0.4445	0.5555	0.6667	0.5555	0.4445	0.3333	0.2222	0.1111	

$(c_0$ to $c_6)$	0.0000	0.2223	0.4444	0.6667	0.8889	1.1111	1.3333
$(c_{12}$ to $c_7)$	0.6667	1.3333	1.3334	1.3333	1.3333	1.3333	
Sums: $(e_0\text{–}e_6)$	0.6667	1.5556	1.7778	2.0000	2.2222	2.4444	1.3333
Differences: $(f_0\text{–}f_5)$	-0.6667	-1.1110	-0.8890	-0.6666	-0.4444	-0.2222	

$(d_1$ to $d_6)$	0.1111	0.2222	0.3333	0.4445	0.5555	0.6667
$(d_{11}$ to $d_7)$	0.1111	0.2222	0.3333	0.4445	0.5555	
Sums: $(g_1\text{–}g_6)$	0.2222	0.4444	0.6666	0.8890	1.1110	0.6667
Differences: $(h_1\text{–}h_5)$	0.0000	0.0000	0.0000	0.0000	0.0000	

$(e_0$ to $e_3)$ 0.6667   1.5556   1.7778   2.0000

$(e_6$ to $e_4)$ 1.3333   2.4444   2.2222

$(h_1$ to $h_3)$ 0.0000   0.0000   0.0000   0.0000

$(h_5$ to $h_4)$ 0.0000   0.0000   0.0000   0.0000

Sums: (j_0-j_3) 2.0000   4.0000   4.0000   2.0000

Differences: (k_0-k_2) -0.6666   -0.8888   -0.4444

Sums: (l_1-l_3) 0.0000   0.0000   0.0000   0.0000

Differences: (m_1-m_2) 0.0000   0.0000   0.0000   0.0000

$j_1 = 4.0000$ $j_2 = 4.0000$ $l_1 = 0.0000$ $k_1 = -0.8888$ $l_2 = 0.0000$ $m_1 = 0.0000$ $m_2 = 0.0000$

$\times\tfrac{1}{2}\ j_1' = 2.0000$ $j_2' = 2.0000$ $l_1' = 0.0000$ $\times 0.866$ $k_1' = -0.7697$ $l_2' = 0.0000$ $m_1' = 0.0000$ $m_2' = 0.0000$

$j_0 = 2.0000$ $j_1 = 4.0000$ $k_0 = -0.6666$ $k_1' = -0.7697$ $j_0' = 2.0000$ $k_0 = -0.6666$

$j_2 = 4.0000$ $j_3 = 4.0000$ $k_2' = -0.2222$ $-j_2' = -2.0000$ $-j_3 = -2.0000$ $k_2 = -0.4444$

$j_2 = 4.0000$ $j_3 = 4.0000$ $k_2' = -0.2222$

Sum col. 1:   6.0000   -0.8888   0.0000

Sum col. 2:   6.0000   -0.7697   0.0000

$-1.6585 = 12a_2$ $0.0000 = 12a_4$ $-0.2222 = 12a_6$

$-0.1191 = 12a_{10}$ $0.0000 = 12a_8$

Sum: 12.0000 $= 12a_0$ $0.0000 = 12a_{12}$

Difference: 0.0000 $= 24a_{12}$

$l_1' = 0.0000$ $l_2' = 0.0000$ $m_1' = 0.0000$ $l_1 = 0.0000$

$l_3 = 0.0000$ $l_3 = 0.0000$ $m_2 = 0.0000$ $l_3 = 0.0000$

Sum col. 1:   0.0000 $0.0000 = 12b_2$ $0.0000 = 12b_4$

Sum col. 2:   0.0000 $0.0000 = 12b_{10}$ $0.0000 = 12b_8$

Sum: $0.0000 = 12b_2$

Difference: $0.0000 = 12b_{10}$ $0.0000 = 12b_6$

TABLE 16.1.—(Continued)

	$f_1 = -1.1110$	$f_3 = -0.6666$	$f_5 = -0.2222$	$g_1 = 0.2222$	$g_3 = 0.6666$	$g_5 = 1.1110$
$\times 0.707$	$f_1' = -0.7855$	$f_3' = -0.4713$	$f_5' = -0.1571$	$g_1' = 0.1571$	$g_3' = 0.4713$	$g_5' = 0.7855$

$f_1' = -0.7855$
$f_5' = -0.1571$

Sum: $-0.9426 = p_1$
Difference: $-0.6284 = p_2$

$g_1' = 0.1571$
$g_5' = 0.7855$

Sum: $0.9426 = s_1$
Difference: $-0.6284 = s_2$

	$f_2 = -0.8890$	$p_1 = -0.9426$	$g_4 = 0.8890$	$s_1 = 0.9426$
$\times 0.866$	$f_2' = -0.7699$	$p_1' = -0.7699$	$g_4' = -0.8163$	$s_1' = 0.8163$

	$f_4 = -0.4444$	$p_2 = -0.6284$	$g_2 = 0.4444$	$s_2 = -0.6284$
$\times \tfrac{1}{2}$	$f_4' = -0.2222$	$p_2' = -0.3142$	$g_2' = 0.2222$	$s_2' = -0.3142$

$f_4' = -0.2222$
$f_2' = -0.7699$

Sum: $-0.9921 = q_1$
Difference: $0.5477 = q_2$

$p_1' = -0.8163$
$p_2' = -0.3142$

Sum: $-1.1305 = r_1$
Difference: $-0.5021 = r_2$

$g_3' = 0.4713$
$s_2' = -0.3142$

$0.7855 = t$

$g_6 = 0.6667$
$g_2' = 0.2222$

$0.8889 = u$

$f_0 = -0.6667$ $f_3' = -0.4713$	$f_0 = -0.6667$ $p_2 = -0.6284$	$f_0 = -0.6667$ $r_2 = -0.5021$	
$g_1 = -0.9921$ $r_1 = -1.1305$	$-f_4 = 0.4444$ $-f_3' = 0.4713$	$g_2 = 0.5477$ $-f_3' = 0.4713$	
Sum col. 1: -1.6588	-0.2223	-0.1190	
Sum col. 2: -1.6018	-0.1571	-0.0308	
Sum: $-3.2606 = 12a_1$	$-0.3794 = 12a_3$	$-0.1498 = 12a_5$	
Difference: $-0.0570 = 12a_{11}$	$-0.0652 = 12a_9$	$-0.0332 = 12a_7$	

$u = 0.8889$ $s_1' = 0.8163$	$s_2 = -0.6234$ $g_2 = 0.4444$	$s_1' = 0.8163$ $u = 0.8889$	
$g_4' = 0.7699$ $t = 0.7855$	$g_3 = 0.4713$ $-g_6 = -0.6667$	$-t = -0.7855$ $-g_4' = -0.7699$	
Sum col. 1 1.6018	-0.1571	0.0308	
Sum col. 2 1.6588	-0.2223	0.1190	
Sum: $3.2606 = 12b_1$	$-0.3794 = 12b_3$	$0.1498 = 12b_5$	
Difference: $-0.0570 = 12b_{11}$	$0.0652 = 12b_9$	$-0.0882 = 12b_7$	

analysis. This can also be carried out in tabular form, and one convenient layout is illustrated in Table 16.1 for the following example.

Example 1

Find the coefficients $a_0, a_1, \ldots, a_{12}, b_1, \ldots, b_{11}$ in the Fourier expansion of the function defined by the following data:

$$
\begin{array}{lll}
y_0 = 0.0000 & y_8 = 0.8889 & y_{16} = 0.4444 \\
y_1 = 0.1667 & y_9 = 0.8333 & y_{17} = 0.3889 \\
y_2 = 0.3333 & y_{10} = 0.7778 & y_{18} = 0.3333 \\
y_3 = 0.5000 & y_{11} = 0.7222 & y_{19} = 0.2778 \\
y_4 = 0.6667 & y_{12} = 0.6667 & y_{20} = 0.2222 \\
y_5 = 0.8333 & y_{13} = 0.6111 & y_{21} = 0.1667 \\
y_6 = 1.0000 & y_{14} = 0.5556 & y_{22} = 0.1111 \\
y_7 = 0.9444 & y_{15} = 0.5000 & y_{23} = 0.0556
\end{array}
$$

Table 16.1 (pp. 548–551) is self-explanatory, and the required expansion is

$$
\begin{aligned}
f(x) = 0.5000 &- 0.2717 \cos x - 0.1382 \cos 2x - 0.0316 \cos 3x - 0.0125 \cos 5x \\
&- 0.0185 \cos 6x - 0.0074 \cos 7x - 0.0054 \cos 9x \\
&- 0.0099 \cos 10x - 0.0048 \cos 11x - \cdots \\
&+ 0.2717 \sin x - 0.0316 \sin 3x + 0.0125 \sin 5x - 0.0074 \sin 7x \\
&+ 0.0054 \sin 9x - 0.0048 \sin 11x - \cdots
\end{aligned}
$$

In this simple illustration, $f(x)$ is actually the function

$$
\begin{aligned}
&\frac{2x}{\pi}, && 0 \leqq x \leqq \frac{\pi}{2} \\
&\frac{2}{3\pi}(2\pi - x), && \frac{\pi}{2} \leqq x \leqq 2\pi
\end{aligned}
$$

and thus the exact values of the Fourier coefficients can easily be calculated from the Euler formulas, giving

$$
\begin{aligned}
a_0 &= 1.0000 \\
a_n &= \frac{8}{3\pi^2 n^2}\left(\cos\frac{n\pi}{2} - 1\right) \\
b_n &= \frac{8}{3\pi^2 n^2}\sin\frac{n\pi}{2}
\end{aligned}
$$

Using these values we obtain the expansion

$$
\begin{aligned}
f(x) = 0.5000 &- 0.2702 \cos x - 0.1350 \cos 2x - 0.0300 \cos 3x - 0.0108 \cos 5x \\
&- 0.0150 \cos 6x - 0.0055 \cos 7x - 0.0033 \cos 9x \\
&- 0.0054 \cos 10x - 0.0022 \cos 11x - \cdots \\
&+ 0.2702 \sin x - 0.0300 \sin 3x + 0.0108 \sin 5x - 0.0055 \sin 7x \\
&+ 0.0033 \sin 9x - 0.0022 \sin 11x + \cdots
\end{aligned}
$$

which differs but little from the 24-ordinate approximation.

EXERCISES

1. The normal maximum and minimum temperatures at New York City on the first and fifteenth of each month are given in the following table:

		Max.	Min.			Max.	Min.
Jan.	1	38	26	July	1	80	64
	15	37	24		15	82	66
Feb.	1	37	24	Aug.	1	82	67
	15	38	24		15	80	67
Mar.	1	41	26	Sept.	1	77	64
	15	45	30		15	74	60
Apr.	1	51	36	Oct.	1	69	55
	15	57	42		15	64	49
May	1	63	48	Nov.	1	57	43
	15	68	52		15	51	37
June	1	73	57	Dec.	1	45	32
	15	77	60		15	41	29

Neglecting the slight irregularities in the spacing of the data, use the 24-ordinate scheme to obtain the harmonic analysis of the maximum temperature and of the minimum temperature.

2. Use the 24-ordinate scheme to obtain the harmonic analysis of the function $f(x) = x(2\pi - x)$, $0 \leqq x \leqq 2\pi$. Check by computing the exact values of the Fourier coefficients from the Euler formulas.

3. Determine the harmonic analysis of the circular arc

$$y = \sqrt{2\pi x - x^2} \qquad 0 \leqq x \leqq 2\pi$$

4. An elliptical cam whose outline is the curve $(x^2/4) + y^2 = 1$ lies in a vertical plane and rotates with uniform angular velocity about a horizontal line through its center. A thin rod which is constrained to lie in a vertical line through the center of the cam maintains contact with the edge of the cam at all times and is driven up and down by it. Find the harmonic analysis of the displacement of the end of the rod as a function of the angle of rotation of the cam.

5. Find the harmonic analysis of the function given in the following table:

x	y	x	y
0.00	0.00	0.55	1.00
0.05	0.23	0.60	0.88
0.10	0.43	0.65	0.74
0.15	0.60	0.70	0.54
0.20	0.75	0.75	0.35
0.25	0.87	0.80	0.22
0.30	0.97	0.85	0.12
0.35	1.05	0.90	0.06
0.40	1.08	0.95	0.02
0.45	1.09	1.00	0.00
0.50	1.07		

16.5 The Method of Stodola. In many, perhaps in most, practical applications involving frequency and deflection calculations for continuous bodies, the properties of the body depart noticeably from constancy, and the partial differential equation describing the system has variable coefficients. In such cases an exact solution is usually impossible, and recourse must be had to some graphical or numerical process. The iterative process of Stodola is admirably suited to the calculation of the first characteristic value, *i.e.*, the lowest natural frequency, and the corresponding characteristic function, or normal mode, and may if necessary be extended to give higher frequencies and modes as well. We shall describe and illustrate the method as applied to the torsional vibration of a shaft of variable cross section. The extension to other second order systems such as the nonuniform string, the nonuniform organ pipe, and the nonuniform bar vibrating longitudinally, and to the important fourth-order case of the nonuniform beam vibrating transversely can easily be made.

For a nonuniform shaft vibrating torsionally, we obtained in Sec. 7.2 the differential equation

$$(1) \qquad \frac{\partial \left[E_s J(x) \, \dfrac{\partial \theta}{\partial x} \right]}{\partial x} = J(x) \, \frac{\rho}{g} \, \frac{\partial^2 \theta}{\partial t^2} \dagger$$

where x = longitudinal coordinate measured from one end of the shaft

θ = angle of twist of the shaft at a general cross section

$J(x)$ = polar moment of inertia of a general cross section of the shaft

E_s = modulus of elasticity in shear of the shaft material

ρ = weight per unit volume of the shaft material

g = acceleration of gravity

As usual when we know that the solution is oscillatory in character, we assume

$$\theta = X(x) \cos \omega t$$

where ω is the frequency to be determined and $X(x)$ is the corresponding

---

$\dagger$ In the derivation of this equation, the product $E_s J(x) \, \dfrac{\partial \theta}{\partial x}$ entered as the torque transmitted through a general cross section of the shaft, on the assumption that the cross sections departed so little from circularity that the formula for circular shafts

$$\text{Torque} = E_s J(x) \, \frac{\partial \theta}{\partial x}$$

could safely be applied. If this is not the case, then

$$E_s J(x) = \frac{\text{applied torque}}{\text{twist per unit length}} \equiv \textbf{torsional rigidity}$$

must be replaced by an empirical expression obtained either by determining experimentally the ratio of the applied torque to the twist per unit length at various points on the shaft or by using some process such as Prandl's membrane analogy. See S. Timoshenko, "Theory of Elasticity," pp. 239, 260, D. Van Nostrand Company, Inc., New York, 1937.

modal shape.   Then substituting into the partial differential equation (1) and dividing out the factor cos ωt, we obtain the ordinary differential equation

$$(2) \qquad \frac{d\left[E_s J(x)\dfrac{dX}{dx}\right]}{dx} = -\omega^2 J(x)\frac{\rho}{g}X(x)$$

To be specific, let us consider first a shaft which is built in at $x = 0$ and free at $x = l$.   Then, integrating Eq. (2) from x to l, we obtain

$$(3) \qquad E_s J(x)\frac{dX}{dx} = \omega^2 \frac{\rho}{g}\int_x^l J(s)X(s)ds$$

Clearly, with these limits on the integral, the free end condition

$$E_s J(x)\frac{\partial\theta}{\partial x}\bigg|_{x=l} \equiv E_s J(x)\frac{dX}{dx}\cos\omega t\bigg|_{x=l} = 0$$

is automatically satisfied.

Now divide (3) by $E_s J(x)$ and integrate again, this time from 0 to x:

$$(4) \qquad X(x) = \frac{\omega^2\rho}{E_s g}\int_0^x \frac{1}{J(r)}\int_r^l J(s)X(s)ds\,dr$$

The limits on the outer integral now guarantee that the fixed end condition

$$\theta\bigg|_{x=0} \equiv X(x)\cos\omega t\bigg|_{x=0} = 0$$

is satisfied for all values of t.

We have thus obtained an expression for the required normal mode $X(x)$, but we have solved the problem only in a paradoxical sense, since in order to find $X(x)$ from Eq. (4) it is necessary to know $X(x)$ in advance! However, if a reasonably good "guess" be made for X, say X_1, and if this be substituted into the integrand in (4), the resulting expression, that is,

$$X_2 = \frac{\omega^2\rho}{E_s g}\int_0^x \frac{1}{J(r)}\int_r^l J(s)X_1(s)ds\,dr$$

will in general be a much better approximation to the required function $X(x)$.   Repeating this process, substituting X_2 into the right member of (4) and computing X_3, and so on, will soon lead to a highly accurate approximation for $X(x)$, from which the frequency ω can be found as follows.

Suppose that the exact solution $X(x)$ is substituted into the right side of Eq. (4), and that by suitable numerical or graphical means the repeated integral is worked out. That is, suppose that

$$(5) \qquad \int_0^x \frac{1}{J(r)} \int_r^l J(s)X(s)ds\, dr$$

has been determined as a function of x. Practically, of course, this will mean that (5) is known for some set of values of x, say $x = 0, 0.1l, 0.2l,$ . . . , $0.9l, l$. Then for every value of x, the integrated result (5), after multiplication by

$$\frac{\omega^2\rho}{E_s g}$$

will be identical with $X(x)$ as originally substituted into the integral. Or to put it otherwise, the ratio of $X(x)$ (as substituted) to the repeated integral (as computed), namely,

$$(6) \qquad \frac{X(x)}{\displaystyle\int_0^x \frac{1}{J(r)} \int_r^l J(s)X(s)ds\, dr}$$

will be a constant for every value of x, and will in fact be equal to

$$\frac{\omega^2\rho}{E_s g}$$

The constancy (or lack of constancy) of the ratio

$$(7) \qquad \frac{X_n}{\displaystyle\int_0^x \frac{1}{J(r)} \int_r^l J(s)X_n(s)ds\, dr}$$

for successive values of x is thus an indication of how well the process of iteration has converged. Moreover, after approximate constancy has been obtained, the frequency ω can be computed at once, since

$$\frac{\omega^2\rho}{E_s g} = \text{constant ratio (7)}$$

and so

$$(8) \qquad \frac{\omega}{2\pi} = \frac{1}{2\pi}\sqrt{\frac{E_s g}{\rho}}\ \sqrt{\text{constant ratio (7)}}$$

The value of $\omega/2\pi$ given by (8) will be in cycles per second if

> x is in in.
> l is in in.
> E_s is in lb/in.^{2}
> g is in in./sec^2
> ρ is in lb/in.^{3}

TABLE 16.2

1	2	3	4	5	6	7	8	9	10	11
x	$J(x)$	$X_n(x)$	$(2) \times (3)$	$\dfrac{(4)_{i+1} + (4)_i}{2}$	Sum (5) ↑	$\dfrac{1}{(2)}$	$(6) \times (7)$	$\dfrac{(8)_{i-1} + (8)_i}{2}$	Sum (9) →	$\dfrac{(3)}{(10)}$
Position along the shaft	Polar moment of inertia of cross section	Current approximation to deflection curve $X_n(x)$. For convenience, take tip deflection = 1	This is the integrand of the inner integral	These averages are for use in the first running integration	This sum, figured from the bottom, gives the inner integral without the factor Δx	This gives the reciprocal $\dfrac{1}{J(x)}$	This gives the integrand of the second integration	These averages are for use in the second running integration	This sum, figured from the top, gives the value of the double integral without the factor $(\Delta x)^2$	This ratio should be a constant if (3) is a correct "guess"
$x_0 = 0$								*****************	0.000	
x_1										
x_2										
$\cdots$										
$x_n = l$		1.000		*****************	0.000					

The dimensions of $J(x)$ and $X(x)$ are irrelevant, since these cancel identically in the ratio (7).

The two running integrations involved in the process can conveniently be performed by the trapezoidal rule, as described in Sec. 16.2. If this method be employed, the whole process can be set up in tabular form as shown on page 557. Using this procedure, we then have

$$\text{Frequency} = \frac{\omega}{2\pi} = \frac{1}{2\pi}\frac{1}{\Delta x}\sqrt{\frac{E_s g}{\rho}}\ \sqrt{\text{column (11), when constant}}$$

The factor $1/\Delta x$ appears here in the formula for the frequency, although it did not enter in the derivation, because, in the practical evaluation of the integrals in columns (6) and (10), the factor Δx was twice suppressed in the denominator of the ratio

$$\text{Column (11)} = \frac{\text{column (3)}}{\text{column (10)}} = \frac{X_n}{\displaystyle\int_0^x \frac{1}{J(r)}\int_r^l J(s)X_n(s)\,ds\,dr} = \frac{\omega^2\rho}{E_s g}$$

Example 1

Find the fundamental frequency of the torsional vibrations of a tapered shaft which is built-in at $x = 0$ and free at $x = l = 10$ in., if the shaft is a solid of revolution for which

$$r = \text{section radius} = \left(\frac{10-x}{10}\right)^{\frac{1}{4}}\text{in.}$$

Take

$$E_s = 12 \times 10^6 \text{ lb/in.}^2$$
$$\rho = 0.285 \text{ lb/in.}^3$$
$$g = 384 \text{ in./sec}^2$$
$$\Delta x = 1$$

As a necessary preliminary we must calculate the polar moment of inertia of the cross section of the shaft at a general station x. This is

$$J(x) = \frac{1}{2}A(x)r^2 = \frac{\pi}{2}r^4 = \frac{\pi}{2}\frac{10-x}{10}$$

As we pointed out above, $J(x)$ occurs once as a factor in the numerator and once as a factor in the denominator in the iteration formula. Hence any *constant* factor in $J(x)$, such as $\pi/20$, can be deleted and forgotten. This we shall do.

It is now necessary to make an initial estimate of the angular deflection curve $X(x)$. To guide us, we have only the meager knowledge, supplied by the boundary conditions, that $X(x)$ should be zero at $x = 0$, and that $X'(x)$ should be zero at $x = l$. How important it is that the initial "guess" satisfy both of these conditions we cannot say. However, for simplicity, we shall neglect the free end condition and choose

$$X_1(x) = \frac{x}{10}$$

With this agreed upon, the routine calculations shown in Table 16.3 can be carried out, leading to the ratios shown in column (11). Since these ratios are far from

Table 16.3

1	2	3	4	5	6	7	8	9	10	11
x	$J(x)$	$X_1(x)$	$(2) \times (3)$	$\dfrac{(4)_{i+1} + (4)_i}{2}$	Sum (5) ↑	$\dfrac{1}{(2)}$	$(6) \times (7)$	$\dfrac{(8)_{i-1} + (8)_i}{2}$	Sum (9) ↓	$\dfrac{(3)}{(10)}$
0	10	0.000	0.000	0.450	16.500	0.1000	1.6500	......	0.0000	......
1	9	0.100	0.900	1.250	16.050	0.1111	1.7831	1.7166	1.7166	0.0583
2	8	0.200	1.600	1.850	14.800	0.1250	1.8500	1.8166	3.5332	0.0566
3	7	0.300	2.100	2.250	12.950	0.1429	1.8505	1.8503	5.3835	0.0557
4	6	0.400	2.400	2.450	10.700	0.1667	1.7837	1.8171	7.2006	0.0556
5	5	0.500	2.500	2.450	8.250	0.2000	1.6500	1.7169	8.9175	0.0561
6	4	0.600	2.400	2.250	5.800	0.2500	1.4500	1.5500	10.4675	0.0573
7	3	0.700	2.100	1.850	3.550	0.3333	1.1832	1.3166	11.7841	0.0594
8	2	0.800	1.600	1.250	1.700	0.5000	0.8500	1.0166	12.8007	0.0625
9	1	0.900	0.900	0.450	0.450	1.0000	0.4500	0.6500	13.4507	0.0669
10	0	1.000	0.000	.....	0.000	......	0.0000	0.2250	13.6757	0.0731

constant, at least one repetition of the process must be undertaken. Before repeating the calculation using $X_2(x)$, it will be convenient to reduce these values, as given in column (10), by dividing each one by the tip deflection, 13.6757. This gives the values of $X_2(x)$ as they appear in column (3) of Table 16.4. In column (11) in Table

Table 16.4

1	2	3	4	5	6	7	8	9	10	11
x	$J(x)$	$X_2(x)$	$(2) \times (3)$	$\dfrac{(4)_{i+1} + (4)_i}{2}$	Sum (5) ↑	$\dfrac{1}{(2)}$	$(6) \times (7)$	$\dfrac{(8)_{i-1} + (8)_i}{2}$	Sum (9) ↓	$\dfrac{(3)}{(10)}$
0	10	0.000	0.000	0.567	20.880	0.1000	2.0880	......	0.0000	......
1	9	0.126	1.134	1.599	20.313	0.1111	2.2568	2.1724	2.1724	0.0580
2	8	0.258	2.064	2.411	18.714	0.1250	2.3393	2.2981	4.4705	0.0577
3	7	0.394	2.758	2.960	16.303	0.1429	2.3297	2.3345	6.8050	0.0579
4	6	0.527	3.162	3.211	13.343	0.1667	2.2243	2.2770	9.0820	0.0580
5	5	0.652	3.260	3.160	10.132	0.2000	2.0264	2.1254	11.2074	0.0582
6	4	0.765	3.060	2.823	6.972	0.2500	1.7430	1.8847	13.0921	0.0584
7	3	0.862	2.586	2.229	4.149	0.3333	1.3829	1.5630	14.6551	0.0588
8	2	0.936	1.872	1.428	1.920	0.5000	0.9600	1.1715	15.8266	0.0591
9	1	0.984	0.984	0.492	0.492	1.0000	0.4920	0.7260	16.5526	0.0594
10	0	1.000	0.000	.....	0.000	......	0.0000	0.2460	16.7986	0.0595

16.4 the ratios are much more nearly constant; however one more iteration is clearly desirable. This is shown in Table 16.5, in which $X_3(x)$ is of course the set of values from column (10) in Table 16.4, each divided by the tip deflection, 16.7986. The ratios in column (11) are now almost exactly the same. Hence we can terminate the process and compute the frequency:

$$f = \frac{1}{2\pi} \frac{1}{1} \sqrt{\frac{(12 \times 10^6)(384)}{0.285}} \sqrt{0.0584}$$

$$= 4{,}890 \text{ cycles/sec.}$$

TABLE 16.5

1	2	3	4	5	6	7	8	9	10	11
x	$J(x)$	$X_2(x)$	$(2) \times (3)$	$\dfrac{(4)_{i+1} + (4)_i}{2}$	Sum $\uparrow$ (5)	$\dfrac{1}{(2)}$	$(6) \times (7)$	$\dfrac{(8)_{i-1} + (8)_i}{2}$	Sum $\downarrow$ (9)	$\dfrac{(3)}{(10)}$
0	10	0.000	0.000	0.581	21.310	0.1000	2.1310	......	0.0000	......
1	9	0.129	1.161	1.645	20.729	0.1111	2.3030	2.2170	2.2170	0.0582
2	8	0.266	2.128	2.482	19.084	0.1250	2.3855	2.3443	4.5613	0.0583
3	7	0.405	2.835	3.041	16.602	0.1429	2.3724	2.3790	6.9403	0.0584
4	6	0.541	3.246	3.291	13.561	0.1667	2.2606	2.3165	9.2568	0.0584
5	5	0.667	3.335	3.226	10.270	0.2000	2.0540	2.1573	11.4141	0.0584
6	4	0.779	3.116	2.866	7.044	0.2500	1.7610	1.9075	13.3216	0.0585
7	3	0.872	2.616	2.250	4.178	0.3333	1.3925	1.5768	14.8984	0.0585
8	2	0.942	1.884	1.435	1.928	0.5000	0.9640	1.1783	16.0767	0.0586
9	1	0.985	0.985	0.493	0.493	1.0000	0.4930	0.7285	16.8052	0.0586
10	0	1.000	0.000	.....	0.000	......	0.0000	0.2465	17.0517	0.0586

The Stodola process can be adapted to other end conditions than the fixed-free, although sometimes a little ingenuity is required. To illustrate, consider a free-free shaft vibrating torsionally. Beginning with the same differential equation (2) and integrating from 0 to x, we obtain

$$(9) \qquad E_s J(x) \frac{dX}{dx} = -\frac{\omega^2 \rho}{g} \int_0^x J(s) X(s) ds$$

From the nature of the limits on the integral it is clear that the left end condition, namely,

$$E_s J(x) \frac{\partial \theta}{\partial x}\bigg|_{x=0} \equiv E_s J(x) \frac{dX}{dx} \cos \omega t \bigg|_{x=0} = 0$$

is satisfied for all values of t. However, it is also necessary that

$$E_s J(x) \frac{\partial \theta}{\partial x}\bigg|_{x=l} \equiv E_s J(x) \frac{dX}{dx} \cos \omega t \bigg|_{x=l} = 0$$

since the right end, like the left, is also free. From (9) it follows that this will hold if and only if

$$(10) \qquad \int_0^l J(s) X(s) ds = 0$$

and at the present stage we have no way of enforcing this condition.

The best we can do is to return to Eq. (9), divide by $E_s J(x)$, and again integrate from 0 to x, getting

$$(11) \qquad X(x) = -\frac{\omega^2 \rho}{E_s g} \int_0^x \frac{1}{J(r)} \int_0^r J(s) X(s) ds \, dr + C$$

With the integration constant C at our disposal it is now possible to impose the condition (10)

To do this, let us define

$$I_n \equiv I(X_n) \equiv \int_0^x \frac{1}{J(r)} \int_0^r J(s)X_n(s)ds \, dr$$

Then, from (11),

$$X_{n+1} = - \frac{\omega^2\rho}{E_s g} I_n + C$$

and thus condition (10) becomes

$$\int_c^l J(s)X_{n+1}(s)ds = - \frac{\omega^2\rho}{E_s g} \int_0^l I_n(s)J(s)ds + C \int_0^l J(s)ds = 0$$

Hence

$$C = \frac{\omega^2\rho}{E_s g} \frac{\int_0^l I_n(s)J(s)ds}{\int_0^l J(s)ds}$$

and therefore the formula of iteration becomes

$$(12) \quad X_{n+1} = \frac{\omega^2\rho}{E_s g} \left[- \int_0^x \frac{1}{J(r)} \int_0^r J(s)X_n(s)ds \, dr + \frac{\int_0^l I_n(s)J(s)ds}{\int_0^l J(s)ds} \right]$$

When, after sufficient repetitions of the process, the ratio

$$\frac{X_n}{- \int_0^x \frac{1}{J(r)} \int_0^r J(s)X_n(s)ds \, dr + \frac{\int_0^l I_n(s)J(s)ds}{\int_0^l J(s)ds}}$$

has become essentially constant, the frequency f can be found, as before, from the ratio by the formula

$$f = \frac{\omega}{2\pi} = \frac{1}{2\pi} \sqrt{\frac{E_s g}{\rho}} \sqrt{\text{constant ratio}}$$

The process in this case also can be conveniently carried out in tabular form.

EXERCISES

1. Rework Example 1, Sec. 16.5, using for X_1 the simplest polynomial function which satisfies both end conditions, and note whether or not the rapidity of convergence is significantly increased by this improved "guess."
2. Rework Example 1, Sec. 16.5, using $X_1 = x/10$, but performing the integrations analytically rather than numerically. Can the Stolcla process be carried out analytically rather than numerically in general?

3. Using the Stodola process, compute the fundamental frequency of the longitudinal vibrations of a uniform steel shaft of length 100 in. and of radius 2 in. if the shaft is built-in at one end and free at the other.

4. Find the fundamental frequency of a free-free steel shaft 50 in. in length, vibrating torsionally, if the shaft is a solid of revolution for which the section radius is

$$r = 5 + \frac{2x}{5} - \frac{x^2}{125} \quad \text{in.}$$

5. Discuss the application of the Stodola process to the problem of the torsional vibrations of a nonuniform shaft, built-in at the left end and bearing a disk of moment of inertia I at the right end.   Indicate how the procedure can be set up in tabular form.   (Hint: The boundary condition at the free end is that the torque transmitted through the end section $E_s J(x) \left.\dfrac{\partial \theta}{\partial x}\right|_{x=l}$ must equal the inertia torque of the disk, $-I \left.\dfrac{\partial^2 \theta}{\partial t^2}\right|_{x=l}$.$\Big)$

Ans.   The iteration formula is

$$X_n(x) = \frac{\omega^2 \rho}{E_s g} \left[\int_0^x \frac{1}{J(r)} \int_r^l J(s) X_{n-1}(s) ds \, dr + \frac{IX(l)g}{\rho} \int_0^x \frac{dr}{J(r)} \right]$$

6. Discuss the application of the Stodola process to the problem of the transverse vibrations of a nonuniform string.   Explain how the procedure can be set up in tabular form.

7. Find the fundamental frequency of a string stretched under a tension of 50 lb between two points 36 in. apart, if the weight of the string per unit length is

$$w = 0.005 + x(36 - x) \times 10^{-5} \text{ lb/in.}$$

8. Discuss the application of the Stodola process to the problem of the transverse vibrations of a nonuniform cantilever.   Explain how the procedure can be set up in tabular form.

Ans.   The iteration formula is

$$X_n(x) = \frac{\omega^2 \rho}{Eg} \int_0^x \int_0^u \frac{1}{I(t)} \int_t^l \int_s^l A(r) X(r) dr \, ds \, dt \, du$$

9. Find the fundamental frequency of a steel cantilever 6 ft long and 3 in. wide if its cross sections are rectangular, and if its depth varies linearly from 5 in. at the built-in end to 3 in. at the free end.

10. Discuss the application of the Stodola process to the problem of the transverse vibrations of a nonuniform simply supported beam.   Explain how the procedure can be set up in tabular form.

16.6 The Iterative Solution of Frequency Equations.   In many problems in dynamics it is necessary to solve systems of linear equations of the form

$$
\begin{aligned}
a_{11}x_1 + a_{12}x_2 + \cdots + a_{1n}x_n &= \lambda b_1 x_1 \\
a_{21}x_1 + a_{22}x_2 + \cdots + a_{2n}x_n &= \lambda b_2 x_2 \\
&\cdots \cdots \cdots \cdots \cdots \cdots \\
a_{n1}x_1 + a_{n2}x_2 + \cdots + a_{nn}x_n &= \lambda b_n x_n
\end{aligned}
$$

(1)

where $a_{ij} = a_{ji}$ and λ is an unknown parameter. By collecting terms on the left-hand side of each equation in (1) it is evident that this system is homogeneous, and hence has no solution other than

$$x_1 = x_2 = \cdots = x_n = 0$$

unless the determinant of the coefficients

$$(2) \quad \begin{vmatrix} a_{11} - \lambda b_1 & a_{12} & a_{13} & \cdots & a_{1n} \\ a_{21} & a_{22} - \lambda b_2 & a_{23} & \cdots & a_{2n} \\ a_{31} & a_{32} & a_{33} - \lambda b_3 & \cdots & a_{3n} \\ \cdots\cdots\cdots\cdots\cdots\cdots\cdots\cdots\cdots\cdots \\ a_{n1} & a_{n2} & a_{n3} & \cdots & a_{nn} - \lambda b_n \end{vmatrix}$$

is equal to zero. Equating the determinant (2) to zero and expanding, gives an equation of order n in the parameter λ. For each of the n roots, $\lambda = \lambda_1, \lambda_2, \ldots, \lambda_n$, of this equation, and for no other values of λ, a non-trivial solution for the x's can be found. In what follows we shall use the notation $x_1^{(i)}, x_2^{(i)}, \ldots, x_n^{(i)}$ to denote the solution corresponding to the root or characteristic value $\lambda = \lambda_i$.

The expansion of (2), the solution of the resulting polynomial equation in λ (by Graeffe's method, for instance), and the subsequent solution of the system (1) for the set of x's corresponding to each of the characteristic values, $\lambda_1, \lambda_2, \ldots, \lambda_n$, presents no theoretical difficulties. However, if n is large, the amount of labor involved in carrying out these steps is excessive, and an alternative method is much to be desired. In this section we shall outline an iterative process for finding the largest and smallest characteristic values λ_1 and λ_n, and the accompanying solutions

$$x_1^{(1)}, x_2^{(1)}, \ldots, x_n^{(1)} \quad \text{and} \quad x_1^{(n)}, x_2^{(n)}, \ldots, x_n^{(n)}$$

To begin with, we note the interesting and important fact that the solutions $x_1^{(i)}, x_2^{(i)}, \ldots, x_n^{(i)}$ and $x_1^{(j)}, x_2^{(j)}, \ldots, x_n^{(j)}$ corresponding to two distinct characteristic values, λ_i and λ_j, satisfy the orthogonality condition

$$(3) \quad \sum_{k=1}^{n} b_k x_k^{(i)} x_k^{(j)} \equiv b_1 x_1^{(i)} x_1^{(j)} + b_2 x_2^{(i)} x_2^{(j)} + \cdots + b_n x_n^{(i)} x_n^{(j)} = 0$$

This is analogous to the vanishing of the dot product of two perpendicular or *orthogonal* vectors, which we discussed in Sec. 15.1, and is also a counterpart of the orthogonality property of the solutions of certain differential equations which we investigated in Sec. 7.5.

To prove (3), we consider the system (1) for two distinct characteristic values λ_i and λ_j, and the corresponding solutions:

$$
\begin{aligned}
a_{11}x_1^{(i)} + a_{12}x_2^{(i)} + \cdots + a_{1n}x_n^{(i)} &= \lambda_i b_1 x_1^{(i)} \\
a_{21}x_1^{(i)} + a_{22}x_2^{(i)} + \cdots + a_{2n}x_n^{(i)} &= \lambda_i b_2 x_2^{(i)}
\end{aligned}
$$

(4)

$$
\cdot \cdot \cdot \cdot \cdot \cdot \cdot \cdot \cdot \cdot \cdot \cdot \cdot \cdot \cdot \cdot \cdot \cdot \cdot \cdot
$$

$$
a_{n1}x_1^{(i)} + a_{n2}x_2^{(i)} + \cdots + a_{nn}x_n^{(i)} = \lambda_i b_n x_n^{(i)}
$$

$$
\begin{aligned}
a_{11}x_1^{(j)} + a_{12}x_2^{(j)} + \cdots + a_{1n}x_n^{(j)} &= \lambda_j b_1 x_1^{(j)} \\
a_{21}x_1^{(j)} + a_{22}x_2^{(j)} + \cdots + a_{2n}x_n^{(j)} &= \lambda_j b_2 x_2^{(j)}
\end{aligned}
$$

(5)

$$
\cdot \cdot \cdot \cdot \cdot \cdot \cdot \cdot \cdot \cdot \cdot \cdot \cdot \cdot \cdot \cdot \cdot \cdot \cdot \cdot
$$

$$
a_{n1}x_1^{(j)} + a_{n2}x_2^{(j)} + \cdots + a_{nn}x_n^{(j)} = \lambda_j b_n x_n^{(j)}
$$

If we multiply the equations in (4) by $x_1^{(j)}$, $x_2^{(j)}$, . . . , $x_n^{(j)}$, respectively, and add, we obtain

$$
\sum_{l,m} a_{lm}x_m^{(i)}x_l^{(j)} = \lambda_i[b_1 x_1^{(i)}x_1^{(j)} + b_2 x_2^{(i)}x_2^{(j)} + \cdots + b_n x_n^{(i)}x_n^{(j)}]
$$

where, in the double sum, the indices l and m range independently over the values 1, 2, . . . , n. Similarly, multiplying the equations in (5) by $x_1^{(i)}$, $x_2^{(i)}$, . . . , $x_n^{(i)}$, respectively, and adding, we find

$$
\sum_{l,m} a_{ml}x_m^{(i)}x_l^{(j)} = \lambda_j[b_1 x_1^{(i)}x_1^{(j)} + b_2 x_2^{(i)}x_2^{(j)} + \cdots + b_n x_n^{(i)}x_n^{(j)}]
$$

However, $a_{lm} = a_{ml}$, by hypothesis, and thus the double sums in the left in the last two equations are identical. Hence, subtracting, we obtain

$$
0 = (\lambda_i - \lambda_j)[b_1 x_1^{(i)}x_1^{(j)} + b_2 x_2^{(i)}x_2^{(j)} + \cdots + b_n x_n^{(i)}x_n^{(j)}]
$$

from which, since λ_i and λ_j are assumed to be distinct, it follows that

$$
b_1 x_1^{(i)}x_1^{(j)} + b_2 x_2^{(i)}x_2^{(j)} + \cdots + b_n x_n^{(j)}x_n^{(j)} = 0
$$

as asserted.

Example 1

For the system

$$
\begin{aligned}
8x_1 - 2x_2 \quad\quad &= 8\lambda x_1 \\
-2x_1 + 3x_2 - x_3 &= 2\lambda x_2 \\
-x_2 + 2x_3 &= 2\lambda x_3
\end{aligned}
$$

it is easy to verify by direct substitution that when

$\lambda = \frac{1}{2}$ we have the solution (1,2,2)
$\lambda = 1$ we have the solution (1,0,−2)
$\lambda = 2$ we have the solution (1,−4,2)

The orthogonality relations for the three possible ways of pairing these solutions are then

$$
\begin{aligned}
8(1)(1) + 2(2)(\ \ 0) + 2(\ \ 2)(-2) &= 0 \\
8(1)(1) + 2(2)(-4) + 2(\ \ 2)(\ \ 2) &= 0 \\
8(1)(1) + 2(0)(-4) + 2(-2)(\ \ 2) &= 0
\end{aligned}
$$

It is now convenient to adopt the notation of matrix algebra (see Sec. A.1). Defining the two $n \times n$ matrices

$$A = \begin{vmatrix} a_{11} & a_{12} & \cdots & a_{1n} \\ a_{21} & a_{22} & \cdots & a_{2n} \\ \cdots\cdots\cdots\cdots\cdots \\ a_{n1} & a_{n2} & \cdots & a_{nn} \end{vmatrix} \quad \text{and} \quad B = \begin{vmatrix} b_1 & 0 & \cdots & 0 \\ 0 & b_2 & \cdots & 0 \\ \cdots\cdots\cdots\cdots\cdots \\ 0 & 0 & \cdots & b_n \end{vmatrix}$$

and the column matrix

$$X = \begin{vmatrix} x_1 \\ x_2 \\ . \\ . \\ . \\ x_n \end{vmatrix}$$

the system (1) can be written

$$(6) \qquad\qquad AX = \lambda BX$$

Now multiplying Eq. (6) on the left by the reciprocal of B, and recalling that $B^{-1}B$ is the identity matrix, we have

$$B^{-1}AX = B^{-1}\lambda BX = \lambda B^{-1}BX = \lambda IX = \lambda X$$

Hence, defining D to be the matrix $B^{-1}A$, we can write

$$(7) \qquad\qquad DX = \lambda X$$

Multiplying Eq. (7) on the left by the matrix D, and then using (7) again on the result, we find

$$D(DX) = D(\lambda X) = \lambda(DX) = \lambda(\lambda X) = \lambda^2 X$$

Continuing in the same way we have, in general,

$$(8) \qquad\qquad D^m X = \lambda^m X$$

Now let

$$C^{(1)} = \begin{vmatrix} c_1^{(1)} \\ c_2^{(1)} \\ . \\ . \\ . \\ c_n^{(1)} \end{vmatrix}$$

be an arbitrary column matrix. If this be substituted for X in the left member of (7), we obtain another column matrix

$$C^{(2)} = DC^{(1)}$$

If we substitute the new column matrix $C^{(2)}$ into the left member of (7), we obtain a third matrix

$$C^{(3)} = DC^{(2)} = D(DC^{(1)}) = D^2C^{(1)}$$

Continuing in this fashion, we obtain in general

$$(9) \qquad\qquad C^{(m+1)} = D^mC^{(1)}$$

If this process of iteration be repeated a sufficient number of times, then, as we shall soon show, the ratio of corresponding elements in $C^{(m+1)}$ and $C^{(m)}$ will approach constancy, and the value of this constant ratio will be the largest characteristic value, λ_1. Moreover, the limit approached by the column matrix $C^{(m+1)}$ will be the solution matrix

$$X^{(1)} = \begin{Vmatrix} x_1^{(1)} \\ x_2^{(1)} \\ \cdot \\ \cdot \\ \cdot \\ x_n^{(1)} \end{Vmatrix}$$

corresponding to the root $\lambda = \lambda_1$. In this respect this process bears a striking resemblance to the method of Stodola.

To establish these properties, we observe first that any column matrix, such as the arbitrary matrix, $C^{(1)}$, with which we begin the iteration, can be expressed in terms of the various solution matrices

$$X^{(1)} = \begin{Vmatrix} x_1^{(1)} \\ x_2^{(1)} \\ \cdot \\ \cdot \\ \cdot \\ x_n^{(1)} \end{Vmatrix} \qquad X^{(2)} = \begin{Vmatrix} x_1^{(2)} \\ x_2^{(2)} \\ \cdot \\ \cdot \\ \cdot \\ x_n^{(2)} \end{Vmatrix} \qquad \cdots \qquad X^{(n)} = \begin{Vmatrix} x_1^{(n)} \\ x_2^{(n)} \\ \cdot \\ \cdot \\ \cdot \\ x_n^{(n)} \end{Vmatrix}$$

as a simple linear combination

$$(10) \qquad\qquad C^{(1)} = \alpha_1 X^{(1)} + \alpha_2 X^{(2)} + \cdots + \alpha_n X^{(n)}$$

The proof of this, and the determination of the constants $\alpha_1, \alpha_2, \ldots, \alpha_n,$ follows almost exactly the pattern of the expansion of an arbitrary function in terms of the members of a set of orthogonal functions, which we carried out first as the Fourier expansion problem in Sec. 5.2, and then in the general case in Sec. 7.5. To find α_i, multiply (10) on the left by the row matrix

$$_bX^{(i)} = \begin{Vmatrix} b_1 x_1^{(i)} & b_2 x_2^{(i)} & \cdots & b_n x_n^{(i)} \end{Vmatrix}$$

This gives us the scalar equation

$$_bX^{(i)}C^{(1)} = \alpha_1{}_bX^{(i)}X^{(1)} + \cdots + \alpha_i{}_bX^{(i)}X^{(i)} + \cdots + \alpha_n{}_bX^{(i)}X^{(n)}$$

which in expanded form is

$$b_1x_1^{(i)}c_1^{(1)} + \cdots + b_nx_n^{(i)}c_n^{(1)} = \alpha_1[b_1x_1^{(i)}x_1^{(1)} + b_2x_2^{(i)}x_2^{(1)} + \cdots + b_nx_n^{(i)}x_n^{(1)}]$$

$$+ \alpha_i[b_1x_1^{(i)}x_1^{(i)} + b_2x_2^{(i)}x_2^{(i)} + \cdots + b_nx_n^{(i)}x_n^{(i)}]$$

$$+ \alpha_n[b_1x_1^{(i)}x_1^{(n)} + b_2x_2^{(i)}x_2^{(n)} + \cdots + b_nx_n^{(i)}x_n^{(n)}]$$

Since the X matrices are orthogonal, as we proved in deriving Eq. (3), every sum on the right will vanish except the one multiplying α_i, leaving

$$\alpha_i = \frac{b_1x_1^{(i)}c_1^{(1)} + b_2x_2^{(i)}c_2^{(1)} + \cdots + b_nx_n^{(i)}c_n^{(1)}}{b_1(x_1^{(i)})^2 + b_2(x_2^{(i)})^2 + \cdots + b_n(x_n^{(i)})^2} = \frac{_bX^{(i)}C^{(1)}}{_bX^{(i)}X^{(i)}}$$

Now from (9) we have

$$
\begin{aligned}
C^{(m+1)} &= D^mC^{(1)} \\
&= D^m(\alpha_1X^{(1)} + \alpha_2X^{(2)} + \cdots + \alpha_nX^{(n)}) \\
&= \alpha_1D^mX^{(1)} + \alpha_2D^mX^{(2)} + \cdots + \alpha_nD^mX^{(n)}
\end{aligned}
$$

Applying (8) to the individual terms in the last equation, we obtain

$$C^{(m+1)} = \alpha_1\lambda_1^mX^{(1)} + \alpha_2\lambda_2^mX^{(2)} + \cdots + \alpha_n\lambda_n^mX^{(n)}$$

Similarly

$$C^{(m)} = \alpha_1\lambda_1^{m-1}X^{(1)} + \alpha_2\lambda_2^{m-1}X^{(2)} + \cdots + \alpha_n\lambda_n^{m-1}X^{(n)}$$

Written at length the last equation is

$$C^{(m)} = \begin{vmatrix} c_1^{(m)} \\ c_2^{(m)} \\ \cdot \\ c_n^{(m)} \end{vmatrix} = \begin{vmatrix} \alpha_1\lambda_1^{m-1}x_1^{(1)} + \alpha_2\lambda_2^{m-1}x_1^{(2)} + \cdots + \alpha_n\lambda_n^{m-1}x_1^{(n)} \\ \alpha_1\lambda_1^{m-1}x_2^{(1)} + \alpha_2\lambda_2^{m-1}x_2^{(2)} + \cdots + \alpha_n\lambda_n^{m-1}x_2^{(n)} \\ \cdots\cdots\cdots\cdots\cdots\cdots\cdots\cdots \\ \alpha_1\lambda_1^{m-1}x_n^{(1)} + \alpha_2\lambda_2^{m-1}x_n^{(2)} + \cdots + \alpha_n\lambda_n^{m-1}x_n^{(n)} \end{vmatrix}$$

Hence the kth component of $C^{(m)}$ is

$$c_k^{(m)} = \alpha_1\lambda_1^{m-1}x_k^{(1)} + \alpha_2\lambda_2^{m-1}x_k^{(2)} + \cdots + \alpha_n\lambda_n^{m-1}x_k^{(n)}$$

and the ratio of corresponding components of $C^{(m+1)}$ and $C^{(m)}$ is

$$\frac{c_k^{(m+1)}}{c_k^{(m)}} = \frac{\alpha_1\lambda_1^mx_k^{(1)} + \alpha_2\lambda_2^mx_k^{(2)} + \cdots + \alpha_n\lambda_n^mx_k^{(n)}}{a_1\lambda_1^{m-1}x_k^{(1)} + \alpha_2\lambda_2^{m-1}x_k^{(2)} + \cdots + \alpha_n\lambda_n^{m-1}x_k^{(n)}}$$

or, factoring λ_1^m from the numerator and λ_1^{m-1} from the denominator,

$$\frac{c_k^{(m+1)}}{c_k^{(m)}} = \lambda_1\frac{\alpha_1x_k^{(1)} + \alpha_2\left(\dfrac{\lambda_2}{\lambda_1}\right)^m x_k^{(2)} + \cdots + \alpha_n\left(\dfrac{\lambda_n}{\lambda_1}\right)^m x_k^{(n)}}{\alpha_1x_k^{(1)} + \alpha_2\left(\dfrac{\lambda_2}{\lambda_1}\right)^{m-1} x_k^{(2)} + \cdots + \alpha_n\left(\dfrac{\lambda_n}{\lambda_1}\right)^{m-1} x_k^{(n)}}$$

Clearly, if λ_1 is the root of largest absolute value, and if m is sufficiently large, the fractions in the numerator and the corresponding fractions in the denominator will be negligibly small, leaving

$$\frac{c_k^{(m+1)}}{c_k^{(m)}} = \lambda_1 \frac{\alpha_1 x_k^{(1)}}{\alpha_1 x_k^{(1)}} = \lambda_1 \qquad \alpha_1 \neq 0$$

independent of k, as asserted.

Similarly, if we consider the ratios of successive components in $C^{(m+1)}$, we have

$$\frac{c_k^{(m+1)}}{c_{k+1}^{(m+1)}} = \frac{\alpha_1 \lambda_1^m x_k^{(1)} + \alpha_2 \lambda_2^m x_k^{(2)} + \cdots + \alpha_n \lambda_n^m x_k^{(n)}}{\alpha_1 \lambda_1^m x_{k+1}^{(1)} + \alpha_2 \lambda_2^m x_{k+1}^{(2)} + \cdots + \alpha_n \lambda_n^m x_{k+1}^{(n)}}$$

$$= \frac{\alpha_1 x_k^{(1)} + \alpha_2 \left(\dfrac{\lambda_2}{\lambda_1}\right)^m x_k^{(2)} + \cdots + \alpha_n \left(\dfrac{\lambda_n}{\lambda_1}\right)^m x_k^{(n)}}{\alpha_1 x_{k+1}^{(1)} + \alpha_2 \left(\dfrac{\lambda_2}{\lambda_1}\right)^m x_{k+1}^{(2)} + \cdots + \alpha_n \left(\dfrac{\lambda_n}{\lambda_1}\right)^m x_{k+1}^{(n)}}$$

and for m sufficiently large this fraction is approximately

$$\frac{c_k^{(m+1)}}{c_{k+1}^{(m+1)}} = \frac{\alpha_1 x_k^{(1)}}{\alpha_1 x_{k+1}^{(1)}} = \frac{x_k^{(1)}}{x_{k+1}^{(1)}} \qquad \alpha_1 \neq 0$$

Thus

$$\frac{c_k^{(m+1)}}{x_k^{(1)}} = \frac{c_{k+1}^{(m+1)}}{x_{k+1}^{(1)}}$$

for all values of k, which proves that the components of $C^{(m+1)}$ are approximately proportional to the components of the solution matrix

$$X^{(1)} = \begin{vmatrix} x_1^{(1)} \\ x_2^{(1)} \\ \cdot \\ \cdot \\ \cdot \\ x_n^{(1)} \end{vmatrix}$$

as asserted.

These results are valid only if $\alpha_1 \neq 0$. However, we have already shown that

$$\alpha_1 = \frac{b_1 x_1^{(1)} c_1^{(1)} + b_2 x_2^{(1)} c_2^{(1)} + \cdots + b_n x_n^{(1)} c_n^{(1)}}{b_1 (x_1^{(1)})^2 + b_2 (x_2^{(1)})^2 + \cdots + b_n (x_n^{(1)})^2}$$

and since the starting matrix $C^{(1)}$ is completely arbitrary, it can surely be chosen so that the numerator of α_1 is different from zero.

If, as is usually the case, we desire the smallest characteristic value rather than the largest, we can proceed as follows. Let $\lambda = 1/\omega$, so that the original system in matrix form (6) becomes

$$AX = \frac{1}{\omega} BX \qquad \text{or} \qquad \omega AX = BX$$

Now multiply this equation on the left by the inverse A^{-1} of the matrix A, getting

$$\omega A^{-1}AX = A^{-1}BX$$

Then, since $A^{-1}A$ is the identity matrix, we have the equivalent matrix equation

$$A^{-1}BX = \omega X \qquad \text{or} \qquad FX = \omega X$$

where $F = A^{-1}B$. Applying our iterative process to this equation, we will obtain, as usual, the largest characteristic value, ω_1, which, because of the relation

$$\lambda = \frac{1}{\omega}$$

leads at once to the smallest value of λ.

This process can be extended in various ways to permit the calculation of characteristic values other than the largest and smallest. One such modification is indicated in Exercise 4 at the end of this section. Another can be found in the book "Elementary Matrices" by R. A. Fraser, W. J. Duncan, and A. R. Collar, p. 143, The Macmillan Company, New York, 1946.

Example 2

By the matrix iteration method find the largest and smallest characteristic values and the corresponding solutions of the system

$$
\begin{aligned}
6x_1 - 3x_2 \qquad\quad &= 6\lambda x_1 \\
-3x_1 + 6x_2 - 3x_3 &= 4\lambda x_2 \\
- 3x_2 + 4x_3 &= 4\lambda x_3
\end{aligned}
$$

In this case

$$
A = \begin{vmatrix} 6 & -3 & 0 \\ -3 & 6 & -3 \\ 0 & -3 & 4 \end{vmatrix} \qquad
B = \begin{vmatrix} 6 & 0 & 0 \\ 0 & 4 & 0 \\ 0 & 0 & 4 \end{vmatrix}
$$

and the system can be written

(11) $$AX = \lambda BX$$

where

$$
X = \begin{vmatrix} x_1 \\ x_2 \\ x_3 \end{vmatrix}
$$

The first step in the solution is the calculation of the reciprocal of B (Sec. A.1). The result is

$$
B^{-1} = \tfrac{1}{12} \begin{vmatrix} 2 & 0 & 0 \\ 0 & 3 & 0 \\ 0 & 0 & 3 \end{vmatrix}
$$

Now multiplying (11) on the left by B^{-1}, we have

$$\frac{1}{12}\begin{vmatrix} 2 & 0 & 0 \\ 0 & 3 & 0 \\ 0 & 0 & 3 \end{vmatrix} \cdot \begin{vmatrix} 6 & -3 & 0 \\ -3 & 6 & -3 \\ 0 & -3 & 4 \end{vmatrix} \cdot \begin{vmatrix} x_1 \\ x_2 \\ x_3 \end{vmatrix} = \frac{\lambda}{12}\begin{vmatrix} 2 & 0 & 0 \\ 0 & 3 & 0 \\ 0 & 0 & 3 \end{vmatrix} \cdot \begin{vmatrix} 6 & 0 & 0 \\ 0 & 4 & 0 \\ 0 & 0 & 4 \end{vmatrix} \cdot \begin{vmatrix} x_1 \\ x_2 \\ x_3 \end{vmatrix}$$

or

$$\begin{vmatrix} 1.00 & -0.50 & 0.00 \\ -0.75 & 1.50 & -0.75 \\ 0.00 & -0.75 & 1.00 \end{vmatrix} \cdot \begin{vmatrix} x_1 \\ x_2 \\ x_3 \end{vmatrix} = \lambda \begin{vmatrix} x_1 \\ x_2 \\ x_3 \end{vmatrix}$$

or simply

$$DX = \lambda X$$

Since the solution corresponding to the largest characteristic value of a system such as we are given usually involves components of alternating sign, it is natural to begin the iteration with the approximation

$$C^{(1)} = \begin{vmatrix} 1 \\ -1 \\ 1 \end{vmatrix}$$

Substituting this into the left side of the last matrix equation gives

$$C^{(2)} = DC^{(1)} = \begin{vmatrix} 1.50 \\ -3.00 \\ 1.75 \end{vmatrix}$$

Since only the ratios of the components are significant, it is convenient, before continuing the iteration with $C^{(2)}$, to reduce one of its components, say the first, to unity by dividing every component by the first. This gives

$$C^{(2)} = \begin{vmatrix} 1.00 \\ -2.00 \\ 1.17 \end{vmatrix}$$

Continuing the process, we have

$$C^{(3)} = \begin{vmatrix} 2.00 \\ -4.63 \\ 2.67 \end{vmatrix} \sim \begin{vmatrix} 1.00 \\ -2.32 \\ 1.33 \end{vmatrix}$$

$$C^{(4)} = \begin{vmatrix} 2.16 \\ -5.23 \\ 3.07 \end{vmatrix} \sim \begin{vmatrix} 1.00 \\ -2.42 \\ 1.42 \end{vmatrix}$$

$$C^{(5)} = \begin{vmatrix} 2.21 \\ -5.45 \\ 3.24 \end{vmatrix} \sim \begin{vmatrix} 1.00 \\ -2.47 \\ 1.47 \end{vmatrix}$$

Already the successive values of C differ but little, and the value of λ_1 can probably be found with satisfactory accuracy after one more iteration:

$$C^{(6)} = \begin{vmatrix} 2.24 \\ -5.56 \\ 3.32 \end{vmatrix}$$

The ratios of successive components of $C^{(6)}$ to the corresponding components of $C^{(5)}$ (as reduced and used in computing $C^{(6)}$) are

$$\frac{2.24}{1.00} = 2.24, \qquad \frac{-5.56}{-2.47} = 2.25, \qquad \frac{3.32}{1.47} = 2.26$$

Hence we take λ_1 to be 2.25, which in this case happens to be the exact value. The corresponding solution (after the first component has been reduced to unity for convenience) is approximately

$$\begin{vmatrix} 1.00 \\ -2.48 \\ 1.48 \end{vmatrix} \qquad \text{or} \qquad x_1^{(1)} = 1.00, \ x_2^{(1)} = -2.48, \ x_3^{(1)} = 1.48$$

It is easy to verify by direct substitution that the exact solution for $\lambda = 2.25$ is $x_1 = 1.00$, $x_2 = -2.50$, $x_3 = 1.50$.

To find the smallest characteristic value, λ_3, we write the system in the form

$$AX = \frac{1}{\omega} BX \qquad \text{or} \qquad BX = \omega AX \qquad \omega = \frac{1}{\lambda}$$

and multiply on the left by the reciprocal of A, which is

$$A = \begin{pmatrix} 6 & -3 & 0 \\ -3 & 6 & -3 \\ 0 & -3 & 4 \end{pmatrix}$$

$$A^{-1} = \frac{1}{18} \begin{vmatrix} 5 & 4 & 3 \\ 4 & 8 & 6 \\ 3 & 6 & 9 \end{vmatrix}$$

$$|D| = 144 - 54 \\ -36 \\ = 54$$

This gives

$$\frac{1}{18}\begin{vmatrix} 5 & 4 & 3 \\ 4 & 8 & 6 \\ 3 & 6 & 9 \end{vmatrix} \cdot \begin{vmatrix} 6 & 0 & 0 \\ 0 & 4 & 0 \\ 0 & 0 & 4 \end{vmatrix} \cdot \begin{vmatrix} x_1 \\ x_2 \\ x_2 \end{vmatrix} = \frac{\omega}{18}\begin{vmatrix} 5 & 4 & 3 \\ 4 & 8 & 6 \\ 3 & 6 & 9 \end{vmatrix} \cdot \begin{vmatrix} 6 & -3 & 0 \\ -3 & 6 & -3 \\ 0 & -3 & 4 \end{vmatrix} \cdot \begin{vmatrix} x_1 \\ x_2 \\ x_3 \end{vmatrix}$$

or

$$\begin{vmatrix} 1.67 & 0.89 & 0.67 \\ 1.33 & 1.78 & 1.33 \\ 1.00 & 1.33 & 2.00 \end{vmatrix} \cdot \begin{vmatrix} x_1 \\ x_2 \\ x_3 \end{vmatrix} = \omega \begin{vmatrix} x_1 \\ x_2 \\ x_3 \end{vmatrix}$$

In general, the components of the solution corresponding to the smallest value of ω will all have the same sign. Hence we begin the iteration with the "guess"

$$C^{(1)} = \begin{vmatrix} 1 \\ 1 \\ 1 \end{vmatrix}$$

Then we have

$$C^{(2)} = \begin{vmatrix} 1.67 & 0.89 & 0.67 \\ 1.33 & 1.78 & 1.33 \\ 1.00 & 1.33 & 2.00 \end{vmatrix} \cdot \begin{vmatrix} 1 \\ 1 \\ 1 \end{vmatrix} = \begin{vmatrix} 3.23 \\ 4.44 \\ 4.33 \end{vmatrix} \sim \begin{vmatrix} 1.00 \\ 1.37 \\ 1.34 \end{vmatrix}$$

$$C^{(3)} = \begin{vmatrix} 3.79 \\ 5.55 \\ 5.50 \end{vmatrix} \sim \begin{vmatrix} 1.00 \\ 1.46 \\ 1.45 \end{vmatrix}$$

$$C^{(4)} = \begin{vmatrix} 3.93 \\ 5.86 \\ 5.84 \end{vmatrix} \sim \begin{vmatrix} 1.00 \\ 1.49 \\ 1.49 \end{vmatrix}$$

$$C^{(5)} = \begin{vmatrix} 3.97 \\ 5.96 \\ 5.96 \end{vmatrix}$$

The ratios of corresponding components of $C^{(5)}$ and $C^{(4)}$ are

$$\frac{3.97}{1.00} = 3.97, \qquad \frac{5.96}{1.49} = 4.00, \qquad \frac{5.96}{1.49} = 4.00$$

Hence we take $\omega_1 = 4.00$ and $\lambda_3 = 1/\omega_1 = 0.25$, which happens to be the exact value. The solution corresponding to $\lambda = 0.25$ (after the first component has been reduced to unity, for convenience) is

$$\begin{vmatrix} 1.00 \\ 1.50 \\ 1.50 \end{vmatrix} \qquad \text{or} \qquad x_1^{(3)} = 1.00, \ x_2^{(3)} = 1.50, \ x_3^{(3)} = 1.50$$

These values are also the exact solution, as direct substitution will verify.

EXERCISES

Find the characteristic values of largest and smallest absolute value and the corresponding solution for each of the following systems:

1. $\quad 2x - 3y + 2z = \lambda x$
$\quad -3x + 4y - z = \lambda y$
$\quad 2x - y + 3z = \lambda z$

2. $\quad 3x - y - 2z = 2\lambda x$
$\quad -x + 2y - 2z = 3\lambda y$
$\quad -2x - 2y + 6z = \lambda z$

3. $\quad 3x_1 - x_2 \qquad\qquad = \lambda x_1$
$\quad -x_1 + 2x_2 - 2x_3 \qquad = \lambda x_2$
$\quad -2x_2 + x_3 - 2x_4 = \lambda x_3$
$\quad -2x_3 + 5x_4 = \lambda x_4$

4. If $C^{(1)}$ is chosen so that $\alpha_1 = 0$, show that the iteration based on $C^{(1)}$ will lead not to the largest characteristic value but to the second largest. Explain how this fact can be used to determine all the characteristic values of a given system of homogeneous linear equations.

5. Find the largest characteristic value and the corresponding solution of the system

$$12x_1 - 3x_2 \qquad\qquad = 3\lambda x_1$$
$$-3x_1 + 9x_2 - 6x_3 = 4\lambda x_2$$
$$-6x_2 + 12x_3 = 3\lambda x_3$$

Then choosing $C^{(1)}$ so that $\alpha_1 = 0$, that is, so that $C^{(1)}$ is orthogonal to the solution $X^{(1)}$, repeat the process and find λ_2 and $X^{(2)}$. Finally, choose $C^{(1)}$ orthogonal to $X^{(1)}$ and $X^{(2)}$ and find λ_3 and $X^{(3)}$. _Ans._ $\lambda_1 = \tfrac{21}{4}, \ \lambda_2 = 4, \ \lambda_3 = 1$

APPENDIX

SELECTED TOPICS FROM ALGEBRA AND CALCULUS

A.1 Determinants and Matrices. By a determinant we mean a certain expression, described in detail in Definition 1, below, associated with a square array of n^2 quantities. The symbol for a determinant consists of the array in question enclosed by single vertical bars:

$$(1) \qquad \begin{vmatrix} a_{11} & a_{12} & a_{13} & \cdots & a_{1n} \\ a_{21} & a_{22} & a_{23} & \cdots & a_{2n} \\ a_{31} & a_{32} & a_{33} & \cdots & a_{3n} \\ \cdot & \cdot & \cdot & \cdots & \cdot \\ a_{n1} & a_{n2} & a_{n3} & \cdots & a_{nn} \end{vmatrix}$$

Ordinarily the word **determinant** is used indifferently to denote the symbol (1) and the expression which this symbol represents.

The number n is called the **order** of the determinant. The individual quantities, a_{ij}, are called the **elements** of the determinant. The horizontal lines of elements are called the **rows** of the determinant; the vertical lines of elements are called the **columns.** In the convenient **double-subscript notation** illustrated in (1), the first subscript attached to an element identifies the row in which the element lies and the second subscript identifies the column. There is of course no reason to suppose that $a_{ij} = a_{ji}$, and in general this will not be so. The sloping line of elements beginning with a_{11} and extending to a_{nn} is called the **principal diagonal** of the determinant.

Determinants of the second and third order and the simple rules for obtaining their expansions are familiar topics in elementary algebra. Thus a second-order determinant is equal to the difference between the product of the elements on the principal diagonal and the product of the elements on the other diagonal:

$$\begin{vmatrix} a & b \\ c & d \end{vmatrix} = ad - bc$$

Similarly a third-order determinant has an expansion containing six terms,

$$\begin{vmatrix} a_1 & b_1 & c_1 \\ a_2 & b_2 & c_2 \\ a_3 & b_3 & c_3 \end{vmatrix} = a_1b_2c_3 + b_1c_2a_3 + c_1a_2b_3 - c_1b_2a_3 - a_1c_2b_3 - b_1a_2c_3$$

573

which can be written down at once by repeating on the right the first two columns of the determinant, and then adding the signed products of the elements on the various diagonals in the resulting array:

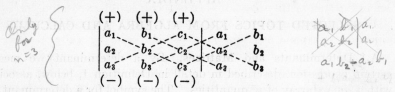

The diagonal method of expanding a determinant is correct *only* for determinants of the second and third order, and will give incorrect results if applied to determinants of order four or more. This fact becomes clear when we consider the definition of the expansion of a general determinant.

Definition 1. The expansion of the determinant (1) is

$$\Sigma(-1)^h(a_{1i_1}\ a_{2i_2}\ a_{3i_3}\ \cdots\ a_{ni_n})$$

where the summation extends over all possible arrangements $(i_1, i_2, i_3, \ldots, i_n)$ of the n second subscripts $(1, 2, 3, \ldots, n)$, and h is the total number of inversions in the sequence of the second subscripts, that is, the total number of times any of the numbers $i_1, i_2, i_3, \ldots, i_n$ precedes a smaller number.

In other words, the expansion of a determinant (thought of as written in the double-subscript notation) consists of the sum of all possible products formed by choosing one and only one element from each row and from each column in the determinant, the products to be plus or minus according to the following rule. Arrange the factors in each product so that the first subscripts run consecutively from 1 to n, and for each product let h be the number of times that one of the second subscripts is followed (consecutively or otherwise) by a smaller one. Then those products for which h is even are to be positive and those for which h is odd are to be negative.

In constructing a typical product in the expansion of a determinant of order n, an element must first be chosen from the first column. This involves n possible choices. Having made such a selection, a second element must be chosen from the second column *but not from the row containing the element already selected*. This involves, then, only $(n - 1)$ possible choices. Similarly only $(n - 2)$ possibilities remain for the third factor, and so on, until the last factor is uniquely determined. Thus there are

$$n(n - 1)(n - 2)\ \cdots\ 3 \cdot 2 \cdot 1 = n!$$

terms in the expansion of an nth-order determinant. Since the diagonal method of expansion applied to a determinant of order n will yield only $2n$ products, it is clear that if n is greater than 3 this method gives only a small fraction of the total number of terms in the expansion.

Since $n!$ increases very rapidly with n, it is completely out of the question to expand a determinant of high order by a direct application of the definition. Fortunately other and more efficient methods are available, based upon the use of one or more of the following theorems.

Theorem 1. If all the elements in any row or in any column of a determinant are zero, the determinant vanishes identically.

Theorem 2. If all the elements in one row or in one column of a determinant are multiplied by the same number, c, the determinant is multiplied by c.

Theorem 3. The value of a determinant is not changed if its columns are written as rows and its rows are written as columns, in the same order.

Theorem 4. Interchanging any two rows or any two columns of a determinant changes the sign of the determinant.

Theorem 5. If corresponding elements of two rows or of two columns of a determinant are proportional, the value of the determinant is zero.

Theorem 6. If the elements in one column of a determinant are binomials, the determinant can be written as the sum of two determinants according to the formula

$$
\begin{vmatrix} a_{11} & \cdots & (a_{1i} + \alpha_{1i}) & \cdots & a_{1n} \\ a_{21} & \cdots & (a_{2i} + \alpha_{2i}) & \cdots & a_{2n} \\ \cdots & \cdots & \cdots & \cdots & \cdots \\ a_{n1} & \cdots & (a_{ni} + \alpha_{ni}) & \cdots & a_{nn} \end{vmatrix} = \begin{vmatrix} a_{11} & \cdots & a_{1i} & \cdots & a_{1n} \\ a_{21} & \cdots & a_{2i} & \cdots & a_{2n} \\ \cdots & \cdots & \cdots & \cdots & \cdots \\ a_{n1} & \cdots & a_{ni} & \cdots & a_{nn} \end{vmatrix}
$$
$$
+ \begin{vmatrix} a_{11} & \cdots & \alpha_{1i} & \cdots & a_{1n} \\ a_{21} & \cdots & \alpha_{2i} & \cdots & a_{2n} \\ \cdots & \cdots & \cdots & \cdots & \cdots \\ a_{n1} & \cdots & \alpha_{ni} & \cdots & a_{nn} \end{vmatrix}
$$

A corresponding formula holds for determinants in which all the elements in one row are binomials.

Theorem 7. The value of a determinant is left unchanged if to the elements of any row or column there be added any constant multiple of the corresponding elements of any other row or column, respectively.

Definition 2. The minor of any element, a_{ij}, of a determinant, D, of order n is the determinant of order $(n - 1)$ which remains when the row and the column which contain a_{ij} are deleted from D.

Definition 3. The cofactor, A_{ij}, of any element, a_{ij}, of a determinant, D, is $(-1)^{i+j}$ times the minor of a_{ij}.

Theorem 8. Any determinant is equal to the sum of the products of the elements of any row or column multiplied by the corresponding cofactors.

In practice, to expand a determinant of order greater than 3, we first apply Theorem 7 one or more times to introduce a number of zeros in some particular row or column. Then we expand the determinant in terms of the elements of this row or column, according to Theorem 8. Because of the presence of zero elements, many of the products of elements and their cofactors drop out, shortening the computation appreciably.

Example 1

To find the value of the determinant

$$\begin{vmatrix} 3 & 1 & -1 & 1 \\ 0 & 3 & 1 & 2 \\ 1 & 4 & 2 & 1 \\ 5 & -1 & -3 & 5 \end{vmatrix}$$

it is convenient to add the third column to the second and to the fourth, and then to add three times the third column to the first. This gives the new but equal determinant

$$\begin{vmatrix} 0 & 0 & -1 & 0 \\ 3 & 4 & 1 & 3 \\ 7 & 6 & 2 & 3 \\ -4 & -4 & -3 & 2 \end{vmatrix}$$

Expanding this in terms of the elements of the first row according to Theorem 8, we obtain

$$0 + 0 + (-1)(-1)^{1+3}\begin{vmatrix} 3 & 4 & 3 \\ 7 & 6 & 3 \\ -4 & -4 & 2 \end{vmatrix} + 0$$

The usual diagonal method of expanding third-order determinants can now be applied, giving the final result 44.

Closely associated with Theorem 8 is the following result, of considerable theoretical importance.

Theorem 9. The sum of the products formed by multiplying the elements of one row (or column) of a determinant by the cofactors of the corresponding elements of another row (or column) is zero.

The concept of minors and cofactors admits of an important generalization, as the following definitions and Theorem 10 indicate.

Let M be the kth order determinant whose elements are common to any k columns and any k rows in an nth order determinant D. Then M is called a kth **minor** of D, and the determinant of order $(n - k)$ which remains when the columns and rows containing M are deleted from D is called the **complementary minor** of M.

Example 2

In the fifth-order determinant

$$\begin{vmatrix} a_1 & b_1 & c_1 & d_1 & e_1 \\ a_2 & b_2 & c_2 & d_2 & e_2 \\ a_3 & b_3 & c_3 & d_3 & e_3 \\ a_4 & b_4 & c_4 & d_4 & e_4 \\ a_5 & b_5 & c_5 & d_5 & e_5 \end{vmatrix}$$

the complementary minor of the second-order minor

$$\begin{vmatrix} b_2 & e_2 \\ b_4 & e_4 \end{vmatrix}$$

is the third-order minor

$$\begin{vmatrix} a_1 & c_1 & d_1 \\ a_3 & c_3 & d_3 \\ a_5 & c_5 & d_5 \end{vmatrix}$$

The **algebraic complement** of a minor, M, of a determinant, D, is the complementary minor of M multiplied by

$$(-1)^{i_1+i_2+\cdots+i_k+j_1+j_2+\cdots+j_k}$$

where $i_1 \ldots i_k$ denote the rows and $j_1 \ldots j_k$ denote the columns of D which contain M.

Theorem 10 (Laplace's Development). Let any k rows (or columns) be selected from a determinant D. Then D is equal to the sum of the products of all the kth minors of D contained in the chosen rows (or columns) multiplied by their corresponding algebraic complements.

Example 3

Expanding the determinant

$$\begin{vmatrix} 1 & 2 & 3 & 4 \\ 4 & 3 & 2 & 1 \\ 0 & -1 & 2 & 3 \\ 1 & 6 & 4 & -2 \end{vmatrix}$$

by Laplace's development, based on minors of the first two rows, we have

$$\begin{vmatrix} 1 & 2 \\ 4 & 3 \end{vmatrix} \cdot \begin{vmatrix} 2 & 3 \\ 4 & -2 \end{vmatrix} - \begin{vmatrix} 1 & 3 \\ 4 & 2 \end{vmatrix} \cdot \begin{vmatrix} -1 & 3 \\ 6 & -2 \end{vmatrix} + \begin{vmatrix} 1 & 4 \\ 4 & 1 \end{vmatrix} \cdot \begin{vmatrix} -1 & 2 \\ 6 & 4 \end{vmatrix}$$

$$+ \begin{vmatrix} 2 & 3 \\ 3 & 2 \end{vmatrix} \cdot \begin{vmatrix} 0 & 3 \\ 1 & -2 \end{vmatrix} - \begin{vmatrix} 2 & 4 \\ 3 & 1 \end{vmatrix} \cdot \begin{vmatrix} 0 & 2 \\ 1 & 4 \end{vmatrix} + \begin{vmatrix} 3 & 4 \\ 2 & 1 \end{vmatrix} \cdot \begin{vmatrix} 0 & -1 \\ 1 & 6 \end{vmatrix} = 150$$

As a practical means of expanding numerical determinants, many workers prefer the so-called **pivotal element method.** Preliminary to applying this method, some convenient element, say a_{ij}, is reduced to unity (if necessary) by dividing either the ith row or the jth column by a_{ij}, and then multiplying the determinant by this same factor. Then the row and column through a_{ij} are crossed out. Finally, from each element in the remaining determinant one subtracts the product of the elements in which the row and column containing a_{ij} are met by the row and column containing the element in question. This yields a new determinant of order one less than the original, and the value of the original determinant is equal to $(-1)^{i+j}$ times the value of the new determinant.

Example 4

To expand the determinant

$$\begin{vmatrix} 2 & 3 & 2 & 4 \\ 3 & 4 & 1 & 5 \\ 4 & -1 & 6 & -2 \\ -2 & 3 & 0 & 5 \end{vmatrix}$$

by the pivotal element method, it is convenient to take the element in the second row and third column as the pivotal element. Then crossing out the second row and third column and applying the given rule, we have

$$\begin{vmatrix} 2 & 3 & 2 & 4 \\ 3 & 4 & 1 & 5 \\ 4 & -1 & 6 & -2 \\ -2 & 3 & 0 & 5 \end{vmatrix}$$

$$= (-1)^{2+3} \begin{vmatrix} 2-(2)(3) & 3-(2)(4) & 4-(2)(5) \\ 4-(6)(3) & -1-(6)(4) & -2-(6)(5) \\ -2-(0)(3) & 3-(0)(4) & 5-(0)(5) \end{vmatrix}$$

$$= - \begin{vmatrix} -4 & -5 & -6 \\ -14 & -25 & -32 \\ -2 & 3 & 5 \end{vmatrix} = 2$$

The most immediate, and one of the most important applications of the theory of determinants is to the solution of systems of simultaneous linear equations. The results which we shall need are embodied in the following pair of theorems.

Theorem 11 (Cramer's Rule). Given a system of n nonhomogeneous linear equations in n unknowns

$$a_{11}x_1 + \cdots + a_{1n}x_n = b_1$$
$$\cdot \cdot \cdot \cdot \cdot \cdot \cdot \cdot \cdot \cdot \cdot \cdot \cdot \cdot \cdot$$
$$a_{n1}x_1 + \cdots + a_{nn}x_n = b_n$$

If the determinant of the coefficients

$$D = \begin{vmatrix} a_{11} \cdots a_{1n} \\ \cdots \cdots \cdots \\ a_{n1} \cdots a_{nn} \end{vmatrix}$$

is different from zero, this system has a unique solution given by

$$x_1 = \frac{D_1}{D}, \quad x_2 = \frac{D_2}{D}, \cdots, \quad x_n = \frac{D_n}{D}$$

where D_i is the determinant obtained from D by replacing the ith column of the a's by the column of the b's.

Theorem 12. A system of n homogeneous linear equations in n unknowns

$$a_{11}x_1 + \cdots + a_{1n}x_n = 0$$
$$\cdots \cdots \cdots \cdots \cdots$$
$$a_{n1}x_1 + \cdots + a_{nn}x_n = 0$$

has a solution other than the trivial solution

$$x_1 = x_2 = x_3 = \cdots = x_n = 0$$

if and only if the determinant of the coefficients is equal to zero.

Theorem 12 is of the utmost importance in large areas of pure and applied mathematics, and must never be forgotten.

Example 5

Determine the values of a for which the system

$$ax + 3y + 5z = 0$$
$$2x - 4ay + az = 0$$
$$-4x + 18y + 7z = 0$$

has nontrivial solutions, and find these solutions.

According to the last theorem there will be nontrivial solutions of this system if and only if the determinant of the coefficients vanishes. Hence we must have

$$\begin{vmatrix} a & 3 & 5 \\ 2 & -4a & a \\ -4 & 18 & 7 \end{vmatrix} = -46a^2 - 92a + 138 = -46(a-1)(a+3) = 0$$

Thus a must be either 1 or -3.

If $a = 1$, the system becomes

$$x + 3y + 5z = 0$$
$$2x - 4y + z = 0$$
$$-4x + 18y + 7z = 0$$

Solving the first two equations for x and y in terms of z, we find

$$x = -\tfrac{23}{10}z, \qquad y = -\tfrac{9}{10}z$$

By direct substitution into the third equation, we can verify the necessary fact that the solution of the first two equations automatically satisfies the third:

$$-4\left(-\frac{23}{10}z\right) + 18\left(-\frac{9}{10}z\right) + 7z = \frac{92z - 162z + 70z}{10} = 0$$

By giving z various values, as we may choose, we thus obtain one family of solutions of the given system.

Similarly, if we consider $a = -3$, we obtain the system

$$-3x + 3y + 5z = 0$$
$$2x + 12y - 3z = 0$$
$$-4x + 18y + 7z = 0$$

This time from the first two equations we have the family of solutions

$$x = \tfrac{23}{14}z, \qquad y = -\tfrac{1}{42}z$$

Of course these also satisfy the third equation identically.

Closely associated with determinants are the mathematical objects known as matrices.

Definition 4. A matrix is a rectangular array of elements represented variously as follows

$$\begin{Vmatrix} a_{11} & \cdots & a_{1n} \\ \cdots & \cdots & \cdots \\ a_{m1} & \cdots & a_{mn} \end{Vmatrix} \equiv \begin{bmatrix} a_{11} & \cdots & a_{1n} \\ \cdots & \cdots & \cdots \\ a_{m1} & \cdots & a_{mn} \end{bmatrix} \equiv \begin{pmatrix} a_{11} & \cdots & a_{1n} \\ \cdots & \cdots & \cdots \\ a_{m1} & \cdots & a_{mn} \end{pmatrix}$$

A matrix consisting of a single column is called a **column matrix.** One consisting of a single row is called a **row matrix.** A matrix with the same number of rows and columns is called a **square matrix.** The significant difference between a determinant and a matrix is the following. A determinant is an expression associated with a square array of n^2 elements. A matrix is an ordered arrangement of $m \times n$ elements. Briefly, a determinant is a *quantity;* a matrix is a *set of elements.*

The **transpose** of a matrix, A, is the matrix obtained from A by interchanging its rows and columns. The symbols A', A^T, and $\tilde{A}$ are all used to denote the transpose of A.

A square matrix in which all elements not on the principal diagonal are zero is called a **diagonal matrix.** A diagonal matrix in which the elements on the principal diagonal are equal is called a **scalar matrix.** A scalar matrix in which the common value of the diagonal elements is 1 is called a **unit matrix.** The symbol I is customarily used to denote a unit matrix.

A square matrix in which $a_{ij} = a_{ji}$ for all values of i and j is called **symmetric.** A square matrix in which $a_{ij} = -a_{ji}$ for all values of i and j is called skew **symmetric.**

A matrix each of whose elements is zero is called a **null** or **zero matrix.**

Two matrices are **equal** if and only if they are identical. In other words, equal matrices, A and B, necessarily have the same number of rows and the same number of columns, and have $a_{ij} = b_{ij}$ for all values of i and j. In particular, a matrix is zero, *i.e.*, is equal to a null matrix, if and only if each of its elements is zero.

The **sum** or **difference** of two matrices having the same number of rows and the same number of columns is the matrix whose elements are the sums or differences of the respective elements of the given matrices. From this it follows that the addition of matrices is commutative and associative. In other words, for any matrices, A, B, and C, having the same number of rows and the same number of columns,

$$A + B = B + A$$
$$A + (B + C) = (A + B) + C$$

The **product of a matrix and a scalar** is the matrix whose elements are those of the given matrix each multiplied by the given scalar.

Two matrices, A and B, are **conformable in the order** AB if the number of columns in A is equal to the number of rows in B. The **product** of two conformable matrices is the matrix in which the element in the ith row and the jth column is the sum of the products of respective elements in the ith row of the first matrix and the jth column of the second matrix. Multiplication is not defined for matrices which are not conformable.

Example 6

$$\rightarrow \begin{Vmatrix} 2 & 1 \\ 3 & 2 \\ 4 & -1 \end{Vmatrix} \cdot \begin{Vmatrix} 1 & 2 & \overset{\downarrow}{4} & 1 \\ 3 & -1 & 2 & 0 \end{Vmatrix}$$

$$= \begin{Vmatrix} (2)(1) + (1)(3) & (2)(2) + (1)(-1) & (2)(4) + (1)(2) & (2)(1) + (1)(0) \\ (3)(1) + (2)(3) & (3)(2) + (2)(-1) & (3)(4) + (2)(2) & (3)(1) + (2)(0) \\ (4)(1) + (-1)(3) & (4)(2) + (-1)(-1) & (4)(4) + (-1)(2) & (4)(1) + (-1)(0) \end{Vmatrix}$$

$$= \begin{Vmatrix} 5 & 3 & 10 & 2 \\ 9 & 4 & 16 & 3 \\ 1 & 9 & 14 & 4 \end{Vmatrix}$$

The law of multiplication for matrices makes it possible to express systems of linear equations very compactly in matrix form. Thus if

$$A = \begin{Vmatrix} a_{11} & \cdots & a_{1n} \\ \cdots & \cdots & \cdots \\ a_{n1} & \cdots & a_{nn} \end{Vmatrix} \qquad X = \begin{Vmatrix} x_1 \\ \cdot \\ x_n \end{Vmatrix} \qquad B = \begin{Vmatrix} b_1 \\ \cdot \\ b_n \end{Vmatrix}$$

then the system of simultaneous linear equations

$$a_{11}x_1 + \cdots + a_{1n}x_n = b_1$$
$$\cdots \cdots \cdots \cdots \cdots$$
$$a_{n1}x_1 + \cdots + a_{nn}x_n = b_n$$

can be written in matrix form as the single equation

$$AX = B$$

Theorem 13. Multiplication of matrices is distributive over addition. That is, if B and C are matrices having the same number of rows and the same number of columns, and if A is a matrix conformable to B and C,

then

$$A(B + C) = AB + AC$$

Theorem 14. Multiplication of matrices is associative. That is, for matrices which are suitably conformable,

$$A(BC) = (AB)C$$

Theorem 15. Multiplication of matrices is not in general commutative. That is, even for matrices A and B which are conformable in either order, in general

$$AB \neq BA$$

Theorem 16. The vanishing of the product of two matrices does not imply that one of the matrices is zero.

Example 7

$$\begin{vmatrix} 6 & 4 & 2 \\ 9 & 6 & 3 \\ -3 & -2 & -1 \end{vmatrix} \cdot \begin{vmatrix} 0 & 1 & -2 \\ -1 & 0 & 3 \\ 2 & -3 & 0 \end{vmatrix} = \begin{vmatrix} 0 & 0 & 0 \\ 0 & 0 & 0 \\ 0 & 0 & 0 \end{vmatrix}$$

The **determinant** of a square matrix is the determinant whose array of elements is identical with the array of the matrix. Clearly only square matrices have determinants. A square matrix whose determinant is equal to zero is said to be **singular**. A square matrix whose determinant is different from zero is called **nonsingular**. The order of the nonvanishing determinant of highest order contained in a matrix (square or not) is called the **rank** of the matrix.

If $A = \|a_{ij}\|$ is a square matrix, and if A_{ij} is the cofactor of a_{ij} in the determinant of A, then the matrix

$$\|A_{ji}\| \equiv \text{transpose of } \|A_{ij}\|$$

is called the **adjoint** of $\|a_{ij}\|$.

The **reciprocal** or **inverse** of a nonsingular matrix, A, is the adjoint of A divided by the determinant of A. The reciprocal of A is usually denoted by the symbol A^{-1}.

Theorem 17. The product of a matrix and its reciprocal is a unit matrix.

Example 8

If $A \equiv \begin{vmatrix} 1 & 2 & 4 \\ -1 & 0 & 3 \\ 3 & 1 & -2 \end{vmatrix}$ then the determinant of A is $\begin{vmatrix} 1 & 2 & 4 \\ -1 & 0 & 3 \\ 3 & 1 & -2 \end{vmatrix} = 7$

The adjoint of A is the transpose of

$$\begin{Vmatrix} \begin{vmatrix} 0 & 3 \\ 1 & -2 \end{vmatrix} & -\begin{vmatrix} -1 & 3 \\ 3 & -2 \end{vmatrix} & \begin{vmatrix} -1 & 0 \\ 3 & 1 \end{vmatrix} \\ -\begin{vmatrix} 2 & 4 \\ 1 & -2 \end{vmatrix} & \begin{vmatrix} 1 & 4 \\ 3 & -2 \end{vmatrix} & -\begin{vmatrix} 1 & 2 \\ 3 & 1 \end{vmatrix} \\ \begin{vmatrix} 2 & 4 \\ 0 & 3 \end{vmatrix} & -\begin{vmatrix} 1 & 4 \\ -1 & 3 \end{vmatrix} & \begin{vmatrix} 1 & 2 \\ -1 & 0 \end{vmatrix} \end{Vmatrix}$$

that is

$$\begin{vmatrix} -3 & 8 & 6 \\ 7 & -14 & -7 \\ -1 & 5 & 2 \end{vmatrix}$$

The reciprocal of A is $\frac{1}{7}\begin{vmatrix} -3 & 8 & 6 \\ 7 & -14 & -7 \\ -1 & 5 & 2 \end{vmatrix}$

Example 9

The matrix $\begin{vmatrix} 1 & 2 & -1 & 3 \\ 3 & 4 & 0 & -1 \\ -1 & 0 & -2 & 7 \end{vmatrix}$ is of rank 2, since

each of the third-order determinants

$$\begin{vmatrix} 1 & 2 & -1 \\ 3 & 4 & 0 \\ -1 & 0 & -2 \end{vmatrix} \quad \begin{vmatrix} 1 & 2 & 3 \\ 3 & 4 & -1 \\ -1 & 0 & 7 \end{vmatrix} \quad \begin{vmatrix} 1 & -1 & 3 \\ 3 & 0 & -1 \\ -1 & -2 & 7 \end{vmatrix} \quad \begin{vmatrix} 2 & -1 & 3 \\ 4 & 0 & -1 \\ 0 & -2 & 7 \end{vmatrix}$$

is zero, while not all second-order determinants vanish. Specifically the second-order determinant in the upper left-hand corner is different from zero.

EXERCISES

Expand each of the following determinants

1. $\begin{vmatrix} 6 & 11 & 1 & -1 & 2 \\ 2 & 4 & -2 & -2 & 2 \\ 1 & 3 & -8 & -6 & 5 \\ 5 & 9 & 2 & 0 & 1 \\ 1 & 0 & -3 & -3 & 1 \end{vmatrix}$ *Ans.* 0

2. $\begin{vmatrix} 1 & 2 & 1 & 3 & 4 \\ 0 & 2 & 3 & 1 & -1 \\ 4 & 1 & 1 & -2 & 1 \\ 3 & 1 & 0 & -3 & 2 \\ -1 & 3 & -2 & 2 & 3 \end{vmatrix}$

3. Solve the following system for t

$$\begin{aligned} x + y - z + 2t &= 3 \\ 2x + 3y - 2z + t &= -5 \\ 4x + 2y + 3z &= 6 \\ -3x + 2y + 4z + 3t &= 0 \end{aligned}$$

Ans. $t = \frac{34}{13}$

4. Solve for $x + 2y - z$ from the following system of equations without finding x, y, or z individually.

$$\begin{aligned} x + y + z + t &= 6 \\ 3y - 2z + 3t &= 0 \\ 2x + 2y + z - t &= 1 \\ 2x - y + 3z + 2t &= 4 \end{aligned}$$

For what values of a does each of the following systems have nontrivial solutions? What are these solutions?

5. $x + ay - 5z = 0$
$2ax - y + 2z = 0$
$ax - ay + 3z = 0$
            Ans. $a = 1, -\frac{1}{2}$

6. $ax + a^2y + z = 0$
$-x + ay + z = 0$
$x + y + az = 0$
            Ans. $a = 1, -1, -\frac{1}{2}$

7. $x + y - 3z + u = 0$
$ax - y + 2az + u = 0$
$3x + 2y + az + 2u = 0$
$(a - 3)x + 3y + z - 3u = 0$

8. $3x_1 - 2x_2 = ax_1$
$-2x_1 + 4x_2 - 2x_3 = ax_2$
$-2x_2 + 5x_3 = ax_3$

9. If the determinant of the system of homogeneous equations

$$a_{11}x_1 + a_{12}x_2 + a_{13}x_3 = 0$$
$$a_{21}x_1 + a_{22}x_2 + a_{23}x_3 = 0$$
$$a_{31}x_1 + a_{32}x_2 + a_{33}x_3 = 0$$

is zero, but if not all second-order determinants in the matrix

$$\begin{vmatrix} a_{11} & a_{12} & a_{13} \\ a_{21} & a_{22} & a_{23} \end{vmatrix}$$

are zero, show that any three numbers, x_1, x_2, x_3, satisfying the continued proportion

$$\frac{x_1}{\begin{vmatrix} a_{12} & a_{13} \\ a_{22} & a_{23} \end{vmatrix}} = \frac{-x_2}{\begin{vmatrix} a_{11} & a_{13} \\ a_{21} & a_{23} \end{vmatrix}} = \frac{x_3}{\begin{vmatrix} a_{11} & a_{12} \\ a_{21} & a_{22} \end{vmatrix}}$$

will satisfy the system. What is the extension of this result to systems of n homogeneous linear equations in n unknowns?

10. Construct an example of a matrix of each of the following types (a) symmetric, (b) skew symmetric, (c) diagonal, and (d) singular.
In Exercises 11 to 15

$$A = \begin{vmatrix} 1 & 3 & 2 \\ 2 & -1 & 1 \\ 4 & 0 & 2 \end{vmatrix} \quad B = \begin{vmatrix} 0 & -2 & 1 \\ 1 & 0 & -3 \\ 2 & 1 & 1 \end{vmatrix} \quad C = \begin{vmatrix} -2 & 1 & 3 \\ 1 & 1 & 1 \\ 1 & 0 & -1 \end{vmatrix}$$

$$D = \begin{Vmatrix} 1 & 2 & 3 \end{Vmatrix} \quad E = \begin{vmatrix} 1 \\ -2 \\ 4 \end{vmatrix}$$

11. (a) What is AB?   (b) What is BA?
12. (a) What is CE?   (b) What is DA?   (c) What is DE?   (d) What is ED?
What fundamental difference is there between DE and ED?
13. Show by direct computation that $A(BC) = (AB)C$.
14. What is the reciprocal of A?   Verify that $AA^{-1} = A^{-1}A = I$.
15. What is the reciprocal of B?   Verify that $BB^{-1} = B^{-1}B = I$.

A.2 Partial Differentiation. If we have a function of two or more variables, say

$$u = f(x,y, \ldots)$$

and if specific values are assigned to all but one of the independent variables, then the dependent variable u becomes in effect a function of the one variable which is left free to change. As a function of this one variable, u can be differentiated according to the usual rules. Such a derivative, calculated upon the assumption that only one of the independent variables of a function is free to change, is called a **partial derivative.** Specifically, if $u = f(x,y)$, then the partial derivatives of u with respect to x and y are, respectively,

$$\frac{\partial u}{\partial x} = \lim_{\Delta x \to 0} \frac{f(x + \Delta x, y) - f(x,y)}{\Delta x}$$

$$\frac{\partial u}{\partial y} = \lim_{\Delta y \to 0} \frac{f(x, y + \Delta y) - f(x,y)}{\Delta y}$$

The symbols u_x and u_y are also used to denote the partial derivatives of u with respect to x and y.

In general, the partial derivatives of a function of several variables will also be functions of the same variables. Hence the partial derivatives themselves have partial derivatives with respect to each of the independent variables. Thus for the function $u = f(x,y)$, we have the four second partial derivatives

$$\frac{\partial}{\partial x}\left(\frac{\partial u}{\partial x}\right) = \frac{\partial^2 u}{\partial x^2}, \qquad \frac{\partial}{\partial y}\left(\frac{\partial u}{\partial x}\right) = \frac{\partial^2 u}{\partial y\,\partial x}$$

$$\frac{\partial}{\partial x}\left(\frac{\partial u}{\partial y}\right) = \frac{\partial^2 u}{\partial x\,\partial y}, \qquad \frac{\partial}{\partial y}\left(\frac{\partial u}{\partial y}\right) = \frac{\partial^2 u}{\partial y^2}$$

As we might expect, it turns out in almost all cases that the two mixed or cross partial derivatives

$$\frac{\partial^2 u}{\partial y\,\partial x} \qquad \text{and} \qquad \frac{\partial^2 u}{\partial x\,\partial y}$$

are equal. In fact, we have the following theorem.

Theorem 1. Wherever $\dfrac{\partial u}{\partial x}$, $\dfrac{\partial u}{\partial y}$, and $\dfrac{\partial^2 u}{\partial x\,\partial y}$ exist and are continuous, $\dfrac{\partial^2 u}{\partial y\,\partial x}$ also exists and is equal to $\dfrac{\partial^2 u}{\partial x\,\partial y}$.

Since a function of two variables, $z = f(x,y)$, can be represented as a surface in three dimensions, the partial derivatives $\dfrac{\partial z}{\partial x}$ and $\dfrac{\partial z}{\partial y}$ have the following significance. In calculating $\dfrac{\partial z}{\partial x}$, y is held fixed; hence the values of z which are involved in the computation are simply those corresponding to the points on the curve in which the surface $z = f(x,y)$ is cut by the plane $y = $ constant. The limit of $\Delta z/\Delta x$ for points on this curve is, as usual, just the slope of this curve. Similarly, $\dfrac{\partial z}{\partial y}$ is the slope of the curve in which the surface $z = f(x,y)$ is met by the plane $x =$ constant (Fig. A.1).

If $z = f(x,y)$ has a maximum or a minimum at the point (x_0,y_0), then each of the planes $x = x_0$ and $y = y_0$ intersects $z = f(x,y)$ in a curve

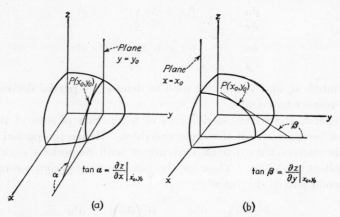

FIG. A.1. The geometrical significance of partial derivatives.

which also has a maximum or a minimum at (x_0,y_0). Hence the slope of each of these curves must vanish at (x_0,y_0),* or in other words

$$\left.\frac{\partial f}{\partial x}\right|_{x_0,y_0} = 0 \qquad \left.\frac{\partial f}{\partial y}\right|_{x_0,y_0} = 0$$

The generalization to functions of more than two variables is immediate, and thus we reach the exceedingly important conclusion that *a necessary condition that the function $u = f(x,y,z, \ldots)$ should have a maximum or a minimum at the point $(x_0,y_0,z_0, \ldots)$ is that each of the first partial derivatives*

$$\frac{\partial f}{\partial x}, \frac{\partial f}{\partial y}, \frac{\partial f}{\partial z} \ldots$$

should vanish at that point. Although not a sufficient condition (any more than $dy/dx = 0$ is a sufficient condition that the curve $y = f(x)$ should have an extremum) this result is adequate for almost all practical problems involving the maxima and minima of functions of several variables.

* This of course assumes that these curves possess slopes at (x_0,y_0), that is, that $z = f(x,y)$ possesses first partial derivatives at (x_0,y_0).

The symbols $\dfrac{\partial u}{\partial x}$, $\dfrac{\partial u}{\partial y}$, $\cdots$, although they resemble fractions, are always to be regarded as indivisible. In other words, we do not attempt to define partial differentials ∂u, ∂x, ∂y, $\ldots$. However, the ordinary concept of the differential of the dependent variable generalizes at once to the **total differential**

$$du = \frac{\partial u}{\partial x}\, dx + \frac{\partial u}{\partial y}\, dy + \cdots$$

This can be shown to be the <u>principal part</u> of the true increment

$$\Delta u = f(x + \Delta x, y + \Delta y, \ldots) - f(x, y, \ldots)$$

and thus in many applications is a satisfactory approximation to the exact change produced in u by changes in x, y, $\ldots$.

If in the function $u = f(x,y)$, x and y are each functions of the independent variable t, then it can be shown that dividing the total differential du by the differential dt gives the correct formula for the derivative of u with respect to t:

$$\frac{du}{dt} = \frac{\partial u}{\partial x}\frac{dx}{dt} + \frac{\partial u}{\partial y}\frac{dy}{dt}$$

As a special case we could of course take $t \equiv x$, getting

$$(1) \qquad \frac{du}{dx} = \frac{\partial u}{\partial x} + \frac{\partial u}{\partial y}\frac{dy}{dx}$$

In the same way, if x and y are functions not of a single variable t, but of several variables, say r and s, we have the formulas

$$(2.1) \qquad \frac{\partial u}{\partial r} = \frac{\partial u}{\partial x}\frac{\partial x}{\partial r} + \frac{\partial u}{\partial y}\frac{\partial y}{\partial r}$$

$$(2.2) \qquad \frac{\partial u}{\partial s} = \frac{\partial u}{\partial x}\frac{\partial x}{\partial s} + \frac{\partial u}{\partial y}\frac{\partial y}{\partial s}$$

Equation (1) provides a means of computing the derivatives of implicit functions. Suppose, for example, that we are given $f(x,y) = 0$ and wish to compute dy/dx. This is a special case of the relation $u = f(x,y)$ for which u is a constant (namely, 0). Hence $du/dx = 0$, and thus from (1)

$$(3) \qquad \frac{\partial f}{\partial x} + \frac{\partial f}{\partial y}\frac{dy}{dx} = 0$$

and

$$(4) \qquad \frac{dy}{dx} = -\frac{\dfrac{\partial f}{\partial x}}{\dfrac{\partial f}{\partial y}}$$

$$\frac{df}{dx} = \frac{\partial f}{\partial x} + \frac{\partial f}{\partial y}\frac{dy}{dx} = 0$$

The higher derivatives of the implicit function y can of course be found by differentiating (3) by the same procedure. Thus to find d^2y/dx^2 we have from (3),

$$\left[\frac{\partial^2 f}{\partial x^2} + \frac{\partial^2 f}{\partial y \, \partial x}\frac{dy}{dx}\right] + \left[\frac{\partial^2 f}{\partial x \, \partial y} + \frac{\partial^2 f}{\partial y^2}\frac{dy}{dx}\right]\frac{dy}{dx} + \frac{\partial f}{\partial y}\frac{d^2y}{dx^2} = 0$$

or, substituting for dy/dx from (4),

$$\left[f_{xx} + f_{xy}\left(-\frac{f_x}{f_y}\right)\right] + \left[f_{xy} + f_{yy}\left(-\frac{f_x}{f_y}\right)\right]\left(-\frac{f_x}{f_y}\right) + f_y\frac{d^2y}{dx^2} = 0$$

Hence solving for d^2y/dx^2,

$$\frac{d^2y}{dx^2} = -\frac{f_y^2 f_{xx} - 2f_x f_y f_{xy} + f_x^2 f_{yy}}{f_y^3}$$

Higher derivatives of y can be found in the same way by differentiating implicitly the expression for d^2y/dx^2.

If we have u defined implicitly as a function of several variables by an equation such as $f(u,x,y) = 0$, we can proceed in essentially the same way to find the partial derivatives of u with respect to x and y. Thus differentiating first with respect to x and then with respect to y, we find

(5.1)
$$f_u\frac{\partial u}{\partial x} + f_x = 0$$

(5.2)
$$f_u\frac{\partial u}{\partial y} + f_y = 0$$

which serve to define the first partial derivatives of u.

If we differentiate (5.1) with respect to x and then with respect to y, we obtain a pair of equations from which we can solve for $\dfrac{\partial^2 u}{\partial x^2}$ and $\dfrac{\partial^2 u}{\partial y \, \partial x}$. Similarly, by differentiating (5.2), we obtain equations from which $\dfrac{\partial^2 u}{\partial x \, \partial y}$ and $\dfrac{\partial^2 u}{\partial y^2}$ can be found. Implicit functions of more than two variables can be handled in the same way.

Sometimes we have several dependent variables, each defined implicitly as a function of other variables by a system of simultaneous equations. For instance, let us suppose that u and v are defined implicitly as functions of the independent variables x and y by the equations

$$f(u,v,x,y) = 0$$
$$g(u,v,x,y) = 0$$

The four partial derivatives $\dfrac{\partial u}{\partial x}$, $\dfrac{\partial u}{\partial y}$, $\dfrac{\partial v}{\partial x}$, $\dfrac{\partial v}{\partial y}$ can then be found as follows. If we differentiate f and g with respect to x, holding y constant, we obtain

$$\frac{\partial f}{\partial u}\frac{\partial u}{\partial x} + \frac{\partial f}{\partial v}\frac{\partial v}{\partial x} + \frac{\partial f}{\partial x} = 0$$

$$\frac{\partial g}{\partial u}\frac{\partial u}{\partial x} + \frac{\partial g}{\partial v}\frac{\partial v}{\partial x} + \frac{\partial g}{\partial x} = 0$$

Regarding these as simultaneous linear equations in the unknown partial derivatives $\dfrac{\partial u}{\partial x}$ and $\dfrac{\partial v}{\partial x}$, we can solve immediately for these derivatives, provided that the **Jacobian**

$$J\left(\frac{f,g}{u,v}\right) \equiv \begin{vmatrix} \dfrac{\partial f}{\partial u} & \dfrac{\partial f}{\partial v} \\[2mm] \dfrac{\partial g}{\partial u} & \dfrac{\partial g}{\partial v} \end{vmatrix}$$

is different from zero.

In the same way, by differentiating f and g with respect to y, we obtain a pair of equations from which the partial derivatives $\dfrac{\partial u}{\partial y}$ and $\dfrac{\partial v}{\partial y}$ can be found at once.

Example 1

If $F(x,y,z)$ is a function such that $\dfrac{\partial^2 F}{\partial x^2} + \dfrac{\partial^2 F}{\partial y^2} + \dfrac{\partial^2 F}{\partial z^2} = 0$, find the equation satisfied by F when F is expressed in terms of cylindrical coordinates r, θ, z by means of the transformation

$$x = r\cos\theta, \qquad\qquad r^2 = x^2 + y^2$$
$$y = r\sin\theta \quad\text{or}\quad \theta = \tan^{-1}\frac{y}{x}$$
$$z = z, \qquad\qquad z = z$$

As a necessary preliminary we have by obvious steps

$$\frac{\partial r}{\partial x} = \frac{x}{r} = \cos\theta, \qquad\qquad \frac{\partial r}{\partial y} = \frac{y}{r} = \sin\theta$$
$$\frac{\partial \theta}{\partial x} = -\frac{y}{x^2+y^2} = -\frac{\sin\theta}{r}, \qquad \frac{\partial \theta}{\partial y} = \frac{x}{x^2+y^2} = \frac{\cos\theta}{r}$$
$$\frac{\partial r}{\partial z} = \frac{\partial \theta}{\partial z} = 0, \qquad \frac{\partial z}{\partial x} = \frac{\partial z}{\partial y} = 0, \qquad \frac{\partial z}{\partial z} = 1$$

Now by regarding F as a function of r, θ, z which in turn depends on x, y, z, we have by an obvious extension of Eqs. (2.1) and (2.2)

$$\frac{\partial F}{\partial x} = \frac{\partial F}{\partial r}\frac{\partial r}{\partial x} + \frac{\partial F}{\partial \theta}\frac{\partial \theta}{\partial x} + \frac{\partial F}{\partial z}\frac{\partial z}{\partial x}$$
$$= \frac{\partial F}{\partial r}\cos\theta - \frac{\partial F}{\partial \theta}\frac{\sin\theta}{r}$$

$$\frac{\partial F}{\partial x} = \frac{\partial F}{\partial r} \cos \theta - \frac{\partial F}{\partial \theta} \frac{\sin \theta}{r}$$

590   ADVANCED ENGINEERING MATHEMATICS

and differentiating again,

$$\frac{\partial^2 F}{\partial x^2} = \frac{\partial \left(\frac{\partial F}{\partial x}\right)}{\partial r} \frac{\partial r}{\partial x} + \frac{\partial \left(\frac{\partial F}{\partial x}\right)}{\partial \theta} \frac{\partial \theta}{\partial x} + \frac{\partial \left(\frac{\partial F}{\partial x}\right)}{\partial z} \frac{\partial z}{\partial x}$$

$$= \left(\frac{\partial^2 F}{\partial r^2} \cos \theta - \frac{\partial^2 F}{\partial r \, \partial \theta} \frac{\sin \theta}{r} + \frac{\partial F}{\partial \theta} \frac{\sin \theta}{r^2}\right) \frac{\partial r}{\partial x}$$

$$+ \left(\frac{\partial^2 F}{\partial \theta \, \partial r} \cos \theta - \frac{\partial F}{\partial r} \sin \theta - \frac{\partial^2 F}{\partial \theta^2} \frac{\sin \theta}{r} - \frac{\partial F}{\partial \theta} \frac{\cos \theta}{r}\right) \frac{\partial \theta}{\partial x}$$

$$(6) \qquad = \left(\frac{\partial^2 F}{\partial r^2} \cos \theta - \frac{\partial^2 F}{\partial r \, \partial \theta} \frac{\sin \theta}{r} + \frac{\partial F}{\partial \theta} \frac{\sin \theta}{r^2}\right) \cos \theta$$

$$+ \left(\frac{\partial^2 F}{\partial \theta \, \partial r} \cos \theta - \frac{\partial F}{\partial r} \sin \theta - \frac{\partial^2 F}{\partial \theta^2} \frac{\sin \theta}{r} - \frac{\partial F}{\partial \theta} \frac{\cos \theta}{r}\right) \left(-\frac{\sin \theta}{r}\right)$$

Similarly,

$$\frac{\partial F}{\partial y} = \frac{\partial F}{\partial r} \frac{\partial r}{\partial y} + \frac{\partial F}{\partial \theta} \frac{\partial \theta}{\partial y} + \frac{\partial F}{\partial z} \frac{\partial z}{\partial y}$$

$$= \frac{\partial F}{\partial r} \sin \theta + \frac{\partial F}{\partial \theta} \frac{\cos \theta}{r}$$

$$\frac{\partial^2 F}{\partial y^2} = \frac{\partial \left(\frac{\partial F}{\partial y}\right)}{\partial r} \frac{\partial r}{\partial y} + \frac{\partial \left(\frac{\partial F}{\partial y}\right)}{\partial \theta} \frac{\partial \theta}{\partial y} + \frac{\partial \left(\frac{\partial F}{\partial y}\right)}{\partial z} \frac{\partial z}{\partial y}$$

$$= \left(\frac{\partial^2 F}{\partial r^2} \sin \theta + \frac{\partial^2 F}{\partial r \, \partial \theta} \frac{\cos \theta}{r} - \frac{\partial F}{\partial \theta} \frac{\cos \theta}{r^2}\right) \frac{\partial r}{\partial y}$$

$$+ \left(\frac{\partial^2 F}{\partial \theta \, \partial r} \sin \theta + \frac{\partial F}{\partial r} \cos \theta + \frac{\partial^2 F}{\partial \theta^2} \frac{\cos \theta}{r} - \frac{\partial F}{\partial \theta} \frac{\sin \theta}{r}\right) \frac{\partial \theta}{\partial y}$$

$$(7) \qquad = \left(\frac{\partial^2 F}{\partial r^2} \sin \theta + \frac{\partial^2 F}{\partial r \, \partial \theta} \frac{\cos \theta}{r} - \frac{\partial F}{\partial \theta} \frac{\cos \theta}{r^2}\right) \sin \theta$$

$$+ \left(\frac{\partial^2 F}{\partial \theta \, \partial r} \sin \theta + \frac{\partial F}{\partial r} \cos \theta + \frac{\partial^2 F}{\partial \theta^2} \frac{\cos \theta}{r} - \frac{\partial F}{\partial \theta} \frac{\sin \theta}{r}\right) \frac{\cos \theta}{r}$$

Finally, since z enters into each coordinate system in exactly the same way, it is clear that

$$(8) \qquad \frac{\partial^2 F}{\partial z^2}\bigg|_{\text{(cartesian)}} \equiv \frac{\partial^2 F}{\partial z^2}\bigg|_{\text{(cylindrical)}}$$

To obtain the equation satisfied by F in cylindrical coordinates, we now merely add Eqs. (6), (7), and (8), taking advantage of the various cancellations and combinations that are possible. The result is

$$\frac{\partial^2 F}{\partial x^2} + \frac{\partial^2 F}{\partial y^2} + \frac{\partial^2 F}{\partial z^2} = \frac{\partial^2 F}{\partial r^2} + \frac{1}{r} \frac{\partial F}{\partial r} + \frac{1}{r^2} \frac{\partial^2 F}{\partial \theta^2} + \frac{\partial^2 F}{\partial z^2} = 0$$

The equation

$$\frac{\partial^2 F}{\partial x^2} + \frac{\partial^2 F}{\partial y^2} + \frac{\partial^2 F}{\partial z^2} = 0$$

is the cartesian form of the exceedingly important partial differential equation known as **Laplace's equation**. What this example has given us, then, is the form of Laplace's equation in cylindrical coordinates.

As a final illustration of partial differentiation, we shall prove the following theorem.

Theorem 2 (Leibnitz' Rule).* If $\phi(x) = \int_{a(x)}^{b(x)} f(t,x)dt$ where a and b are differentiable functions of x, and $f(t,x)$ and $\dfrac{\partial f(t,x)}{\partial x}$ are continuous in both x and t, then

$$\frac{d\phi}{dx} = \int_{a(x)}^{b(x)} \frac{\partial f(t,x)}{\partial x}\,dt + f[b(x),x]\frac{db(x)}{dx} - f[a(x),x]\frac{da(x)}{dx}$$

[margin handwriting: used on p. 164 b(s) = ∝ considered differentiable]

To prove this, we resort to the fundamental definition of a derivative and compute the change in ϕ corresponding to an arbitrary change in its independent variable x:

$$\Delta\phi = \int_{a(x+\Delta x)}^{b(x+\Delta x)} f(t,x+\Delta x)dt - \int_{a(x)}^{b(x)} f(t,x)dt$$

Breaking the first integral into three parts, $\Delta\phi$ can be written

$$(9)\quad \Delta\phi = \int_{a(x+\Delta x)}^{a(x)} f(t,x+\Delta x)dt + \int_{a(x)}^{b(x)} f(t,x+\Delta x)dt$$
$$\int_{b(x)}^{b(x+\Delta x)} f(t,x+\Delta x)dt - \int_{a(x)}^{b(x)} f(t,x)dt$$

The second and fourth of these integrals have the same limits and hence can be combined into a single integral, to whose integrand the law of the mean for derivatives (see Sec. A.7) can then be applied:

$$(10)\quad \int_{a(x)}^{b(x)} [f(t,x+\Delta x) - f(t,x)]dt = \int_{a(x)}^{b(x)} [f_x(t,x+\theta\,\Delta x)\Delta x]dt$$
$$0 < \theta < 1$$

Next, by an obvious application of the law of the mean for integrals, (see Sec. A.7) the first and third integrals in (9) can be written

$$(11)\quad \int_{a(x+\Delta x)}^{a(x)} f(t,x+\Delta x)dt = -f(t_1,x+\Delta x)[a(x+\Delta x) - a(x)]$$

$$(12)\quad \int_{b(x)}^{b(x+\Delta x)} f(t,x+\Delta x)dt = f(t_2,x+\Delta x)[b(x+\Delta x) - b(x)]$$

where $a(x) < t_1 < a(x+\Delta x)$ and $b(x) < t_2 < b(x+\Delta x)$.

Substituting (10), (11), and (12) into (9) and dividing by Δx, we have

$$\frac{\Delta\phi}{\Delta x} = \int_{a(x)}^{b(x)} f_x(t,x+\theta\,\Delta x)dt + f(t_2,x+\Delta x)\frac{b(x+\Delta x) - b(x)}{\Delta x}$$
$$- f(t_1,x+\Delta x)\frac{a(x+\Delta x) - a(x)}{\Delta x}$$

---

* Gottfried Wilhelm Leibnitz (¹646–1716) was a great German mathematician and philosopher. He and Sir Isaac Newton (1642–1727) independently, but almost simultaneously, founded the differential calculus.

As $\Delta x \to 0$, t_1 approaches $a(x)$ and t_2 approaches $b(x)$, while the two difference quotients become, respectively, $db(x)/dx$ and $da(x)/dx$. Hence in the limit

$$\frac{d\phi}{dx} = \int_{a(x)}^{b(x)} f_x(t,x)dt + f[b(x),x]\frac{db(x)}{dx} - f[a(x),x]\frac{da(x)}{dx}$$

as asserted.

EXERCISES

1. If $z = x^3 + y^3 - 3xy$, find all the first and second partial derivatives of z.
2. If $w = x^2 y e^{yz^2}$, find all the first and second partial derivatives of w.
3. If $z = (x^2 + 2y^2)(\log x - \log y)$, show that $x\dfrac{\partial z}{\partial x} + y\dfrac{\partial z}{\partial y} = 2z$.
4. Two sides of a triangle are measured to be 58 ft and 77 ft, plus or minus errors of at most 0.1 per cent. The angle included between these sides is measured to be 64°, plus or minus an error of at most 0.2 per cent. What is the maximum error to be anticipated in the area of the triangle as computed from these data?
5. If $z = xy^2 + ye^x$, and if $x = \sin t$ and $y = t + t^3$, find dz/dt, when $t = 2$.
6. If $z = \dfrac{2x + y}{xy}$ and if $x = u \log v$ and $y = u^2 + 2uv$, find $\dfrac{\partial z}{\partial u}$ and $\dfrac{\partial z}{\partial v}$.
7. If $x^2 + xy - 2y^3 = 3$, find dy/dx and d^2y/dx^2.
8. If $x^2y + 2xy^2 = 1$, find dy/dx and d^2y/dx^2.
9. If $xy^2 + yz^2 + 2xyz = 2$, find $\dfrac{\partial z}{\partial x}$ and $\dfrac{\partial z}{\partial y}$.
10. If $z = f(x,y)$ and $g(x,y) = 0$, show that

$$\frac{dz}{dx} = \frac{\dfrac{\partial f}{\partial x}\dfrac{\partial g}{\partial y} - \dfrac{\partial f}{\partial y}\dfrac{\partial g}{\partial x}}{\dfrac{\partial g}{\partial y}}$$

11. If $x^2 + 3y^2 = ty$ and $x^3 - 2ty^2 + t^2 = 1$, find dx/dt and dy/dt.
12. If $u^3 + xv^2 - yu = 0$ and $u^2 + xyv + v^2 = 0$, find $\dfrac{\partial u}{\partial x}, \dfrac{\partial u}{\partial y}, \dfrac{\partial v}{\partial x}, \dfrac{\partial v}{\partial y}$.
13. If $u^2 + xv^3 = x + y$ and $v^3 + yu^2 = x - y$, find $\dfrac{\partial u}{\partial x}, \dfrac{\partial u}{\partial y}, \dfrac{\partial v}{\partial x}, \dfrac{\partial v}{\partial y}$.
14. If $x = u + v + w$, $y = u^2 + v^2 + w^2$, $z = u^3 + v^3 + w^3$, show that

$$\frac{\partial u}{\partial x} = \frac{vw}{(u - v)(u - w)}. \quad \text{What is } \frac{\partial v}{\partial x}? \quad \frac{\partial w}{\partial y}?$$

15. If $f(t) = \displaystyle\int_0^t e^x \sin xt \, dx$, what is df/dt?
16. If $f(t) = \displaystyle\int_t^{t^2} e^{tx^2} \, dx$, show that

$$\frac{df}{dt} = \frac{5t^2 e^{t^5} - 3te^{t^3} - f(t)}{2t}$$

17. If $f(t) = \int_0^t t^2 e^{xt} \int_0^x e^{-st} \, ds \, dx$, compute df/dt (a) by Leibnitz' rule and (b) by integrating first and then differentiating.

18. If $y = ax^2 + bx^3$, determine a and b so that the quotient $\dfrac{\displaystyle\int_0^1 (y'')^2 \, dx}{\displaystyle\int_0^1 y^2 \, dx}$ will be a minimum.

19. Find the minimum distance between the parabolas $2y = x^2$ and $y = -(x - 9)^2$.

Ans. $3\sqrt{5}$

20. A hopper is to have the form of an inverted right circular cone surmounted by a right circular cylinder. If the volume of the hopper is fixed, find the proportions that will make the surface area a minimum.

A.3 Infinite Series. If to every positive integral value of n there corresponds a quantity u_n, the set

$$(1) \qquad u_1, u_2, u_3, \ldots, u_n, \ldots$$

is called an **infinite sequence,** and the indicated sum

$$(2) \qquad u_1 + u_2 + u_3 + \cdots + u_n + \cdots$$

is called an **infinite series.** The symbols $\{u_n\}$ and $\displaystyle\sum_{n=1}^{\infty} u_n$ are frequently used to represent the sequence (1) and the series (2), respectively.

By the nth **partial sum** of (2) we mean the finite sum

$$S_n = u_1 + u_2 + u_3 + \cdots + u_n$$

If S_n approaches a limit as n becomes infinite, we call this limit the **sum** of the series (2). Technically, the series (2) has a sum S if and only if for any $\epsilon > 0$ there exists an integer N such that

$$|S - S_n| < \epsilon \qquad \text{for all } n > N$$

A series which possesses a sum according to this definition is called **convergent.** If a series has no sum, it is called **divergent.** Clearly, deleting a finite number of terms from the beginning of an infinite series will not affect the convergence or divergence of the series (though it may affect the value of the sum if the series is convergent) since it will merely change each partial sum by a fixed amount equal to the algebraic sum of the omitted terms. Similarly, multiplying every term of an infinite series by the same quantity will not affect the convergence or divergence of the series.

When some of the terms in (2) are positive and some are negative, it is often convenient to consider the related series of absolute values

$$(3) \qquad |u_1| + |u_2| + |u_3| + \cdots + |u_n| + \cdots$$

If this series of positive terms converges, the given series (2) is said to be **absolutely convergent.** If (2) converges but the series of absolute values (3) does not, then (2) is said to be **conditionally convergent.** In the special case in which the terms of (2) are alternately positive and negative, the series is said to be **alternating.**

Usually it is inconvenient to determine whether a particular series converges or diverges by a direct application of the definition of convergence, and thus it is desirable to have available more efficient general tests. The simplest and most useful of these are contained in the following theorems.

Theorem 1. A necessary (though not sufficient) condition that the series $u_1 + u_2 + u_3 + \cdots + u_n + \cdots$ should converge is that $\lim\limits_{n \to \infty} u_n = 0$.

Theorem 2 (The Integral Test). If for all x equal to or greater than some positive integer m, $f(x)$ is a positive monotone decreasing function which takes on the values $f(n) = u_n$ for integral values of x equal to or greater than m, then the series of positive terms

$$u_1 + u_2 + u_3 + \cdots + u_n + \cdots$$

converges if the improper integral

$$\int_m^\infty f(x)dx$$

exists, and diverges if this integral fails to exist.

Theorem 3 (The Comparison Test for Convergence). If the terms of the series $u_1 + u_2 + u_3 + \cdots + u_n + \cdots$ are all positive and are, respectively, equal to or less than the terms of a known convergent series of positive terms $A = a_1 + a_2 + a_3 + \cdots + a_n + \cdots$, then the given series converges to a value which is not greater than A.

Theorem 4 (The Comparison Series for Divergence). If the terms of the series $u_1 + u_2 + u_3 + \cdots + u_n + \cdots$ are all positive and are, respectively, equal to or greater than the terms of a known divergent series of positive terms $b_1 + b_2 + b_3 + \cdots + b_n + \cdots$, then the given series is divergent.

To use the comparison tests for convergence and divergence, it is necessary to have available known series of each type. For most applications, the **geometric series**

$$a + ar + ar^2 + ar^3 + \cdots$$

which converges for $|r| < 1$ and diverges for $|r| \geqq 1$, and the p **series**

$$\frac{1}{1^p} + \frac{1}{2^p} + \frac{1}{3^p} + \frac{1}{4^p} + \cdots$$

which converges for $p > 1$ and diverges for $p \leqq 1$, provide adequate examples of each sort.

Theorems 2 to 4 are valid only for series whose terms are all positive. However, because of the following theorem it is often possible to use them in establishing the convergence or divergence of series which contain both positive and negative terms.

Theorem 5. An infinite series is convergent if it is absolutely convergent.

The important special case of series whose terms are alternately positive and negative is usually best handled by the following theorem.

Theorem 6. If each term of an alternating series is numerically less than the preceding term and if the nth term approaches zero as n becomes infinite, then the series is convergent.

In most cases it is impossible to find the exact value of the sum of a convergent series, and for computational purposes the partial sums S_n must be used as approximations to the true sum S. The difference $S - S_n$ is usually known as the **remainder after n terms,** R_n, and its estimation is an important (and often difficult) part of calculations involving infinite series. For alternating series, the remainder after n terms can often be estimated by means of the following theorem.

Theorem 7. If the terms of an alternating series decrease monotonically and eventually approach zero, the remainder after n terms is numerically less than the $(n + 1)$st term.

One of the most useful tests for convergence for all types of series is the **ratio test,** which is contained in the following theorem.

Theorem 8. The infinite series $u_1 + u_2 + u_3 + \cdots + u_n + \cdots$ is absolutely convergent if

$$\lim_{n \to \infty} \left| \frac{u_{n+1}}{u_n} \right| < 1$$

and divergent if

$$\lim_{n \to \infty} \left| \frac{u_{n+1}}{u_n} \right| > 1$$

If

$$\lim_{n \to \infty} \left| \frac{u_{n+1}}{u_n} \right| = 1$$

the test gives no information about the series.

For series whose convergence can be established by the ratio test, an estimate for the remainder after n terms is provided by the following theorem.

Theorem 9. If

$$\lim_{n \to \infty} \left| \frac{u_{n+1}}{u_n} \right| < 1$$

and if N is any value of n such that

$$\left| \frac{u_{n+1}}{u_n} \right| \leq r < 1 \qquad \text{for all } n \geq N$$

then

$$|R_N| \leq \frac{r}{1-r} |u_N|$$

The ratio test is especially useful in studying the convergence of series of functions, particularly series of the form

(4) $\qquad a_0 + a_1(x - x_0) + a_2(x - x_0)^2 + a_3(x - x_0)^3 + \cdots$

which are known as **power series in** $(x - x_0)$. For such series, the limit of the ratio $|u_{n+1}/u_n|$ will, in general, depend upon x, and may be less than 1 for some values of x and greater than 1 for other values of x. In other words, a series such as (4) may converge for some values of x and diverge for others. The set of values of x for which (4) converges is known as the **interval of convergence** of the series. The distance between the mid-value of the interval of convergence and either extreme value is frequently called the **radius of convergence.**

Example 1

For what values of x does the series

$$1 + \frac{x}{3} + \frac{x^2}{5} + \frac{x^3}{7} + \cdots + \frac{x^{n-1}}{2n - 1} + \cdots$$

converge? Estimate the remainder after n terms.

The test ratio for this series is

$$\left| \frac{u_{n+1}}{u_n} \right| = \frac{2n - 1}{2n + 1} |x|$$

and clearly

$$\lim_{n \to \infty} \frac{2n - 1}{2n + 1} |x| = |x|$$

Hence the series converges for any value of x for which $|x| < 1$ and surely diverges for any value of x for which $|x| > 1$. The borderline case in which $|x| = 1$ cannot be decided by the ratio test, but must be analyzed by other means. In particular, if $x = -1$, the series becomes

$$1 - \tfrac{1}{3} + \tfrac{1}{5} - \tfrac{1}{7} + \cdots$$

which is an alternating series whose terms decrease monotonically in numerical value and eventually approach zero. Hence by Theorem 6 this series is convergent. On the other hand, if $x = 1$, we have the series

$$1 + \tfrac{1}{3} + \tfrac{1}{5} + \tfrac{1}{7} + \cdots$$

which is term for term greater than the series

$$\tfrac{1}{2} + \tfrac{1}{4} + \tfrac{1}{6} + \tfrac{1}{8} + \cdots = \tfrac{1}{2}(1 + \tfrac{1}{2} + \tfrac{1}{3} + \tfrac{1}{4} + \cdots)$$

which is surely divergent. Hence by Theorem 4 the series arising when $x = 1$ diverges. The interval of convergence for the original series is therefore $-1 \leqq x < 1$.

Since $\left|\dfrac{u_{n+1}}{u_n}\right| < |x|$ for all values of n, the remainder after n terms can be estimated by Theorem 9 and we find

$$|R_n| \leqq \frac{|x|}{1 - |x|} \cdot \left|\frac{x^{n-1}}{2n-1}\right| = \frac{|x|^n}{(2n-1)(1-|x|)} \qquad n = 1, 2, \ldots$$

If $0 < x < 1$, so that all terms of the series are positive, this is the only estimate available. However, if $-1 \leqq x < 0$, Theorem 7 can also be applied, giving the estimate

$$|R_n| < \left|\frac{x^n}{2n+1}\right| = \frac{|x|^n}{2n+1} \qquad n = 1, 2, \ldots$$

For values of x between -1 and 0, this estimate of $|R_n|$ is sharper than the one obtained from Theorem 9.

EXERCISES

Test the following series for convergence or divergence.

1. $\dfrac{1}{2 \cdot 4} + \dfrac{1}{3 \cdot 5} + \dfrac{1}{4 \cdot 6} + \dfrac{1}{5 \cdot 7} + \cdots$ *Ans.* Convergent

2. $\dfrac{1}{2^2} + \dfrac{\sqrt{2}}{3^2} + \dfrac{\sqrt{3}}{4^2} + \dfrac{\sqrt{4}}{5^2} + \cdots$ *Ans.* Convergent

3. $\tfrac{1}{2} - \tfrac{1}{3} + \tfrac{1}{5} - \tfrac{1}{7} + \tfrac{1}{11} - \tfrac{1}{13} + \tfrac{1}{17} - \cdots$ *Ans.* Convergent

4. $\dfrac{1!}{10} - \dfrac{2!}{10^2} + \dfrac{3!}{10^3} - \dfrac{4!}{10^4} + \cdots$ *Ans.* Divergent

5. $\dfrac{0.001}{11} - \dfrac{0.002}{21} + \dfrac{0.003}{31} - \dfrac{0.004}{41} + \cdots$

6. $\dfrac{1}{1 + 2{,}000} + \dfrac{2^2}{2^3 + 3{,}000} + \dfrac{3^2}{3^3 + 4{,}000} + \dfrac{4^2}{4^3 + 5{,}000} + \cdots$

7. $\dfrac{1}{2^3 - 1} + \dfrac{1}{3^3 - 2^3} + \dfrac{1}{4^3 - 3^3} + \dfrac{1}{5^3 - 4^3} + \cdots$

8. $\dfrac{1 \cdot 3}{3} + \dfrac{2 \cdot 4}{3^2} + \dfrac{3 \cdot 5}{3^3} + \dfrac{4 \cdot 6}{3^4} + \cdots$

9. Prove that the geometric series

$$a + ar + ar^2 + ar^3 + \cdots$$

is convergent if $|r| < 1$ and divergent if $|r| \geqq 1$. (Hint: Use the definition of convergence.)

10. Prove that the p series

$$\frac{1}{1^p} + \frac{1}{2^p} + \frac{1}{3^p} + \cdots$$

is convergent if $p > 1$ and divergent if $p \leqq 1$. (Hint: Use the integral test.)

Determine the interval of convergence of each of the following series.

11. $1 - \dfrac{2x}{3} + \dfrac{3x^2}{9} - \dfrac{4x^3}{27} + \dfrac{5x^4}{81} - \cdots$ *Ans.* $-3 < x < 3$

12. $1 + \dfrac{(x+1)}{2^2 - 2} + \dfrac{(x+1)^2}{2^3 - 2^2} + \dfrac{(x+1)^3}{2^4 - 2^3} + \cdots$ *Ans.* $-3 \leqq x < 1$

13. $1 + \dfrac{2x}{11} + \dfrac{3x^2}{21} + \dfrac{4x^3}{31} + \cdots$

14. $\dfrac{1}{2^2 - 1} + \dfrac{(x-2)}{3^2 - 1} + \dfrac{(x-2)^2}{4^2 - 1} + \dfrac{(x-2)^3}{5^2 - 1} + \cdots$

15. $1 + (ax)^2 + (ax)^4 + (ax)^6 + \cdots$

16. $1 + \dfrac{(x+2)}{2^2} + \dfrac{(x+2)^2}{3^2} + \dfrac{(x+2)^3}{4^2} + \cdots$

17. $1 + \dfrac{x}{2!} + \dfrac{x^2}{3!} + \dfrac{x^3}{4!} + \dfrac{x^4}{5!} + \cdots$

18. $1 + \dfrac{2}{x} + \dfrac{2^2}{2!x^2} + \dfrac{2^3}{3!x^3} + \dfrac{2^4}{4!x^4} + \cdots$ *Ans.* All $x \neq 0$

19. $\dfrac{1}{2} + \dfrac{2(7x - x^3)}{3 \cdot 6} + \dfrac{3(7x - x^3)^2}{4 \cdot 6^2} + \dfrac{4(7x - x^3)^3}{5 \cdot 6^3} + \cdots$

            Ans. $-3 < x < -2,\ -1 < x < 1,\ 2 < x < 3$

20. $\dfrac{1}{(2x+1)} + \dfrac{2}{(2x+1)^2} + \dfrac{3}{(2x+1)^3} + \dfrac{4}{(2x+1)^4} + \cdots$

21. $1 + \dfrac{(x^2 - 3)}{2} + \dfrac{(x^2 - 3)^2}{3} + \dfrac{(x^2 - 3)^3}{4} + \cdots$

22. How many terms of the series

$$\frac{1}{2^2} - \frac{2}{2^3} + \frac{3}{2^4} - \frac{4}{2^5} + \cdots$$

must be used in order that its sum shall be approximated with an error numerically less than 0.001?   *Ans.* Twelve

23. How many terms of the series

$$\frac{1}{2 \cdot 3 \cdot 4} - \frac{5}{6 \cdot 7 \cdot 8} + \frac{9}{10 \cdot 11 \cdot 12} - \frac{13}{14 \cdot 15 \cdot 16} + \cdots$$

must be used in order that its sum shall be approximated with an error numerically less than 0.0001?

24. Estimate the error made in using the first five terms of the series

$$\frac{1}{3} + \frac{2^2}{3^2} + \frac{3^2}{3^3} + \frac{4^2}{3^4} + \frac{5^2}{3^5} + \cdots$$

as an approximation to the sum of the series.

25. How many terms of the series in Exercise 24 must be used in order that its sum shall be approximated with an error less than 0.01?

A.4 Taylor's Series. In general, infinite series, as such, do not exist among the data of problems, and their use in particular applications is a matter of solution technique. Hence in addition to a knowledge of the general properties of infinite series, it is necessary that one know how to expand a given function into an infinite series when the need arises.

Of the various expansions which can be found for a function $f(x)$, the simplest and most natural is probably the power series

(1) $f(x) = a_0 + a_1(x - a) + a_2(x - a)^2 + \cdots + a_n(x - a)^n + \cdots$

where a is a given constant and $a_0, a_1, a_2, \ldots$ are coefficients given by the formula

$$a_n = \frac{f^{(n)}(a)}{n!}$$

This result is known as the **Taylor series of** $f(x)$ or the **Taylor expansion of** $f(x)$ **around the point** $x = a$. The important special case in which $a = 0$ is known as the **Maclaurin*** expansion of $f(x)$. Questions on the convergence and validity of these expansions are discussed in advanced calculus. In our work, we shall when necessary establish the convergence of such representations by means of the ratio test and shall assume that wherever they converge they converge to the function which generated them.

By an easy application of this method, we can obtain the following important series:

(2) $e^x = 1 + x + \dfrac{x^2}{2!} + \dfrac{x^3}{3!} + \dfrac{x^4}{4!} + \cdots$ $-\infty < x < \infty$

(3) $\cos x = 1 - \dfrac{x^2}{2!} + \dfrac{x^4}{4!} - \dfrac{x^6}{6!} + \cdots$ $-\infty < x < \infty$

(4) $\sin x = x - \dfrac{x^3}{3!} + \dfrac{x^5}{5!} - \dfrac{x^7}{7!} + \cdots$ $-\infty < x < \infty$

(5) $\log x = (x - 1) - \dfrac{(x - 1)^2}{2} + \dfrac{(x - 1)^3}{3} - \cdots$ $0 < x \leqq 2$

If we assume that the series for e^x is valid for imaginary as well as for real values of x, we find without difficulty that

$$e^{i\theta} = 1 + (i\theta) + \frac{(i\theta)^2}{2!} + \frac{(i\theta)^3}{3!} + \frac{(i\theta)^4}{4!} + \frac{(i\theta)^5}{5!} + \frac{(i\theta)^6}{6!} + \cdots$$

$$= \left(1 - \frac{\theta^2}{2!} + \frac{\theta^4}{4!} - \cdots\right) + i\left(\theta - \frac{\theta^3}{3!} + \frac{\theta^5}{5!} - \cdots\right)$$

(6) $= \cos \theta + i \sin \theta$

Similarly,

(7) $e^{-i\theta} = \cos \theta - i \sin \theta$

* Brook Taylor (1685–1732) and Colin Maclaurin (1698–1746) were early English mathematicians.

By adding and subtracting (6) and (7), we obtain the important **Euler**[*]
formulas

(8)
$$\cos \theta = \frac{e^{i\theta} + e^{-i\theta}}{2}$$

(9)
$$\sin \theta = \frac{e^{i\theta} - e^{-i\theta}}{2i}$$

The striking formal resemblance which series in general, and power series in particular, bear to polynomials is a dangerous temptation to the indiscriminate manipulation of infinite series as though they were finite sums. That this is not always possible should be clear from the fact that many simple series converge only for certain values of x, and diverge, *i.e.*, mean nothing at all, for all other values. A still more striking precautionary illustration is the following. Consider the convergent series

$$S = 1 - \tfrac{1}{2} + \tfrac{1}{3} - \tfrac{1}{4} + \tfrac{1}{5} - \tfrac{1}{6} + \cdots$$

By writing it first in the form

$$S = (1 - \tfrac{1}{2}) + (\tfrac{1}{3} - \tfrac{1}{4}) + (\tfrac{1}{5} - \tfrac{1}{6}) + \cdots$$

and then in the form

$$S = 1 - (\tfrac{1}{2} - \tfrac{1}{3}) - (\tfrac{1}{4} - \tfrac{1}{5}) - (\tfrac{1}{6} - \tfrac{1}{7}) - \cdots$$

it is clear that its sum lies between $\tfrac{1}{2}$ and 1. However, by a simple rearrangement of its terms we have

$$S = (1 - \tfrac{1}{2}) - \tfrac{1}{4} + (\tfrac{1}{3} - \tfrac{1}{6}) - \tfrac{1}{8} + (\tfrac{1}{5} - \tfrac{1}{10}) - \tfrac{1}{12} + (\tfrac{1}{7} - \tfrac{1}{14}) - \cdots$$
$$= \tfrac{1}{2} - \tfrac{1}{4} + \tfrac{1}{6} - \tfrac{1}{8} + \tfrac{1}{10} - \tfrac{1}{12} + \tfrac{1}{14} - \cdots$$
$$= \tfrac{1}{2}(1 - \tfrac{1}{2} + \tfrac{1}{3} - \tfrac{1}{4} + \tfrac{1}{5} - \tfrac{1}{6} + \tfrac{1}{7} - \cdots)$$
$$= \tfrac{1}{2}S$$

Thus without omitting any terms from S, but merely by changing the order of the terms initially present, we have shown that

$$S = \tfrac{1}{2}S$$

which is possible if and only if $S = 0$! Contradictions of this sort, which cannot arise in handling finite sums, are the rule rather than the exception in the case of infinite series which are not absolutely convergent. In fact, it is possible to prove that *given any conditionally convergent series of real constants and any real number α, it is always possible to rearrange the terms of the series so that the resulting series will converge to α.* It is thus clear that a knowledge of the conditions under which familiar oper-

[*] Named for the Swiss mathematician Leonard Euler (1707–1783), the most prolific and one of the greatest mathematicians of all time.

ations can correctly be performed with infinite series is indispensable. For most purposes the results of the following theorems will suffice.

Theorem 1. If $f(x) = \sum_{n=0}^{\infty} a_n x^n$ and $g(x) = \sum_{n=0}^{\infty} b_n x^n$, then for all values of x for which both series converge, the sum $f(x) + g(x)$ can be found by termwise addition of the two series.

Theorem 2. If $f(x) = \sum_{n=0}^{\infty} a_n x^n$ and $g(x) = \sum_{n=0}^{\infty} b_n x^n$, then for all values of x for which both series converge, the product $f(x)g(x)$ can be found by multiplying the two series as ordinary polynomials.

Theorem 3. If $f(x) = \sum_{n=0}^{\infty} a_n x^n$ and $g(x) = \sum_{n=0}^{\infty} b_n x^n$ are both convergent, and if $b_0 \neq 0$, then for sufficiently small values of x the quotient $f(x)/g(x)$ can be found by dividing the two series as ordinary polynomials.

Theorem 4. The power series $y = \sum_{n=0}^{\infty} b_n x^n$ can legitimately be substituted into the series $\sum_{n=0}^{\infty} a_n y^n$ for all values of x for which $\sum_{n=0}^{\infty} |b_n x^n|$ is less than the radius of convergence of the series $\sum_{n=0}^{\infty} a_n y^n$.

Theorem 5. If $f(x) = \sum_{n=0}^{\infty} a_n x^n$, then for all values of x interior to the interval of convergence, the derivative, $f'(x)$, can be found by termwise differentiation of the series.

Theorem 6. If $f(x) = \sum_{n=0}^{\infty} a_n x^n$, then $\int_a^b f(x)dx$ can be found by termwise integration of the series, provided that a and b are values of x interior to the interval of convergence.

The extension of these results to power series in $(x - a)$ is obvious.

Theorem 7. If a function possesses a power series expansion about the point $x = a$, that expansion is unique.

Example 1

What is $\int_0^{\frac{1}{2}} e^{-x^2} \sin x \, dx$?

Since no elementary antiderivative exists for the function $e^{-x^2} \sin x$, it is necessary to evaluate the integral by some approximate means. To do this let us first expand the integrand in a Maclaurin series, and then integrate term by term between the required limits. The expansion of the integrand is most easily carried out by substituting $-x^2$ for x in the known series for e^x, and then multiplying this result by the known series for $\sin x$:

$$\int_0^{\frac{1}{2}} e^{-x^2} \sin x \, dx = \int_0^{\frac{1}{2}} \left(1 - x^2 + \frac{x^4}{2} - \frac{x^6}{6} \cdots \right) \left(x - \frac{x^3}{6} + \frac{x^5}{120} - \frac{x^7}{5,040} \cdots \right) dx$$

$$= \int_0^{\frac{1}{2}} \left(x - \frac{7x^3}{6} + \frac{27x^5}{40} - \frac{1,303x^7}{5,040} + \cdots \right) dx$$

$$= \frac{1}{8} - \frac{7}{384} + \frac{9}{5,120} - \frac{1,303}{10,321,920} + \cdots$$

Retaining the first three terms, we find the value of the integral to be approximately 0.10853. This is evidently a little too high, the error being less than the first term neglected, or 0.00013.

Taylor's expansion admits of an important generalization to functions of more than one independent variable. Restricting ourselves, for convenience, to the case of a function of two variables, our problem is to expand $f(x,y)$ in the neighborhood of the point (a,b) in terms of powers of the differences $x - a \equiv h$ and $y - b \equiv k$. To do this, let us consider the related function

$$f(a + ht, b + kt)$$

When $t = 1$, this reduces to $f(a + h, b + k)$ which, regarding h and k as variables, represents the given function $f(x,y)$ in the neighborhood of (a,b).

On the other hand, we can also regard $f(a + ht, b + kt)$ as a function of the variable t, say $\phi(t)$, and from this point of view the theory of Taylor's series for functions of one variable becomes applicable. Thus we can write

$$(10) \quad f(a + ht, b + kt) \equiv \phi(t) = \phi(0) + \phi'(0)\, t + \phi''(0) \frac{t^2}{2!}$$

$$+ \phi'''(0) \frac{t^3}{3!} + \cdots$$

Now since $\phi(t) \equiv f(a + ht, b + kt)$ is nothing but $f(x,y)$ with $x = a + ht$ and $y = b + kt$, we have

$$\frac{d\phi}{dt} = \frac{\partial f}{\partial x} \frac{dx}{dt} + \frac{\partial f}{\partial y} \frac{dy}{dt} = h \frac{\partial f}{\partial x} + k \frac{\partial f}{\partial y}$$

$$\frac{d^2\phi}{dt^2} = h \left(\frac{\partial^2 f}{\partial x^2} \frac{dx}{dt} + \frac{\partial^2 f}{\partial y \, \partial x} \frac{dy}{dt} \right) + k \left(\frac{\partial^2 f}{\partial x \, \partial y} \frac{dx}{dt} + \frac{\partial^2 f}{\partial y^2} \frac{dy}{dt} \right)$$

$$= h^2 \frac{\partial^2 f}{\partial x^2} + 2hk \frac{\partial^2 f}{\partial x \, \partial y} + k^2 \frac{\partial^2 f}{\partial y^2}$$

and similarly

$$\frac{d^3\phi}{dt^3} = h^3 \frac{\partial^3 f}{\partial x^3} + 3h^2 k \frac{\partial^3 f}{\partial x^2 \, \partial y} + 3hk^2 \frac{\partial^3 f}{\partial x \, \partial y^2} + k^3 \frac{\partial^3 f}{\partial y^3}$$

. . . .

The general derivative of $\phi(t)$ can be expressed most conveniently through the use of the differential operator

$$h\frac{\partial}{\partial x} + k\frac{\partial}{\partial y}$$

and its various powers. To do this, we agree to attach the following meaning to the expression

$$\left(h\frac{\partial}{\partial x} + k\frac{\partial}{\partial y}\right)^n f(x,y)$$

The binomial $\left(h\dfrac{\partial}{\partial x} + k\dfrac{\partial}{\partial y}\right)$ is to be raised to the nth power by a formal application of the binomial theorem. Then the various powers of $\dfrac{\partial}{\partial x}$ and $\dfrac{\partial}{\partial y}$ are to be regarded as symbols indicating repeated differentiation. Finally, this expanded operator is to be multiplied on the right by $f(x,y)$, and the individual terms in the product are to be interpreted as the indicated derivatives, giving

$$h^n\frac{\partial^n f}{\partial x^n} + nh^{n-1}k\frac{\partial^n f}{\partial x^{n-1}\,\partial y} + \frac{n(n-1)}{2!}h^{n-2}k^2\frac{\partial^n f}{\partial x^{n-2}\,\partial y^2} + \cdots + k^n\frac{\partial^n f}{\partial y^n}$$

In this notation, the derivatives of $\phi(t)$, as calculated above, can be written

$$\frac{d\phi}{dt} = \left(h\frac{\partial}{\partial x} + k\frac{\partial}{\partial y}\right)f(x,y)$$

$$\frac{d^2\phi}{dt^2} = \left(h\frac{\partial}{\partial x} + k\frac{\partial}{\partial y}\right)^2 f(x,y)$$

$$\frac{d^3\phi}{dt^3} = \left(h\frac{\partial}{\partial x} + k\frac{\partial}{\partial y}\right)^3 f(x,y)$$

$$\cdots \cdots \cdots \cdots \cdots$$

Evaluating the derivatives of $\phi(t)$ at $t = 0$, that is, at $x = a$ and $y = b$, and substituting these results into the series (10), we obtain

$$f(a + ht, b + kt) = f(x,y)\Big|_{a,b} + \left[\left(h\frac{\partial}{\partial x} + k\frac{\partial}{\partial y}\right)f(x,y)\right]_{a,b}t$$

$$+ \left[\left(h\frac{\partial}{\partial x} + k\frac{\partial}{\partial y}\right)^2 f(x,y)\right]_{a,b}\frac{t^2}{2!}$$

$$+ \cdots \cdots \cdots \cdots \cdots$$

$$+ \left[\left(h\frac{\partial}{\partial x} + k\frac{\partial}{\partial y}\right)^n f(x,y)\right]_{a,b}\frac{t^n}{n!}$$

$$+ \cdots \cdots \cdots \cdots \cdots$$

If we now set $t = 1$, we find

$$(11) \quad f(a + h, b + k) = f(a,b) + \left(h\frac{\partial}{\partial x} + k\frac{\partial}{\partial y} \right) f(x,y) \Big|_{a,b}$$

$$+ \frac{1}{2!} \left(h\frac{\partial}{\partial x} + k\frac{\partial}{\partial y} \right)^2 f(x,y) \Big|_{a,b} + \cdots$$

which is one form of **Taylor's expansion for a function of two variables.** If we put $x = a + h$ and $y = b + k$ in (11), we obtain the alternative form

$$(12) \quad f(x,y) = f(a,b) + \left[(x - a)\frac{\partial}{\partial x} + (y - b)\frac{\partial}{\partial y} \right] f(x,y) \Big|_{a,b}$$

$$+ \frac{1}{2!} \left[(x - a)\frac{\partial}{\partial x} + (y - b)\frac{\partial}{\partial y} \right]^2 f(x,y) \Big|_{a,b} + \cdots$$

The resemblance of this to the Taylor's series for a function of one variable is unmistakable. Its generalization to functions of more than two variables is equally clear.

EXERCISES

Obtain at least the first three terms of each of the following expansions. Wherever possible find the general term and the interval of convergence.

1. x^6 about $x = -1$ **2.** e^x about $x = 1$

3. $\sin x$ about $x = \dfrac{\pi}{4}$ **4.** $e^x \sin 2x$ about $x = 0$

5. $\tan x$ about $x = 0$ *Ans.* $\tan x = x + \dfrac{x^3}{3} + \dfrac{2x^5}{15} + \dfrac{17x^7}{315} + \cdots$

6. $\sec x$ about $x = 0$ *Ans.* $\sec x = 1 + \dfrac{x^2}{2} + \dfrac{5x^4}{24} + \dfrac{61x^6}{720} + \cdots$

7. $\cos(e^x)$ about $x = 0$ **8.** $f(a) = \displaystyle\int_0^a e^{(x-a)^2} \, dx$ about $a = 0$

9. $\dfrac{(3 - x)}{2 + x - x^2}$ about $x = 0$ **10.** $\dfrac{(3 - x)}{2 + x - x^2}$ about $x = 1$

11. $\dfrac{x}{e^x - 1}$ about $x = 0$ *Ans.* $\dfrac{x}{e^x - 1} = 1 - \dfrac{x}{2} + \dfrac{x^2}{12} - \dfrac{x^4}{720} + \cdots$

12. How many terms of the Maclaurin expansion of $\cos x$ must be used in order that for all values of x between 0 and $\pi/4$, $\cos x$ can be computed with an error not exceeding 0.000005? (Hint: Use Theorem 7 of Sec. A.3.)

13. How many terms of the Maclaurin expansion of e^{-x^2} must be used in order that for all values of x between 0 and 2 the error in e^{-x^2} shall not exceed 0.00005?

Using infinite series, evaluate each of the following integrals:

14. $\displaystyle\int_0^1 \frac{\sin x}{x} \, dx$ *Ans.*   0.9461

15. $\displaystyle\int_0^1 \frac{\cos x}{\sqrt{x}} \, dx$ **16.** $\displaystyle\int_0^1 \frac{dx}{\sqrt[3]{1 - x^4}}$

17. $\displaystyle\int_5^7 \frac{dx}{\sqrt[3]{64 + 12x - x^2}}$ [Hint: Expand in terms of powers of $(x - 6)$.]

18. Expand z in terms of powers of $(a - 2)$ if $z^3 - 3z^2 + a = 0$.

19. Obtain a series expansion valid around $a = b = 0$ for the root of the equation $x^3 + ax^2 + bx + 1 = 0$, which is in the neighborhood of $x = -1$.

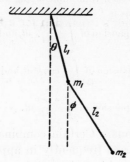

FIG. A.2.

20. Obtain the expression for the potential energy of the double pendulum shown in Fig. A.2, and expand the result in a generalized Maclaurin series in terms of θ and ϕ.

21. What is $\displaystyle\lim_{x \to 0} \frac{x(1 - \cos x)^2}{x^3 - \sin^3 x}$? *Ans.* $\dfrac{1}{2}$

(Hint: Replace each function by its Maclaurin expansion and simplify.)

22. What is $\displaystyle\lim_{x \to 0} \frac{e^x \log (1 + x) + \cos x - \sin x - 1}{x \tan^2 x}$? *Ans.* $\dfrac{1}{2}$

23. What is $\displaystyle\lim_{x \to 0} \frac{e^x \sin x - xe^{\sin x}}{\tan^3 x}$?

24. Obtain the Maclaurin expansion of $f(x)$, if it is known that $f(0) = 1$, $f'(0) = 0$, and $f''(x) = xf(x)$.

[Hint: Compute the higher derivatives of $f(x)$ by differentiating the relation connecting $f''(x)$ and $f(x)$.]

$$\text{Ans.} \quad f(x) = 1 + \frac{x^3}{3!} + \frac{1 \cdot 4}{6!}x^6 + \frac{1 \cdot 4 \cdot 7}{9!}\frac{x^9}{} + \cdots \qquad x^2 < \infty$$

25. Obtain the Maclaurin expansion of $f(x)$ if $f(0) = 1$ and $f'(x) = 2xf(x)$.

26. Obtain the Maclaurin expansion of $f(x)$ if $f(0) = 0$, $f'(0) = 1$, and if

$$f''(x) + f'(x) + xf(x) = \sin x$$

27. Show that for all values of x greater than zero

$$\int_x^\infty e^{-t^2}\, dt = e^{-x^2}\left[\frac{1}{2x} - \frac{1}{2^2 x^3} + \frac{1 \cdot 3}{2^3 x^5} - \cdots (-1)^{n-1}\frac{1 \cdot 3 \cdots (2n - 3)}{2^n x^{2n-1}}\right]$$
$$+ (-1)^n \frac{1 \cdot 3 \cdots (2n - 1)}{2^n}\int_x^\infty \frac{e^{-t^2}}{t^{2n}}\, dt$$

Show that the infinite series obtained by extending to infinity the integrated portion of the last expression does not converge for any x but that this expression can nevertheless be used to compute the value of the integral with considerable accuracy if x is moderately large. Illustrate by computing $\int_2^\infty e^{-t^2}\, dt$. A series of powers of $1/x$ which does not converge for any x but which if terminated at the appropriate point is a good approximation to a function is called an **asymptotic expansion** of that function. (Hint: In deriving the given expression, use integration by parts repeatedly, each time multiplying and dividing the integrand by t so that dv can be taken as $te^{-t^2}\, dt$.)

28. Obtain the asymptotic expansion of $\int_x^\infty \dfrac{\sin t}{t}\, dt$, and use it to evaluate the integral if $x = 2\pi$.

29. Obtain the asymptotic expansion of $\int_x^\infty \cos t^2\, dt$, and use it to evaluate the integral if $x = 5$.

30. Obtain the asymptotic expansion of $\int_x^\infty \dfrac{e^{-t}}{t}\, dt$.

A.5 Hyperbolic Functions.   Certain combinations of the exponential functions e^x and e^{-x} occur so frequently in applied mathematics and in engineering that they have been given names, and are studied as functions in their own right.   The most important of these are the **hyperbolic cosine**

$$(1) \qquad\qquad \cosh x = \frac{e^x + e^{-x}}{2}$$

the **hyperbolic sine**

$$(2) \qquad\qquad \sinh x = \frac{e^x - e^{-x}}{2}$$

and the **hyperbolic tangent**

$$(3) \qquad\qquad \tanh x = \frac{e^x - e^{-x}}{e^x + e^{-x}} = \frac{\sinh x}{\cosh x}$$

Three other hyperbolic functions, of somewhat lesser importance, are defined from these by analogy with the trigonometric or circular functions.   These are the **hyperbolic secant**

$$(4) \qquad\qquad \operatorname{sech} x = \frac{1}{\cosh x} = \frac{2}{e^x + e^{-x}}$$

the **hyperbolic cosecant**

$$(5) \qquad\qquad \operatorname{csch} x = \frac{1}{\sinh x} = \frac{2}{e^x - e^{-x}}$$

and the **hyperbolic cotangent**

$$(6) \qquad\qquad \coth x = \frac{1}{\tanh x} = \frac{e^x + e^{-x}}{e^x - e^{-x}} := \frac{\cosh x}{\sinh x}$$

If we set $x = 0$ in (1), (2), and (3), we find

$$\cosh 0 = 1, \qquad \sinh 0 = 0, \qquad \tanh 0 = 0$$

If we replace x by $-x$ in (1), (2), and (3), we find

$$\cosh(-x) = \cosh x, \quad \sinh(-x) = -\sinh x, \quad \tanh(-x) = -\tanh x$$

From (1) and (2) it is evident that both $\cosh x$ and $\sinh x$ increase rapidly and without limit as x gets larger and larger. It is also clear that $\cosh x$ is always a little larger than $\sinh x$. From (3) it follows that $\tanh x$ is always less than 1 and that it approaches 1 as x approaches $+\infty$. With these facts and a table of the exponential functions (or better still a table of the hyperbolic functions themselves, which can be found in almost any mathematical or engineering handbook) it is an easy matter

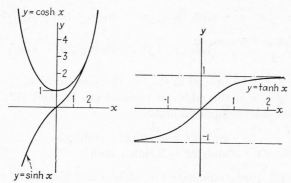

Fig. A.3. Plot showing the hyperbolic functions $y = \cosh x$, $y = \sinh x$, and $y = \tanh x$.

to plot the graphs of $\cosh x$, $\sinh x$, and $\tanh x$. Figure A.3 shows these curves. Evidently the hyperbolic functions are not periodic.

If we add and subtract Eqs. (1) and (2), we obtain

(7) $$e^x = \cosh x + \sinh x$$
(8) $$e^{-x} = \cosh x - \sinh x$$

Moreover, since

$$\left(\frac{e^x + e^{-x}}{2}\right)^2 - \left(\frac{e^x - e^{-x}}{2}\right)^2 = \frac{e^{2x} + 2 + e^{-2x}}{4} - \frac{e^{2x} - 2 + e^{-2x}}{4} = 1$$

we have the important relation

(9) $$\cosh^2 x - \sinh^2 x = 1$$

Dividing this by $\cosh^2 x$ and using (3) and (4), we obtain

(10) $$1 - \tanh^2 x = \operatorname{sech}^2 x$$

The derivation of further results of importance requires the two formulas

$$(11) \qquad \cosh (x \pm y) = \cosh x \cosh y \pm \sinh x \sinh y$$
$$(12) \qquad \sinh (x \pm y) = \sinh x \cosh y \pm \cosh x \sinh y$$

To prove the first of these, we merely substitute definitions (1) and (2) into the right member:

$$\cosh x \cosh y \pm \sinh x \sinh y = \frac{e^x + e^{-x}}{2} \frac{e^y + e^{-y}}{2} \pm \frac{e^x - e^{-x}}{2} \frac{e^y - e^{-y}}{2}$$

$$= \frac{e^{x+y} + e^{x-y} + e^{-x+y} + e^{-(x+y)}}{4} \pm \frac{e^{x+y} - e^{x-y} - e^{-x+y} + e^{-(x+y)}}{4}$$

$$= \frac{e^{x+y} + e^{-(x+y)}}{2} = \cosh (x + y) \qquad \text{(using the + sign)}$$

$$= \frac{e^{x-y} + e^{-(x-y)}}{2} = \cosh (x - y) \qquad \text{(using the − sign)}$$

Equation (12) can be proved in exactly the same fashion.

If we let $y = x$ in the addition versions of (11) and (12), we obtain the important double angle formulas

$$(13) \qquad \cosh 2x = \cosh^2 x + \sinh^2 x$$
$$(14) \qquad \sinh 2x = 2 \sinh x \cosh x$$

By using Eq. (9) to eliminate first $\sinh^2 x$ and then $\cosh^2 x$ from (13), we obtain the alternative forms

$$(15) \qquad \cosh 2x = 2 \cosh^2 x - 1$$
$$(16) \qquad \cosh 2x = 1 + 2 \sinh^2 x$$

Solving these for $\cosh^2 x$ and $\sinh^2 x$, we find

$$(17) \qquad \cosh^2 x = \frac{\cosh 2x + 1}{2}$$

$$(18) \qquad \sinh^2 x = \frac{\cosh 2x - 1}{2}$$

Just as in trigonometry, so too in the study of hyperbolic functions, there are numerous occasions when a function is given and it is required to find the corresponding "angle." This relationship is expressed by a notation just like that used for the inverse trigonometric functions. Thus we write $y = \cosh^{-1} x$ to indicate that y is the "angle" having x for its hyperbolic cosine. The other inverse hyperbolic functions are similarly denoted.

There are important relationships connecting the inverse hyperbolic functions and certain frequently occurring logarithmic expressions. In fact, one of the important uses of hyperbolic functions in practical problems is to replace such logarithmic combinations by their hyperbolic equivalents, which can then be found in tables with much less computational labor. For instance, if we consider $y = \cosh^{-1} x$ and write it in the form

$$x = \cosh y = \frac{e^y + e^{-y}}{2}$$

we are led at once to the quadratic equation

$$(e^y)^2 - 2x \, (e^y) + 1 = 0$$

Solving this for e^y, we find

$$e^y = x \pm \sqrt{x^2 - 1}$$

Taking the natural logarithm of both sides gives

$$y = \log \, (x \pm \sqrt{x^2 - 1})$$

or, recalling the original definition of y,

$$(19) \qquad \cosh^{-1} x = \log \, (x \pm \sqrt{x^2 - 1}) \qquad x \geqq 1$$

Similarly we can show that

$$(20) \qquad \sinh^{-1} x = \log \, (x + \sqrt{x^2 + 1})$$

$$(21) \qquad \tanh^{-1} x = \frac{1}{2} \log \left(\frac{1 + x}{1 - x}\right) \qquad x^2 < 1$$

$$(22) \qquad \coth^{-1} x = \frac{1}{2} \log \left(\frac{x + 1}{x - 1}\right) \qquad x^2 > 1$$

The differentiation formulas for the hyperbolic functions can be obtained immediately from the original definitions. For instance,

$$\frac{d(\cosh x)}{dx} = \frac{d\left(\dfrac{e^x + e^{-x}}{2}\right)}{dx} = \frac{e^x - e^{-x}}{2} = \sinh x$$

or more generally

$$(23) \qquad \frac{d(\cosh v)}{dx} = \sinh v \, \frac{dv}{dx}$$

In the same way we can show that

$$(24) \qquad \frac{d(\sinh v)}{dx} = \cosh v \, \frac{dv}{dx}$$

$$(25) \qquad \frac{d(\tanh v)}{dx} = \operatorname{sech}^2 v \, \frac{dv}{dx}$$

For the inverse hyperbolic functions, we have the formulas

(26)
$$\frac{d\left(\cosh^{-1}\dfrac{v}{a}\right)}{dx} = \frac{1}{\sqrt{v^2 - a^2}}\frac{dv}{dx} \qquad v > a > 0$$

(27)
$$\frac{d\left(\sinh^{-1}\dfrac{v}{a}\right)}{dx} = \frac{1}{\sqrt{v^2 + a^2}}\frac{dv}{dx}$$

(28)
$$\frac{d\left(\tanh^{-1}\dfrac{v}{a}\right)}{dx} = \frac{a}{a^2 - v^2}\frac{dv}{dx} \qquad v^2 < a^2$$

(29)
$$\frac{d\left(\coth^{-1}\dfrac{v}{a}\right)}{dx} = \frac{a}{a^2 - v^2}\frac{dv}{dx} \qquad v^2 > a^2$$

These may be derived from Eqs. (19), (20), (21), and (22), although it is perhaps a little easier not to use the logarithmic equivalents, but to work with the functions themselves. Thus if $y = \cosh^{-1}(v/a)$, then

$$\frac{v}{a} = \cosh y \qquad \text{and} \qquad \frac{1}{a}\frac{dv}{dx} = \sinh y \frac{dy}{dx}$$

Hence

$$\frac{dy}{dx} = \frac{1}{a\sqrt{\cosh^2 y - 1}}\frac{dv}{dx} = \frac{1}{\sqrt{v^2 - a^2}}\frac{dv}{dx}$$

which establishes (26). Equations (27), (28), and (29) can be derived in exactly the same way.

By integrating various ones of the differentiation formulas we have derived, we obtain important integral formulas for hyperbolic functions. Chief among these are

(30)
$$\int \sinh v \, dv = \cosh v + c \qquad\qquad \text{[from (23)]}$$

(31)
$$\int \cosh v \, dv = \sinh v + c \qquad\qquad \text{[from (24)]}$$

(32)
$$\int \frac{dv}{\sqrt{v^2 - a^2}} = \cosh^{-1}\frac{v}{a} + c \qquad v > a > 0 \quad \text{[from (26)]}$$

(33)
$$\int \frac{dv}{\sqrt{v^2 + a^2}} = \sinh^{-1}\frac{v}{a} + c \qquad\qquad \text{[from (27)]}$$

(34)
$$\int \frac{dv}{a^2 - v^2} = \frac{1}{a}\tanh^{-1}\frac{v}{a} + c \qquad v^2 < a^2 \quad \text{[from (28)]}$$

(35)
$$\int \frac{dv}{v^2 - a^2} = \frac{1}{a}\coth^{-1}\frac{v}{a} + c \qquad v^2 > a^2 \quad \text{[from (29)]}$$

Infinite series for the hyperbolic functions can easily be obtained by the expansion methods of the last section. However, for the hyperbolic cosine and hyperbolic sine, it is easier merely to combine the known series for e^x and e^{-x}. Thus

$$(36) \quad \cosh x = \frac{e^x + e^{-x}}{2} = \frac{1}{2}\left(1 + x + \frac{x^2}{2!} + \frac{x^3}{3!} + \frac{x^4}{4!} + \cdots\right)$$

$$+ \frac{1}{2}\left(1 - x + \frac{x^2}{2!} - \frac{x^3}{3!} + \frac{x^4}{4!} - \cdots\right) = 1 + \frac{x^2}{2!} + \frac{x^4}{4!} + \cdots$$

In the same way we find

$$(37) \qquad\qquad \sinh x = x + \frac{x^3}{3!} + \frac{x^5}{5!} + \cdots$$

Since the series for e^x and e^{-x} converge everywhere, so do the series for $\cosh x$ and $\sinh x$.

Example 1

Find the equation of the curve in which a perfectly flexible, uniform, unloaded cable will hang when suspended between two points at the same level.

In assuming that the cable is perfectly flexible, we mean that it can transmit stresses only in the direction of its length, and is incapable of sustaining any transverse stress.

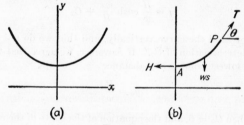

(a)   (b)

Fig. A.4.

Physical cables all have some slight stiffness which keeps them from being perfectly flexible, but in spite of this, the agreement between theory and experiment is usually very good.

Let the cable under consideration be as shown in Fig. A.4a. The weight of the cable per unit length we suppose to be w. Now on a general length of the cable, $AP = s$, extending upward from the lowest point, we have the forces shown in Fig. A.4b. These are

a. The weight of the length of cable being considered, ws.

b. The constant but unknown horizontal tension H at the lowest point A.

c. The variable, unknown tension T acting along the tangent to the curve of the cable at a general point P.

Since the cable is in equilibrium, the sum of the horizontal forces and the sum of the vertical forces which act upon any portion of it must be zero. Hence

$$H = T \cos \theta$$
$$ws = T \sin \theta$$

and thus, by division,

(38)
$$\tan \theta = \frac{dy}{dx} = \frac{ws}{H}$$

If we differentiate (38) with respect to x, we obtain

$$\frac{d^2y}{dx^2} = \frac{w}{H}\frac{ds}{dx} = \frac{w}{H}\sqrt{1 + \left(\frac{dy}{dx}\right)^2}$$

or

(39)
$$\frac{dy'/dx}{\sqrt{1 + (y')^2}} = \frac{w}{H}$$

Integrating Eq. (39) with respect to x, with the help of Eq. (33), gives

$$\sinh^{-1} y' = \frac{wx}{H} + C_1$$

From our choice of axes it is clear that $y' = 0$ when $x = 0$. Hence in the last equation, $C_1 = 0$, and we have simply

$$\sinh^{-1} y' = \frac{wx}{H}$$

or

$$y' = \sinh \frac{wx}{H}$$

Integrating again, we find

$$y = \frac{H}{w} \cosh \frac{wx}{H} + C_2$$

We have not as yet fixed the curve vertically, and thus we do not have information available for the determination of C_2. If, however, we agree that the curve shall be so located that its lowest point is at a distance

$$y_0 = \frac{H}{w}$$

above the x-axis, then $C_2 = 0$, and the equation of the curve of the cable becomes

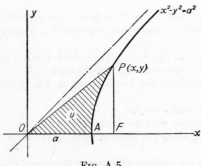

FIG. A.5.

$$y = \frac{H}{w} \cosh \frac{wx}{H}$$

This curve is commonly called the **catenary,** after the Latin word *catenarius,* meaning chain.

The hyperbolic functions are intimately connected with the rectangular hyperbola, and may be defined in relation to it just as the trigonometric, or circular, functions are defined in relation to a circle. To uncover this relation, let us begin by calculating the area of the hyperbolic sector OAP, shown in Fig. A.5. Clearly the area of the sector

u is given by

$$u = \text{area } OFP - \text{area } AFP = \tfrac{1}{2}xy - \int_a^x \sqrt{x^2 - a^2}\, dx$$

To evaluate this integral, it is convenient to let

$$x = a \cosh v, \qquad dx = a \sinh v\, dv$$

Then

$$u = \frac{1}{2} xy - \int \sqrt{a^2 \cosh^2 v - a^2}\,(a \sinh v\, dv)$$

$$= \frac{1}{2} xy - a^2 \int \sinh^2 v\, dv$$

$$= \frac{1}{2} xy - a^2 \int \frac{\cosh 2v - 1}{2}\, dv \qquad\qquad \text{[by (18)]}$$

$$= \frac{1}{2} xy - \frac{a^2}{2}\left(\frac{\sinh 2v}{2} - v\right)$$

$$= \frac{1}{2} xy - \frac{a^2}{2}(\cosh v \sinh v - v) \qquad\qquad \text{[by (14)]}$$

Replacing $\cosh v$, $\sinh v$, and v by their equivalents in terms of x from the substitution equation, $x = a \cosh v$, and evaluating the result between the limits a and x, we have

$$u = \frac{1}{2} xy - \frac{a^2}{2}\left(\frac{x}{a}\sqrt{\frac{x^2}{a^2} - 1} - \cosh^{-1}\frac{x}{a}\right)$$

$$= \frac{a^2}{2} \cosh^{-1}\frac{x}{a} \qquad\qquad (\text{since } y = \sqrt{x^2 - a^2})$$

Hence

(40) $$\cosh\frac{2u}{a^2} = \frac{x}{a}$$

Moreover, from the equation of the hyperbola, $y = \sqrt{x^2 - a^2}$, we have

$$y = \sqrt{a^2 \cosh^2\frac{2u}{a^2} - a^2}$$

and thus

(41) $$\sinh\frac{2u}{a^2} = \frac{y}{a}$$

Since x/a and y/a, when read from the circle $x^2 + y^2 = a^2$, are, respectively, the ratios which define the familiar cosine and sine functions, it is clear from (40) and (41) that the names **hyperbolic cosine** and **hyperbolic sine** are well chosen.

One apparent flaw in the analogy between the hyperbolic functions and the circular functions is that the independent variable in the former is not an angle but the ratio of two areas. That this difference is only superficial is evident when we recall that the area of any circular sector, such as OAP in Fig. A.6a, is

$$u = \tfrac{1}{2}\,(\text{radius})^2\,(\text{central angle in radians}) = \tfrac{1}{2}a^2\theta$$

and thus

$$\theta = \frac{2u}{a^2}$$

In other words, the familiar angle θ, which we normally regard as the independent variable of the trigonometric functions, can also be expressed as the ratio of two areas in a manner entirely similar to the hyperbolic case. The complete analogy between the two systems is shown in the following tabulation.

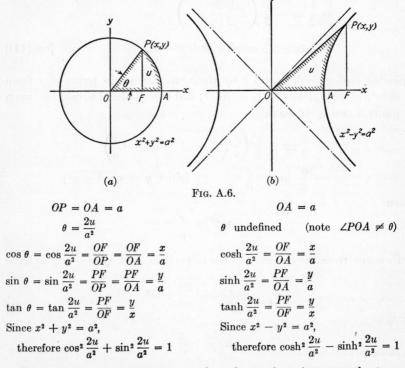

(a)   (b)

Fig. A.6.

$$OP = OA = a \qquad\qquad OA = a$$

$$\theta = \frac{2u}{a^2} \qquad\qquad \theta \text{ undefined} \quad (\text{note } \angle POA \neq \theta)$$

$$\cos\theta = \cos\frac{2u}{a^2} = \frac{OF}{OP} = \frac{OF}{OA} = \frac{x}{a} \qquad \cosh\frac{2u}{a^2} = \frac{OF}{OA} = \frac{x}{a}$$

$$\sin\theta = \sin\frac{2u}{a^2} = \frac{PF}{OP} = \frac{PF}{OA} = \frac{y}{a} \qquad \sinh\frac{2u}{a^2} = \frac{PF}{OA} = \frac{y}{a}$$

$$\tan\theta = \tan\frac{2u}{a^2} = \frac{PF}{OF} = \frac{y}{x} \qquad\qquad \tanh\frac{2u}{a^2} = \frac{PF}{OF} = \frac{y}{x}$$

Since $x^2 + y^2 = a^2$,   Since $x^2 - y^2 = a^2$,

$$\text{therefore } \cos^2\frac{2u}{a^2} + \sin^2\frac{2u}{a^2} = 1 \qquad \text{therefore } \cosh^2\frac{2u}{a^2} - \sinh^2\frac{2u}{a^2} = 1$$

We must be careful to observe that the analogy between the two sets of functions depends not only upon interpreting the trigonometric variable $\theta = \angle POA$ as $2u/a^2$, but also upon replacing the radius vector OP in the circular case by its equal $OA = a$. Neither $\angle POA$ nor the radius vector OP is of significance in the definition of the hyperbolic functions.

The fact that the hyperbolic functions can be defined from the rectangular hyperbola exactly as the trigonometric functions are defined from the circle is not merely a mathematical curiosity. The line-segment definitions of the hyperbolic cosine, sine, and tangent provide a convenient means of keeping in mind the initial values of the functions, their symmetry properties, their lack of periodicity, and their general variation as the independent variable ranges from $-\infty$ to $+\infty$.

EXERCISES

Establish the following identities:

1. $\tanh (x \pm y) = \dfrac{\tanh x \pm \tanh y}{1 \pm \tanh x \tanh y}$. What is $\tanh 2x$?

2. $\sinh \dfrac{x}{2} = \pm \sqrt{\dfrac{\cosh x - 1}{2}}$. Why must the $\pm$ sign be included?

3. $\cosh \dfrac{x}{2} = \sqrt{\dfrac{\cosh x + 1}{2}}$. Why would the $\pm$ sign be incorrect?

4. $\cosh x \cosh y = \dfrac{\cosh (x + y) + \cosh (x - y)}{2}$. What is $\sinh x \sinh y$? What is $\sinh x \cosh y$?

5. $\sinh x + \sinh y = 2 \sinh \dfrac{x + y}{2} \cosh \dfrac{x - y}{2}$. What is $\cosh x + \cosh y$?

6. $\cosh 4x = 8 \cosh^4 x - 8 \cosh^2 x + 1 = 8 \sinh^4 x + 8 \sinh^2 x + 1$

7. $\sinh 4x = 4(\sinh^3 x \cosh x + \cosh^3 x \sinh x)$

8. $\cosh^4 x = \dfrac{3 + 4 \cosh 2x + \cosh 4x}{8}$

9. $\sinh^4 x = \dfrac{3 - 4 \cosh 2x + \cosh 4x}{8}$

10. $\cos^2 \theta \cosh^2 \phi + \sin^2 \theta \sinh^2 \phi = \dfrac{\cosh 2\phi + \cos 2\theta}{2}$

11. $\cos^2 \theta \sinh^2 \phi + \sin^2 \theta \cosh^2 \phi = \dfrac{\cosh 2\phi - \cos 2\theta}{2}$

12. $\sinh^{-1} x = \log (x + \sqrt{x^2 + 1})$

13. $\tanh^{-1} x = \dfrac{1}{2} \log \dfrac{1 + x}{1 - x} \qquad x^2 < 1$

14. $\coth^{-1} x = \dfrac{1}{2} \log \dfrac{x + 1}{x - 1} \qquad x^2 > 1$

15. Derive the differentiation formulas for $\sinh^{-1} \dfrac{v}{a}$, $\tanh^{-1} \dfrac{v}{a}$, and $\coth^{-1} \dfrac{v}{a}$.

16. Show that the derivative of $y = \dfrac{\cosh x - \sinh x}{\cosh x + \sinh x}$ is $y' = \dfrac{-2}{\cosh 2x + \sinh 2x}$.

17. Examine the function $y = 3 \sinh x - \cosh 2x$ for maxima and minima.

18. A particle moves with uniform velocity v along the curve $y = \cosh x$. Show that its total acceleration at any instant is v^2/y^2.

19. Where does the curve $y = \sinh x$ have maximum curvature?

20. What is $\lim\limits_{x \to 0} \dfrac{2 \cosh x - 2 - x^2}{x^4}$?

21. Prove that for all values of A and B the function

$$y = A \cosh kx + B \sinh kx$$

satisfies the relation $y'' = k^2 y$.

22. Prove that for all values of A, B, C, and D the function

$$y = A \cosh kx + B \sinh kx + C \cos kx + D \sin kx$$

satisfies the relation $y^{iv} = k^4 y$.

23. If $\tanh \lambda = \tan \lambda$, prove that at $x = 1$ the curve $y = \sinh \lambda \sin \lambda x - \sin \lambda \sinh \lambda x$ has zero slope.

24. If $\cosh \lambda \cos \lambda = -1$, prove that at $x = 1$ the curve

$$y = (\cosh \lambda + \cos \lambda)(\sinh \lambda x - \sin \lambda x) - (\sinh \lambda + \sin \lambda)(\cosh \lambda x - \cos \lambda x)$$

has both y'' and y''' equal to zero.

Integrate the following:

25. $\int x \cosh x^2 \, dx$

26. $\int \tanh x \, dx$

$$Ans. \quad \frac{1}{3} \sinh^{-1} \frac{3x + 1}{2} + c$$

27. $\int \dfrac{dx}{\sqrt{9x^2 + 6x + 5}}$

28. $\int \dfrac{x \, dx}{9 - x^4}$

29. $\int \dfrac{dx}{\sqrt{x^2 - 2x - 8}}$

30. $\int \dfrac{\sinh 2x \, dx}{1 + \cosh 2x}$

31. $\int \cosh^2 2x \, dx$

32. $\int \cosh^{-1} 2x \, dx$

$$Ans. \quad x \cosh^{-1} 2x - \frac{\sqrt{4x^2 - 1}}{2} + c$$

33. Obtain the first three terms of the Maclaurin expansion of $\tanh x$.

34. How much volume is generated when the area in the first quadrant between $x = 0$ and $x = 1$ under the curve $y = \sinh x$ is revolved about the y-axis?

35. What is the area in the first quadrant between the curve $y = \tanh x$ and its asymptote?

36. How much surface is generated when the arc of $y = \cosh x$ between $x = 0$ and $x = 1$ is revolved about the y-axis?

37. Where is the center of gravity of the area bounded by the curve $y = \cosh x$ and the line $y = \cosh 1$?   *Ans.* $x = 0, y = 1.324$

38. Where is the center of gravity of the arc of the curve $y = \cosh x$ between $x = -1$ and $x = 1$?

39. Show that the tension at any point in a uniform cable is $T = wy$, where w is the weight of the cable per unit length and y is the ordinate of the catenary curve in which the cable hangs.

40. Show that any root of the equation $\tanh x = \tan x$ is also a root of the equation $\cosh 2x \cos 2x = 1$. Is the converse true?

A.6 The Gamma and Beta Functions.

One of the important new functions which are encountered in advanced mathematics is the **gamma** or **generalized factorial function,** defined by the equation

(1)
$$\Gamma(x + 1) = \int_0^\infty e^{-t} t^x \, dt$$

To determine the simple properties of this function, and its relation to the familiar factorial

$$n! = n(n-1)(n-2) \cdots 3 \cdot 2 \cdot 1$$

defined in elementary algebra for positive integral values of n, let us apply integration by parts to the definitive integral (1):

$$\int_0^\infty e^{-t}t^x \, dt \xrightarrow[\substack{u=t^x \\ du = xt^{x-1}dt}]{\substack{dv = e^{-t}dt \\ v = -e^{-t}}} -e^{-t}t^x \Big|_0^\infty + x\int_0^\infty e^{-t}t^{x-1} \, dt$$

On the assumption that $x > 0$, the integrated portion vanishes both at $t = 0$ and at $t = \infty$, leaving

$$\int_0^\infty e^{-t}t^x \, dt = x\int_0^\infty e^{-t}t^{x-1} \, dt$$

Hence, applying the definition (1) to each of these integrals, we have the fundamental relation

$$(2) \qquad\qquad \Gamma(x+1) = x\Gamma(x) \qquad x > 0$$

Moreover, we have specifically

$$\Gamma(1) = \int_0^\infty e^{-t} \, dt = -e^{-t} \Big|_0^\infty = 1$$

Therefore, using (2),

$$\Gamma(2) = 1\Gamma(1) = 1 \cdot 1 = 1$$
$$\Gamma(3) = 2\Gamma(2) = 2 \cdot 1 = 2!$$
$$\Gamma(4) = 3\Gamma(3) = 3 \cdot 2! = 3!$$

and in general

$$(3) \qquad \Gamma(n+1) = n! \qquad n = 1, 2, 3, 4, \ldots$$

The connection between the gamma function and ordinary factorials is now clear. However, the gamma function constitutes an essential extension of the idea of a factorial, since its argument x is not restricted to positive integral values, but can vary continuously.

Since (2) can be written

$$(4) \qquad\qquad \Gamma(x) = \frac{\Gamma(x+1)}{x}$$

and since $\Gamma(1) = 1$ it is evident that $\Gamma(x)$ approaches ∞ as x approaches zero. In other words $\Gamma(0)$ is undefined. In the same way, taking $x = -1, -2, -3, \ldots$ in turn, it is clear that the gamma function is undefined for all negative integral values of x. For all other values of x, however, $\Gamma(x)$ is well defined, the use of the recurrence formula (4) effectively removing the restriction that x be positive, which the integral definition (1) requires. By methods which need not concern us here, tables of $\Gamma(x)$ have been constructed and can be found [usually as tables of $\log_{10} \Gamma(x)$] in most elementary handbooks. Because of the recurrence formula which the gamma function satisfies, these tables ordinarily cover

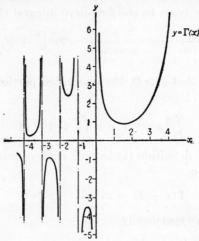

FIG. A.7.   Plot of the function $y = \Gamma(x)$.

only a unit interval on x, namely, the interval $1 < x \leqq 2$. A plot of $\Gamma(x)$ is shown in Fig. A.7.

Example 1

What is the value of $I = \displaystyle\int_0^\infty \sqrt{x}\, e^{-\sqrt[3]{x}}\, dx$?

This integral is typical of many which can be reduced to the standard form of the gamma function by a suitable substitution. In this case it is clear that we should let

$$x = t^3, \qquad dx = 3t^2\, dt$$

getting

$$I = \int_0^\infty (t^3)^{\frac{1}{2}} e^{-t}(3t^2\, dt)$$
$$= 3 \int_0^\infty e^{-t} t^{\frac{7}{2}-1}\, dt$$
$$= 3\Gamma(\tfrac{9}{2})$$
$$= 3 \cdot \tfrac{7}{2} \cdot \tfrac{5}{2} \cdot \tfrac{3}{2}\Gamma(\tfrac{3}{2})$$
$$= \tfrac{315}{8}(0.8861)$$
$$= 34.89$$

$\Gamma(\tfrac{3}{2}) = \tfrac{1}{2}\Gamma(\tfrac{1}{2})$
$= \sqrt{\pi}$
$= .88622$

The value $\Gamma(\tfrac{1}{2})$ occurs frequently in applications, and it is a matter of some interest to determine its exact value. To do this, we begin with the integral definition

$$\Gamma(\tfrac{1}{2}) = \int_0^\infty e^{-t} t^{\frac{1}{2}-1}\, dt = \int_0^\infty e^{-t} t^{-\frac{1}{2}}\, dt$$

and let
$$t = x^2, \qquad dt = 2x\,dx$$
Then

(5)
$$\Gamma(\tfrac{1}{2}) = \int_0^\infty e^{-x^2}\,(x^2)^{-\frac{1}{2}}(2x\,dx)$$
$$= 2\int_0^\infty e^{-x^2}\,dx$$

Equally well, of course, we can change the variable of integration from x to y, and write

(6)
$$\Gamma(\tfrac{1}{2}) = 2\int_0^\infty e^{-y^2}\,dy$$

If we multiply (5) and (6), we obtain

$$\Gamma^2(\tfrac{1}{2}) = 4\int_0^\infty e^{-x^2}\,dx \int_0^\infty e^{-y^2}\,dy$$
$$= 4\int_0^\infty \int_0^\infty e^{-(x^2+y^2)}\,dx\,dy$$

Interpreted geometrically, this double integral represents the volume over the entire first quadrant under the surface

$$z = e^{-(x^2+y^2)}$$

Recognizing this, let us transform this equation to polar coordinates, getting

$$z = e^{-r^2}$$

and then compute the same volume using

$$dV = z\,dA = e^{-r^2}(r\,dr\,d\theta)$$
This gives

$$\Gamma^2\left(\frac{1}{2}\right) = 4\int_0^{\pi/2}\int_0^\infty e^{-r^2}r\,dr\,d\theta = 4\int_0^{\pi/2}\left[\frac{e^{-r^2}}{-2}\right]_0^\infty d\theta = 2\int_0^{\pi/2} d\theta = \pi$$

Hence

(7)
$$\Gamma(\tfrac{1}{2}) = \sqrt{\pi}$$

Example 2

Evaluate
$$I = \int_0^\infty e^{-a^2x^2}\cos bx\,dx$$

In many cases, a useful first step in evaluating definite integrals which depend on one or more parameters is to differentiate the integral with respect to one of the parameters.   In this problem it is convenient to regard I as a function of b and compute dI/db by Leibnitz' rule (Sec. A.2):

$$\frac{dI}{db} = \int_0^\infty e^{-a^2x^2}(-x \sin bx)dx$$

The factor x which this differentiation has introduced into the integrand now makes it possible to integrate by parts with

$$u = \sin bx \qquad\qquad dv = -xe^{-a^2x^2}\, dx$$
$$du = b \cos bx\, dx \qquad v = \frac{e^{-a^2x^2}}{2a^2}$$

getting

$$\frac{dI}{db} = \int_0^\infty -xe^{-a^2x^2} \sin bx\, dx = \frac{e^{-a^2x^2} \sin bx}{2a^2}\Big|_0^\infty - \int_0^\infty \frac{b}{2a^2} e^{-a^2x^2} \cos bx\, dx$$

The integrated portion vanishes at both limits.   The remaining integral is just $-(b/2a^2)$ times I itself.   Hence I satisfies the relation

$$\frac{dI}{db} = -\frac{b}{2a^2} I$$

By an obvious rearrangement this can be written

$$\frac{dI}{I} = -\frac{b}{2a^2}\, db$$

Hence, integrating,

$$\log I = -\frac{b^2}{4a^2} + c$$

Therefore

(8) $I = e^{-(b^2/4a^2)+c} = ke^{-(b^2/4a^2)}$.

where $k = e^c$ is a constant which remains to be determined.

As a first step in finding k, it is convenient to set $b = 0$ in the integral I.   Then

$$I\Big|_{b=0} = \int_0^\infty e^{-a^2x^2}\, dx$$

If we make the substitution $ax = y$, this becomes

$$I\Big|_{b=0} = \int_0^\infty e^{-y^2} \frac{dy}{a}$$

Hence, recalling Eqs. (5) and (7), we have

$$I\Big|_{b=0} = \frac{1}{2a} \Gamma\left(\frac{1}{2}\right) = \frac{\sqrt{\pi}}{2a}$$

Finally, putting $b = 0$ and $I = \sqrt{\pi}/2a$ in (8), we obtain $k = \sqrt{\pi}/2a$ and thus

$$I = \frac{\sqrt{\pi}}{2a} e^{-(b^2/4a^2)}$$

Closely associated with the gamma function is the **beta function**

$$(9) \qquad B(m,n) = \int_0^1 z^{m-1}(1-z)^{n-1}\,dz \qquad m, n > 0$$

To evaluate this in terms of gamma functions, we proceed very much as in the evaluation of $\Gamma(\tfrac{1}{2})$. First we take the definitive integrals

$$\Gamma(m) = \int_0^\infty e^{-s}s^{m-1}\,ds$$
$$\Gamma(n) = \int_0^\infty e^{-t}t^{n-1}\,dt$$

and transform them by the respective substitutions

$$s = x^2, \qquad t = y^2$$

into

$$\Gamma(m) = 2\int_0^\infty x^{2m-1}e^{-x^2}\,dx$$
$$\Gamma(n) = 2\int_0^\infty y^{2n-1}e^{-y^2}\,dy$$

Multiplying these integrals, we next obtain

$$\Gamma(m)\Gamma(n) = 4\int_0^\infty x^{2m-1}e^{-x^2}\,dx \int_0^\infty y^{2n-1}e^{-y^2}\,dy$$
$$= 4\int_0^\infty \int_0^\infty x^{2m-1}y^{2n-1}e^{-(x^2+y^2)}\,dx\,dy$$

Now changing to polar coordinates, we have

$$(10) \quad \Gamma(m)\Gamma(n) = 4\int_0^{\pi/2}\int_0^\infty (r\cos\theta)^{2m-1}(r\sin\theta)^{2n-1}e^{-r^2} r\,dr\,d\theta$$
$$= 4\int_0^{\pi/2}(\cos\theta)^{2m-1}(\sin\theta)^{2n-1}\int_0^\infty e^{-r^2}r^{2m+2n-1}\,dr\,d\theta$$

In the inner integral let $r = u^{\frac{1}{2}}$ and $dr = \tfrac{1}{2}u^{-\frac{1}{2}}\,du$. Then this integral becomes

$$\int_0^\infty e^{-u}(u^{\frac{1}{2}})^{2m+2n-1}(\tfrac{1}{2}u^{-\frac{1}{2}}\,du) = \tfrac{1}{2}\int_0^\infty e^{-u}u^{m+n-1}\,du$$

which is precisely $\tfrac{1}{2}\Gamma(m+n)$. Hence, substituting into (10) and dividing by $2\Gamma(m+n)$, we obtain the useful formula

$$(11) \qquad \int_0^{\pi/2}(\cos\theta)^{2m-1}(\sin\theta)^{2n-1}\,d\theta = \frac{\Gamma(m)\Gamma(n)}{2\Gamma(m+n)}$$

Next let

$$\cos^2\theta = z, \qquad \sin^2\theta = 1-z, \qquad d\theta = -\frac{dz}{2\cos\theta\sin\theta} = -\frac{dz}{2\sqrt{z}\sqrt{1-z}}$$

Then (11) becomes

$$\int_1^0 z^{(2m-1)/2}(1-z)^{(2n-1)/2}\left(-\frac{dz}{2\sqrt{z}\sqrt{1-z}}\right) = \frac{\Gamma(m)\Gamma(n)}{2\Gamma(m+n)}$$

or finally

(12) $$\int_0^1 z^{m-1}(1-z)^{n-1}\,dz \equiv B(m,n) = \frac{\Gamma(m)\Gamma(n)}{\Gamma(m+n)}$$

Example 3

What is $\int_0^1 \sqrt{x}\,\sqrt[3]{1-x^2}\,dx$?

In an attempt to reduce this to the standard form (11), let us put $x = t^{\frac{1}{2}}$ and $dx = \frac{1}{2}t^{-\frac{1}{2}}\,dt$. Then the integral becomes

$$\int_0^1 t^{\frac{1}{4}}(1-t)^{\frac{1}{3}}\left(\frac{1}{2}t^{-\frac{1}{2}}\,dt\right) = \frac{1}{2}\int_0^1 t^{\frac{3}{4}-1}(1-t)^{\frac{4}{3}-1}\,dt = \frac{1}{2}\frac{\Gamma(\frac{3}{4})\Gamma(\frac{4}{3})}{\Gamma(\frac{25}{12})}$$

EXERCISES

Evaluate the following definite integrals:

1. $\int_0^\infty \sqrt{x}\,e^{-x^2}\,dx$

2. $\int_0^\infty \frac{e^{-x}}{\sqrt{x}}\,dx$

3. $\int_0^\infty e^{-x^3}\,dx$

4. $\int_0^\infty (1+x^2)^2 e^{-x}\,dx$

5. $\int_0^\infty \frac{x^c}{c^x}\,dx$ *Ans.* $\dfrac{\Gamma(c+1)}{(\log c)^{c+1}}$

6. $\int_0^1 x^{m-1}\left(\log\frac{1}{x}\right)^{n-1}\,dx$ (Hint: Let $x = e^{-y}$.)   *Ans.* $\dfrac{\Gamma(n)}{m^n}$

7. $\int_a^b (b-x)^{m-1}(x-a)^{n-1}\,dx$ *Ans.* $(b-a)^{m+n-1}B(m,n)$

8. $\int_0^1 \frac{dx}{\sqrt{1-x^3}}$

9. $\int_0^1 \sqrt[3]{x}\,\sqrt{1-x^3}\,dx$

10. $\int_0^1 \sqrt{\frac{1-x^2}{1+x^2}}\,dx$

11. $\int_0^{\pi/2} \sqrt{\tan\theta}\,d\theta$

12. Find the entire length of the lemniscate $r^2 = a^2\cos 2\theta$ *Ans.* $a\sqrt{\pi}\,\dfrac{\Gamma(\frac{1}{4})}{\Gamma(\frac{3}{4})}$

13. Find the area enclosed by the curve

$$\left(\frac{x}{a}\right)^{2m} + \left(\frac{y}{b}\right)^{2n} = 1 \qquad m, n \text{ positive integers.} \quad Ans. \quad \frac{ab}{mn}\frac{\Gamma\left(\dfrac{1}{2m}\right)\Gamma\left(\dfrac{1}{2n}\right)}{\Gamma\left(\dfrac{1}{2m}+\dfrac{1}{2n}+1\right)}$$

14. Find the volume enclosed by the surface

$$\left(\frac{x}{a}\right)^{2m} + \left(\frac{y}{b}\right)^{2n} + \left(\frac{z}{c}\right)^{2p} = 1$$

15. A pendulum consisting of a particle of mass m on the end of a weightless rod of length l is displaced until it is horizontal. If it is released from rest in this position, determine how long it will take for the weight to reach its lowest position.

[Hints: (*a*) At any instant the sum of the kinetic and potential energies of the weight is a constant.   (*b*) At any instant the linear velocity of the weight is equal to $\sqrt{2gh}$ where h is the vertical distance the weight has fallen from its initial position.]

$$Ans. \quad \frac{3}{2} \sqrt{\frac{\pi l}{2g}} \frac{\Gamma(\frac{5}{4})}{\Gamma(\frac{7}{4})}$$

A.7 Glossary

Aperiodic : Not periodic, not possessing a period.

Arbitrary : Capable of taking on any value, unrestricted; as an *arbitrary* constant.

Argument : The independent variable of a function.   Also, more specifically, the angle of a complex number.

Binomial theorem : The expansion

$$(a + b)^n = a^n + na^{n-1}b + \frac{n(n-1)}{2!} a^{n-2}b^2$$
$$+ \frac{n(n-1)(n-2)}{3!} a^{n-3}b^3 + \cdots + b^n$$

Center of gravity : For a material body, the point with coordinates

$$\bar{x} = \frac{\int x \, dm}{\int dm}, \qquad \bar{y} = \frac{\int y \, dm}{\int dm}, \qquad \bar{z} = \frac{\int z \, dm}{\int dm}$$

the integrations extending over the entire body.   For a plane area, taken to lie in the xy-plane, the point with coordinates

$$\bar{x} = \frac{\int x \, dA}{\int dA}, \qquad y = \frac{\int y \, dA}{\int dA}$$

the integrations extending over the entire area.

Circuit laws :

The algebraic sum of the potential diffences around any closed path in an electrical network is equal to zero.

The potential difference E across a resistance (symbol —⋀⋀⋀⋀—) through which a current i is flowing is

$$E = iR$$

The potential difference E across a condenser (symbol —⊣⊢—) of capacitance C on which there is a charge Q is

$$E = \frac{Q}{C} = \frac{1}{C} \int i \, dt$$

The algebraic sum of the currents flowing toward any point in an electrical network is equal to zero.

The current i flowing through a resistance R across which there is a potential difference E is

$$i = \frac{E}{R}$$

The current i flowing toward or (apparently) through a condenser of capacitance C across which the potential difference E is changing at the rate dE/dt is

$$i = C \frac{dE}{dt}$$

The potential difference E across a coil (symbol ⦚⦚⦚) of inductance L through which the current i is changing at the rate di/dt is

$$E = L \frac{di}{dt}$$

The current i flowing through a coil of inductance L across which a potential difference E has been acting is

$$i = \frac{1}{L} \int E \, dt$$

Coulomb friction (also called **dry** or **solid friction**): Friction which is proportional to the normal force N pressing two objects together, but independent of the area of contact between the objects and of the relative velocity of one with respect to the other. In the analytical formulation, $F = \mu N$, μ is known as the **coefficient of friction.**

Current (electric): The time rate of change of the quantity of electricity.

$$i = \frac{dQ}{dt}$$

Curvature: The change of direction of the tangent to a curve per unit distance along the curve. In cartesian coordinates

$$K = \frac{y''}{[1 + (y')^2]^{\frac{3}{2}}}$$

Cylindrical coordinates: The coordinates r, θ, z which serve to locate a point in space as shown in Fig. A.8. Cylindrical coordinates are con-

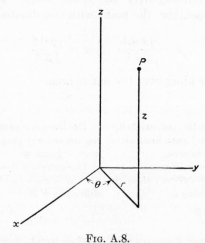

Fig. A.8.

nected with cartesian coordinates through the equations

$$x = r \cos \theta$$
$$y = r \sin \theta$$
$$z = z$$

Dashpot: A device which introduces (or represents) friction proportional to the velocity in a mechanical system. The conventional symbol for a dashpot is ⊣⊢.

Density: The mass per unit volume of a given material.

Descartes's rule of signs: A polynomial equation, $f(x) = 0$, with real coefficients and arranged in descending powers of x, can have no more positive roots than there are variations of sign between successive terms in $f(x)$, and can have no more negative roots than there are variations of sign between successive terms in $f(-x)$.

Difference quotient: The quotient

$$\frac{f(x + \Delta x) - f(x)}{\Delta x}$$

whose limit as $\Delta x \to 0$ is the derivative $f'(x)$.

Differential of arc: The expression $ds = \sqrt{1 + (y')^2}\, dx$ [or $ds = \sqrt{1 + (x')^2}\, dy$]. The infinitesimal ds is related to the infinitesi-

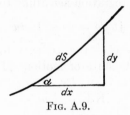

Fig. A.9.

mals dx and dy and the inclination angle of the curve in question by the formulas

$$dx = \cos \alpha\, ds$$
$$dy = \sin \alpha\, ds$$

Figure A.9 is useful in recalling these relations.

Dummy variable of integration: The variable of integration in a definite integral, so called because it can be replaced at pleasure by any other symbol, without affecting the value of the integral.

Free body: A physical body, or portion thereof, considered as isolated from all other bodies, but acted upon by forces equivalent to those actually applied to it by the parts originally in contact with it.

Geometric progression: A finite series in which each term is obtained from the one preceding it by multiplying it by a constant called the **common ratio.** The sum of a geometric progression of n terms is

$$s = a\frac{r^n - 1}{r - 1}$$

where r is the common ratio and a is the first term of the progression.

Improper integral: An integral with one or both of the following characteristics.

a. At one or more points within the range of integration its integrand becomes infinite.

b. One or both of its limits is infinite.

By definition

$$\int_a^\infty f(x)dx = \lim_{T\to\infty} \int_a^T f(x)dx$$

$$\int_{-\infty}^\infty f(x)dx = \lim_{S\to\infty} \int_{-S}^c f(x)dx + \lim_{T\to\infty} \int_c^T f(x)dx, \qquad c \text{ any real number}$$

and if $f(x)$ is infinite for $x = d$, where $a < d < b$,

$$\int_a^b f(x)dx = \lim_{\epsilon_1\to 0} \int_a^{d-\epsilon_1} f(x)dx + \lim_{\epsilon_2\to 0} \int_{d+\epsilon_2}^b f(x)dx$$

Infinitesimal: A variable whose limit is zero.

Integration by parts: Integration according to the formula

$$\int u\,dv = uv - \int v\,du$$

Kinetic energy: Energy (*i.e.*, the capacity for doing work) possessed by a body by virtue of its state of motion. For a particle of mass m moving with velocity v,

$$\text{K.E.} = \tfrac{1}{2}mv^2$$

For a body of moment of inertia I rotating with angular velocity ω,

$$\text{K.E.} = \tfrac{1}{2}I\omega^2$$

Lateral: Synonymous with transverse.

Law of the mean for derivatives (mean value theorem for derivatives): If $f(x)$ and its derivative $f'(x)$ are single-valued and continuous for all values of x in the interval $a \leq x \leq b$, then there exists at least one value of x between a and b, say x_1, such that

$$\frac{f(b) - f(a)}{b - a} = f'(x_1)$$

or

$$f(b) - f(a) = (b - a)f'(x_1) \qquad a < x_1 < b$$

This is frequently written in the alternative form

$$f(x + h) - f(x) = hf'(x + \theta h) \qquad 0 < \theta < 1$$

where $x = a$, $x + h = b$, $b - a = h$, and $x_1 = x + \theta h$.

Law of the mean for integrals (first mean value theorem for integrals): If $f(x)$ is a continuous function over the interval $a \leq x \leq b$, then there exists at least one value of x between a and b, say x_1, such that

$$\int_a^b f(x)dx = (b - a) f(x_1) \qquad a < x_1 < b$$

Left-hand limit: The value approached by a function, $f(x)$, as x approaches a given point, say a, from the left. The left-hand limit is frequently denoted by the symbol $f(a^-)$.

L'Hospital's rule: If for $x = a$, the fraction $f(x)/g(x)$ is an indeterminate of the form $0/0$ or ∞/∞, but if $f'(x)/g'(x)$ is not indeterminate, then

$$\lim_{x \to a} \frac{f(x)}{g(x)} = \frac{f'(a)}{g'(a)}$$

This holds whether a is infinite or not.

Linear combination: The result of adding together a group of quantities after each has been multiplied by an arbitrary constant.

Linearly dependent: If a relation of the form

$$c_1 f_1 + c_2 f_2 + \cdots + c_n f_n = 0$$

where not all of the c_i are zero, exists among the quantities $f_1, f_2, \ldots f_n$, the quantities are said to be linearly dependent. From this it follows that there is always at least one member of a set of linearly dependent quantities which can be expressed as a linear combination of the remaining quantities. When only two functions are involved, linear dependence is equivalent to simple proportionality.

Linearly independent: If a set of quantities $f_1, f_2, \ldots, f_n$ is such that the relation

$$c_1 f_1 + c_2 f_2 + \cdots + c_n f_n = 0$$

implies $c_1 = c_2 = \cdots = c_n = 0$, the quantities are said to be linearly independent. From this it follows that no one of the members of a set of linearly independent quantities can be expressed as a linear combination of the remaining quantities.

Longitudinal: In the direction of the length of something, as the *longitudinal* vibrations of a shaft.

Mass: A measure of the resistance a body offers to being set in motion. It is connected with the weight of a body through the formula

$$m = \frac{w}{g}$$

Moment of inertia: For physical bodies, the integral

$$\int_M r^2 \, dM$$

For plane areas, the integral

$$\int_A r^2 \, dA$$

If the axis from which r is measured in the latter case is perpendicular to the plane of the area, the integral is called the **polar moment of inertia** of A.

Partial fractions: The simplest real fractions into which the quotient of two polynomials, $p(x)/q(x)$ (q of higher order than p), can be broken down. Specifically, the partial fraction expansion of $p(x)/q(x)$ will contain a fraction of the form

$$\frac{A}{x - a}$$

for every unrepeated linear factor, $x - a$, of $q(x)$; a set of fractions

$$\frac{A_1}{x - a} + \frac{A_2}{(x - a)^2} + \cdots + \frac{A_r}{(x - a)^r}$$

for every r-fold linear factor, $(x - a)^r$, of $q(x)$; a fraction of the form

$$\frac{Ax + B}{x^2 + ax + b}$$

for every unrepeated irreducible quadratic factor, $x^2 + ax + b$, of $q(x)$; and a set of fractions

$$\frac{A_1 x + B_1}{x^2 + ax + b} + \frac{A_2 x + B_2}{(x^2 + ax + b)^2} + \cdots + \frac{A_r x + B_r}{(x^2 + ax + b)^r}$$

for every r-fold irreducible quadratic factor, $(x^2 + ax + b)^r$, of $q(x)$.

Periodic function: A function which in successive intervals of fixed length repeats itself exactly. Analytically, a function, $f(x)$ for which there exists a constant p, called the **period,** such that

$$f(x + p) = f(x)$$

for all values of x.

Piecewise continuous: A function is said to be piecewise continuous in a finite interval if that interval can be divided into a finite number of subintervals over each of which the function is continuous and at the ends of each of which $f(x)$ possesses finite right- and left-hand limits.

Potential energy: The energy (or capacity for doing work) which a body possesses by virtue of its position or its state of strain. The most important cases are the potential energy of a weight w in the gravitational field,

$$\text{P.E.} = wh = mgh$$

where h is the vertical distance of the weight above an arbitrary reference level; and the potential energy of a stretched spring

$$\text{P.E.} = \tfrac{1}{2}ks^2$$

where s is the elongation of the spring over its unstretched length and k is the force required to stretch the spring a unit distance.

Radius of curvature: The reciprocal of the curvature. In cartesian coordinates,

$$R = \frac{[1 + (y')^2]^{\frac{3}{2}}}{y''}$$

Right-hand limit: The value approached by a function, $f(x)$, as x approaches a given point, say a, from the right. The right-hand limit is frequently denoted by the symbol $f(a^+)$.

Root-coefficient relations: In any polynomial equation

$$a_0x^n + a_1x^{n-1} + a_2x^{n-2} + \cdots + a_{n-1}x + a_n = 0$$

$(-1)^k \dfrac{a_k}{a_0}$ = sum of all possible products of the roots of the equation taken k at a time.

Semi-infinite: Extending to infinity in one direction, as a *semi-infinite* bar.

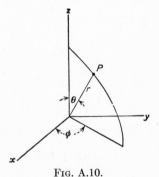

Fig. A.10.

Spherical coordinates: The coordinates r, θ, and ϕ which serve to locate a point in space as shown in Fig. A.10. Spherical coordinates are related to cartesian coordinates through the equations

$$x = r \sin \theta \cos \phi$$
$$y = r \sin \theta \sin \phi$$
$$z = r \cos \theta$$

Transverse: Perpendicular to the length of something, as the *transverse* vibrations of a beam.

Work: The product of force times distance. If the force varies with the distance, then the work done by the force must be computed as an integral

$$W = \int F\, ds$$

Zero of a function: A value of the independent variable of a function for which the function assumes the value zero; in other words, a root of the equation obtained by equating the function to zero.

INDEX

The letter *e.* after a page number refers to an exercise, the letter *n.* to a footnote